BOTTOM LINE
YEAR BOOK
1993

BY THE EDITORS OF

Bottom Line
PERSONAL

First Printing
10   9   8   7   6   5   4   3   2   1

Boardroom® Classics publishes the advice of expert
authorities in many fields. But the use of a book
is not a substitute for legal, accounting, or other professional services. Consult a competent professional for
answers to your specific questions.

**Library of Congress Cataloging in Publication Data
Main entry under title:**

Bottom Line Yearbook 1993.

     1. Life skills—United States.   I. Bottom line
personal.
ISBN 0-88723-043-1

Boardroom ® Classics is a registered trademark of
Boardroom ® Reports, Inc.
330 W. 42nd Street, New York, NY 10036

Printed in the United States of America

Contents

9 • CAREER SUCCESS

10 • RETIREMENT PLANNING

11 • PREPARING YOUR ESTATE

12 • YOUR HOME, YOUR FAMILY

18 • MORE FUNTIME

1

Well-Being Secrets

How To Say No To Back Pain

Four of five Americans report they've had back trouble—making the back-pain* industry a $30-billion-a-year business.

Conventional medical wisdom: Back pain is caused by structural abnormalities of the spine (such as arthritic and disc disorders), or by a vague group of muscle conditions linked to poor posture, lack of exercise or overexertion.

Conventional treatments: Surgery, traction, acupuncture, nerve blocks, biofeedback, deep massage and extended bed rest.

These approaches may bring temporary relief (through what I think is a placebo effect), but fail to resolve the problem.

As a result, the pain recurs...and recurs. And millions of people have barred themselves from normal physical activity—from raking leaves to going to work. Back pain is the leading cause of worker absenteeism.

*For my purposes, back pain refers to discomfort in the neck, shoulders, back or buttocks.

What's going on:

These semidisabled men and women have been imprisoned by a myth—that their backs are delicate, vulnerable structures, easy to throw out of whack and difficult to restore.

The personal and financial cost of this problem is staggering—and largely unnecessary. After 17 years of monitoring thousands of patients, I've concluded that the overwhelming majority of back-pain sufferers have been misdiagnosed...that their doctors have been treating merely the symptoms of their problem, rather than its underlying cause.

Back pain, I have found, is nearly always a stress-related problem. I call it Tension Myositis Syndrome (TMS). TMS almost invariably affects the soft tissue (muscles, nerves, tendons), and not the spine, discs or vertebrae.

The good news: TMS is a harmless (though often excruciating) disorder. Most back-pain sufferers can be cured without surgery, drugs or special exercise. Key: The patient must fully recognize that back pain is essentially a trick played on the body by the subconscious mind.

1

Who gets TMS:

The notion of a mind-body connection is hardly revolutionary.

Tension is widely accepted as the primary cause of peptic ulcer, for one example. Other mind-related disorders: Constipation, irritable bowel syndrome, tension or migraine headaches, cardiac palpitations, eczema, hay fever.

People who fall prey to these syndromes—including TMS—are generally competitive, perfectionist types who feel compelled to excel in both family and business matters. They strive to be the best parent, the best manager, the best golfer. They are their own worst critics when they fall short.

TMS sufferers build up large stores of anxiety and anger. Because these feelings are painful, frightening and inappropriate, they are repressed.

Examples: A new father may resent the sleep he's losing...or a middle-aged woman may resent having to care for her elderly parents. Since they cannot vent their frustration at the people who are causing it, they bottle it up.

But the story doesn't end there. To divert our attention and keep hidden emotions from becoming conscious, the brain creates a defense—which diverts attention from our unkind, childish, angry, selfish feelings.

Thirty years ago, fewer people complained of back pain, but there was a much higher incidence of peptic ulcers then. When doctors and laymen came to realize ulcers were caused by tension, ulcers no longer served the brain's purpose of hiding tension. Note: More effective medication also has helped.

By contrast, the medical profession still ignores the emotional basis for TMS—making it the perfect camouflage for unrevealed feelings.

How TMS works:

The autonomic nervous system (a part of the brain) controls the body's involuntary functions, including heart rate, digestion and breathing. It can increase or decrease the flow of blood to any part of the body with total precision.

TMS is an abnormal autonomic activity that reduces blood flow to various tissues in the back region. Although the nervous system may be triggered by a physical event (an auto accident, a fall, a day of heavy lifting), it is responding to a psychological need.

Result: The tissues get less oxygen than normal. Depending on which tissues are affected (muscles, nerves, tendons-ligaments or a combination), the body responds with many symptoms—sharp, aching or burning pain...tingling and numbness...pressure or weakness.

All of these symptoms should be thoroughly investigated, to rule out the possibility of tumor or some other organic illness. After that, however, patients should be highly suspicious when a doctor diagnoses a structural problem.

Example: When scans reveal that a patient's last intervertebral disc has flattened (and that its shock-absorbing fluid has dried up or leaked through the disc wall), there is a standard diagnosis—a herniated disc. The patient's back pain is promptly blamed on this condition. Typical treatment: Surgery.

In my experience, however, this disc pathology is a normal process of aging, almost universal after age 20. It rarely causes pain. It is no more pathological than graying hair or wrinkling skin.

I recently studied 109 patients with herniated discs. Of that group, 88% became free or nearly free of pain (with unrestricted physical activity) after following my techniques. Another 10% showed some improvement. Only two patients, who had unusually severe psychological problems, were unchanged.

I have seen similar results with people diagnosed for spinal stenosis, pinched or inflamed nerves, osteoarthritis, scoliosis, tendinitis and bursitis.

Treatment and cure:

When I see patients with acute back pain (often caused by a muscle spasm), I advise bed rest and painkillers as needed —but urge them to keep testing their ability to move around. If they assume they will be immobilized for days or weeks, they will slow their recovery.

My emphasis, however, is on the prevention of TMS attacks. Best weapon: The patient's own awareness of what is going on—what I call knowledge therapy.*

Once a person is truly convinced that TMS is not serious—that it is a charade to be ridiculed rather than feared—the pain stops. The brain's ruse simply doesn't work any more. To reach that point, patients must:

• Think psychological, rather than physical. As they become aware of pain, they must shift attention from their body to something they are worried about. The particular worry isn't important. The refocusing process short-circuits the brain's deception.

• Talk to their brain. Although this may sound silly at first, it is critical to take charge and tell your subconscious that you refuse to put up with TMS any longer.

• Resume physical activity as soon as pain has subsided. Patients must feel free to bend, lift, jog or perform any other common physical acts. Since their backs are essentially normal, there is nothing to fear—except for the fear itself, the emotion that goes hand in hand with TMS.

• Discontinue all physical treatment. Until patients renounce all structural explanations for either the pain or its cure, symptoms will persist.

Bottom line: Victory over TMS does not require any change in personality, nor a commitment to stop repressing anxiety and anger. (If this were the case, my cure rate would approach zero.)

Once patients understand and accept the true nature of their pain, they are on the path to permanent relief.

*Most patients master the therapy after two two-hour seminars, and achieve permanent pain relief within two to six weeks. On occasion, small-group, follow-up sessions are required.

Source: John E. Sarno, MD, professor of clinical rehabilitation medicine at the New York University School of Medicine and attending physician at the Howard A. Rusk Institute of Rehabilitation Medicine at New York University Medical Center. His revolutionary book, *Mind Over Back Pain* (1984) has helped thousands of sufferers overcome back problems. Dr. Sarno's most recent book is *Healing Back Pain*, Warner Books, 666 Fifth Ave., New York 10103.

Beware Of Eating Fatty Meals

Eating a fatty meal causes men's testosterone levels to drop significantly one to four hours afterwards. In a study of healthy men aged 23 to 35, their testosterone levels fell about 30% after they ate a meal deriving 57% of its calories from fat. Eating a meal with no fat or very little fat (2% of calories from fat) had no impact on testosterone levels. The researchers believe that if a man eats a fatty meal only occasionally, it probably won't affect his sexual performance but that a man's habitual consumption of fatty foods may have a negative effect.

Source: Wayne Meikle, MD, professor of medicine, University of Utah Medical Center, 50 N. Medical Dr., Salt Lake City 84132.

Changing Blood Types

Blood types can change. Organ transplants and certain infections can change a person's blood type—sometimes just temporarily...but sometimes permanently.

Source: Lawrence Petz, MD, UCLA Medical Center, Los Angeles, writing in The New England Journal of Medicine, 10 Shattuck St., Boston 02115.

The Vitamin D Dilemma

Too much—or too little—vitamin D added to milk is not the health problem the media now is claiming that it is. Researchers have found that some dairies add much more—or much less—than the standard 400 International Units (IU) per quart. But vitamin D, used by the body to regulate calcium absorption, is available from many sources other than milk—your body even manufacturers it when you stand in the sun. Lack of vitamin D is rarely a problem in the US. The danger comes from consuming too much. Infants who take in more than about 1,800 IU/day may not grow as well as those who consume less. Adults consuming more than 60,000 IU/day risk vitamin D poisoning—with symptoms much like drunkenness.

Problem:

The kidneys can absorb so much calcium that they can eventually fail. Only one dairy—so far—was found to have dangerous levels of vitamin D in its milk.

Self-defense:

Wherever possible, limit intake of dairy products fortified with vitamin D.

Source: Robban Sica-Cohen, MD, Center for the Healing Arts, 325 Post Rd., Orange, Connecticut 06477.

Best Cavity Fighters

Dental sealants help children avoid tooth decay...and the dentist's drill. Although 70% of all school-age children could benefit from this harmless and painless procedure, less than 10% have had it done.

Sealants are film-like plastics "painted" onto the biting surfaces of the molars (the back teeth). It takes just a few minutes to protect a tooth from cavities for about five years. Cost: $15–$30 per tooth—much less than a cavity filling.

Not every tooth needs to be sealed. A dentist should examine a child's back teeth for cavities.

If any are evident, all back teeth with deep crevices—which make them prone to decay—should be sealed. Once decay has developed on the sides of teeth, sealants can't be used. Sealants also can't be applied over metal fillings.

Note:

Although fluoride protects the sides of teeth, it doesn't protect the biting surfaces. It is important that children with sealants still floss regularly and brush at least twice daily with a fluoride toothpaste.

Source: Lawrence Kotlow, DDS, a pediatric dentist in Albany, NY, and past president of New York State Association of Pediatric Dentists.

Leukemia Link

Electric blanket warning. Childhood leukemia risk increased 70% in children who used an electric blanket or whose mothers used an electric blanket during pregnancy. Leukemia risk did not increase from exposure to any other electric appliance studied (heating pad, heated water bed, television, portable heaters, bedside electric clock). Recommended: Although it's not certain that electric blanket use actually causes leukemia, if you want to warm up your bed with an electric blanket, avoid exposure by turning off the blanket before you get in...from David Savitz, PhD, associate professor, department of epidemiology, University of North Carolina, Chapel Hill.

Herbal Remedies: How To Use Them Safely

Herbs have been used for thousands of years to treat illnesses and injuries.

But herbs can be toxic, as well as healing. And because herbs are not regulated by any government agency, it is very difficult to find out which one works for what and how to use them.

Traps: Much of the literature written about herbs and herbal remedies contains exaggerated claims...some handed down from 17th-century books. And many commercial preparations contain little of the actual herbs. Most popular herbs:

Aloe. Sold as an ingredient in lotions, etc. Effectiveness: There is no proof that aloe products purchased off the shelf offer any benefit whatsoever. Fresh aloe gel, however, does facilitate wound healing. For a minor burn, you can pull a leaf off an aloe plant and use the gel that oozes out of the center to help heal the burn.

Chamomile. Sold in tea bags. Effectiveness: There is substantial evidence that chamomile is an antispasmodic and an anti-inflammatory that also aids digestion. Chamomile products are marketed in Europe, where herbs are more closely regulated. Drawback: Chamomile is potentially allergenic. But only about half a dozen mild cases have been reported in this century.

Comfrey. Sold as loose leaves, used to make tea. Effectiveness: Facilitates wound healing to some degree by causing cells to reproduce more rapidly. Danger: It has been removed from the market in Europe and Canada because the root contains toxic alkaloids shown to cause liver cancer in small animals and liver malfunction in humans.

Feverfew. Sold as dried leaves in capsules or tablets. Effectiveness: Clinical studies have shown that it helps prevent migraines. There is good evidence that a relatively small amount is effective if used periodically. Problem: Because there are no government standards, it's almost impossible to obtain properly prepared feverfew. Tests show that many commercial feverfew products contain few active ingredients.

Garlic. Sold everywhere. Effectiveness: We now know that raw garlic can reduce hypertension, even in quantities as small as a half-ounce per week.

Ginseng. Sold in capsules, extracts and teabags. Originally used in the Orient as an aphrodisiac, it has been used as a tonic for about 20 years. Effectiveness: Although ginseng seems to fight fatigue in small animals, there have been no controlled studies in the US to prove its effectiveness in humans. Caution: Pure ginseng is expensive. Most products sold in the US are extracts that are subject to adulteration—some contain no ginseng.

Peppermint. Sold in capsules. Effectiveness: Oil of peppermint is a digestive aid—it warms the stomach and facilitates digestion.

Sassafras. Sold as strips of bark, and formerly in tea bags. Called a blood purifier because it was once used to treat venereal disease, sassafras tea later became popular as a tonic. Danger: The Food & Drug Administration (FDA) has forbidden its use as a food additive or drug because it contains safrole, a toxin that, ironically, is also responsible for its pleasant flavor and aroma. Although the toxic effect is cumulative over time, a single cup of sassafras tea contains three to four times the amount that would be considered a maximum dosage.

Using herbal remedies:

Because most of the available literature is written to promote or sell a product, it's very difficult to learn how to use herbs and herbal remedies. It's also hard to determine if the purveyors of herbal products really know what they're doing and are offering something useful. Self-defense:

Read helpful literature.

Buy the right products. Look for items processed by companies that are making an effort to standardize their products and control quality.

Use herbs wisely. They're best used for occasional problems—indigestion, minor burns, headaches, etc.—for which you'd buy an over-the-counter remedy.

Warning: There are some conditions—heart trouble, worsening arthritis, etc.—for which you definitely should not use herbs.

Example: Some people take yucca tablets to relieve arthritis symptoms. But it has not proven to be effective...and using it can delay someone from getting proper treatment.

Source: Varro E. Tyler, PhD, dean of the Purdue University School of Pharmacy for more than 20 years. He is the author of *The New Honest Herbal*, J.B. Lippincott Co., East Washington Square, Philadelphia 19106.

The Most Misunderstood Cardiac Condition

Mitral valve prolapse is an often misdiagnosed heart condition that occurs when the mitral valve, which lets blood drain from the top to the bottom chamber of the heart, buckles back during the heart's contraction.

Mitral valve prolapse syndrome (MVPS) refers to a cluster of symptoms that often occur when the heart has this abnormality.

Common symptoms: Heart palpitations, chest pain, dizziness, fatigue, anxiety or panic attacks, headaches, mood swings. Symptoms may be made worse by physical or emotional stress, caffeine, dehydration, skipping meals or being in a hot, dry environment.

MVPS affects 4% to 18% of Americans—as many as 40+ million people. It afflicts about three times as many women as men.

The physical abnormality is believed to be inherited.

Whether it actually causes the symptoms associated with it—and if so, how—is unknown.

Other physiological changes associated with mitral valve prolapse include:

• High sensitivity to catecholamines, the adrenaline-like substances released by the nervous system to help the body deal with emergencies.

• Problems with the body's salt-regulating mechanism.

• Decreased intravascular volume—the amount of blood circulating through the body.

• In some people, the buckling back of the valve is accompanied by a murmur, during which a small amount of blood flows back into the top chamber of the heart. (The blood doesn't stay there, but gets pumped out on the next beat.)

Not all physicians are familiar with MVPS. Too often, symptoms are not taken seriously by doctors, or are wrongly attributed to other conditions—usually hypoglycemia, chronic fatigue syndrome, an inner ear problem or anxiety disorder.

Many people with the condition go from doctor to doctor, terrified they're on the brink of a heart attack—only to be told there's nothing wrong with them or that the problem is psychological.

The good news:

Despite being classified as a heart condition, mitral valve prolapse does not cause heart attacks, and it's believed that the majority of people with MVPS have a normal life span.

Sometimes, just learning that the condition has a name—and that it's not life-threatening — is enough to make the syndrome manageable.

However, patients with mitral valve prolapse are advised to use antibiotics when undergoing "dirty surgery"—procedures, such as root canal work, during which bacteria could be released into the blood, making the valve more vulnerable to infection.

Diagnosing MVPS:

In addition to noting the presence of symptoms, a physician can usually diagnose MVPS by listening to the patient's heartbeat for a click (made by the buckling back of the valve)—or murmur (the swooshing sound caused by the flow of blood back into the top chamber). These sounds, though, aren't always detectable. The diagnosis may be confirmed with an echocardiogram, or ultrasound examination.

Living with MVPS: There is no cure for mitral valve prolapse. Fortunately, the symptoms can usually be controlled through changes in diet, exercise and other life-style habits.

Nutrition management:

• Avoid caffeine and other stimulants. Because MVPS patients are sensitive to adrenaline-like substances, stimulants can aggravate symptoms. Cut out coffee, tea, chocolate, caffeinated soft drinks and over-the-counter drugs containing caffeine, such as Anacin and Vivarin. Also avoid drugs that contain the stimulants ephedrine and pseudoephedrine, including Actifed, Benadryl, Chlor-Trimeton, Sudafed and many other antihistamines.

• Increase salt and fluid intake, especially if you feel dizzy when you stand up. People tend to think *heart problem—cut down on salt,* but the opposite is true of MVPS. The condition is often accompanied by problems with salt regulation and circulating blood volume, so taking in enough salt and fluids—at least eight glasses of water or juice a day—is important.

Exception: People with high blood pressure should not add salt to their diet.

• Eat a well-balanced diet, not too high in calories—or sweets. A high caloric intake—and the metabolization of simple carbohydrates and fats—can greatly increase the activity of the sympathetic nervous system, the body's "accelerator," making symptoms worse.

• Never go on crash or fad diets. Not only are they ineffective over the long term, but most of the weight loss achieved is through water depletion—just the opposite of what someone with MVPS needs.

• If you suffer from migraine headaches, avoid tyramine. Tyramine is a food component that has been associated with migraines. It is found in chocolate, citrus fruit, avocados, raspberries, pickled herring and some foods that have undergone fermentation, such as cheese and wine.

Exercise management:

My research has shown that many MVPS sufferers experience a dramatic improvement in symptoms simply by following an exercise program. For best results, workouts should be:

• Aerobic (brisk walking, bicycling, swimming, etc.).

• Done a minimum of three times a week, preferably on alternate days.

• Twenty to 45 minutes long, plus time to warm-up and cool down muscles.

• Performed at a level where work load feels somewhat difficult but not too intense. Taking pulse rate to measure workout intensity is not recommended for people with MVPS. If you feel out of breath, overexerted or dizzy, you're exercising too hard.

Very important: Start slow. If you're out of shape, begin with a 10-minute session and add a few more minutes each time. And don't expect symptoms to vanish overnight. Our research subjects didn't begin to show improvement until they'd been exercising regularly for six weeks or more.

Coping with panic attacks:

A number of people with MVPS have recurrent anxiety attacks accompanied by heart palpitations, light-headedness, shortness of breath, extreme apprehension or fear, chest pain and/or the feeling that they're about to pass out.

For many, the unexplained presence of frightening symptoms, such as a pounding heart, triggers an outflow of anxiety. The person may think, *I'm having a heart attack,* and these kinds of thoughts further intensify the physical symptoms.

Panic attacks rarely come from nowhere. If you think about it, you may be able to identify a source of anxiety—or remember eating a type of food you're sensitive to—preceding the attack.

Helpful: Cognitive therapy, as described in books by Dr. David Burns of the University of Pennsylvania.* You can change the way you react to events by altering how you perceive them. Key steps:

1. Be aware of automatic thoughts—*there is a clutching in my chest…I'm about to die.*

2. Identify the cognitive distortions, or irrational patterns of thinking, that lead to anxiety and depression.

Examples:

• Catastrophizing—*I'm going to pass out in the middle of the supermarket. I'll be humiliated.*

• Overgeneralization—*This panic attack will make me late for work and ruin my whole week…and my boss will probably fire me.*

• *Should* statements.

• Focusing on negative information and discounting the positive.

• Expecting the worst—*This must be a heart attack.*

• All-or-nothing thinking—*I can't take control of my health. I must be a total failure.*

3. Challenge your irrational thoughts with rational, contradictory evidence. Write your argument down if you have to.

Unfortunately, it's hard to think clearly enough to use cognitive therapy techniques when you're in the middle of a panic attack. Good on-the-spot measures:

• Get up and move around. By lying in the dark worrying, you'll only make it worse. Focus your attention on something else, such as housework or an absorbing book. Call a friend and touch base with reality.

• Breathe. Pursed-lip breathing is very effective in combating shortness of breath. Don't worry about taking a deep breath—just breathe in, then slowly exhale through your mouth with your lips pursed, as though blowing out a candle. Repeat three or four times until you can breathe comfortably.

Medications:

The non-drug interventions just described can bring about great improvement for the

Feeling Good: The New Mood Therapy and The Feeling Good Handbook, William Morrow & Company, Inc., 1350 Avenue of the Americas, New York 10019.

vast majority of people with MVPS. However, if excessive symptoms continue to interfere with the activities of daily life, medication may be helpful.

Most commonly prescribed: Beta-blockers and anti-anxiety drugs. Both have side effects, so discuss them with your doctor and make sure he/she carefully monitors their effects.

Source: Kristine Scordo, PhD, RN, clinical director of The Cardiology Center of Cincinnati and Mitral Valve Prolapse Program of Cincinnati, 10525 Montgomery Rd., Cincinnati, Ohio 45242. She is the author of *Taking Control: Living with the Mitral Valve Prolapse Syndrome*, Camden House, Inc., Drawer 2025, Columbia, South Carolina 29202.

Alcohol Dangers

High alcohol intake—particularly beer intake—has been shown in a recent study to be associated with an increased risk of rectal cancer among men. Reason: Unknown. Possible explanations: Alcohol may stimulate an increase in bile acids, which now seem to be involved in both colon and rectal cancers …beer contains a high level of nitrosamine, a known carcinogen…ethanol has been linked to rapid cell growth in the rectum. At highest risk: Men who drink two or three beers per day—or men who drink a total of four alcoholic drinks per day. This group was shown to have an 85% increased risk of rectal cancer. (In women, the association between alcohol and rectal cancer could not be confirmed because those women studied did not drink as heavily as the men.) Note: Approximately four percent of all new cancers in the United States are rectal cancers.

Source: Jo L. Freudenheim, PhD, assistant professor of social and preventive medicine, State University of New York, Buffalo.

AIDS Defense

Circumcision and AIDS. Uncircumcised men may be up to eight times more susceptible to the AIDS virus during heterosexual intercourse than men who are circumcised. Theories: The intact foreskin may provide the warm, moist environment that the AIDS virus needs in order to survive…the foreskin may be traumatized during intercourse, enabling the virus to enter the body…the foreskin may contain cells that have receptors for the AIDS virus.

Source: Alan Ronald, MD, head of the Department of Internal Medicine, University of Manitoba, Winnipeg, Canada. Dr. Ronald is working in conjunction with Francis Plummer, MD, who is the Canadian head of the Cooperative Sexually Transmitted Disease Research Program in Nairobi, Kenya.

Unnecessary Cataract Surgery

Unless cataracts interfere with normal activities, surgery isn't recommended. Trap: Many doctors routinely remove cataracts before it's truly necessary. Because cataracts vary in size, density and location in the lens, they can exist for a lifetime without creating major vision problems. Time for surgery: When you can't read a newspaper because of cataracts.

Source: Dr. Stephen Bloomfield, associate professor of ophthalmology at Cornell University Medical School.

Coffee Dangers

Is coffee really all that dangerous? Here's what our expert told us…

Although coffee has no nutritive value, its use is so common that no one thinks of it as what is really is—a recreational drug.

Problem: Coffee contains several potent pharmacological agents categorized as methylxanthines—caffeine is one of them. Coffee plants use these as natural pesticides. Scary: Some insects that eat coffee beans die immediately.

Because we're bigger than insects, the effects on people are less noticeable…but may, nevertheless, be harmful in the long run. Coffee and the heart:

Large-scale studies on coffee's effect on the heart contradict each other. Some conclude that coffee is dangerous...others find it safe. Common sense suggests that it is a hazard. Reason: Coffee activates our adrenergic system—the fight-or-flight mechanism that produces adrenaline.

In addition to making us alert—usually the effect we seek—this adrenaline accelerates our heart rate and constricts the blood vessels, often for hours.

Result: If you drink four cups of coffee each day, your heart will beat thousands of extra times. And to overcome the constriction of the blood vessels in the periphery, it will beat harder, raising your blood pressure.

These extra, harder beats strain the heart and increase the risk of heart disease and heart attack.

In addition, coffee can provoke cardiac arrhythmia in people prone to this problem. And if a person has another factor that could cause arrhythmia, that factor will be compounded by caffeine. Result: Caffeine greatly increases the person's risk of developing cardiovascular problems.

More trouble: Because coffee is so bitter, many people counter that taste by adding sugar. This creates a host of additional problems for the cardiovascular and other systems. Other negative effects:

In addition to causing heart problems, coffee can...

• Increase cholesterol levels.

• Magnify the effects of stress on the cardiovascular system.

• Cause ulcers and prevent ulcers from healing.

• Provoke or exacerbate anxiety disorders.

• Induce fibrocystic breast disease—a benign condition that scares many women by creating lumps in the breast.

• Generate migraines.

• Increase the risk of stroke. This risk has shown to be even greater when caffeine is consumed in combination with phenylpropanolamine, a drug found in nasal decongestants and over-the-counter diet preparations—many of which also contain caffeine.

How to give up coffee:

If you're addicted to coffee, don't stop cold turkey. This could make you extremely irritable...perhaps even cause a migraine headache. And such an unpleasant experience would make it less likely that you'd try to quit again, if your first attempt fails.

Better: Decrease consumption by a quarter cup to a half cup every few days. If you start getting headaches, increase your dose slightly, and then start decreasing it again—slowly.

Switching to tea or decaffeinated coffee is not the answer. Reason: Although decaffeination removes caffeine from the beverage, several other methylxanthines are still present. These naturally occurring pesticides can be found in decaffeinated coffee, decaffeinated teas, black tea, colas and chocolate.

Although it is reasonable to use decaf and these other beverages as a transition from drinking coffee with caffeine to no coffee, your mental and physical health can be greatly improved by eliminating the consumption of these beverages as much as possible.

Only the fact that these beverages are so widely consumed has made us lose sight of just how dependent we are on drugs.

Source: Richard M. Carlton, MD, a psychiatrist who has discovered that many psychological as well as physical problems can be solved through proper nutrition. He maintains a private practice at 333 W. 57 St., New York 10019.

Lowering Cholesterol

Lower cholesterol by adding fiber supplements to your diet—but they must be the right type of fiber. Of the three common fiber supplements, only psyllium significantly lowers LDL (bad) cholesterol. Calcium polycarbophil and methylcellulose don't lower LDL cholesterol significantly...in fact, they may actually increase it.

Source: Study led by James Anderson, MD, University of Kentucky and Veterans' Administration Medical Center, reported in The Medical Post, 777 Bay St., Toronto, Ontario M5W 1A7.

The Well-Stocked Medicine Cabinet

What you shouldn't have in your medicine cabinet is as important as what you put in it.

General guideline: Check with your doctor before purchasing any over-the-counter medication...or if your symptoms persist longer than a few days.

What to include:

• Pain, fever and anti-inflammatory medicines. Recommended: Acetaminophen (Tylenol, Datril and Panadol). It reduces pain and fever without damaging the intestinal tract. However, it is not an anti-inflammatory—it will not reduce swelling.

Aspirin and ibuprofen (Advil, Nuprin and Medipren) relieve pain and inflammation...aspirin also relieves fever. Warning: At high doses, both can lead to internal bleeding and wearing away of the stomach lining. At greatest risk: the elderly.

Aspirin is also associated with ulcers and tinnitus (ringing in the ears)...ibuprofen with kidney toxicity. Self-defense: Always take aspirin or ibuprofen with food or liquid antacids, and never exceed the recommended dosage—no more than eight regular-strength tablets a day.

• First-aid materials: Hydrogen peroxide for cleaning wounds (not alcohol, which is drying and more irritating), antibiotic creams, cotton swabs, gauze pads, surgical tape, adhesive bandages, blunt scissors and tweezers.

• Skin protectors: Petroleum jelly or mild moisturizers for dry skin...over-the-counter vaginal cream for mild yeast infections... hydrocortisone cream (no more than 0.5% strength) for poison ivy or other rashes.

Caution: Do not use hydrocortisone on face or genitals without consulting a doctor. And don't use it on fungal infections, such as athlete's foot or jock itch—it will make the problem worse.

• Syrup of Ipecac...to induce vomiting after ingesting a poison.

Caution: Call a poison-control center before administering—vomiting makes certain kinds of toxins more destructive.

What to use less of:

• Over-the-counter cold remedies. These fight symptoms but don't cure colds. And by drying out mucous membranes, they can hamper the body's natural defenses, slowing recovery.

Antihistamines can be sedating—don't drive or operate machinery while using them.

Decongestants can constrict blood vessels and increase heart rate, making them dangerous for people who are experiencing heart problems or hypertension. Talk to your doctor before taking them.

Cough medicines may contain alcohol, as well as added decongestants and antibiotics. Read the label carefully, and don't exceed recommended dosages.

What to leave out:

• Diet pills. These are completely ineffective over the long term—they work only as long as you take them. They can be addictive. And they are very, very dangerous for people with heart problems—especially undiagnosed heart problems—or high blood pressure.

• Decongestant nose drops. These create a rebound effect—when you stop using them, you become as congested as before...if not more. Better: Steroid nasal sprays, available by prescription only.

Source: Robert L. Perkel, MD, clinical associate professor of family medicine at Thomas Jefferson University, Philadelphia 19107.

Better Summer Care For Your Skin

As you head outdoors this summer, be prepared to protect your skin from permanent damage. Don't fall for these myths:

• Myth: That a slight tan is a safe tan. Even a slight tan indicates that the skin has been damaged and is at risk for developing premalignant and malignant lesions.

• Myth: That sun blocks prevent long-term damage to the skin. Suntan lotions that contain sun-protection factors (SPFs) protect against burning...but the sun's rays continue to penetrate and damage the skin.

Trap: People slather themselves and their children with sun blocks...and then spend hours in the sun, thinking they're safe.

• Myth: That the sun can help improve acne. The sun actually causes only a short-lived cosmetic improvement in acne. Ultimately, the sun dries out the skin, stimulating the oil glands to start pumping, pumping, pumping, worsening the condition.

Because exposure to the sun toughens the skin, it also causes the formation of enlarged pores and blackheads.

• Myth: That ocean water is good for the skin. Salt from the ocean depletes the skin's moisture; the result is that it becomes dry and prone to wrinkles.

Source: Mary Ellen Brademas, MD, assistant clinical professor of dermatology at New York University School of Medicine...and chief of dermatology at St. Vincent's Hospital...and director of the Venereal Diseases Clinic at Bellevue Hospital. All are in New York City.

Safer Telephone Use

Don't use telephones while you're near water—doing dishes, bathing, etc. If the phone gets wet, it can give you—and the person you're speaking to—an electrical shock. Also: Avoid using the phone during an electrical storm—lightning can travel through phone lines.

Source: *Rodale's Complete Home Products Manual,* Rodale Press, 33 E. Minor St., Emmaus, PA 18098.

Right Way To Remove A Tick

Grab the tick as close to the victim's skin as possible. Use tweezers or fingers covered in rubber gloves or a paper towel. Pull upward, without squeezing the tick's body, until it becomes detached. Disinfect the bite with Betadine. Do not squeeze, twist or jerk the tick out (you may break off the mouthparts

and inject yourself with infected fluids). Do not crush the tick once you've removed it—you want to avoid all contact with its fluids. Once it has been safely removed, flush the tick down the toilet. Encouraging: Generally, ticks must be attached for at least 24 hours or more in order to transmit illness.

Source: Dr. Glen Needham, tick physiologist, quoted in *Hippocrates,* 475 Gate Five Rd., Sausalito, California 94965.

Allergy News

Good news for allergy sufferers: With various preventive measures and allergy treatments now available, you can make yourself more comfortable during hay fever season this year.

Allergies: The new basics. An allergic reaction is an abnormal physical response to one of the millions of proteins in the environment. For reasons that are not entirely clear, the immune system perceives this protein—usually a totally benign substance—as being dangerous to the body and mounts an attack against it. The immune system's offensive against airborne allergens like pollen include hives, a runny (itchy, swollen) nose and teary eyes, as well as sneezing or wheezing.

In cases of food allergy, symptoms include cramps and diarrhea, often accompanied by swelling of the lips, eyes, face, tongue and throat.

Most common food allergens: milk, eggs, fish, shellfish, peanuts, soy and other nuts. Treatment: Complete avoidance of the allergens. Peanuts and fish can be lethal.

The capacity to develop allergies is an inherited trait that affects about 20% to 25% of the population. Airborne or "inhalant" allergies to ragweed, dust, cats and pollen are more common than allergies to food or drugs.

If you think you may have an allergy but you're not sure what's causing it, your doctor will probably recommend the standard allergy "scratch" test.

Procedure: Small amounts of suspected allergens are placed on the skin of the forearm, upper arm or back. The area is then pricked or scratched to introduce the allergen below the skin surface. The test site is examined after 15 to 20 minutes, and if swelling and redness of the skin have developed where a particular allergen was applied, the test is considered positive for that allergen. Treating and preventing allergic reactions:

Drug therapy for allergies will follow one of two approaches...

• it will either treat symptoms of the allergic reaction...

• or prevent the reaction from occurring.

• Antihistamines and decongestants: Either over-the-counter or prescription strengths treat allergy symptoms. In cases of mild-to-moderate allergies, such medications can probably clear up the runny nose, watery eyes and itchy mouth and throat that can make spring pollen season such a trial. Seldane and Hismanal, which produce no sedative effect, are both available by prescription.

• Anti-inflammatories: For more severe allergies, it may be preferable to prevent or moderate the allergic reaction itself with one of the corticosteroids administered as a nasal spray, or an anti-inflammatory drug—cromolyn sodium. Nasal cromolyn is a safe drug with few, if any, side effects. Nasal corticosteroids are topically potent agents that are quickly degraded after absorption. Therefore, the body sees only tiny amounts of steroid if the medication is used in recommended doses.

Important: If you have been relying on over-the-counter medication to control your allergy symptoms for years, it's time to consult a doctor about a more effective therapeutic regimen.

• Immunotherapy: Also known as "allergy shots," it is a third allergy treatment strategy. It is usually recommended only for people with at least moderate—but more likely severe—allergies. The goal of immunotherapy is to make allergy sufferers less responsive to their particular allergens. The starting dose is too small to be effective, but it is necessary to start with tiny doses to avoid allergic reactions to the shots themselves. Therefore, don't expect to see much improvement until you reach a maintenance dose.

How it works: Small amounts of known allergens are injected into the body once or twice a week. The dose is gradually increased until an effective or maintenance dose is achieved. This controlled introduction of small quantities of "foreign" proteins provokes the immune system into producing neutralizing antibodies, but not into a full-scale counterattack that would result in an allergic reaction. Once a sufficient amount of these antibodies are circulating in the body, strong allergic reactions (and their accompanying annoying symptoms) can be prevented or significantly reduced. Once a maintenance dose has been achieved, the interval between shots can be stretched out to every four to six weeks.

Two new classes of drugs:

Nasal atrovent and antileukotriene drugs are two new classes of drugs that are being studied for their effects on allergies. Neither is commercially available yet.

Relief without drugs:

The simplest way to eliminate the unpleasant symptoms of an allergy attack is to find out what you're allergic to and avoid it.

This advice is relatively easy to follow in the case of allergies to foods or animals. But avoiding airborne allergens can be a bit more difficult to accomplish. And because people allergic to pollen or ragweed may also be sensitive to other allergens (house dust) or irritants (perfume, cigarette smoke), exposure to these secondary triggers during hay fever season may exacerbate the pollen allergy and produce some very uncomfortable symptoms.

House dust is a common allergen that often acts as a secondary trigger in people with allergies to pollen, animal dander, etc. And one of the principal constituents of house dust is the house-dust mite—a microscopic insect that feeds off of discarded bits of dead skin. These mites thrive in places where you'd expect to find sloughed skin cells—in rugs, upholstered furniture, pillows, mattresses and box springs.

Battle plan:

Concentrate on the bedroom. It's where people spend most of their time—and where the house dust mite tends to spend most of its time. Put allergen-proof casings (which you can get from an allergy-supply house or a department store) on the pillows, box spring and mattress.

Important: These coverings must have a plastic layer and a zipper, and they must completely enclose the pillow, box spring or mattress. (The more expensive cases will have a cotton layer for greater comfort.) Also: Simplify the bedroom furnishings so it is easier to keep the room dust-free. Eliminate venetian blinds, heavy curtains, bed ruffles and canopies, stuffed furniture and bookcases that are difficult to keep dusted. Dust the room thoroughly twice a week.

Air-filtration system. This can be helpful in reducing indoor exposure to dust and other allergens. Recommended: An electrostatic system able to filter particles down to a level of five microns. If you have a central forced-air heating/air conditioning unit, a filtration device can easily be added to your existing system. If you don't have central heating, a room air purifier may handle the job adequately. Rule: Don't look for a bargain. The cheaper ones don't work as well as the more expensive units.

During spring allergy season, if you're allergic to pollens, grasses and other things found outdoors, reduce your exposure to these allergens when you're indoors by keeping your doors and windows closed. The same principle applies when you're traveling by car. And on dry windy days when there is a high pollen count, stay indoors if you can.

When to see a doctor:

If allergy symptoms—or the side effects of over-the-counter medications—begin to interfere with your lifestyle or your ability to work, or if they're just generally making you miserable, it's time to see a doctor about your allergies. (On the other hand, if your allergies are bothersome for only a few days each year, it's probably okay to self-treat with allergy pills bought at the drugstore.)

If you decide that you need to see a doctor, meet with your regular internist, pediatrician or family doctor first. He/she can prescribe appropriate first-line therapy to control your allergy symptoms. If, however, your symptoms don't respond to treatment, or if the side effects of the prescribed medications become difficult to tolerate, you should ask to be referred to an allergy specialist.

Source: Martha V. White, MD, senior staff fellow at the National Institute of Allergy and Infectious Diseases, National Institutes of Health, Bethesda, Maryland 20892.

Artificial Sweetener News

For years, artificial sweeteners have been hailed as the dieter's dream come true. Great taste. No calories. What could be better?

Problem: The sweeteners have not lived up to their publicity. Most don't really taste all that good. And the more tests we conduct, the more bad news we get about their adverse effects on our health.

The truth about:

• Saccharin. Widely available as Sweet-'n-Low. The first noncaloric artificial sweetener, saccharin was discovered in 1879, when it was accidentally produced by a student at Johns Hopkins University.

Saccharin is used in canned fruits and chewing gums and in unexpected places, including toothpaste. Its use has declined somewhat since the advent of newer sweeteners (see below).

Pros: 350 times sweeter than sugar.

Cons: Produces a bitter aftertaste. Saccharin creates a slightly increased risk of bladder cancer in humans. Products containing saccharin are required to carry a warning label regarding the cancer risk.

• Acesulfame K. Widely available as Sunette and Sweet-One.

The newest substance to be approved for use as a tabletop sweetener. It has not yet been approved for any additional uses.

Pros: 200 times sweeter than sugar.

Cons: Although it has not been thoroughly tested, long-term rat studies produced lung, breast and other tumors. It may slightly increase the risk of cancer and should not have been approved.

• Aspartame. Widely available as Equal and NutraSweet. Used in soft drinks and in countless types of diet foods. It breaks down at high temperatures, however, and can't be used in baked or cooked foods.

Pros: 150 to 200 times sweeter than sugar.

Cons: Early tests showed that aspartame may have caused an increased incidence of brain tumors in rats. (Other animals tested showed no tumors.)

A board of public inquiry revoked the Food and Drug Administration's (FDA) 1974 approval of aspartame on the grounds that the research did not conclusively show that aspartame does not cause brain tumors. Three of five members of an FDA panel selected to review the board's decision agreed with it. But the FDA commissioner overturned the board's decision and reapproved aspartame anyway.

The rat study has not been repeated, so the question of brain-tumor risk remains unresolved. Also, the medical literature is peppered with reports of headaches and other reactions associated with aspartame.

Recommended: People who seem to be sensitive to aspartame should avoid it.

Products containing aspartame also must carry a warning label for people with phenylketonuria (PKU), a genetic problem that afflicts one in 20,000 people. People with PKU can't metabolize a component of aspartame.
Warning for travelers:

Cyclamate, a popular sweetener in the 1950s and 1960s, was banned in the US in 1970. It was linked to bladder cancer, shrinking testes and other health risks in laboratory animals.

But US manufacturers still market cyclamate to many other countries, where it is used alone, or combined with saccharin. When you travel, read labels very carefully to avoid products that contain cyclamate.
Do we really need them?

More and more evidence shows that artificial sweeteners are not all they're cracked up to be. Reasons:

• Each presents some health risk.

• Despite the popularity of artificial sweeteners, people are consuming more sugar than ever. Theory: Sugar substitutes may be stimulating our appetite for sugar.

• Although artificial sweeteners have no calories, they have no nutritive value either.

Bottom line: Most people probably would be better off using moderate amounts of sugar.

One teaspoon of sugar contains fewer than 25 calories. Used in moderation, its only adverse effect (except in people with diabetes and some other medical conditions) is to promote tooth decay, which is easily preventable and treatable.

Source: Lisa Y. Lefferts, staff scientist at the Center for Science in the Public Interest, 1875 Connecticut Ave. NW, Suite 300, Washington, DC 20009. She is a specialist in food safety.

Are You Overweight?

Sixty-two out of 100 people consider themselves overweight. Reality: Only 20%–30% of the population is actually overweight.

Source: *Tufts University Diet & Nutrition Letter,* 53 Park Pl., New York 10007.

Food And Our Moods Food And Our Bodies

All food has its poisons, says an ancient Chinese proverb. Self-defense: Balance your poisons. In other words…eat a varied diet.

In modern society, most of us eat the same things day in and day out. We consume so much sugary, fatty, unhealthful food it's like living in an endless birthday party.

Sad result: We develop not just physical ailments but psychological problems—anxiety, depression, insomnia and hyperactivity, even schizophrenia and paranoia.

Good news: In many cases, it's possible to eliminate or lessen the severity of these problems simply by altering our diets.
What's going on:

Mainstream medical doctors and psychotherapists often overlook the role of food in psychological disturbances. That's unfortunate, because research over the years from MIT, the National Institutes of Health and other top institutions has shown that food does have an effect on brain processes.

In my years as a psychiatrist, I've witnessed countless instances in which a simple change of diet led to a rapid recovery of mental health. It's now clear to me that what we eat has a profound effect on what we think and how we feel.

Food, of course, is not always the culprit. Many psychological problems take years of psychotherapy before they respond, regardless of what the patient eats. But people who are experiencing emotional problems out of context to events with no discernible cause may be feeling the effects of a food hypersensitivity.

Different foods affect people differently, and any food can cause problems. But I found coffee, chocolate, milk, sugar and wheat to be the most common culprits. In many cases, my patients have been especially fond of the very food that was causing them the trouble.

Remarkable recoveries:

• **Anxiety and milk.** A married nurse in her 20s suffered from intense, pervasive anxiety, including terrifying choking and gagging attacks, often in public places.

So intense were these attacks that she considered herself an emotional basket case and had decided never to have children. She couldn't see how such an anxious person could be a good parent.

But in taking this woman's medical history, I began to suspect that her problem wasn't psychological at all but dietary. She had been subsisting primarily on dairy products. I suggested that she give up dairy products, at least for a while, and she did.

Result: Her anxiety and choking disappeared. Within a year, she and her husband had their first child. Note: Resuming the consumption of dairy products would reprovoke the symptoms.

• **Anxiety and coffee.** Psychiatrists have long known that too much coffee can cause anxiety. In fact, caffeine is implicated in anxiety so frequently that the *Diagnostic and Statistical Manual*—a guide used to diagnose mental illness—instructs psychiatrists to exclude caffeineism before diagnosing a patient with anxiety disorder.

Surprise: What many doctors don't know is that caffeine isn't the only troublesome compound in coffee. All coffees and teas—including decaf—also contain methylxanthines, naturally occurring pesticides that are a common cause of anxiety attacks. People troubled by anxiety or panic attacks should give up all coffee, tea, caffeine-containing soft drinks and chocolate.

Caution: Going cold turkey when giving up caffeine often causes severe headaches, sweating episodes and other symptoms of withdrawal. Give up caffeine gradually.

• **Chest pains and milk.** A 31-year-old lawyer was terrified by recurrent chest pains that he thought were heart attacks. So severe was the pain that he had been visiting emergency rooms and cardiologists' offices several times a week for more than two years.

Repeated electrocardiograms and blood tests indicated that his heart was healthy, and his doctors told him his pain was caused by hypochondria brought on by anxiety.

As it turned out, the real culprit was not anxiety but dairy products—which apparently irritated his esophagus. He gave up milk, and the pain disappeared.

• **Depression and milk.** A young filmmaker under my care was eager to give up film for a medical career, but he was too fearful to take the leap. Instead, he became a part-time emergency medical technician.

One day he came into my office complaining of intestinal pain, a symptom often caused by consumption of dairy products. I told him to give up milk, because it can not only cause gripping intestinal pains but also give him the cranky frown that he always had.

Two weeks later, his scowl was gone, and he was cheerful for the first time in years. His relationships with friends and family members had shown signs of improvement after years of decline.

Two months later, he applied to medical school. Today he is a physician.

• Chronic fatigue and chocolate. A middle-aged businesswoman was troubled by foggy thinking and chronic fatigue so severe that it often kept her in bed for days on end. I learned that she ate chocolate two to three times a week. Although this didn't sound excessive, I suggested that she give it up anyway to see what happened.

Result: During her first chocolate-free month, she felt clear-headed for the first time in years. Then she ate a slice of chocolate cake at a dinner party...and spent the next three days in bed. This convinced her that chocolate was to blame.

• Schizophrenia and wheat. A woman in her 30s had long endured symptoms of schizophrenia, including auditory and visual hallucinations that made a normal life impossible. Her symptoms were so bad at times that hospitalization was necessary—and when I first saw her, she had recently ended her fifth stay in a psychiatric hospital.

Yet even then, hallucinations continued to plague her. She was able to function in society only because she was taking a powerful tranquilizer, Thorazine.

I asked about her eating habits and discovered that she was eating a great deal of wheat-based products, including pasta, cakes, cookies, etc. I prescribed a wheat-free diet, and almost immediately her hallucinations vanished. A few weeks later she again ate wheat, and the hallucinations recurred within minutes.

At that point she gave up wheat, and she continues to be hallucination-free years later.

Diet has not worked in every case of schizophrenia, of course. But this case illustrates the ancient saying, "One man's food is another's fierce poison." The poison (for some people) in wheat is two peptides that act as false neurotransmitters in the brain.

• Paranoia and wheat. An obese computer executive sought my help in an effort to lose weight. I persuaded her to give up wheat, and she quickly lost 10 pounds.

Bonus: Her mood and general outlook brightened markedly. In retrospect, she realized that wheat had contributed not only to her obesity but also to a low-grade paranoia—thinking "the boss is saying that just to get me," which could be reprovoked on ingesting wheat again. Off wheat, she lost weight and gained equanimity.

• Drowsiness and wheat. A lawyer in his 30s was plagued by midafternoon sleepiness so overwhelming that he would often fall dead asleep at inopportune times—even in the middle of conversations.

Once, while visiting my home, he fell asleep in my living room. When he woke up, I asked about his eating habits and discovered that he had been eating lots of bread (wheat) at fancy lunches with clients. When he gave up the bread, his afternoon sleepiness disappeared.

If you have a problem:

Ask yourself which food you would be least willing to give up—then give it up.

Wean yourself off it slowly over a few (one to three) weeks, then take note of your symptoms. Have they diminished? If so, you have probably pinpointed the culprit. If not, try giving up another food.

Good news: In many cases, it's possible to resume eating the culprit food—on occasion, and in small quantities—without having symptoms reappear.

Source: Richard M. Carlton, MD, a psychiatrist in private practice at 333 W. 57 St., New York 10019. A specialist in the relationship between food and psychological disorders, Dr. Carlton is now studying the relationship between nutrition and learning disabilities.

Crystal Decanter Danger

Crystal decanters, the lovely, sparkling glass containers that are popular wedding gifts, pose a health threat if you store wine or other alcoholic beverages in them. Good crystal is made with lead, and the lead leaches into liquids, particularly acidic liquids, over time. Less threatening: Crystal wineglasses, because the liquid is consumed quickly. However, pregnant women should avoid crystal glasses altogether. Baby alert: Crystal baby bottles shouldn't be used at all. Babies are more sensitive to lead poisoning than adults and the risks are too high.

Source: *FDA Consumer*, United States Superintendent of Documents, Washington, DC 20402.

Too Much Good Food Is Bad For Your Health...Too

In attempting to revise bad eating habits, some people go too far in striving to eat healthful foods. Hidden danger: Even "good" foods can be bad for you if they're eaten in excess.

• Too much fiber. Most Americans get too little dietary fiber and could benefit from eating more. But too much fiber causes abdominal cramps, flatulence and poor absorption of iron, calcium, magnesium and other essential minerals.

Guidelines: Eat no more than 150 grams of fiber a day (about 20 ounces of unprocessed bran). If you're trying to boost fiber consumption, do so gradually. This gives your body a chance to adapt.

• Too much protein. Recent studies confirm that excessive protein causes irreversible kidney damage, and most Americans consume too much.

Guidelines: Eat one gram of protein a day for each kilogram (2.2 pounds) of body weight. An ounce of chicken contains about seven grams of protein. An ounce of milk contains about eight grams.

• Too many fruits and vegetables. Eating too many carrots (10 or more per day), and other fruits and vegetables high in beta-carotene results in hypercarotenemia, a cosmetic condition characterized by orangy skin.

Guidelines: Eat two to three servings of fruit and two to three servings of vegetables a day.

Source: Ronald Rudin, MD, an internist and nutritionist in private practice at 121 E. 84 St., New York 10028.

Kids Are What They Eat: Self-Defense Strategies

It's common knowledge that children must eat the right foods in order to grow up healthy and strong. But it is not so well understood that children's mental functioning can suffer if they eat the wrong foods at the wrong times even if they are well nourished.

One of the nation's leading authorities on how food affects learning and behavior explores the subject...

How does food affect the brain?

Almost all the fuel for the brain's work comes from glucose, a sugar manufactured from carbohydrates in the diet.

In addition, the brain's neurotransmitters—the vehicles for the chemical messages sent throughout the body—are composed of the same amino acids (or their by-products) that are found in food proteins.

Like drugs, foods are psychoactive. They affect how we think, feel and relate to others. Recent studies show that some foods can enhance problem-solving abilities, increase alertness and improve mood and behavior. New research also has shown that the wrong foods can impair behavior and learning.

In the long run, food has been found to affect basic intelligence by shaping brain growth and development.

Is there a difference between the food-brain dynamic of children and adults?

A child's behavioral control system is generally more fragile, and it takes less to disrupt it.

Example: Many adults skip breakfast without any noticeable ill effects. But when schoolchildren miss breakfast—as one in four frequently does—most research suggests that their attention span and performance suffer. The effect is most pronounced among children with attention or learning impairments, but many normal children are also breakfast-sensitive.

What should kids eat at breakfast?

Based on a recent study at Duke University, we concluded that high-carbohydrate breakfasts—toast, waffles and syrup, potatoes, doughnuts —tend to have a sedative effect on the brain as the morning wears on.

Again, this effect is most severe in the hyperactive and other impaired populations. Children perform better when the carbohydrates are balanced with high-protein foods—including milk, eggs and cheese.

Is milk really the ideal food it's cracked up to be?

Milk is rich in calcium, an essential nutrient not only for bones and teeth but for the proper functioning of nerve cells.

When schoolchildren who missed breakfast were given morning snacks of either milk or calcium supplements, they became both calmer and more alert.

We've heard a lot about the dangers of high-fat and high-cholesterol diets, even in children. Is skim milk healthier?

Children have different nutritional needs than adults. In particular, they need appropriate amounts of fat in their diets to insulate their brain nerve cells and prevent nerve crosstalk. In extreme cases, a low-fat diet can lead to brain damage.

Breast milk is ideal for infants, followed by 2%-fat milk for preschoolers, then 1%-fat milk for older children through adolescence.

Can excess sugar really make children more hyperactive?

The evidence, as reflected in numerous studies over the past 10 years, is conflicting. Some research suggests that refined sugar induces inappropriate behavior, poor attention and even—in some hyperactive children—aggression. But other studies show no clear effect.

In our breakfast study at Duke, we found that hyperactive children seemed to benefit when they received a sugar drink in conjunction with a high-protein meal—they quieted down considerably.

But their behavior worsened when they got the sugar drink with other carbohydrates. Note: When they had the sugar drink by itself, they behaved as they did after drinking a placebo. Normal children responded similarly, though less dramatically.

Again, balance was the key factor.

Are you saying that sugar itself isn't bad for kids?

I'm saying that a child's sugar craving may serve a physiological purpose—and that a parent's challenge is to manage that craving rather than to try to eliminate it.

A child typically goes through three spurts of brain growth—between 3 and 5 years of age…9 and 11…and 12 and 14.

During each growth spurt, the brain requires more fuel, or glucose, than at other times—which might account for a child's desire for high-carbohydrate foods, including refined sugar or sucrose.

That said, fructose—the sugar found in fruits—can provide brain fuel just as well as sucrose and will create less havoc with the child's blood sugar along the way.

How do you handle this issue in your home?

I allow my child one refined sugar treat a day, but only one—be it a Popsicle, a candy bar or a cupcake. It's a mistake to give children uncontrolled access to the refrigerator.

Is there any food that you would ban from a child's diet altogether?

I would not give a child any drink sweetened with aspartame (NutraSweet). This substance has no nutritional value, and there is some evidence that it can provoke hyperactivity.

Do you believe in dietary supplements for children?

When children eat a balanced diet, very few need any supplementation. In fact, they are better off without it, since supplements can throw off the body's mineral balance.

The one positive exception is iron supplementation for adolescent females, who lose iron in menstruation.

Source: C. Keith Conners, PhD, director of the Center for Attention Deficiency Disorders in Children at Duke University Medical School. He is the author of *Feeding the Brain/How Foods Affect Children*, Plenum Publishing, 233 Spring St., New York 10013.

Generic Drugs Myth

Generic drugs aren't always cheaper than brand name equivalents. While pharmacies pay less for generic drugs, many mark them up to match the price of their brand-name competitors.

Nosophobia: How Fear Of Disease Is Making Us Sick

Nosophobia—defined as a morbid dread of disease—has become a national psychosis, and it's on the increase, we learned from Dr. Elizabeth Whelan, president of the American Council on Science and Health, Inc., when we spoke with her recently. What Dr. Whelan thought that we should know about the problem...

Nowhere is nosophobia more evident than in recent panics about "cancer-causing" chemicals in food. We're choosing superstition over science, with dangerous implications for our society.

Example: The Alar scare. Because high doses of Alar were reported to cause cancer in mice, intelligent and educated Americans behaved irrationally, throwing out apples and apple products. One New York mother even called the state police to stop her daughter's school bus because the girl was carrying a "poison" apple in her lunch.

The scientific reality is that trace levels of pesticide residue have never been implicated in ill health in any human being, ever. There has never been a documented case of ill health related to pesticide residues from the regulated, approved use of pesticides. Obviously, if you were to drink a couple of quarts or so of Alar—or any other concentrated chemical, including the arsenic that occurs naturally in potatoes—you'd probably wind up getting sick.

Many foods contain chemicals that, in high doses, cause cancer in rodents—including table pepper, mushrooms, peanuts, soy sauce ...and even bread. That doesn't mean these foods aren't safe for human beings to eat, in the doses we're exposed to.

We assume new risks when we ban chemicals...and those risks can be much more threatening to public health than the imagined "cancer" risk. Bugs may penetrate food and cause microbial damage, which can make food dangerous to eat. Without additives to preserve food, rancidity can occur.

If crops are widely destroyed by insects, we'd face the ultimate public health threat, starvation. We're far from that...but we are seeing increased food prices as producers try to comply with ever-more-complicated regulations.

In fact, I'd make the charge that nosophobia is causing cancer rather than preventing it. While lecturing to a fourth-grade class in New York last spring, I told them that cigarette smoking causes cancer—a link that is certain. One of the students said, "So do apples. What's the point?" When everything is thought to cause cancer, people are less likely to take real threats seriously.

Also last spring, I saw a nosophobic neighbor loading all her applesauce into the car. She said she was returning it to the store because she was concerned about her child's health. The next morning I saw the same woman riding her bicycle on a sandy road, with her child on the back of the bicycle—and no helmet on the child. The truly insidious result of nosophobia is that you lose your perspective on real danger. This woman had deprived her child of apples—that are actually wholesome yet she put her at risk of epilepsy or death by not having her wear a helmet.

If we were to take the funds that go into testing and regulating supposed carcinogens in food, and channel that money into efforts that we know would help to prevent cancer—helping people stop smoking, educating them to avoid the excessive sun exposure that can lead to skin cancer, encouraging early detection of cervical and colon cancer—we'd see an enormous decrease in cancer deaths in our country.

If people want to extend their longevity, they should stop throwing out wholesome food and focus on real risks...smoking, alcohol abuse, illicit drug use, not eating a moderate diet, failing to use lifesaving technology—

like seat belts or smoke detectors. I don't want to sound unsympathetic to people's fears. Food is an emotional issue, particularly when children are involved. Having acknowledged that, it's time to get back to reality: Do we believe in science or superstition?

If you're worried about a possible carcinogen, ask whether the results are related to animals or humans. If related to humans (which these scares rarely are), look at the evidence. Has the link been shown in more than one study? What are the credentials of the source making the claim? A university scientist with training in epidemiology or toxicology is a better expert than a movie star.

The reason that our society has reached its current level of sophistication and affluence is that we are not superstitious. We've come a long way with science. Americans are living longer than ever before. Unchecked nosophobia puts both the public health and the high standard of living in the US at risk.

Source: Dr. Elizabeth Whelan, president of the American Council on Science and Health, Inc., 1995 Broadway, New York 10023. Dr. Whelan is the author of 21 books on health-related subjects.

Teddy Bears Can Make Children Sick

Teddy bears can cause allergic symptoms in children. Like other stuffed toys, bears are favorite dwellings for dust mites and may release clouds of allergenic mite excrement when squeezed. Alternative: Washable toys made of plastic or vinyl.

Source: *Rodale's Allergy Relief,* 33 E. Minor St., Emmaus, PA 18098.

Hair Cream Warning

Prolonged use of hair creams and lotions containing estrogen has caused breast enlargement in men and young children. Also: One hair product led to vaginal bleeding in women as old as 82. Problem: Because cosmetics are not regulated, no one knows which products contain estrogen.

Source: *The Harvard Medical School Health Letter,* 79 Garden St., Cambridge, MA 02138.

Lead Poisoning Warning

The danger of lead poisoning is greater than most of us think. Biggest source: Lead plumbing or copper plumbing soldered with lead. If your water pipes are a dull gray color instead of copper, or if they have dull gray soldering at the joints, you have a potential lead problem. Protection:

• Let the water run for at least three minutes before using it for drinking or cooking. That allows water that's been sitting in the pipes collecting lead to drain off.

• Drink and boil only cold water. Hot water dissolves lead much more quickly.

Source: *Tufts University Diet & Nutrition Letter.*

Tamper-Proof Capsules

A pharmaceutical manufacturing process produces capsules that are tamper-proof, leak-proof, and gas-tight (contents will not degrade on contact with oxygen). Bonus: The capsules, made of hard gelatin, are thinner and cheaper than the soft-gelatin capsules and have always been used with liquid and oil fillings. Key: Hermetic sealing of capsule halves makes it possible to reduce the gripping surface on the lower half of the capsule…so tampering cannot take place without damaging the original capsule. Final heat-sealing step locks capsule halves in place but does not alter the contents in any way. The inventors find the new capsules suitable for encasing powders, pastes, liquids, oils, pellets, microspheres or any combination of these.

Source: Capsugel AG (Division of Warner-Lambert), Basel, Switzerland.

Getting Fast Medical Care

If your condition is very serious: Call the police—always dial 911. Police response with an ambulance—or transport by the police themselves if no ambulance is available—will help facilitate matters at the hospital. Helpful: Call the ambulance a "bus"—the inside term used by police. Aim: To get them to assume that you or a close relative is a cop and render service accordingly.

Source: Harry Alberts, MSW, certified social worker, Box 402, Commack, NY 11725, 718-353-HELP. Mr. Alberts was formerly with the New York State Department of Health.

Cancer Test Failure

The usual test for cancer of the colon and rectum fails to find existing cancers 70% of the time. For this reason it may not be useful as a primary screening tool. The test looks for blood in the stool. But early-stage cancers of the colon and rectum do not cause bleeding and may have no overt symptoms at all—making the test a poor method of detecting them.

Source: A National Cancer Institute study of the test's effectiveness on more than 12,000 people, led by David Ahlquist, MD, Mayo Clinic, Rochester, MN.

Moderate Activity A Plus

Even moderate activity improves health, reduces stress and extends life. Just doing household chores can be beneficial—lawn mowing burns as many calories as cycling, and gardening uses almost as many as moderate swimming. Bottom line: Performing some physical activity is important—even if you have neither the time nor the temperament for extensive aerobic workouts.

Source: *University of Texas Lifetime Health Letter,* 1100 Holcombe Blvd., Houston 77030.

Calf-Cramp Self-Defense

Gently stretch the knotted muscle by grabbing your toes and pulling the ball of your foot toward the kneecap. Even better: Stand two feet from a wall with knees straight and feet flat on the ground. Press palms against the wall and slowly lean into the wall until your nose touches.

Source: *Listen to Your Body: A Head-to-Toe Guide to More Than 400 Common Symptoms, Their Causes and Best Treatments* by the editors of *Prevention* magazine, Rodale Press, 33 E. Minor St., Emmaus, Pennsylvania 18098.

The Stress Of A Cold Or The Flu Greatly Increases Your Body's Need For Nutritious Foods

Problems: A sore throat may make swallowing painful…stuffed nasal passages may interfere with your sense of smell, leaving food tasteless…and your appetite may grow very weak.

Why you still must eat right: When your body is fighting an infection, your immune system needs even more vitamins and minerals than it normally does. When you have a fever, you utilize protein more rapidly.

Realistic solution: Eat as nutritiously as you possibly can while you are ill. Emphasize foods that are rich in protein, vitamins and

minerals yet are also soothing and easy to swallow. If you find raw fruits and vegetables totally unappealing when you're ill, forget them. Take vitamin and mineral supplements if you know you aren't eating right.
Good foods to choose:

• Soups combining meat or poultry with vegetables. Pureed soups are especially palatable when swallowing hurts.

• Yogurt or cottage cheese. Both are high in protein, and they go down easily. Also try frozen yogurt or even popsicles.

• Baked potatoes. Provide minerals and vitamins, including vitamin C. Try topping it with yogurt.

• Blended juices. Drink the milder mixed juices—such as banana-pineapple-orange—for vitamin C if straight orange or grapefruit juice seems too acidic.

• Hot breakfast cereals diluted with warm milk. Especially valuable: Those fortified with vitamins and minerals.

• Soft scrambled eggs—or to reduce fat, use an egg substitute.

• Baked custard.

• High-protein drinks such as Carnation Instant Breakfast, Sustagen, Sustacal or Ensure. For a soothing feeling, drink them warm.

The convenience factor:

Prepare in advance for cold and flu season. Smart steps:

• Always keep at least some of the above-listed foods on hand throughout the winter.

• Stock your freezer with homemade or high-quality commercial soups.

Advance planning is especially important for those who live alone and tend to keep little food on hand.

Reason: A cold or the flu can strike very suddenly and leave you unable to shop or cook.

Source: Judith J. Wurtman, PhD, professor of brain and cognitive science at the Massachusetts Institute of Technology. She is the author of *Managing Your Mind and Mood Through Food,* HarperCollins, 10 E. 53 St., New York 10022.

2

More Travel—Smarter Travel

Best Time To Take A Vacation

The best time to take a break from it all is just before or after the busy season of your desired locale. You can save up to 50% on airfare, the weather will be the same and the destination will be less crowded.

Source: Mark Eisenson, editor, *The Banker's Secret Bulletin*, Box 78, Elizaville, New York 12523.

Travel Tips For The Organized Executive

Before you go:

- Keep a prepacked overnight kit ready at all times.
- Prepare three packing lists...overnight trips...longer, single-location trips...and multiple-location trips.

- Collect papers—notes for meetings, memos, etc.—for your trip in a special trip folder.
- Stock a travel briefcase with pads and pens, calculator, dictation machine and cassettes, prestamped mailers and supplies such as scissors, tape, etc.
- Organize your travel briefcase. One manager packs work for his first flight in the first compartment, for his second flight in the second compartment and so on.

On the road:

- Process mail daily with your secretary by phone.
- Have urgent mail shipped via overnight mail or faxed to you.
- Send tapes of meeting notes back to your secretary.
- Take expense forms with you and write them up as you go.

For smooth reentry:

- Return to the office in late afternoon or early morning.

• Slide back into the routine with an easy project you've left on your desk.

Source: Stephanie Winston, founder of the New York–based time-management consulting firm, The Organizing Principle, and the author of *The Organized Executive*, Warner Books, 1271 Avenue of the Americas, New York 10020.

Better Packing

Put your suitcase out several days before a trip—and toss in items you want to take along as you come across them.

Source: *Super Memory: A Quick-Action Program for Memory Improvement* by Douglas J. Herrmann, PhD, former research psychologist at the National Institutes of Health, Rodale Press, 33 E. Minor St., Emmaus, Pennsylvania 18098.

Hotel Savvy

Guarantee your room for late arrival—even if you plan to arrive early. Flight delays may cause you to arrive later than expected. Most hotels won't hold a room after 6 pm—unless the reservation is guaranteed with a credit card.

Source: *The Complete Financial Guide to the 1990s* by Gary L. Klott, business correspondent for *The New York Times,* Times Books, 201 E. 50 St., New York 10022.

Hotel Room Rate Trap

The trap: paying the rack rate—the price listed in the hotel brochure—for a night's lodging. Call the hotel directly and ask for the best possible rate—weekend packages, seasonal specials or senior discounts. These will likely be lower than the rate quoted by travel agents and 800-number reservation operators. Also helpful: Ask for the corporate rate— available even to individual travelers—which is usually 10% to 15% off the rack rate.

Source: Herb Teison, editor, *Travel Smart*, 40 Beechdale Rd., Dobbs Ferry, New York 10522.

Vacation Traps...And Wonderful Alternatives

It's a shame to waste money on a vacation that fails to meet your expectations. Overrated destinations:

• Trap: Hawaiian "fantasy" resorts. In both architecture and amenities, these multi-million dollar resorts completely lack any feel for the culture of Hawaii. Guest activities include Clydesdale horse riding and gondola sailing on man-made lakes. If fantasy is what you're looking for, go to Disney World instead.

Better: The island of Lanai. Once home to pineapple plantations, the island has recently seen the opening of its first major resorts. Result: It still retains the atmosphere of early Hawaii.

• Trap: Bermuda in winter. Many vacationers don't realize that this island is located in the Atlantic Ocean, not the Caribbean—at about the same latitude as North Carolina. Winter weather is often rainy and chilly.

Better: Cancun or Cozumel on the Mexican Caribbean. Both offer good winter rates.

• Trap: Venice in the summer. Poor sanitation, hoards of tourists and heat and humidity combine to make Venice smelly and unpleasant in the summer. Visit at another time of year.

Better: If you want both art and canals, try Amsterdam.

• Trap: Miami Beach. The city lost its luster long ago. Hotel Row has become crowded and expensive.

Better: Fort Morgan Island on the Alabama Gulf Coast. This 25-mile breaker island is quiet and offers a pleasing southern atmosphere. Drawback: Winter weather isn't as mild as in South Florida.

• Trap: The overbuilt Caribbean islands. These include Nassau/Paradise Islands in the Bahamas, the Montego Bay area in Jamaica and the Dutch side of St. Maarten.

Better: The quieter Bahamian islands of Eluthera and Exuma. If you want quiet and excitement, Anguilla is only a 20-minute ferry ride from the shopping and casinos of St. Maarten.

• Trap: All-inclusive resort packages. Offered primarily in the Caribbean and Mexico (and coming soon to Cuba), these packages include room, meals and activities all for one price and all under one roof. Drawbacks: You pay for amenities (rhumba lessons, for example) that you may not use and you never experience the surrounding countryside.

Better: Villas, equipped with kitchens and bedrooms, are a better choice. They give you privacy at a good value.

• Trap: Traditional cruises. The ships that sail the Caribbean and Alaskan coast make ports of calls that, in recent years, have become fake places that are designed to take as much money from tourists as quickly as possible.

Better: Cruise ships and schooners sailing the New England and Canadian coast…or the fjords of Scandinavia offer great cruises. And you don't have to fend off people selling beads every time you step ashore.

• Trap: Eastern Europe. Many who traveled to the newly free countries of Eastern Europe last year returned home disappointed. Problem: They expected to stay in reasonably comfortable hotels and enjoy exciting sightseeing. Reality: These countries have neither the hotels nor the tourism infrastructure (guides, buses, etc.) to handle tourists.

Exception: Visit Hungary, where years of goulash capitalism have created a modicum of tourist comforts. Or stay in a bordering country and take day trips to the East. Bonus: The Eurail Pass is now good for train travel in Eastern Europe.

• Trap: The most popular national parks in summer. Yellowstone and Yosemite are overrun with tourists and tour buses during the summer months.

Better: Visit the undiscovered—but more difficult to get to—jewels of the park system: Glacier in Montana, Boundary Waters Wilderness Area—a canoeist's dream—in Wisconsin and Big Bend in Texas.

• Trap: Vermont during the fall foliage season. During a few weeks in autumn, tour buses wend their way through the mountains of Vermont tail-to-trunk like parades of elephants.

Better: Visit the nearby, less crowded and nearly as breathtaking states of Maine, New Hampshire and upstate New York.

• Trap: Aspen in the winter. Both the prices and the crowds are out of this world.

Better: Visit Aspen in summer when the crowds have abated and the scenery is beautiful in an altogether different way. In winter, try Crested Butte, Colorado. It's less glitzy, a better value and has equally fine skiing.

Source: An expert who has been writing about travel for more than two decades.

Safer Air Travel

Pick off-peak flights, which are less likely to be full. Reason: The chances of dying in a crash increase significantly if a flight is heavily booked. Heaviest booking times: Rush hours and holidays.

Source: Study of major airline crashes in the United States over a 15-year period, led by Arnold Barnett, PhD, professor of operations research, Sloan School of Management, Massachusetts Institute of Technology.

Travel Discount For Seniors

Senior-citizen discounts offered by most airlines are applicable for one companion, regardless of the companion's age—a great travel opportunity for grandparents and grandchildren.

Source: *Bill & Pam Bryan's Off the Beaten Path*, 109 E. Main St., Bozeman, Montana 59715.

How To Get Satisfaction From Travel Companies

Every year Americans experience thousands of problems with travel arrangements. Travel and recreation are ranked sixth on the

US Department of Commerce's list of the products and services consumers complain about most—up there with other such "top ten" headaches as cars, banks and insurance.

Here's how to register a meaningful complaint in the travel industry—and how to pursue it until you get results.

Before you complain:

• Ask questions beforehand. Be extremely specific about your wants and needs when making arrangements. Aim: To accommodate special needs and avoid disappointing "mismatches."

Example: A couple instructed their travel agent to book them for a cruise they'd seen advertised. Although their cabin was comfortable and the food delicious, they didn't have much fun because most of their fellow passengers were retirees. They were expecting a younger, livelier group.

• Keep expectations realistic. A certain amount of inconvenience is an unavoidable part of life, whether you are at home or traveling. Problem: People may expect their vacations to be perfect. They often complain about hitches that occur while they are traveling that they would not attach blame to at home.

Example: A bus tour is held up in traffic due to an accident on the highway. The delay is clearly not the agent's—nor the carrier's—fault.

• Make sure your complaint is legitimate. Specifically, if a service promised in your contract is not delivered, and/or you suffer damages due to some negligence on the part of the party you are complaining against, you have a legitimate complaint.

Example: A bus that was chartered to take a group to a Broadway show is delayed due to a flat tire. The driver grumbles that he has repeatedly advised the bus company to replace the worn tires. The delay causes the group to miss the entire first act and was clearly caused by the bus company's failure to provide a reliable vehicle.

If your complaint is minor:

The majority of travel complaints are minor problems that can be easily corrected.

Examples: You don't receive the double room, non-smoking table or aisle seat you reserved.

Best: Complain politely—immediately. In most cases, the personnel in charge will resolve your problem right away. If necessary, call your travel agent for extra clout.

In the event you are asked to put up with a minor inconvenience, such as taking the window seat or keeping the single room until a double becomes available, avoid becoming angry or rude.

Better: Ask for a concession that will satisfy you—a price reduction, a complimentary bottle of wine, a voucher for a future service. You may need to speak to the management to get your request honored.

Don't expect to collect a refund if you accept the unacceptable. For instance, if the air conditioner in your hotel room is too noisy but you don't change your room—or your hotel.

Helpful: Inform the management or company representative of problems you encounter as a courtesy—even if you expect no recompense.

Examples: Tell the tour guide that he/she's talking too quickly...tell the hotel manager that the pool furniture needs cleaning.

Handling serious complaints

Step one: Collect the names of witnesses and company employees you deal with, copies of contracts, reservations, tickets or receipts, photos and/or witness statements if appropriate, and any other material that can document the incident and any losses.

Step two: Write directly to the president of the firm by name. Your letter should be brief and clearly typed. Include the following:

• Who you are. Include any identification that may add weight to your complaint (you are a steady, old customer, a stockholder, a member of the travel industry, the chairperson of a travel committee).

• An objective description of what happened. Do not whine! Include: Your assertions as to why what happened was their fault, and a description of the damages caused, if any.

• What you expect in the way of compensation. This can be a refund, reimbursement of damages, voucher for future service, etc.

• Wait 30 days. If you receive no reply, follow up with a copy of the letter along with a note requesting a response. Also send copies of your letter to the Consumer Protection Division in the office of the Attorney General of your state (use his/her name), and to any other governing body responsible for regulating the company or service in question.

Accept the settlement offered if you believe it is in good faith. Unless your losses have been great, your complaint is probably not worth the time and expense involved in a lawsuit.

Last recourse: Talk to an attorney to see if your case is worth litigating.

Source: Herbert J. Teison, editor and publisher of the monthly newsletter *Travel Smart*, 40 Beechdale Road, Dobbs Ferry, New York 10522.

When Traveling Abroad

Consider carrying an ATM (Automated Teller Machine) card instead of traveler's checks. The Cirrus and Plus ATM networks now operate internationally, tying into your US bank account via satellite. Using an ATM card allows you to avoid check-cashing fees and standing in check-cashing lines, and provides access to cash 24 hours a day. It also eliminates charges for taking a cash advance on a credit card. Helpful: Before leaving home, ask your bank for a list of its international ATM locations.

Source: *Successful Meetings,* 633 Third Ave., New York 10017.

Boarding Passes May Not Be Guarantees Of Getting Onto A Plane

Airlines say that advance boarding passes issued by travel agents are usually honored if passengers arrive at least 10 minutes before flight time. But when flights are overbooked, or a plane must pick up passengers from a canceled flight, the advance passes may not be accepted. Recommended: Arrive early enough to check in at the gate, even if you have a boarding pass.

Source: Consensus of airline officials, reported in the *New York Times.*

Secrets Of Flying Safely In Unsafe Times

Despite new technology, there's no evidence that airlines are appreciably safer today than they were a decade ago. Over the past 10 years, US airlines have averaged one fatal accident for every 2,000,000 departures.

Part of the problem is an unintentional consequence of deregulation. During the era of federal control, many airlines exceeded minimum safety requirements. But today fewer airlines exceed the standards because deregulation has toughened competition, thereby creating financial problems that have forced some airlines to divert resources away from safety.

But more information about airline performance is now available, and it gives passengers new ways to choose safer airlines and increase their chances of surviving a crash. How to choose safer airlines:

Rule #1: If possible, don't fly on an airline that's having financial difficulty. There's no certainty that a money-troubled airline will be less safe. But the FAA itself increases safety surveillance of such airlines on the assumption that they're under pressure to cut corners on safety and maintenance.

For similar reasons, think twice about flying on an airline that is experiencing severe labor problems, especially those that disrupt maintenance operations.

Right now American, Delta and United seem to be in excellent financial shape and have no major labor problems. Continental, Pan American and TWA appear less healthy. Eastern still has serious labor trouble.

Rule #2: Avoid small regional airlines whenever possible. While some regionals have good safety records, statistics show that you're three times more likely to die in a crash on a plane with 30 seats or fewer than on a larger craft. Among other problems, regionals often use small airports that aren't as well equipped to guide planes in at night and in bad weather as are larger airports. Also, small airplanes often lack the more sophisticated instrumentation for bad-weather flying, and regional pilots are generally not as experienced as those who fly for major carriers.

Trap: Airlines don't always tell passengers that they're routed on a regional carrier for a particular leg of their trip. For that reason, always ask which airline you'll be flying on each leg. You may find that another major airline will fly directly to your destination or that you can rent a car and drive from a nearby major city.

Safest planes…safest seats:

The National Transportation Safety Board* keeps records on the accidents of specific planes, and these are available to the public. Challenge: The accident data are difficult to interpret because problems may originate with the different kinds of engines that a single type of aircraft may use. And some aircraft that are flown over more dangerous routes may appear statistically less safe than others when they're really not.

Nevertheless, if for no other reason than peace of mind, travelers can avoid specific types of planes, particularly the DC-10 that's been involved in several recent disasters. And avoiding a certain type of plane is easier than most passengers realize.

When you make reservations, ask the ticket or travel agent what kind of plane is scheduled on your flight. If he/she balks, be insistent. Agents virtually always have that information. If you have qualms about the plane, ask for another flight or make reservations with another airline.

Before you leave for the airport, check with the airline again to see if there's been a change in planes. If there has been, and if you

*800 Independence Ave. SW, Washington, DC 20594. Phone: 202-382-6600.

don't want to fly on the craft, you again have the option of making other travel arrangements (unless you have a nonrefundable ticket).

Even if you have a nonrefundable ticket, don't give up. Go to the airport and use persuasion on the ticket agent. Unfortunately, you have no other power to ask him/her to switch your flight.

Agents are under no obligation to help travelers in that situation. But if you make it clear that the only reason you want to switch is to fly on another type of aircraft, the agent may accommodate you to earn goodwill for the airline.

Choosing the safest seats:

Myth: That the safest seats on all commercial aircraft are those next to emergency exits.

Reality: Aisle seats close to the over wing emergency exits are safer. These seats are commonly in the mid-front section of the plane. If you sit in the window seat next to an emergency exit, you may be worse off in the event of a crash that jams the exit. Aisle seats near several exits give you more escape options in the event of a crash.

Lifesaving precaution: When you take your seat in the plane, count and memorize the number of rows to the nearest exits. Reason: If smoke fills the cabin after a crash, you may have to feel your way in the dark to an exit. This precaution is based on the tactics that crash survivors have actually used to get out of a plane.

Other lifesavers:

• To maximize protection against fire, wear full-length clothing, suits or dresses made of wool or cotton and sturdy shoes and eyeglasses with an attachable lanyard. Avoid wearing shorts or clothing made of synthetics like polyester, which can melt to your body in a fire.

• Women should not wear high-heeled shoes on a plane. They can cause you to trip, and they can snag on the emergency exit slide.

• If the plane fills with smoke, stay low, even if you have to crawl. Two or three breaths of toxic smoke can kill you. If there's enough warning before a crash, place a damp cloth over your mouth in order to breathe through the smoke.

• Get as far away from the plane as possible if you're lucky enough to escape it after a crash. People on the ground are often killed when a downed plane explodes.

• Learn how to open the exits by reading the emergency instructions soon after you board the plane. That's something you don't want to learn as the aircraft bursts into flames.

Source: Chris Witkowski, director, Aviation Consumer Action Project, an advocacy group for airline safety and passenger rights, 2000 P St. NW, Washington, DC 20036. The organization also publishes *Facts and Advice for Airline Passengers*, a booklet that gives more information on safety and consumer rights, ACAP, Box 19029, Washington, DC 20036.

Frequent Flying Increases Cancer Risks

Flying frequently increases cancer risk because of the higher level of radiation that exists at high altitudes. Among passengers and crew members who fly frequently: There are 1,000 more cancer-related deaths per 100,000 people who fly cross-country 98 times per year over a 20-year period. Flyers who take 54 cross-country flights each year for 20 years have 500 more deaths from cancer per 100,000. There are 1,200 more cancer deaths per 100,000 among flyers who take 74 flights per year over the North Pole between New York and Tokyo for 10 years.

Source: Study conducted by the Department of Transportation, reported in *International Living*, 824 E. Baltimore St., Baltimore 21202.

Money-Saving Strategies For Frequent Flyers

You don't have to be a regular flyer to join an airline's frequent flyer program. Most offer tangible benefits even to occasional flyers. Some of the best strategies to take advantage of these popular programs:

• Join every program possible. The "frequent" in frequent flyer programs is a misnomer. Airlines use them as marketing programs to communicate with their customers, even occasional travelers.

• Timing is everything. Don't cash in a frequent flyer award for flights during the off-season or when airlines are in the midst of a fare war. Save it for when fares go back up or you can't meet advance-purchase and other restrictions.

• Upgrades vs. free tickets. Airlines closely monitor the number of free seats allotted on any one flight. There are, however, no such controls on the number of upgrades allowed from coach to first or business class.

Example: A friend traveling to Paris was told he couldn't use his frequent flyer mileage for a first-class seat because first class was sold out. Reality: Seats were available...but for paying customers only because the allotted number of free seats had been reached. So my friend bought a coach-class ticket and upgraded into first.

• Unconventional wisdom. It isn't always best to use free travel for the longest trip possible.

Example: Most travelers will use an award for travel within the continental US to fly as far as possible, say, from New York to Los Angeles. But airlines often run promotional fares as low as $119 between such "glamour" destinations. Better—sometimes: Use awards for shorter, more expensive flights, such as Dallas/Fort Worth to Wichita, Kansas, which can cost as much as $333, or New York to Chicago, which is $419.

• The recognition factor. Airlines value their frequent-flyer program members. So don't hesitate to flash your frequent flyer membership card to airline personnel. You'll be surprised how many doors it opens. These include advanced boarding, priority wait-listing, and separate check-in lines. Many airlines have separate telephone-reservation lines exclusively for program members.

• Bunch your mileage. It's better to accumulate 60,000 miles in one airline program than to have 20,000 miles in three different programs.

Reason: Award values increase geometrically, not arithmetically, at higher mileage levels.

• Avoid using hotel discount coupons. Airline awards often include hotel discount coupons. Reality: These discounts are off the published (rack) rate. Most travelers can take advantage of the many other discounts available—corporate rates, senior citizen rates, special promotions—to save more than the discount coupon.

Example: A 50%-off coupon on a $300-per-night room doesn't mean a great deal when the hotel is running a special $99 weekend promotion.

Source: Joe Brancatelli, executive editor of *OAG Frequent Flyer Magazine*, 1775 Broadway, New York 10019.

Overlooked Airfare Saver

Many airlines will reimburse you for the amount of any drop in the price of an airline ticket that occurs after you buy it but before you use it. But you won't get a reimbursement if you don't ask. Advice: Before getting on your flight, ask the ticket agent to check the computer for the current price of your ticket, and see if you are entitled to a refund.

Source: The *Wall Street Journal*.

How To Travel Free

There are hundreds of budget guides that tell you how to cut costs on trips. Many of these books contain low-cost travel tips, but they don't give you the ultimate scoop on no-cost travel. Instead of traveling cheap, you could be traveling free—from transportation by air—or sea—or lodgings, meals and entertainment. Most free travel requires no special skills, credentials or contacts. And it can be just as luxurious—and often more pleasurable—than the most expensive paid vacation. Complimentary Cruises:

Cruise lines generally offer free passage to anyone who recruits 10 to 15 paying passengers. (Many airlines offer similar deals.) If you can't lure that many customers, you can get a prorated reduction on your fare.

You can also cruise free as an expert in a pertinent subject. Historians, anthropologists, naturalists and ornithologists are in especially high demand. Your job on the cruise would be to present a series of lectures and be available for informal questioning. It helps to have a PhD (or at least a master's) and to have published articles on the subject, but an affable personality and a willingness to share your knowledge with others can stretch your credentials. After your first cruise in this capacity, a good reference will ease the way at other lines.

Free cruises are available to doctors and nurses who are willing to be on 24-hour call (here a salary is an added inducement)…to athletic directors and coaches who can help organize recreational activities…to musicians and entertainers who are willing to perform—to cosmetologists who can barter their services for a ride.

There is also a strong demand for "hosts"—distinguished single gentlemen who are usually 55 years old and up. They serve by dining and dancing with the many unattached older women taking these vacation cruises. Besides free room and board, hosts are encouraged to make use of an unlimited bar tab available to them and their new female friends.

Free foreign tours:

Enlist enough people and get a whole trip—long or short—free. Some travel agencies recruit teachers, who receive a free trip if they bring six students. With 12 students, the teacher's spouse also travels free.

The same deal is available to anyone who is willing to organize a special-interest tour. An auto-racing fan might lead a group to Le Mans…an opera aficionado might arrange a trip to Milan and La Scala. Similar trips focus on photography, architecture, theater, music, golf or winetasting. The group leader sets the itinerary, chooses lodgings and arranges for side trips. Travel experience and linguistic skills are usually helpful but not essential.

Source: Robert William Kirk, author of *You Can Travel Free*, Pelican Publishing Co., 1101 Monroe St., Gretna, LA 70053.

Getting A Refund On Nonrefundable Airline Tickets

Nonrefundable airline tickets are refundable—under certain circumstances. All the major airlines will refund such a ticket if you show you couldn't use it because of an unexpected emergency. Examples: Death or serious illness of a family member is an excuse accepted by all airlines. Delta will accept a change of military orders, and Continental will accept a military or civilian job reassignment. TWA and United will accept jury duty and subpoenas. And all airlines will consider unique individual circumstances.

Free Medical Assistance While Traveling

Source: your credit-card company. This traveler-assistance program will help you arrange for eyeglasses or medication, or provide names of reputable local physicians and medical facilities free of charge.

Other services: locating an interpreter, relaying an urgent message or delivering emergency cash, arranging transportation to a US hospital and handling the booking of trips for relatives who fly in to help.

More information: American Express, 800-843-2273; Diners Club, 800 688-2273. Gold MasterCard or Visa Gold card holders should check with the bank that issued their card.

Source: *Money*, Rockefeller Center, New York 10020.

Traveler's Checks

Stiff competition among issuers means many good deals right now. Thomas Cook charges no commission if checks are bought and cashed in any of its 72 US or 1,500 foreign outlets. And 65% of all American Express checks are offered without fees through local banks and major organizations.

Source: *Money*, Rockefeller Center, New York 10020.

Traveler's Checks Trap

Don't use traveler's checks for major expenses when you are traveling abroad. Reason: Airlines, car-rental companies, hotels and many merchants and restaurants will give you a very unfavorable exchange rate. Strategy: Pay these charges by credit card—the charge-card company will get you a much better exchange rate. Use your traveler's checks as a source of cash for walking-around expenses after changing them at a bank or travel-service office, again to get the best possible rate.

Source: *Money*, Rockefeller Center, New York 10020.

The Earlier, The Better

The earlier in the day the flight, the less likely it is to be delayed. Also: Avoid booking the last flight of the day—if it's canceled, you could get stuck overnight.

Source: *Runzheimer Reports on Travel Management*, Runzheimer International, management consultants for travel, Runzheimer Park, Rochester, Wisconsin 53167.

Beware Of US Customs Inspections

US Customs inspections give travelers few rights. If inspections detain you so long that you miss a connection, you have no re-

31

course—although most airlines will book you on the next flight at no extra charge. If Customs damages personal items, you can report it...but Customs has no obligation to pay. Rights that you do have: A pat-down search of your person requires a supervisor's approval, two officers must be present at the search and you cannot be searched by someone of the opposite sex.

Source: *Travel & Leisure*, 1120 Avenue of the Americas, New York 10036.

Fly Direct

Growing air-traffic congestion will lead to more frequent delays, increasing the odds that you—or your luggage—will miss your connecting flight.

Source: *The Complete Financial Guide to the 1990s* by Gary L. Klott, business correspondent for *The New York Times,* Times Books, 201 E. 50 St., New York 10022.

Airport X Rays And Film

Signs still say it is safe to put film through, but increased security has led to the use of stronger X rays at most airports. Film may be fogged. Recommended: Pack film in clear plastic bags and ask to have it inspected by hand.

Source: *Self,* 350 Madison Ave., New York 10017.

3

The Winning Edge

The Power Of Self-Esteem

Self-esteem is not merely an emotional luxury enjoyed by a rare breed of super-content individuals. It is a prerequisite for attaining maximum success in business.

Times of accelerating change, choices and challenges demand managers with great capacity for innovation, self-management, personal responsibility and self-direction. These are some of the basic qualities that mark individuals with high self-esteem.

Success and the self-esteem: the myth:

Self-esteem is the immune system of consciousness. It provides resilience, strength and a capacity for regeneration individuals need to cope with life's challenges. High self-esteem often leads to success...but not all successful executives enjoy high self-esteem.

Example I: The successful head of a mid-size company complains: I've accomplished so much. Why don't I feel proud of myself?

Why am I depressed? He then confides that he had always wanted to be a research scientist but abandoned that dream and conformed to his parents' strong preference that he make a career in business.

Result: He felt only superficial pride in his business success...while he deeply felt the wounds of having surrendered his excellent mind, intense energy and his values to the wishes of others—in order to earn their "love."

He built genuine self-esteem by becoming more involved in his company's own research—and made time for it by delegating much of the other work that he never liked doing anyway. Outside of work, he began spending more of his life in activities that he really enjoyed.

Example II: A brilliant businessman complained: Why do I feel my failures so much more acutely than my victories— even though I know that my victories far outweigh my failures? A few minutes later, he mentioned that he often had an image of his father looking at

33

him contemptuously, suggesting that he would never amount to much.

Result: He was unable to enjoy for any length of time his own achievements. His response to every success was to plan his next accomplishment…one more deal, one more victory. He was successful—but not nearly as successful as he would be if he didn't have to force himself to strive.

What will help him build self-esteem: Making a disciplined internal effort to be aware each time he feels that he has not done "enough" to identify the source of that inner voice prodding him on to the next goal.

Key: Making an honest commitment to his own self-acceptance, to understanding that he is "enough" and that he does not have to spend his life "proving" his worth.

Real vs. phony self-esteem:

Self-esteem is: Confidence in your ability to think and cope with the challenges of life.

Self-esteem is: Confidence in your right to be happy, to feel worthy and deserving and to enjoy the fruits of your labors.

People with healthy self-esteem generally assess their abilities and accomplishments realistically, neither denying nor exaggerating them.

Authentic self-esteem comes from the choices you make for yourself. It is not a function of the family you were born into and what they have accomplished, nor the color of your skin nor your religion.

Trap: The possibilities for self-deception in the search for self-esteem are endless. Instead of earning self-esteem through conscious behavior and choices, through taking responsibility and through personal integrity, some successful people seek it through popularity, fame, prestige, material acquisitions or sexual exploits. Instead of focusing on their own personal worth, they become obsessed with living in the "right" neighborhood, belonging to the "right" country clubs or the "right" political party.

Instead of striving to build the power of their own competence, these people seek power by manipulating or controlling others.

Attaining this form of "success" without acquiring positive self-esteem, however, usu-

ally condemns these individuals to feeling like impostors anxiously fearing exposure.

What genuine self-esteem feels like:

People without genuine self-esteem are always proving…proving…proving…how worthy they are. Often, they suffer physical illness, because the intense drive to prove—to cover up the actual lack of genuine self-esteem causes harmful stress that can result in heart disease, depression or exhaustion.

By contrast, people who do enjoy high self-esteem express their joy about being who they are—not about being better than someone else. They feel alive, more able to enjoy what they do—including their work. They have a good sense of internal equilibrium. Characteristics of genuine self-esteem:

• A manner and way of talking and moving that projects pleasure in being alive.

• Ease in talking about one's own accomplishments as well as shortcomings, directly and honestly.

• Comfort in giving and receiving compliments, gifts, expressions of affection and appreciation.

• Openness to criticism and ability to acknowledge mistakes because self-esteem is not tied to some impossible image of perfection.

• Openness and curiosity about new ideas, new experiences, and new challenges and opportunities.

• Ability to remain undaunted by feelings of anxiety or insecurity when they occur because they're confident they will not be overwhelmed by them.

• Flexibility in responding to situations and challenges, moved by a spirit of inventiveness—even playfulness—since they don't see life as doom or defeat.

Source: Nathaniel Branden, PhD, a pioneer in the psychology of self-esteem. He is the author of *The Power of Self-Esteem,* Health Communications, 3201 SW 15 St., Deerfield Beach, Florida 33442. He practices psychology and consults to businesses, Box 2609, Beverly Hills, California 90213.

Great Ideas Are Not Enough Anymore

Most people think that getting a good idea is the hardest part of bringing a new product to market. But they couldn't be more wrong. An idea alone is not enough. Undeveloped ideas are everywhere.

They are difficult to protect and all but impossible to sell.

To succeed, you must demonstrate that a new product can be made, and that people will buy it. This is true whether you intend to sell your idea to a company or produce it yourself. Lessons I've learned in operating the many new businesses I've started up...

• Research, research, research. Without good information, you are merely dreaming. Idea development requires constant research. The more you know about your concept, the better your chances are for selling it. You may indeed have a great idea, but if someone else is out there with the same product already, you need to step back. But just because someone else beat you to the punch doesn't mean your concept is doomed to failure. Perhaps they're doing a mediocre job, or maybe there's an angle they've overlooked.

Many of the essential research aids are in public libraries or available free, or at modest cost, from government agencies. Others are as close as the neighborhood shopping mall. Two of the most available research tools are the telephone and the Yellow Pages.

• Be ruthless in evaluating the viability of an idea. Your favorite new product concepts will often be the ones you should discard first. "I like it" or "It's so cute" are not adequate reasons for risking your time and money.

• Newness alone is not enough. Successful new products and services must provide a consumer benefit, either real or perceived. There are many ways in which something can be "new." Products may contain qualitative changes or unprecedented technical advances. Or the newness may consist of a change in packaging, a different styling detail or a revised advertising slant.

• Determine whether or not you are an en-trepreneur. Business is extremely competitive, and it is essential to know your capabilities and limitations. The most crucial business decision you will make is how to develop your favorite brainchild. Will you sell your best concept to someone else, who will take all the headaches...and rewards? Or will you do the job yourself?

Clue: Entrepreneurs tend to be active, impatient people who "just do it" once they get an idea. They're the kind of folks who, when they buy a new electronic gadget, throw away the assembly instructions and simply plunge right in without bothering to read the directions.

A common start-up problem is not having enough expertise. There may be a part of your product you can't design, or a part of your burgeoning business that you can't manage. Instead of feeling guilty that you can't do it all, recognize instead that no single individual can successfully bring a new product to market in today's technologically complex world without some backup help.

• Don't assume that you must patent your idea. First, many ideas aren't patentable. And even those that are, such as technological breakthroughs, are very difficult to defend. Reality: Obtaining a patent is a long, costly, frustrating ordeal. The process consumes your time, money and, most important, your energy. Usually you are better off devoting these resources to developing and marketing your product.

On the other hand, there are some good reasons for obtaining a patent. It may discourage others from trying to compete with you. If you're trying to sell your idea to an existing manufacturer, the fact that you have applied for a patent makes you appear serious, knowledgeable and confident in the uniqueness of the product. And it can be an effective document for demonstrating exactly what the product is.

• Be flexible and cover all angles. Keep an open mind for better ideas and consider all possibilities for how your product should look, feel, be produced and be marketed. If a company has a problem with your original concept, suggest another way of looking at it. Or restructure the concept slightly and present it to another firm.

If you market something yourself, you should constantly monitor consumer response, the reaction of competitors and new technology. You must be ready to react quickly and effectively on all fronts.

• Target your audience. Although you should remain flexible, you must also start with a well-defined analysis of what your target audience is and how to reach it. This includes not only potential consumers of your product but also companies to which you will be presenting your idea.

• Understand distribution. Manufacturing is typically a minor part of overall new product development. You can have the best product in the world, but if you can't manage to get it into the stores, it doesn't matter. The key to distribution is people. Distribution will probably involve much more expense and effort than you anticipate. To find out how the distribution system works for the industry into which your product fits, make a point of attending industry trade shows. Talk with distributors there, and later call them to discuss standard markups, demand, pricing and terms. Find out if they would handle a product like yours.

• Don't confuse selling with marketing. Marketing is creating demand for a product, whereas selling is closing the deal. All too often, people choose to market something for which there is already strong demand or sell something that nobody wants.

Don't expect to avoid mistakes: They are inevitable. There are no crystal balls in the new-product business. So instead of taking your failures personally, or letting your ego take over, learn from them. With luck, your mistakes won't be too costly. And those that hurt the most often provide valuable insights and wisdom.

Don't be put off by all these potential dangers. Act now. If you want to try to sell an idea or develop a new product or service on your own, do it. Don't procrastinate, and don't stop halfway. You will find new, educational and fascinating experiences at every step.

Source: Tony Husch, who co-founded the first computer dating service while he was an undergraduate at Harvard University and is the former owner of about 15 businesses, including a winery and distributorship of Good Karmal candy. He is the co-author (with attorney Linda Foust) of the book *That's a Great Idea*, Ten Speed Press, Box 7123, Berkeley, California 94707.

How To Make More Good Decisions, Fewer Half-Decisions

Individually and collectively, Americans have been making many bad decisions. Our country—and, for many of us, our personal lives—are in a mess today because we made too many decisions in the 1980s based on *wishful thinking* rather than on *reality*.

It doesn't have to be that way anymore. I have found a system that teaches us, reliably, to make better decisions than the trial-and-error method that most people use nowadays. Many leading business organizations have found that managers and workers trained in this system consistently make better corporate decisions…and when they get home and try it out together with their spouses and children, they make better personal decisions, there, too. Half-decisions don't work:

Today most people don't think through their decisions with both their head and their heart…so they make only half-decisions— and they're not happy with the results. But I have found that by asking ourselves a few questions that can be answered by a simple yes or no, we can arrive at decisions that satisfy both our intellect and our emotions.

Think ahead: When faced with a decision of any kind, we must first analyze what we really need…not merely what we want. There's an easy way to do this—don't look at what you want to do now but on what you will like to have done when you're able to look back at the decision.

Example of needs vs. wants: When deciding whether you should get up from the couch and go out for some exercise or stay put, you'll make a better choice if you focus on your future well-being, not on your current comfort.

Once we decide what we need, we have to think through our options—and list them. We can usually find options we weren't originally considering by gathering information...not only facts, but how people feel about the facts.

Armed with a knowledge of our needs and options, we can think each option through. For each option, imagine what situation may occur.

Ask yourself: What would probably happen then?...And then what?

Thinking options through will take some time...but if you make the wrong decision because you didn't want to spend that time at the beginning, it will take you a lot longer to straighten things out at the end.

The heart helps:

So far, I have explained the first half of better decision making...using our heads to figure out whether our decisions rate a yes or a no answer to the practical question, Am I meeting the real need, informing myself of the options and thinking it through?

A yes to that question alone is not enough. To make a better decision, we must also use our heart to see if our decisions fit our personal beliefs.

For most of us, that's not easy to do. We have become uncomfortable looking deeply into ourselves. But we can be sure our decisions are better if they reflect our true character. A good decision depends on three key character traits...

• Integrity: We don't fool ourselves.

• Intuition: We feel that we can trust ourselves.

• Insight: We know we really want to do better.

And we need all three in order to make the right decision.

Though our ego often encourages us to fool ourselves, we can replace illusions with reality if we put our ego aside and ask others

for advice—people who aren't attached to our illusions, people we admire.

Or we can ask ourselves what decision we would advise a friend to make. Parking our ego can help us to arrive at the truth and make better decisions much sooner because we are honest with ourselves.

Our experience with past decisions that worked—or didn't work—has given us an intuition that makes us feel better not only about the right decision when we have made it but also about the way we made it.

Intuition signals our body to give an answer in terms of feeling. If our intellect tells us that the answer to the practical question we first asked is only maybe, then we must rely on our intuition for a better answer.

Our intuition tells us when we're making a sound decision by making us feel clear rather than confused about the problem...calm rather than stressed about the process...enthusiastic rather than afraid about the outcome.

In addition to integrity and intuition, we need to develop insight. Otherwise we may go ahead with a decision we know is not the best one that we can make...or we may not bother to get all the information we know that we need.

We may sabotage ourselves because, in our hearts, we don't really want to make the best decision...because we don't really believe that we deserve it. To consistently make good decisions, we must really believe that we deserve to succeed.

Putting it all together:

A good decision is one that allows us to give a yes answer to both the practical and the personal questions we must ask ourselves. Does my head tell me that it meets my needs...not merely my wants? Have I explored all the options? Have I thought it through? Does my heart tell me I am being honest with myself? Do I trust my intuition? Do I really believe I deserve better?

Bottom line:

I believe we all deserve better. I've turned my own life around since I began practicing the yes–no system six years ago.

Try it out in both your business decisions and your personal life. Once you find how well it works, I hope you'll share it with others whom you care about.

Source: Spencer Johnson, MD, co-author of the bestselling book *The One Minute Manager.* Dr. Johnson's latest book is *"Yes" or "No": The Guide to Better Decisions,* HarperCollins, 10 E. 53 St., New York 10022.

How To Become A Power Talker

Power talkers speak the language of success. They transmit positive expectations both to themselves and to others. While used mostly in business, power talking also helps people communicate better with their children, friends and acquaintances.

Anyone who wants to can become a power talker by following a few simple rules, because we are all already conscious of the principles of power talking.

Just think how you feel when a hotel clerk tells you, "You won't have your room before 1 o'clock" rather than "We'll have the room ready for you at 1 o'clock." Both messages convey the same information…but they give the listener totally different impressions of the attitude of the clerk—and the hotel.

Power talking isn't a destination, it's a journey. You become a power talker when you consciously decide the effect that you want your speech to have on others and elevate your consciousness so that you always seek the more powerful phrasing.

Nobody can totally avoid slips. I catch some of my own every day. However, everyone can work at it—phrase by phrase, day by day—to increase awareness of those phrases that should be replaced by more positive expressions.

Example: Start with one simple phrase. Instead of saying, "I'll try to do it," say, "I will do it." Reason: I'll try means I'm not sure I'll succeed…but when you say "I will," both you and the person you're talking to can be more confident that the job will get done.

Power traits:

Each night list the expressions you came up with during the day that can help you project the positive thinking that's the key to power talking. You'll find these basic traits as you work on your skills.

• Project positive expectations:

• Don't say, "I have to"…say, "I'll be glad to."

• There are no problems in life…only opportunities.

• Don't say you're no good at anything…say you're getting better.

• Give credit wherever it's due:

• When someone gives you a compliment, don't excuse yourself…simply accept the compliment graciously.

• When other people succeed, don't tell them how lucky they are…compliment them on their skill and effort.

• Rebound resiliently. Lots of "bad" things happen to successful people because they're always trying something new. But they bounce back to greater success. When faced with a setback:

• Don't say, "I failed"…say, "Here's what I learned."

• Don't say, "I'm going under"…say, "I'm going to bounce back."

• Don't say, "This is terrible, and it could get worse"…say, "It's over. Now I'm going to work on making things better."

• Accept responsibility. Don't blame others for what happens to you, but see yourself as being in control of your fate.

• Don't say, "This rush-hour traffic drives me crazy"…say, "I can find a better way to deal with my commuting challenges."

• Don't say, "I can't do anything about it"…say, "It's my responsibility to change things."

• Encourage cooperation and reduce conflict. Eliminate conflict-producing words like *but* and *disagree* from your vocabulary.

• Don't say, "It's a good product, but it's expensive"…say, "It's good, and it's expensive."

• When someone makes a suggestion that doesn't impress you too much, don't say, "I disagree"…say, "That's an interesting idea, and I'd like to suggest a few more."

• Speak decisively:

• Don't say, "We should have it ready by the end of the week"…say, "We will have it ready by Friday."

• Don't say, Generally speaking, I tend to think such-and-such…say, I believe such-and such.

• Don't say, "Do you have any questions?"… say, "What questions do you have?"

• Always tell the truth. Power talking is not a way to fool people with language. It's a way to communicate effectively. And effective communication must be consistently credible.

• Don't use phrases like "Well, to be perfectly honest"…the listener will get the idea that sometimes you're not perfectly honest.

• When you're asked to do something you really think you cannot, or should not, do…politely say no.

• Get back to basics:

• Don't forget to say the words *please* and *thank you.*

• When you make a mistake, don't say "It's not my fault. I couldn't help it"…say, "I'm sorry. It was my responsibility."

• Share your pride when others do their job well:

• If an airline ticket clerk makes a complicated reservation well, say, "Thank you for explaining that so clearly and for doing it so efficiently."

• If your child excels scholastically and socially, don't just tell your friends, "I have a great kid." Tell your child, "You're a terrific student, you have great friends and I'm proud of you."

Bottom line:

If you want to become a power talker, you should get started right away. Become more aware of the powerless phrases you have been using until now and replace them with more positive expressions.

Enlist partners to support you…and co-workers, close friends, your spouse and children to cue you in when you slip. As you

listen to the way other people talk, you'll see how far you can progress in just a short time.

Source: George R. Walther, president of TelExcel in Seattle, the author of *Power Talking: 50 Ways to Say What You Mean and Get What You Want,* Berkley Publishing Group, 200 Madison Ave., New York 10016.

Understanding Happiness

Many of the most popular ideas about what makes people happy are wrong.

By and large, studies by psychologists have measured little difference in happiness between teenagers, the middle-aged and the elderly. Knowing whether someone is rich or poor, black or white, healthy or handicapped, does not make it possible to predict how happy he/she is likely to be. Women are as happy as men. And, in general, people are as happy today as their parents were 30 years ago.

In short, researchers have established that external circumstances have little effect on psychological well-being. However, they have identified four inner traits that foster happiness—self-esteem, a sense of personal control, optimism and socializing.

Self-esteem:

Happy people like themselves. People who agree with such statements as *I'm a lot of fun to be with and I have good ideas* suffer less from ulcers and insomnia…are less likely to abuse drugs…are more resistant to pressures to conform…are more persistent at difficult tasks. And conversely, low self-esteem goes together with psychological disorders—especially depression.

Most people, in fact, protect themselves from anxiety and depression by feeling good about themselves. As long as their positive outlook is based on genuine achievement of realistic goals, that self-esteem is healthy.

Personal control:

The 15% of Americans who have a strong sense that they control their own lives and feel satisfied with themselves are twice as likely to be very happy as the national average.

People who agree with statements like *what happens to me is my own doing* or *the average person can influence government decisions* typically do better in school, cope better with stress and live more happily than those who lack that sense of personal control.

Those given little control over their environment—in prisons or even in nursing homes, factories and colleges—suffer from lower morale, greater stress and worse health. It is not surprising that people are happiest in nations where democratic traditions give them a high degree of personal freedom.

On a personal level, effective time management is one important way to gain a sense of control. People who can't plan their time and fill it purposefully are left feeling empty. Those who are happy tend to be punctual and efficient.

You can reach very ambitious goals more easily than you expect by breaking down big tasks into manageable daily objectives. As each mini-deadline is met, you will savor the taste of achievement and personal control.

Optimism:

Optimistic people are not only happier, but healthier. They suffer less illness...recover better from heart surgery and cancer...and have stronger immune defenses.

Those who think in positive terms get positive results, succeeding better in business than pessimists. Psychologist Martin Seligman found that new Metropolitan Life salesmen with an optimistic outlook sold more policies and were half as likely to quit during their first year—one of the optimists he tested even sold a policy to Seligman himself.

Optimism does have a flip side, however. Unrealistic optimism can make people believe they are invulnerable and stop them from taking sensible steps to avoid danger.

And if the future doesn't match up to their glowing expectations, they may be shattered by disappointment.

The recipe for well-being comprises ample optimism to provide hope...a dash of pessimism to prevent complacency...and enough realism to understand the difference between those things we can control and those we can't.

Socializing:

People with sociable, outgoing personalities tend to be happier and more satisfied with life than introverts.

Extroverts are cheerful and high-spirited people who like themselves. When they walk into a roomful of strangers, they are confident the strangers there will like them as well, which becomes a self-fulfilling prophecy.

Their friendliness makes it easier for them to find friends, mates and jobs. And the support they get from their large circle of friends makes them even happier.

Can we make ourselves happier?:

Basic personal traits like optimism and extroversion persist from childhood to old age.

Important: We have the power to improve our future happiness by the way we act now.

Our actions leave a residue within us, so by acting in the way happy people act, it is possible for us to make ourselves into happier people. You can carry out a simple experiment yourself...fake a scowl and you'll feel angrier...fake a smile and you'll feel more cheerful.

The same effect occurs in a more general way. People who have been asked by experimenters to fake high self-esteem have actually developed better feelings about themselves. In short, if you begin acting in a way that shows self-esteem, optimism or sociability, you will end up developing that trait.

One way to become a happy person is to act like one.

Source: *David G. Myers*, PhD, who teaches psychology at Hope College in Holland, Michigan. He is the author of *The Pursuit of Happiness: Who is Happy—and Why,* William Morrow and Co., 1350 Avenue of the Americas, New York 10019.

Guide To A Wonderful Social Life

Whether you dream of elegant white-tie social balls...long for 12-course formal dinners…or crave a mailbox stuffed with exotic invitations, take heart. Whatever your fantasy of the ideal social life, you can have it. I know because I've had that great life—and I'm willing to share my secrets with you.

The four Ps:

•Popularity is the key. If people want to be around you, you're doing something right. It's a trap to think that you need Cindy Crawford's looks or Steve Ross's fiscal power in order to be popular. Beauty, bucks, and celebrity can bring instant party appeal, but anyone can have the key to real popularity…a winning personality.

•Personality is how you project inner beauty, goodness, and giving. Too often we focus on our flaws—thinning hair, less-than-perfect body. But we're all our own worst critics—no one notices our flaws as well as we do. When you're well-groomed and sparkling, others pay attention to your energy…and what you say and do.

•Pleasing others is essential to a winning personality. The most loved people live to give, not get. Make others feel good about themselves and they will feel good about you. See that others have a good time and you will have a good time. Beware of expecting returns. While some people will reciprocate, don't "count receipts at the end of the day." Trust that goodies will come back to you from some source in some way eventually.

Mistake: Being so desperate to gain approval or acceptance you become a doormat—revealing low self-esteem—who repels other people. When you feel satisfied with yourself and your life—no matter what it is—your giving is genuine rather than a demand to be given to.

Useful exercise: On meeting someone, think, What does he/she need to feel good? and fulfill the need as much as you can. Give reassurance that the person is liked…encouragement over an imminent move…support after a recent loss, etc. When inviting someone, or requesting a favor, offer what he stands to gain first.

Example I: I know you're interested in art. A wonderful painter is coming to my party Friday evening. I'd love you to be there.

Example II: If you're going abroad, instead of saying, Can you do me a favor and give me your contacts? say, Can I do a favor for you? Do you want me to bring you back anything or bring anything there, or call anyone to say hello for you?

•Being positive is the second key to a pleasing personality. Smile and the whole world smiles back at you. Frown and they run away. Check what I call your "twinkle factor"—when your eyes twinkle with enthusiasm, your warmth is a magnet to others.

How do you help yourself if you're stuck in a depressed mood? Get rid of negative thoughts.

Exercise I: Imagine your mind like a light switch. Flick off dark thoughts, turn on ones that brighten your mood.

Exercise II: Use affirmations. Tell yourself, I'm having a good time…This is fun…I'm as talented as anyone here. Find value in every person and experience.

Communication skills:

To put your positive, pleasing, popular personality into effect, you should know not only how to treat others, but how to talk to them, as well.

•Give compliments. Say something nice about a person's looks, actions or experience. Asking for advice is very pleasing to a person.

Examples: George says you're an excellent golfer. If I'm just starting, where's the best place to go?…You look great. What fitness routine do you do?

Phony flattery or lying is obvious and obnoxious. But…you can always find something you genuinely admire.

•Always try to be nice. If you don't have something nice to say, keep quiet. If you're nasty about someone, it reflects poorly on you.

You don't have to stay "trapped" by someone who has engaged you in conversation. Get away respectfully. Invent an excuse…I have to make a phone call or Let's try some hors d'oeuvres. Then you can talk to someone else.

•Make people comfortable. People are put at ease when they know what to say after they say hello.

Example: In introductions, repeat names and common ground, like John Smith, this is Susan Katz, who's the account executive for the sportswear I saw you wearing. Susan, John's an excellent tennis player.

• Self-disclosure. Be willing to admit if you feel very self-conscious and shy. Trap: Thinking that openness is vulnerability or weakness. People, in general, like to help others out.

Example: If you're new in town, approach a friendly-looking person. Say, I just moved here and sure would love some help in picking the best gourmet food shop, since I love to cook.

Also, hearing your mistakes makes others feel better about their own. But avoid sounding too self-denigrating or feeling sorry for yourself.

• Be a good listener. Focus on others, not "I." Ask, What do you think? Ask questions about the other person's work, family, hobbies, travels, etc. President Kennedy's secret to his great conversational skill was genuine interest in others.

• Practice using a pleasant voice—one with low pitch, medium pace and volume. Smile with your voice. Exercise: Breathe from your solar plexus.

• Use good body language to reinforce your communications. Capture and keep a person's attention with eye contact. Avoid "Hollywood hellos"—talking to someone while looking over his/her shoulder to find someone more important in the room. Avoid distracting movements like hair pulling, tie tugging or over-obvious flirting that makes others uncomfortable.

• Be a good storyteller. Keep a file of story clippings. Practice saying them in a mirror, into a tape recorder (so you really know what your voice sounds like) or to a close friend or family member. Avoid catty gossip (what an ugly dress she wore), constant complaints (the food's always bad) or terrible tragedies that throw wet blankets on the mood or show you can't be trusted. For great stories…

• Be positive.

• Be surprising: Use jokes—they are a terrific tension breaker.

• Be anything but pushy.

• Share pet passions, not pet peeves. (A person who's always "down" receives very few dinner invitations.)

• Be provocative, too: Example: Barbara Walters asked, What kind of tree are you?

Overcoming blocks:

• The shyness block. Anyone, including famous actresses and eloquent politicians, even the zany, extroverted comedienne Phyllis Diller, can admit to being shy. Shyness is a defense against anxiety. Recognize the source of your anxiety, but then force yourself to come out of your shell.

Exercise: Visualize yourself at the end of a seesaw. You want balance in the conversation. It's your turn to talk. Be sensitive to the situation for the appropriate time to speak. Walk the fine line between being assertive, too withdrawn or too pushy.

• The fear-of-rejection block. Trap: Thinking others have the power to destroy you with disapproval or uninterest. They can't.

Exercise: Don't be afraid to approach others. If you're shy, always go into a new situation with a mental list of what you have to offer any group. It may be a great new story you've just heard, or a piece of news or the results of your latest personal poll on the exact definition of a nerd.

Positive actions for adding new friends to your roster:

• Take the initiative. Speak up first. Ask questions. Suggest lunch with someone of interest to you. (You are paying.) Hand out your business card to people at a cocktail party who have acted interested in what you've had to say. Tell someone who was interrupted during your conversation that you would like to hear the end of his story. Then make a point to call him.

• Start small and build up your confidence.

Example: Invite two close friends over for a rehearsal dinner before undertaking a large party, to work out the "kinks."

•Track your progress. Keep a self-improvement notebook with goals, a step-by-step plan, diary of your feelings, problems, successes. Accentuate the positive. Suggestion: Post your plan or picture of how you would like to look on your refrigerator door or bathroom mirror.

•Keep up contacts. Memorize facts (children's names, anniversary dates, favorite color) to bring up in conversation. People will be delighted that you remembered. Drop occasional notes to friends, just to stay in touch with them and their families.

•Always look your best. Apply the mirror test: Observe yourself clinically in the mirror. Don't be aghast, just appreciate the good points, and assess possible changes. Always go out of the house dressed for action—social or business.

•Appreciate yourself, your friends and your peers for who you truly are. Trap: Social climbing is downright unattractive.

Where to go:

Go where like-minded people will be on weekends. Do what turns you on and go where you'd like, and where you can make a contribution as well as have a good time. You'll meet people with similar interests—the best foundation for a good relationship.

You can meet interesting people at sporting matches, health clubs, electronics stores, wine tastings, cooking classes, shopping malls, group meetings at religious or community centers, even self-help groups (insuring common interests and support). Check local papers for listings of meetings, events, clubs. Very timely now: Volunteering for political candidates and to try to improve the social problems of your city.

Example: Volunteer for a charity benefit. Offer to do the grunt work no one else wants and eventually you'll be noticed and welcomed by a new group of friends.

Source: Letitia Baldrige, author of 13 books, including *Letitia Baldrige's Complete Guide to the New Manners for the 90's,* Rawson Associates, 866 Third Ave., New York 10022, drawing on her experience in the business world, in diplomatic life, and in the John F. Kennedy administration in the White House.

How To Boost Your Mental Energy

We'd all like more mental energy—the drive and focus that help us go after what we really want. But many of us try to boost that energy in the wrong ways.

Examples: Smoking cigarettes, eating sugary foods, drinking coffee. These give a short-term burst of energy, but can drain resources over the long run.

Boosting basics:

•Get out of your rut. Do something different from what you did yesterday. It doesn't have to be drastic—very simple changes will stimulate your mind. If you usually read biographies, try a mystery. Take a new route into the city.

•Take more risks. Exercise your mind with greater challenges.

Example: Take a course in Latin. Learn all about the new business systems.

•Give yourself a "mental health" day. You don't have to be physically sick to take a day off from responsibility—once in a while. Spend it on whatever renews you mentally, whether it's browsing for antiques or just lying on the beach.

•Believe in yourself. Worry and self-criticism are mentally fatiguing. Never put yourself down. Give yourself frequent pep talks instead. Rather than twisting yourself into a pretzel to please other people, make sure you are satisfied with your life and actions.

•Visualize your goals. Picture them vividly. Fill your environment with reminders of prizes for achievement—such as a picture of your dream house on your bulletin board. Visualizing what you want will help sustain the energy you need to go after it.

•Improve your ability to focus. We exhaust ourselves by scattering our attention among many different projects and ideas at once...instead of concentrating on the task at hand. Dr. Mihaly Csikszentmihalyi of the University of Chicago has written about the highly satisfying flow state experienced by artists, athletes, musicians and others who concentrate on performing an action to the best of their ability.

You can achieve flow in everyday activities, too. Absorb yourself in each task—no matter how mundane it seems. Say to yourself: This is the most important project on Earth. Ask yourself: How can I do this better...more efficiently...more pleasingly?

•Meditate. Sit quietly, relax your entire body and concentrate for 10 minutes on your breathing, a favorite proverb or a syllable such as the word "one." When other thoughts intrude, let them drift away. If you do this at least once a day, you will find yourself feeling calmer and more mentally energetic.

•Take care of your body. Physical energy affects mental energy, and vice versa. Keep a regular sleep schedule...eat a variety of healthful foods...gradually cut back on fat and caffeine...exercise regularly. A five-minute walk will give you greater and longer-lasting mental energy than a cup of coffee.

•Reflect on your mission in life. Who and what are most important to you? When you have a strong sense of inner direction, you will bring more energy to everything you do.

Source: Russell Wild, senior editor of Prevention Magazine Health Books and co-author of *Boost Your Brain Power,* Rodale Press, 33 E. Minor St., Emmaus, Pennsylvania 18098.

How To Keep A Lid On Emotional Upset

Events and other people don't upset us. We upset ourselves by what we tell ourselves about these events.

We take desires and preferences and turn them into shoulds and musts.

Example: This situation is terrible. It should not—must not—exist. Other people are rotten for doing this to me.

Making yourself miserable is more than unpleasant—it's unethical.

You're hurting the most important person in your life—you—as well as the people closest to you, who want you to be happy.

That doesn't mean you should never feel

anxious, angry or disappointed. These feelings are appropriate and even helpful. But panic, rage and depression are inappropriate...and irrational.

Example: If you perform badly at a job interview, your disappointment at being turned down for the job may motivate you to evaluate your performance...and do better next time. But if you are horrified and put yourself down for "failing," you might avoid all interviews for the next three months—which would keep you out of work and give you even more to complain about.

How to think and feel better:

•Acknowledge...that the event or person you are upset with did not upset you—you largely upset yourself.

•Look for the "should," look for the "must"...with which you made yourself upset.

Example: I should have made a better impression on the interviewer. I must get a job this week. The world should give me what I want when I want it.

•Dispute, challenge and question those "musts." Change them to preferences.

Example: I would prefer to have aced the interview, but it didn't work out that way. I'll learn what I can and try to do better next time.

You may have to voice these new statements very strongly, in order to fight the strength of your habitual, gloom-and-doom response.

With practice, the rational way of thinking will become your automatic reaction. You'll find you tell yourself immediately...That was unpleasant, but it's not the end of the world. I can probably succeed next time.

Rational thinking is not the Pollyanna-ish, "positive" thinking espoused by many popular speakers.

It's not rational to tell yourself, I can always hit this tennis ball...and I know I'll become a champion.

You may hit the ball well for a while, but it's highly unlikely that you'll become a tennis champion—and that could lead to disillusionment.

It's more constructive to say, I can hit that tennis ball better—but if I miss it, too bad...if

I don't win this next match, tough —I'm still a worthwhile person. Key attitude: I can do it…I'd like to do it…but I don't have to.

Source: Albert Ellis, PhD, originator of Rational-Emotive Therapy and founder of the Institute for Rational-Emotive Therapy, which has branches throughout the US and around the world. He has written more than 50 books, including *How to Stubbornly Refuse to Make Yourself Miserable About Anything—Yes, Anything!,* Lyle Stuart/Carol Publishing Group, 600 Madison Ave., New York 10022.

All About Priorities

Priorities are the key to managing your time and yourself.

Many of us make To-Do lists. But few people take enough time to weigh the activities on the list for their relative importance—professionally and personally.

Without that essential step of priority setting, a To-Do list is useless. We may seem to be constantly busy, yet we fritter away our time on tasks that don't advance us toward our major goals…and we don't accomplish anything of real value.

How to set daily priorities:

•Make a list of everything you think you should do tomorrow—complicated or routine. Don't worry about the order or importance of each task—just list them all.

•Weigh each task for its relative importance. Ask yourself:

•Which jobs are high payoff—ones that will give me the best return on my investment of time and energy?

•Which are essential to my goals?

•Which are essential to the goals of my company?

•Which do my boss view as most important? (Obviously, these should also be important to you.)

•Which can only be done by me—and no one else?

Use this information to number the items on your list—#1 for top priority, #2 for second-highest priority….

Example: A salesperson may find his/her top priority is servicing a high-volume account…his second priority is contacting a new prospect with the potential to be highly lucrative…his third is to begin compiling monthly sales figures. He may also recognize that some of the preparation for his sales reports, which he has always done himself, could be delegated to his secretary.

Important: Take sufficient time for this step. If you rush through it, you'll wind up with a To-Do list that doesn't reflect your true priorities.

It's not necessary to split hairs, however. Don't agonize over which of two equally important priorities should be #1 or #2. Just make sure both are toward the top of your list.

Hint: Many successful businesspeople use their evening commuting time for priority-setting.

Acting on priorities:

Early each morning, review your priorities. Start your day with the top-priority jobs, and stick with them. Otherwise, lower-priority tasks will eat up your day.

Helpful: Delegate low-priority jobs. If you absolutely cannot delegate them, schedule a five- or 10-minute break to devote to them. If these smaller tasks take more than the few minutes you have set aside, drop them and schedule another short break for them later.

Long-term planning:

Set long-range as well as daily priorities. If you know what your long-term goals are, you can make sure your daily actions are building toward those goals. You'll get more satisfaction out of each day…and you'll be more likely to stick with your plans. To identify long-range goals, think about:

•What makes you happy. Do you prefer more or less responsibility? What activities—business and personal—bring you the most pleasure? What would you enjoy learning more about?

•Where your skills lie. What do you do better than anyone else?

•Areas that need strengthening. In what ways do you want to grow and develop? What important areas have you been avoiding because you're afraid you'll fail? What skills would you need in order to succeed in those areas?

•What the trends are. Is your company

moving away from traditional markets? Is management promoting people with expertise in financial analysis rather than sales? Are more and more functions becoming computerized?

• Whether you can get the cooperation of others. A working mother who wants to go to law school at night will find her goal far more difficult if her husband and children aren't behind her all the way.

Don't be shy about selling others on your priorities. To accomplish them, you will need the help of those around you—family, colleagues, friends. Make sure the valued people in your life know how important the priority is to you.

On your daily list of priorities, include items from the long-term list that will move you toward your goals. Make sure you take some action on your top long-range priorities each day.

You can't always close the door on interruptions. But you can find 15 minutes to give some thought to the department's five-year plan...outline objectives...and decide who has the data you need.

Starting and sticking with priorities:

You will probably never finish every item on your daily To-Do list. That's why it's essential to do the most important tasks first. Many people fall into the trap of spending most of their time on less important tasks. These low-priority tasks are often easier, or may seem urgent—but they only seem more rewarding. Result: Long-term projects with a much greater potential payoff are neglected.

"Not having enough time" is an avoidance tactic. Everyone has time to complete one small step...and then another. The first step is always the hardest—once started, a project tends to develop a momentum of its own. How to get started...

• Visualize yourself completing the task. Vividly picture the rewards you'll get—a promotion, a raise, the gratitude and respect of others, the satisfaction of a job well done. Make sure those rewards are personal and meaningful to you.

Time-saving basics:

Once you've started, continue to use this visualization technique whenever your motivation lags.

• Avoid pessimists. They will poke holes in your ideas and discourage you from even trying.

• Turn off the TV. You'll gain hours of extra time each week.

• Fight perfectionism. Anxiety about not doing a perfect job keeps many people from doing any job. Combat anxiety by refocusing that energy into your priorities.

• Don't be afraid to make mistakes. With careful thinking most of them can be avoided. But, it's important to remember that mistakes are useful—they show us what works and what doesn't. Learn from them. If you never try anything new, you might not make any blunders—but you won't learn anything, either. Get started, profit from your mistakes and move on.

Changing your priorities:

Priorities aren't cast in stone. External circumstances, or your internal needs, may change. Your priorities should change along with them.

• Your company may be taken over and adopt a new corporate philosophy.

• You could find you prefer field work to management.

• You may have miscalculated the direction your industry was heading.

Another good reason to change priorities: Feeling overwhelmed. If chasing after too many goals is sapping your energy and enjoyment of life, it might be necessary to modify your goals.

Changing your priorities does not mean that you've failed. Successful people are flexible enough to evaluate the environment and adjust their course accordingly.

There is great benefit in priority-setting, whether or not you achieve every goal. You learn what you really value. You develop the ability to take action. And you build pride in your achievements...which increases your motivation to accomplish even more.

Source: William J. Bond, who conducts career- and time-management seminars for major corporations. He is the author of *1001 Ways to Beat the Time Trap* and *199 Time-Waster Situations,* both published by Frederick Fell Publishers, Inc., 2131 Hollywood Blvd., Hollywood, Florida 33020.

How To Do What You Want To Do Effectively

Dr. Edward de Bono, the world's leading authority on the teaching of thinking skills and author of the widely acclaimed *Six Thinking Hats** has now focused his attention on action.

His new book, *Six Action Shoes,* offers practical ways to focus on the type of action that is appropriate to deal with a particular challenge—and get it done. It's a very worthwhile read in its entirety.

As with his *Six Thinking Hats*—used by many major corporations—de Bono adopts a simple metaphor, this time different colored shoes, to symbolize six different modes of action that can be followed by anyone who wants to get things done effectively...

The Six Action Shoes:

This idea came to me when I was challenged by senior police officers who were expected to train perfect policemen—so that they would always take the right action in each occasion. I recommended establishing categories of action that could then be learned...and used appropriately...

• Navy formal shoes: Routine and formal procedures. Routines are crystallizations of the best way of doing something.

Example: The checklist that airline pilots use on takeoffs and landings.

Procedures remove the need to think something through each time. The goal is to perform the routine as perfectly as possible, reducing the chances of error.

Routines can be changed from time to time. They should also allow for some flexibility.

Important: Never try to improve a routine while you're using it. That defeats the very purpose of a routine.

• Gray sneakers: Collecting and analyzing information. Gray suggests brain matter...also

**Available from the International Center for Creative Thinking, 805 W. Boston Post Rd., Mamaroneck, New York 10543. 800-32-THINK. Both *Six Thinking Hats* and *Six Action Shoes* are copyrighted materials, which may not be reproduced in any media or included in any training materials without written permission of the copyright holders.*

fog and mist...sneakers are unobtrusive and casual. This mode is for collecting information—and thinking about it. Those are the only goals. Persistence and near invisibility are the most important characteristics needed for this kind of action.

Information can be collected in a systematic way by creating and following procedures...or it may be necessary to work from hunch, theory or hypothesis. Be as comprehensive and neutral as possible.

Best: Keep at least two hypotheses in mind. Avoid choosing a single hypothesis too early. Fully check out the reasonableness of each theory.

• Brown brogues: Down to earth practicality. Brown—color of earth, mud—brogue, a hard-wearing shoe suitable for most occasions. The emphasis here is on pragmatism and practicality—doing what is doable in a given situation. Action is guided by basic values, basic principles, basic good sense about what is possible under the circumstances.

The goal is simplicity and, above all, effectiveness.

Important: Enough flexibility to make minute-by-minute adjustments as a situation changes. Try to stay in control of the situation even as you are adjusting to it.

• Orange gumboots: Response to crisis and danger. Orange shrieks...alarm bells ring... gumboots are for emergency situations... police...firemen...surgeons. Focus, urgency and sense of priorities characterize orange gumboot action. The dangers need to be assessed carefully. Often human lives may be at stake. The risks of action versus inaction must be constantly reassessed within a tight framework of well-coordinated teamwork. Everyone needs to know what is to be done and who is doing what.

When situations are unstable, unpredictable and likely to get worse, urgent action may be required to get medical attention...to reduce danger...to remove people from the danger area.

Sometimes inaction may have strategic value...waiting to see what develops.

Obtain as much information and expert advice as possible. Determine who is in charge and establish communication between the various parties. Work out a strategic plan including backup, follow-through and fallback considerations...but remain flexible and keep reassessing the situation. Despite the fact that emotions are heavily involved, courage is vital to making hard decisions—and taking necessary action.

•Pink slippers: Human caring, compassion and sympathy. Pink—a gentle, feminine color—slippers...comfort and domesticity. Pink slipper action is concerned with human caring—with sympathy, compassion and help. People matter as people, and caring applies to all people. Even if the feeling is not there, the intention to act in a caring way can still result in caring actions.

Listening and understanding the perceptions and values of others are key parts of caring. Sometimes caring is the prime purpose of the action. At other times, pink slipper action may be used to modify, or mollify, other actions that are taking place.

•Purple riding boots: Performing authoritative roles. Purple...traditional color of authority, as in ancient Rome...boots suggest a special function...an official role. Whoever uses the purple riding boot action mode is not acting as a normal person but is performing as though he/she is an official. Actions must be consistent with the duties, obligations and expectations of that role.

Important: Signal to those around you when you're switching into purple action mode—by, for instance, acting official.

Once you have indicated that to those around you, be consistent and don't switch back and forth. Duties must be performed, but they can be changed by pink slipper considerations.

Decisions...decisions:

There are many situations that call for a mixture of action styles. For example, a crisis may call for both emergency action (orange gumboots) and human care (pink slippers). Another combination might be gray sneakers and brown brogues—where initiative must be used in collecting information.

By getting to know the different styles of action, we can be much more effective as individuals. And, when we ask someone else to act, knowing the sort of action to ask for is also important.

Example: Navy shoe formality may be called for in collecting data...that data may lead to additional gray sneaker intelligence activity...which, in turn, may lead to brown brogue (or other) practical action.

As with the six thinking hats, people can change their action stance when advised, say, that this is a brown brogue assignment...or this is strictly gray sneakers...or I need a pink slipper approach to this problem.

Source: Edward de Bono, PhD, International Center for Creative Thinking, author of more than 30 books and audio programs. His book, *Six Action Shoes,* is available at your bookstore—or from Harper Business, 10 E. 53 St., New York 10022.

Mental Fitness Made Easy...Almost

Just as it takes energy and attention to stay physically healthy, it takes time and effort for us to keep fit mentally. And, just as we've learned to exercise and watch our diets, we can learn to "think like a shrink" for optimum mental health.

What is mental fitness? The ability to overcome self-pity, anger, guilt and emotional isolation, in favor of self-esteem, usefulness, wonder, intimacy...and the other joyful feelings that give life meaning.

Therapists who focus on solving problems quickly use an active, systematic approach to help patients identify and resolve troubling issues and emotional problems. They are called short-term therapists. We can use their techniques in our daily lives as ongoing strategies to maintain mental fitness.

How a shrink thinks:

An effective therapist helps the patient address the universal issues with which we all struggle...

•Dependence versus independence.

•Inappropriate attachment versus the ability to separate.

•Self-sabotage versus self-actualization.

•Chronic grief versus acceptance of loss.

•Emotional isolation versus the ability to feel one's feelings.

•Distancing versus intimacy.

All of us have developed ways to avoid examining our most troublesome behaviors and feelings. The short-term therapist takes an "observant posture" to identify the patient's defenses—the common techniques we all use to shield ourselves from painful truths about our present or past experiences.

Defenses always conceal hidden feelings. So the therapist intervenes when the patient makes a defensive statement, and pursues the defense rather than the content of the statement.

Here is a sample session, greatly condensed. A hypothetical patient, Mr. J., age 52, has been laid off from his job and is very depressed.

Therapist: How did you feel when you lost your job?

Mr. J: Well, the economy is bad, and they needed to make cut-backs, so…

Therapist…hears Mr. J. rationalizing: Yes, but how did you feel?

Mr. J.: Like there's nothing I can do about it. I'm too old to start again.

Therapist…challenging defense of helplessness: You're taking a helpless posture here. How did you feel?

Mr. J: Angry, lousy. After all I had done for that company!

Therapist…hears defensive anger: What was underneath the anger?

Mr. J.: I felt betrayed, and foolish for having expected the company to protect me, to be loyal. And I was scared. Where would I find another job? What would happen to my family?

Therapist: Anything else?

Mr. J.: I felt ashamed, that I was a failure.

Therapist: What do these feelings bring to mind?

Mr. J.: My father, telling me I will never amount to anything, and letting me down when I needed his help.

Therapist…after further exploring the association with Mr. J's father: Were there any positive feelings the day you lost your job?

Mr. J.: I felt relief, like I was suddenly free, and a strange sort of excitement that I might get to start over again doing something new.

Therapist: Anything in particular?

Mr. J.: Well, I've always wanted to teach French cooking classes.

Therapist: That doesn't seem like a viable occupation now. Are you going to put your energy into proving your father right? What are you going to do about solving this problem?

By actively challenging a patient's defenses, the therapist helps him/her to recognize the underlying emotions and associations. The therapist can then issue a call to action: What are you going to do about remedying your problem?

The "work" of therapy involves learning to take an inventory of our mixed emotions. We can learn to do this on our own.

Required: A sensitivity to—and understanding of—common defenses…and unrelenting honesty.

The aim: To reach a sense of emotional balance. This lets us see our options clearly, to let go of our anxiety or fear of intimacy, to take action on our own behalf, change our self-defeating behaviors and move forward.
The defenses:

Each of us favors certain defenses over others. When you notice yourself being defensive, challenge yourself to search for the emotions and associations beneath the defense. There are three types of defenses: Helpless, emotional and intellectual.

•The defenses of helplessness often reflect a lack of self-esteem.

•Vagueness. I guess I feel…Maybe, I don't know…I suppose.

•Passivity and helplessness. I can't do anything about it…really means I won't do anything, I won't change.

•The emotional defenses are used to mask underlying pain.

•Crying is an appropriate response to sadness or loss. But often it masks anger, hurt or guilt. I got so frustrated I cried.

•Depression is also an appropriate response to grief. But defensive depression usually has a self-devaluing quality, and tends to come and go. My life is worthless.

• Anger is an appropriate response to an attack or threat. Defensive anger is a way to feel powerful to mask feelings of hurt, insecurity, inadequacy or powerlessness.

• The intellectual defenses are used to avoid dealing with the emotions.

• Rationalization. Explaining or making excuses to hide feelings. She only said that because she was under a lot of stress.

• Intellectualization. Retreating into philosophy to avoid taking action. Man was meant to be alone.

• Avoidance. Distancing from situations that are painful or intimate. Leaving the room to avoid conflict, avoiding social situations, using sarcasm to keep people away, being bossy or controlling to avoid feeling out of control.

• Denial. Denying that feelings or behaviors exist. I wasn't drunk, the cop was a moron. I wasn't upset at all.

• Projection. Attributing one's own unacceptable feelings or qualities to another.

Example: A man who is afraid to admit he is attracted to a woman not his wife says, All these young guys want to do is chase girls. Society's defenses:

Defenses work on a community level as well as a personal one. The more we understand about how defenses work in our own lives, the better we are able to understand the greater issues that trouble us.

Example: Many Americans responded defensively to the Japanese accusation that American workers are lazy and illiterate, angrily Japan-bashing and smashing cars. If we were mentally fit, we would have accepted the comment in a spirit of challenge, rather than in rage. Underlying truth: Faced with a rather long, demoralizing recession, we have lost faith in ourselves. Our anger is a shield against the pain of believing the Japanese message.

Balance yields wisdom:

The therapeutic process produces a growing awareness that an array of conflicting feelings usually lies beneath our defenses…that among them are positive feelings that can help balance the negative ones. (I am angry at my father's coldness, I feel the hurt of wanting intimacy, and I also feel love and gratitude for the lessons he taught me and our moments of tenderness.)

In taking responsibility for our own contributions to our problems, we learn to stop searching for outside solutions and are no longer hostages to situations.

The quest for balance—pro and con…Yin and Yang—yields wisdom: understanding of the world's complexity.

Source: Christ Zois, MD, co-author of *Think Like A Shrink: Solve Your Problems Yourself with Short-Term Therapy Techniques,* Warner Books, 1271 Avenue of the Americas, New York 10020. Dr. Zois is a member of the faculty of New York Medical College and director of the New York Center for Short-Term Dynamic Psychotherapy, 350 E. 54 St., New York 10022.

Focus On Achievement

Write down the 15 accomplishments you would most like to attain–both on and off the job. Look at the list and decide which are real desires rather than mere wishes. Then examine those desires and ask yourself: How do they relate to one another? How can attaining one further another? What skills do they demand in common? Is there a course to follow to attain them, one leading to another? Finally, get on with it—act to build the skills you need and take the steps necessary to make your most valued goals come true.

Source: *The Achiever's Profile,* by Allan Cox, Amacom, 135 W. 50 St., New York 10020.

Secrets Of Getting Organized

How can people set their priorities more effectively?

Beyond developing a daily to-do list and prioritizing it, the following may be helpful:

• Give yourself at least one hour of screened/prime time every day to work on top-priority work. Screened time is quiet, uninterrupted time allowing you to concentrate, and prime time is the time of day when you are most effective.

Screening options: Coming in an hour early, staying an hour later, having your calls screened by a secretary or colleague (and offering to do the same for them), working in another location (at home or in a quiet, inaccessible office), closing your door, activating your voice mail system or your answering machine and writing in a one-hour appointment with yourself on your calendar.

•Make time every day to work on B priorities. These are priorities that closely tie in with your goals. Most people tend to put Bs on the back burner, selecting only the more pressing, fire-fighting A priorities.

Do you have any recommendations for time-management tools?

In addition to using some kind of calendar, consider using a computer-based time-management system if you can take a portable computer around with you. These software programs include time- and information-management features such as a calendar, to-do lists and tickler functions. They not only have more capacity to record information, but they can enable you to retrieve more in a variety of ways. Computer-based systems also allow you to print out your day's schedule. In general, programs for an office or laptop computer are far superior to the new, hand-held computers. Recommended: Metro, OnTime or PrimeTime, each available at most larger computer stores. Prices range from approximately $85 for Metro to $190 for PrimeTime.

What can people do to minimize interruptions?

Interruptions throw off the best-laid time management plans. Minimizing them requires several steps:

• Jot down as many kinds of interruptions as you can think of from other people—as well as those you initiate yourself. How many ways do you interrupt yourself every day to handle things that should be handled later?

•For every interruption, ask, Is it truly necessary?

•Using your imagination, jot down the things you could do to influence each interruption. Some interruptions could be handled later, perhaps consolidated with similar interruptions.

How can people handle telephone calls more efficiently?

Set up your office so that you can handle calls without the distraction of other work. You'd need an ample writing surface and proximity to current files.

Also helpful: A headset. It enables you to handle a lot of calls quickly without an aching neck. I've used one for years.

Planning will help you minimize time wasted playing telephone tag:

•Whenever possible, set up telephone appointments.

•Consolidate and prioritize all callbacks.

•Make as many calls as possible at times when you're likely to reach people. For instance, after Monday morning staff meetings or after 5:00 pm, when most business of the day is over.

•Prepare for each outgoing call or telephone appointment by having all necessary material in front of you and writing down in advance any key questions or topics to cover as well as a projected time limit for each call.

How do you make filing more useful?

The problem is what you might call a filing phobia. Most people don't know what to call papers, so they're called nothing, and unnamed stacks accumulate. Things get lost. In addition, many people are afraid of discarding things—things that might be needed someday!

Be aggressive. Categorize files as active or inactive. Get inactive files out of your filing system.

Write out your filing system categories and subcategories on paper. Work on it with others who will be involved with the system.

Mark everything clearly. Aim: Others can find their way through your system—to help a customer when you're away…etc.

How can tasks be delegated more effectively?

Of course, you must look for tasks which could be delegated and train someone else to handle those tasks.

Be clear about when you need a task completed. Get the staff person to agree to the due date—or to speak up if it's unrealistic. Let him/her see you write the due date on your calendar. You might want to try putting up a wall calendar so everyone can see what is due when. This helps maintain quiet pressure to perform, so everyone can plan their work.

Few people provide enough praise for a job well done. That's important to motivate your staff.

Source: Susan Silver, president of Positively Organized!, a time-management consulting firm based in Los Angeles She is the author of *Organize to Be the Best!: New Time-Saving Ways to Simplify and Improve How You Work,* Adams Hall Publishing, Box 491002-BL, Los Angeles 90049.

How To Use The Power Of Empowerment

Dr. William Byham, author of *Zapp! The Lightning of Empowerment,* founded and heads an international consulting organization, Development Dimensions International, which is using its long experience in helping US companies adopt team-building and empowerment techniques to help struggling new businesses in Eastern Europe survive.

Dr. Byham writes about his latest discoveries about empowerment—the process of giving employees…and teams…responsibility for their jobs…

There's suddenly no shortage of stories about companies that are magically boosting quality, productivity and customer service because management has empowered the workers to continuously improve the way they get their work done. Some suspect it's just another management fad. Is it?

Managers and workers are understandably skeptical about these programs because so many have come—and gone—in recent years. And why shouldn't they be skeptical…with all the layoffs that have occurred in recent years? Employees feel that any new program will only make matters worse, heightening their chances of termination.

Of course skepticism is all bosses deserve if they attend a management seminar and return to boldly announce they've decided to empower everyone in the company.

Giving people an opportunity to develop a personal commitment to improving the way they work must be approached as a long-term effort. You can't just talk about it. You must show you are serious by your actions.

But many managers are reluctant to make a long-term commitment to changing the way they manage. Why is that?

They're scared. One of the biggest misunderstandings about empowerment is that managers think they abdicate their responsibilities. They think that what they do is tell people they are empowered and the workers then go off and do what they want. Then, if the work is fouled up, the manager's head will be cut off.

Well, what powers do managers actually retain?

Many managers think empowerment means they must accept every idea from every employee, and that their own judgment as managers or supervisors isn't valued any more.

True, you get wonderful ideas from people closest to the work and to customers—when you convince employees that their ideas are valued. But not every single one of them is wonderful. Supervisors must learn the skill and tact of turning down unworkable ideas constructively without harming an employee's enthusiasm about coming back with more.

The easiest thing in the world for a supervisor to do is turn off a worker by saying something like: Oh, that's an interesting idea. But there's this major problem with it. The worker's thought is: Okay. You still are…or think you are…smarter than me. So, you take care of the problem. I'm out of it.

Better: Managers must learn how to maintain the self-esteem of workers as they guide them. Listen to them carefully…and prove it by responding with empathy.

Is it necessary for managers to define the areas of work in which workers can exercise their power?

There's a difference between Americans

and the Japanese on this. The Japanese don't believe in carving up areas of responsibility. Everybody sticks his fingers into everybody's pie. They overlap areas of responsibility.

But we find that does not fit American companies very well. Empowerment programs work better when you give Americans clear areas of responsibilities within which they can see the results of their work.

But American managers also have a problem with measuring results for long-term improvement. It's fine to measure results and grade them for quality. It's quite another to use the measurement to spur future improvement. Managers must learn that the company can't continuously improve unless it can constantly measure its progress. Tinker a bit, change. Then measure the result. Is it better or not? You need feedback all the time. Otherwise it's like trying to improve your bowling score at a bowling alley that has a curtain between you and the pins.

What's needed to make measurements successful?

One of the hidden costs of empowerment for many companies is the time and effort needed to develop better management information systems to get feedback to their workers.

People must know the level of waste in a job process before they can begin measuring how successful their efforts are to reduce it. They must know the quality of their output...and whether it is going up.

Aim: To reduce the number of people who work at jobs where they have no way to measure what they are doing. These people shouldn't be deprived of the benefit...the joy...of empowerment by having to ask a supervisor how they're doing. They should be able to monitor results themselves.

How do you put these measurements in place?

Measures are often specific to a job or even to an individual doing that job. Discuss with each individual how he would measure results. Compare that information with the company's perspective.

Coming up with fair measures takes a lot of time and practice. But it is one of the most

powerful steps management can take to energize employee efforts and keep those efforts going in the right direction.

What about direction and priorities?

Workers often have a big misunderstanding of what empowerment means, too. They think it means total independence...that they can do what they think is best, without checking with a boss or with fellow workers.

But empowerment is not independence. It's interdependence. There are no islands in a company.

Also, workers can be naive about the value of ideas. They may need to learn why when they come up with a better way, it takes a long time to implement the concept. This requires learning the subtleties of company politics—where other people and often other departments have an interest in how things are done.

Workers often must be trained to see that they can't do it all themselves. They will create better ideas and better implementation of their ideas if they use input from other key people in the company.

Source: Dr. William C. Byham, president and cofounder of Development Dimensions International, a human resource training and development consultant, 1225 Washington Pike, Bridgeville, Pennsylvania 15017. He is also the coauthor of *Zapp! The Lightning of Empowerment,* Fawcett Columbine, 201 E. 50 St., New York 10022.

Lessons In Living Life To Its Very Fullest

When David Brown was a young man, the number-one best seller was *Life Begins at Forty,* by Walter B. Pitkin.

Today, that view is outmoded...it's puberty that begins at 40. Life doesn't get better until after 50...and it gets even better later on, Brown says in his new book, *The Rest of Your Life is the Best of Your Life: David Brown's Guide to Growing Gray (Disgracefully).*

The years between 65 and 75 have been the best years of his life...best for work, best for making money, best for making love.

While he admits that he had a lot of fun before 50—as his friend Alan J. Lerner put it, he's glad he's not young anymore. Youth is too fragile, too easily intimidated, unsure of itself.

At 75, David Brown likes himself, and now he says and does what he wants—without worrying much about what others may think. The sense of freedom one can have after passing 50 is exhilarating.

Simple rules for staying young:

• Don't retire. Brown intends to work until his death. What keeps him going is his involvement in work. The work is the machine, the motive.

Almost everybody he knows who feels young, vital and sexy—no matter what his/her age—is working. He is certain that if he stopped working and started getting up late, his machine would slow down...and stop.

With his friends Richard and Lili Zanuck, David Brown produced the movie Cocoon. They discovered that the older actors they selected to play retirees—Hume Cronyn, Jessica Tandy, Jack Gilford, Maureen Stapleton, Don Ameche, Gwen Verdon—looked too young to play their own ages. They had to be aged with makeup and taught to limp and bend over. They had kept on working and never had time to grow old!

How powerfully retirement can affect your health was shown by a recent study of airline pilots. When they retired at age 55, this group of pilots was in certifiably good health. At the time Brown wrote his book—only a few years later—their mortality rate was higher than that of the general public.

Many people hate their work, he observes, and can't wait for "the machine to stop." But if you retire from one thing, you can always go on and do something you really love.

• Start planning your second career while you're in your first one. Brown believes that when you get a job, you should start looking for the next one—or for the next career—however covertly you do it. If you're 35, prepare to deal with getting fired when you're 55 or 60. If you don't get fired, the planning won't hurt you. But you must start thinking

creatively while there's time. Identify what interests you, and what you can develop on the outside as an independent person.

It's very tough for people who work in companies to do this because they've been programmed to depend upon the system. They come to work knowing they'll be required to do certain tasks that have been laid down for them.

But so many companies now are in a desperate state. Those that can't pay their bills pare down their work forces. The economists are saying that most of those who are being let go will not be rehired. What is going on, in Brown's opinion, is not a temporary shrinkage. It's a basic restructuring. So always keep your eye on your options 10 or 20 years down the road.

• Be prepared to start over. What can you do if you are a company man who didn't want to stop working—but got retired?

Brown says he would cut his standard of living, possibly by moving to a much less costly place. Next, he would look around to see what services were needed. Is a messenger service required? Is there something else that isn't being provided in the community?

Then he would go and try to raise money...a modest amount of capital. In other words, he would try to get someone else interested in staking him to a business, after he had done some careful research.

When Brown and Richard Zanuck founded their own movie-production company—after being thrown out of executive posts that they thought they had for life—they decided that never again would they let their lives be controlled by others. But—they weren't certain that they would succeed on their own.

Twice in his fifties, Brown was jobless, a former top executive reduced to collecting unemployment insurance and sending out resumes. What saved him was his refusal to face facts.

If he had held onto his old job, Brown, as an over-65 employee, would have had to retire long ago. Launching out on his own was the best thing that ever happened to him, he feels.

• Worship your body. Even if your body

doesn't look as good to you as it did in your twenties, his best advice is to take good care of your body. You won't get far without it. This means paying attention to what you eat and drink, to how much exercise you get, and to the right kind of medical care.

An old friend of his, a gerontologist at Rockefeller University, says that the best recipe for a long, healthy life is to eat half of what you do now...exercise regularly...and make love every day.

Watching your weight is just common sense, and it may have life-extending virtues, too. Experiments at Cornell University and UCLA have shown that underfed mice lived longer than mice who were fed as much as they wanted. Most of the men and women he knows who have reached the age of 80 or more are thin. But don't get too thin, he cautions. There's no advantage to being emaciated. Moderation in all things is a good rule.

The same goes for exercise. There's no medical evidence that hard exercise extends life, and some doctors believe it shortens it. On the other hand, the authors of *Total Fitness in Thirty Minutes a Week* say 10 minutes of peak effort every day gives you 80% of the cardiovascular conditioning benefits of hours of exercise.

About medical care: Remember, doctors aren't gods. If you get a diagnosis that is ominous, or if your doctor wants to do a little fancy tailoring on your interior, get a second opinion. And maybe a third.

One phenomenally successful producer, David Geffen, dropped out of the entertainment business for three years, after being told he was dying of cancer. He wasn't. The diagnosis was wrong.

Actress Peggy Cass came out of surgery to discover that the wrong knee had been operated on.

You can save yourself a lot of worry by being your own medical consultant. Pay attention to how your body feels and what it needs. Make sure you understand and agree with any medical treatment that's suggested.

Finally, there's the question of drinking. As early as your late forties you will notice a decrease in your ability to consume alcohol.

Brown has found that even a small amount—a few drinks—can cause his voice to slur and his mind to fog...even though he feels as if he is sharper than ever.

Drinking can also release sudden and inexplicable combativeness, repressed aggressions and paranoia. Brown came closest to wrecking his marriage and friendships while drinking, even drinking moderately. Avoid alcoholic beverages entirely when there is pressure or tension...or when you're tired.

• Keep your friends—including friends of the opposite sex. People who stay young all their lives never stop being interested in the opposite sex. There is hardly a day or an hour when Brown is not aware of the women around him. Whether you're married or single, friends of the opposite sex can be a joy and a rejuvenation.

Brown says his wife, Cosmopolitan's pioneering editor, Helen Gurley Brown, cautions older men to beware of women who are too young. Women closer to your own age understand life better—and they are much more interesting than younger women. And Brown agrees.

Source: David Brown, producer of *The Sting, Jaws, Cocoon* and other successful films. He is the author of *The Rest of Your Life is the Best of Your Life: David Brown's Guide to Growing Gray (Disgracefully),* Barricade Books, 1530 Palisade Ave., Fort Lee, New Jersey 07024.

How To Uncomplicate Your Life

The complaint I most often hear from friends and clients alike as a time management and organization consultant is, I just don't seem to have time for myself these days.

But most of us don't really lack time, no matter how busy we are. Lack of time is a symptom. Real problems: Unclear priorities and lack of simple systems for dealing with everyday life.

Solution: Streamlining. Use streamlining to develop and maintain uncomplicated systems wherever life is driving you crazy—from your sock drawer to your social calendar.

Benefits: More time to do what you really want to do, improved relationships with people who really matter, an increased focus on meaningful living, a sense of control. In my five-step plan for uncomplicated living, the first step is often the hardest, while the second is most important...

Adjust your attitude:

•Make a commitment to change. Streamlining is a change, so you must be willing to change. Most common obstacle: Fear of letting go of habits, possessions and people that are no longer relevant to your life.

•Take control of problems rather than letting them control you. Most common obstacles: An addiction to worrying—an addiction to feeling like a victim.

Helpful: Put the same energy into solving problems that you would normally put into worrying...

•Resolve to be productive.

• Concentrate on one problem at a time.

•Take responsibility for your problems, but avoid thinking you should or must do everything yourself.

•When searching for solutions, ask others for advice. Find professional help when necessary: An accountant, a consultant, a teacher, a therapist.

• Learn to let go and move on from problems that are not within your power to solve.

•Control perfectionism. Striving for perfection can be counter-productive and self-sabotaging. Warning signs: Trouble delegating, frequent turnover among assistants—often due to unrealistic demands and expectations...inability to finish tasks quickly and simply. Most common obstacle: Failure to accept excellence in lieu of perfection. Helpful: Be willing to lower your standards. Often "good" is good enough.

Example: It's better to have a relatively clean house than to put off any cleaning until you have time to make it immaculate. Focus on results, not on how they are achieved or whether they are done your way.

•Stop procrastinating. Delay creates problems. Most common obstacle: Excuse-making, blaming others for why you're not doing what needs to be done, waiting for the "right time." Helpful:

•Divide large projects into manageable pieces. Do the hardest part first.

•Set deadlines and trick yourself into action if necessary.

•Reward yourself when you meet your deadlines.

•If you are putting off doing something you really hate or don't know how to do, hire someone to do it for you.

Prioritize and plan:

•Identify your life mission, goals and priorities. On the first page of a new loose-leaf notebook, briefly describe your purpose in life. What would you most like to be remembered for?

List your goals—one per page—everything from buying a house in the country to losing 20 pounds. People who write down their goals are far more likely to achieve them. Give each goal a realistic deadline, whether it's one week or five years. Next, make a "To Do" list of all of your unfinished business and projects: Take an exercise class...clean out the attic.

Review your mission, goals and list to determine project categories: Career, House, Finances, Self-Improvement, etc. Transfer "To Do" items to the appropriate category page, and prioritize each with a number.

•Plan and schedule regularly. Transfer errands and daily obligations to your calendar. Then schedule time for work on your top-priority projects, including time for yourself. Helpful:

•Devote specific, uninterrupted periods to one project at a time, and finish what you start.

•Be realistic about the amount of time projects take. Use your calendar to schedule time for bill-paying, chores, volunteering, play.

•Build in some flexibility for the unexpected, but say no to unreasonable demands or invitations that don't interest you.

•Practice preventive maintenance.

Examples: Schedule regular check-ups for your family, teeth, cars, etc.

•Continue to review your goals, priorities and schedule weekly. Aim: Increased awareness of what's really important to you…motivation to simplify and eliminate what isn't. Are you really spending more hours maintaining a finicky foreign car than reading to your children?

Eliminate the extraneous:

•Prioritize the people in your life. Time spent with people you don't care about means less time for those who are important to you. Clarify your priorities and learn to say no. Helpful: Improved communication skills can minimize time spent explaining, arguing, placating, etc.

•Reevaluate your possessions. Many people spend more time taking care of their "stuff" than they do taking care of themselves. Get rid of things you don't use or that no longer suit your life-style. Be ruthless.

Key: Separate need from want. You may want a gourmet popcorn popper, but you don't actually need it. Make an attempt to let go of the things that have accumulated from your "past lives."

Helpful: Give things away, right away. Someone else does need your extra china.

•Avoid fads, sales and shopping from habit.

•Rent rather than own equipment you seldom use.

•Don't store stuff in the garage!

•Evaluate what you do need to function efficiently.

Example: Keep scissors in the desk and in the kitchen.

Organize what's left:

•Establish a convenient place for everything. Tackle each area once and for all… kitchen, workspace, closets.

Stick to a system:

•Maintain systems at home and at the office. For ongoing efficiency and serenity, devise a system for handling the mail, keys, eyeglasses, shopping, cooking, filing, laundry, bills, etc. My books offer suggestions for organizational systems of every kind. Enjoy the newfound time and focused productivity of your streamlined life.

Source: Stephanie Culp, whose firm, The Organization, in Oconomowoc, Wisconsin, helps individuals and businesses develop systems to get—and stay—organized. Her book is *Streamlining Your Life: A Five-Point Plan for Uncomplicated Living,* Writer's Digest Books, 1507 Dana Ave., Cincinnati 45207.

More Effective Thinking

Should we condemn our traditional thinking methods, which were set in place by the last Renaissance? Surely they have served us well in science, in technology, in democracy and in the development of civilization itself?

There is no doubt that our existing thinking culture has taken us very far. It is pointless to speculate that a different thinking culture might have taken us even further—especially in human affairs—because such speculation can never be tested. We can be duly appreciative of our traditional thinking culture and also realize that it is inadequate. It may have been adequate for the period in which it was developed (ancient Greece and medieval Europe), but at that time there were stable societies, agreed perceptions and limited technical change. Today there are problems caused by rapidly accelerating change and the uneven nature of that change. In part these things are caused by the "cleverness" of our traditional thinking systems and a lack of "wisdom."

The inadequacy of our traditional thinking culture may be pinpointed as follows:

•We need to shift from a destructive type of thinking to a much more constructive type.

•We need to change from argument to genuine exploration of a subject.

•We need to lessen the esteem in which we hold critical thinking and to place it below constructive thinking.

•We need to match skills of analysis with an equal emphasis on skills of design.

•We need to do as much idea-work as we

do information-work. We need to realize that the analysis of data is not enough.

• We need to shift from an obsession with history to a concern for the future.

• We need to emphasize "operacy" as much as knowledge. The skills of doing are as important as the skills of knowing.

• We need, for the first time, to realize that creative thinking is a serious and essential part of the thinking process.

• We need to move from our exclusive concern with the logic of processing to the logic of perception.

Source: *I Am Right—You Are Wrong,* by Dr. Edward de Bono, Viking Penguin, 375 Hudson St., New York 10014. Dr. de Bono has written over 20 books on thinking and creativity. Reprinted by permission.

---

17 Principles Of Success

Napoleon Hill and W. Clement Stone were two of this century's pioneers in motivational thinking. For decades, their books, lectures and seminars have inspired millions to strive for the best of which they are capable.

Hill and Stone developed their philosophies independently. They joined forces in the 1950s to further develop their secrets of success. These principles are still relevant today—they are the same principles used to achieve career and life success by the most successful people in our society.

As I studied these principles during my work with Mr. Stone and the Napoleon Hill Foundation in Chicago, I realized that they fell into five categories…attitudinal…personal…fraternal…intellectual…spiritual.

The key to success is balance in all five areas. Money, influence and power are traditional ingredients of success—but they aren't the whole story. One CEO of a major company told me that the most successful person he knew was his gardener—a man loved by his family, respected by his friends, who worked hard and had a full life.

Attitudinal principles:

The first two principles—Stone's Positive Mental Attitude and Hill's Definiteness of Belief—are the foundations of success. You must master these two principles in order to apply any of the others.

• Positive Mental Attitude (PMA). If you expect success, you will succeed. If you expect failure, you'll fail. It's as simple as that.

Negative thinking is a learned habit. We can condition our minds to think positively by replacing negative thoughts with positive ones—hour by hour, day by day.

We can't control all of the circumstances of our lives, but we can control our attitude toward them. PMA means having the appropriate attitude under the circumstances.

This is not the Pollyanna-ish approach that says, "If I just look on the bright side, everything will be perfect." It requires analyzing your circumstances, minimizing the risk and maximizing the advantages…then approaching the situation with the belief that you will succeed.

Example: An insurance salesman who tells himself, "I can sell this policy to anybody," will wind up wasting hours trying to persuade prospects who are never going to buy. But the salesman who says, "The more people I present this policy to, the more sales I'll make—and I won't give up until I reach my goal," is setting himself up for success.

• Definiteness of purpose. To get where you want to go, you must have a definite vision of your overall goal.

This is the source of your burning desire—the dream that wakes you up in the middle of the night, the thing that makes work a pleasure instead of a chore because it's part of the path to your goal.

Example: A newspaper reporter's overall goal might be to own his/her own newspaper someday…or to win the Pulitzer prize.

Hill's 4-point formula—plus:

• Write down your goal—make it clear and concise.

• Outline a plan for getting there. Include the interim steps needed to achieve your goal.

• Set a timetable for reaching the goal—a planned timetable for each step.

• Memorize both your overall goal and your plan…and repeat them to yourself several times a day.

If you're focused on an overriding goal, you'll find that you set priorities almost automatically. Actions that help you reach the goal take priority over everything else.

• Going the extra mile. Essayist Elbert Hubbard wrote, "Folks who never do any more than they get paid for never get paid for any more than they do."

In our age of instant gratification, this principle might seem unfashionable—but it works. In business and all other areas of life, if you give more than is asked of you, you will reap great rewards.

• Learning from defeat. People who lack the courage to fail big also lack what it takes to achieve big successes. Coping with failure builds strength and wisdom. If you learn from it and refuse to give up, every defeat can be another step toward success.

Personal principles:

• Personal initiative.

• Enthusiasm.

• A pleasing personality. People prefer to do business with someone they like—no matter how technical or expensive the purchase. People want to associate with those who are pleasant to be around...who act on their ideas...who believe in themselves and others...who are cheerful, generous and considerate of others.

Important: Follow the golden rule: Think about how you would like to be treated if you were in the other person's shoes. There's no better business or social advice.

• Self-discipline.

• Budgeting time and money.

• Maintaining sound physical and mental health. Even if you are already enthusiastic and positive, you must be able to control your mental and physical habits in order to succeed. Rest and relaxation are vital to renewing your energy and maintaining your focus. And, of course, good nutrition and exercise are essential if your mind and body are to function at their peak.

Fraternal principles:

• Master-mind alliance. Napoleon Hill began his study of success principles in 1908, in response to a challenge from steel magnate Andrew Carnegie. "Master-mind alliance" was a term Carnegie coined to describe the almost miraculous power unleashed when two or more people work together in harmony toward a common goal.

Carnegie believed his greatest strength in building US Steel was in hiring people who would not only get the job done but work in perfect harmony together with a shared sense of mission.

When the right spirit is present, the power generated is incredible—far beyond that of gifted individuals working alone with equal or even greater intensity.

The master-mind alliance is truly high-order networking. You may have experienced this phenomenon yourself during a brainstorming session, when ideas flowed and everything seemed to click.

This kind of relationship is not easy to achieve, but it's worth working toward.

• Teamwork. Members of an effective team may not always share a common purpose... but they always cooperate to achieve success.

Developing a smoothly functioning team takes empathy and the willingness to encourage the best from others—even if their approach is different from yours.

Intellectual principles:

• Creative vision. Creativity is nothing more than using your imagination to look at something in a different way.

W. Clement Stone advises setting aside at least half an hour every day just for creative thinking. Take an idea and turn it over in your mind, looking at it from every possible angle until you see it as you never have before.

Listen to your subconscious mind. Write down the ideas that come to you in dreams or when you're thinking about something completely unrelated.

Once you've gathered information about an idea and mulled it over, let the information incubate for a period of time...until your subconscious produces flashes of insight.

• Controlled attention. This means being able to focus and make sure you spend the time needed to get your idea right.

• Accurate thinking. Imagination creates ideas...attention and accurate thinking shape them into action.

Look at your ideas objectively. List the positives and negatives. Evaluate alternatives and their possible consequences. Draw on the advice of experts as well as on your own knowledge and experience.

Stone's R2A2 Formula can be very useful: Recognize and Relate, Assimilate and Apply. You can use the knowledge gained from any field to produce greater understanding of the situation at hand.

Spiritual principles :

• Applied faith. You can have all the money, fame and power you desire, but without the knowledge that you are making a contribution to the world, these superficial signs of success will leave you feeling empty.

Even if you don't subscribe to an organized religion, having faith in something greater than yourself—God, cosmic consciousness, the power of love—will enhance your success by bringing out your highest qualities.

• Cosmic habit force. Both good and bad habits are formed in the same way—through repetition. Understanding and mastering this simple principle gives you the power to change any negative habit or form any positive one.

Repeat positive suggestions, affirmations or commands to yourself over and over—aloud and with conviction—morning and night until they become absorbed into your subconscious.

Success, too, is a habit. You can form the habit of success by repeating, reinforcing and practicing the success principles I have outlined until they become a part of you.

Source: Samuel A. Cypert, director of communications at Masco Corp., a *Fortune 500* manufacturer of building products, and the author of *Believe and Achieve: W. Clement Stone's 17 Principles of Success,* Avon Books, 1350 Avenue of the Americas, New York 10019.

4

Personal Money Management

It's Almost Impossible To Get Rich Quick Now— Here's How To Get Rich...Slowly

Now that money market rates have dropped to the 5% area, everybody is looking for alternative ways to get the high returns that they've become accustomed to. There are still many ways to get higher returns, but each alternative comes with its own risks and rewards...

• Junk bonds. The riskiest alternatives. They are currently paying 12% to 15%. Junk bonds are usually issued by highly leveraged companies. In the best of times, they have enough cash flow to pay back debt, but in a recession they may be dangerous.

Important: Some junk issues are much, much better than other ones. Example:

• Kroger. 1999, 12⅞%. A solid company with good cash flows.

Caution: If the economy doesn't turn around as fast as anticipated, the company could default on its debt. Result: You could wind up losing both interest payments and capital.

• Other low-rated corporate bonds are a bit more secure—with yields between 10% and 11%. Although they aren't considered junk, they may have received different or split ratings from various rating agencies. Example:

• United Telecommunications. 2000, 11%. Rated Baa3 by Moody's and BBB—by Standard and Poor's.

• Common and preferred stock. You can get high yields from some common stocks. Although the average dividend is now 3.2%, some companies are paying dividends of 10% or higher.

Risk: You wind up losing principal if the stock price drops...and dividends may drop as well if earnings begin to deteriorate. Examples:

• Northeast Utilities. NYSE: NU. Recent share price: $23. Current yield: 7.7%.

• Ohio Edison. NYSE: OEC. Recent share price: $19⅞%. Current yield: 7.5%.

You can get additional security by purchasing preferred stock of financial service companies. Owners of preferred stock are paid dividends before owners of common stock. Although they don't benefit when the stock prices go up, preferred stock provides a more secure income stream because the dividend and yield is predetermined. Attractive:

• Household International Inc. pfA:* NYSE:HI. Recent share price: $25½%. Yield: 9.3%.

• Wells Fargo pf: NYSE:WFC. Recent share price: $36¾. Yield: 9.1%.

• Certificates of deposit. Bank certificates of deposit now pay 5.19%, on national average.

You may be able to get an additional percentage point of yield by purchasing repackaged bank certificates of deposit from your stock broker. Insurance companies and other institutional investors buy huge blocks of bank CDs. When the issues of those CDs are downgraded, some institutions will sell them to brokers at discounts of up to 5%. Brokers then repackage them to their clients in $10,000 units. Right now, you can buy repackaged one-year CDs yielding 5.3%.

Even though the banks issuing the CDs may be downgraded, you're still protected by the FDIC if you hold less than $100,000 at each bank.

The FDIC pledge may mean less than it did a few years ago, but it is considered an important plus—right now. When you buy a repackaged CD, just make sure that it is registered in your name rather than the name of your broker.

• Top-rated corporate bonds. AAA-rated corporations yield returns of about 8.8%, considerably higher than that offered by a bank CD. Although your money isn't guaranteed by the federal government, top-rated corporate bonds provide a high degree of security.

*"pfA" designates one of several classes of Household International preferred stock.

Source: Peter H. Heerwagen, chief investment officer at The Ayco Corp., the financial counseling subsidiary of American Express Co., 1 Wall St., Albany, New York 12205.

Two Smart Money Strategies

Here are two smart ways to keep your money safe:

• Stick with strictly credit-risk-free investments.

Suggestion: Zero coupon bond funds. They can be volatile on a day-to-day basis (that's market risk as distinct from credit risk). The yield is guaranteed if you hold to maturity, but if you sell before that, you could wind up with a big profit...or a big loss.

Note: Although zero coupon bonds, which are sold at a big discount, pay no cash dividend, you are liable for annual income taxes on what the IRS calls imputed interest.

• Caution: Reconsider keeping your money in government-insured bank accounts. The Federal Deposit Insurance Corp. (FDIC) had—before the Bank of New England takeover—reserves of only $.60 per $100 of bank deposits. Steps are underway to improve that to $1.25 per $100 of deposits by 1995, but that's still only marginal protection.

The good news: You can put your money in money market mutual funds that invest 100% in US Treasury bills. These funds are not insured by the FDIC...they're safer because they have $100 in reserves backing up $100 in investments.

Source: William E. Donoghue, publisher of *Donoghue's Moneyletter,* Box 6640, Holliston, MA 01746.

How To Erase Bad Credit

About 70% of all people have at least one negative item in their personal-credit reports. They are collected and distributed by nationwide consumer-reporting agencies.

That single bad item can jeopardize a loan or an application for a credit card...and, more troublesome, it can even hurt a person's chances of getting a job or being admitted to a private club. Since many credit reports contain errors, and these reports can remain active for years, it's wise to get any errors corrected as soon as possible.

It's not difficult to clean up a report. Except for unusual situations, a credit-report cleanup is a do-it-yourself project.

How to get a report: A credit bureau must send you a copy of its report on you free of charge if you've been denied credit within the past 30 days because of negative information provided by it. Otherwise, you can buy a copy for $5 to $15 from any credit reporting agency—any agency that compiles credit information and reports it to subscribers. The four largest...

• TRW Credit Information Systems, 505 City Parkway West, Orange, California 92667.

• Trans Union Credit Information, 444 N. Michigan Ave., Chicago 60611.

• CBI/Equifax, Box 4091, Atlanta 30302.

• Associated Credit Services, Inc., 624 East North Belt, Suite 400, Houston 77060.

Alarming: It's estimated that nearly 75% of all personal-credit reports have at least one error. Mistakes are so widespread that many industry professionals joke about the credit reports regularly.

How to correct errors:

• Legal basis: The Federal Fair Credit Reporting Act requires that all bad credit items be removed from a report after a specified period—usually after seven years. A personal bankruptcy action, however, is allowed to remain for up to 10 years. Positive information, stays in the report for only five years.

The law also provides opportunities for correcting reports that are either in error, misleading or obsolete (older than the legal retention period).

When disputing an item, never write, for example, "I was late in this payment because..." That could add negative information to your report. Instead, just list the errors.

Unless the credit agency can show that your request is "frivolous and irrelevant," it must undertake a reinvestigation of a claim within a "reasonable amount of time."

There's the catch: The law doesn't say how soon it must start the reinvestigation. It only says it must be completed within 20 working days after the start of the agency's order for reinvestigation—but be prepared for foot-dragging. If the agency sends you a "frivolous

and irrelevant" letter, fire back a demand for immediate action and even threaten suit.

• Explanation option: If a reinvestigation fails to resolve the dispute, the law allows you to add a brief statement (about 100 words) to explain why you were not at fault.

• Circumvention: If you're the victim of a clerical error that you can't get corrected (because you no longer have the necessary paperwork, for example), you may want to use a circumvention strategy. Be aware, however, that, although the method is effective, its ethics are questionable. How it works...

Send the letter requesting a reinvestigation to a branch office of the credit bureau—not the one in your area or the main office. That makes it difficult for the bureau to meet the deadline, and once it misses it, you can demand removal of the offensive item. You can get addresses of branch offices either from the agency or from the Directory of Consumer Credit Services.*

• Alternative method: If an error on a billing is several years old or the purchased service or merchandise was defective, you may want to file the dispute directly with the creditor and demand that your credit report be corrected. Direct the letter to an official of the firm, not just the accounting department.

• Negotiation strategy: If you are severely pressed for funds and are indeed in arrears on a debt, it's still possible to clean your report. Contact an officer of the creditor and level with him about your financial situation. Then offer to pay the debt or some portion of it in exchange for an amendment to your file. Usually a creditor will accept a partial payment (70% or so is not unusual in exchange for clearing the slate).

Get the agreement in writing and signed by the officer before you make the payment. Do not accept such changes as "paid collection account" or "paid charge-off." That will not clear your credit report. Instead, demand such notations as "paid satisfactorily" or "current account."

• Legal action: If a credit bureau refuses to reinvestigate a disputed item, federal law al-

*Available from Consumer Research Associates, Box 20161, Riverside, California 92516.

lows you to file a complaint with the Federal Trade Commission (Sixth St. and Pennsylvania Ave. NW, Washington, DC 20580). Or you can take the credit bureau to court—including your local small claims court, where you can litigate an action for a few dollars and without a lawyer.

Source: Bob Hammond, financial consultant, president of Hammond & Associates, Box 1253, Moreno, CA 92337, and author of *Credit Secrets: How to Erase Bad Credit.*

Financial Independence: 10 Commonsense Rules

Many ordinary, middle-class folks are put off by the term "financial planning." But good financial planning is nothing more than common sense. The KISS formula is—Keep It Simple...Sweetheart.

You don't have to earn a doctor's or a lawyer's salary to achieve financial security. Anyone, regardless of his/her job or income, can become financially independent as long as he follows these 10 simple principles of financial planning...

• Spend less than you make. This sounds incredibly basic, but unfortunately most people can't manage to live within their means. Obviously, you cannot become financially independent if your spending regularly exceeds your income...unless you marry or inherit wealth. Generally, that's not something that you can count on.

• Budgeting in order to save is doomed to failure. Theoretically, budgeting makes a lot of sense. You allot so much of your income for each expense, and at the end of the month, there should be a certain amount left over to invest.

Trap: Budgets are almost always sabotaged by human nature. You tell yourself that you're budgeting for your needs, but what happens is that you wind up budgeting for your wants. Do you really need that winter vacation in the Caribbean, or a new car for your business? Or do you simply want those things so much that

they have become needs? Very few people budget successfully, and most of them aren't much fun to be around.

• Pay off your credit card balances. The interest on these balances, like the interest on personal, installment and car loans, is no longer tax-deductible. And at annual interest rates of 18% or more, eliminating these non-deductible debts is one of the best financial decisions you'll ever make.

• Buying a house is a good investment. I still believe this even though the double-digit growth in real estate values that we saw in the 1980s in some areas will probably not be repeated. Too many people have felt that the only investing they have to do is to buy a home. Not true. It's just one element in fashioning a sound approach to investing, and has to be done in conjunction with other financial planning.

• Aim to save at least 10% of your net income. That's the money left over after you've paid federal, state and local taxes. Saving one-tenth of that amount may seem like an impossibly ambitious undertaking, but if you use the next two suggestions, after a few months, you won't even miss the money you're stashing away.

• Pay yourself first. This sounds simple—and it is. Point: You can't spend what you don't see. By establishing a routine of automatically diverting some of your paycheck into savings each month, you become accustomed to making ends meet with less income than before. The money you save goes into building a portfolio that can be used for a retirement nest egg, a downpayment on a house, college education fund for your children, etc.

• Use payroll deductions or preauthorized checking for painless savings. The most effective method is to have the money you plan to invest come straight out of your paycheck or bank account. The 401 (k) plans that many companies now offer are the ultimate in the payroll deduction approach to saving. These plans allow you to reduce your income (and your income taxes) by automatically making monthly contributions to a tax-deferred savings plan with a variety of investment options, ranging from stocks to bonds to insurance contracts. Bonus: Many companies will match your contributions, up to a certain point.

• Be an owner, not a loaner, over the long term. If you're relatively young and have a decade or more to go before retirement, contribute the bulk of your savings to stocks—not bonds or bank certificates of deposit. Reason: Over the long term, equities have had a much higher rate of return than fixed-income securities, and I expect that pattern to continue in the future. Even though our country has huge deficits, major environmental problems and serious social ills, I believe that we will address them, and that the next 20–30 years will present some of the greatest investment opportunities ever. And the only way to share in the successes is through ownership.

I do not, however, recommend owning individual common stocks directly. To do well on your own in the stock market, you must have a rare combination of guts and brains. You have to not only become familiar with the management teams of various companies, but you also have to know what questions to ask them. And most of all, you have to have a sixth sense that enables you to recognize value. Best: Invest in a carefully selected mutual fund, where you buy into a diversified portfolio of stocks and gain access to a professional money manager who has those qualities you need to succeed in the market.

• Don't try to time the market. Market timing requires using key indicators, to predict major shifts in the stock and bond markets… and to shift your money from one investment to another.

Example: When the indicators point to a decline in the stock market, you're supposed to move your money out of equities into the "safe" haven of a money market fund. Conversely, when the indicators suggest the stock market is poised for a major upturn, you're supposed to move out of the money market fund and back into equities to catch the predicted upturn. In theory this sounds great, but in practice it seldom works…except for brokers, who reap big commissions from such trading. Sector fund switching—from a mutual fund that specializes in one type of industry to another—is usually not any more successful.

• Your biggest enemy is procrastination. The earlier you start investing, and reaping the benefits of compounding (the earning of interest on interest), the better…and it's never too late to start. Don't get sidetracked by agonizing over whether to buy Fund A or Fund B. Spend a reasonable amount of time researching the long-term track records of funds you are interested in. Make sure that the portfolio managers responsible for the good performance are still at the helm and that the expenses of the funds are in line with those of similar funds. Then go ahead and buy.

I'm a big believer in finding a few good mutual funds, leaving my money (including reinvested dividends and capital gains) there and forgetting about it. You'll be astounded at how much your money will grow over the years.

Source: David Chilton, a former stockbroker and financial planner who now travels across the country speaking to company employees and individuals about their finances. He is the author of *The Wealthy Barber*, Prima Publishing, Box 1260, Rocklin, California 95677.

A Personal Budget Is Smart Planning

A personal budget shouldn't be a fiscal straightjacket that dictates how each dollar must be spent. Better: Use a budget first as a planning tool. Decide what you want to accomplish with your money—and budget to meet those goals. Build in some flexibility for comfort…and to help you meet unexpected needs. Then, after the budget is up and running, use it as a warning system. When you stray from your financial plan, the budget warns you that trouble is approaching, and gives you time to take money-saving steps.

Source: *Make Your Money Grow*, edited by Theodore J. Miller, Kiplinger Books, 1729 H St. NW, Washington, DC 20006.

The 14-Day Fraud Window

You are entitled to full reimbursement if a bank cashes a check on which someone has forged your name—even if you fail to report that your checkbook was stolen. But if you fail to report a forgery within 14 days of the time the bank mails your statement, and the same person keeps cashing fraudulent checks, you will not be reimbursed for later losses.

Source: *Making the Most of Your Money* by financial writer Jane Bryant Quinn, Simon & Schuster, 1230 Avenue of the Americas, New York 10020.

Dumbest Money Mistakes

Being ashamed to invest small amounts of money…having inadequate savings—six months of take-home pay is a minimum… operating too many accounts—service fees can add up rapidly…failing to diversity—no one investment is profitable or safe enough for all your money…procrastinating—the sooner you start investing, the sooner funds start appreciating. Most important: Developing the saving habit.

Source: *How to Invest $50–$5,000* by financial writer Nancy Dunnan, HarperCollins, 10 E. 53 St., New York 10022.

Credit Card Traps

Don't just throw credit cards away. Your credit file will show that you have an open line of credit…even if you never use it. Then, when you do want credit, you may be denied—on the grounds that you have too much already. What to do: If you get a card that you don't want, cut it up and return it to the issuer with a letter stating that you do not want the card or the account.

Source: *Money Troubles: Legal Strategies to Cope with Your Debts* by attorney Robin Leonard, Nolo Press, 950 Parker St., Berkeley, California 94710.

Unauthorized Use Of Your Card

If your credit card is lost or stolen, and you report it to the card issuer before anyone uses the card, you are not liable for any fraudulent charges.

If you either didn't know about the problem or didn't contact the card issuer promptly, you could be held liable for the first $50 of charges per card. There is no time limit on disputing unauthorized charges.

If a friend or family member uses your card, that person is authorized to charge items only to the extent that you have authorized him/her.

If the actual credit card is not used in the transaction—if someone gets one of your carbons, or a store copy of your credit card receipt—you cannot be held liable for any unauthorized charges at all…not even the first $50.

Note: It is now illegal for companies to send unsolicited credit cards through the mail. If you receive a credit card you have not applied for, cut up the card, send it back to the issuer and complain to the comptroller of currency in your city—listed in the government blue pages of your phone book.

Always Keep Your Records Straight

Always keep your own records of investment transactions made through brokers—brokerage firms do make mistakes. With each order, write down the date, time, security, price and whether it was a buy or a sell. Compare your records with brokerage reports on a regular basis. Trap: If you don't keep your own records, you'll have no way of knowing whether the brokerage reports you get are correct or not.

Source: *Trader Vic: Methods of a Wall Street Master* by Victor Sperandeo and T. Sullivan Brown, John Wiley & Sons, 605 Third Ave., New York 10158.

Better Checkbook Balancing

It isn't necessary to balance your checkbook to the last penny. Helpful: Enter every deposit and withdrawal immediately, including ATM and debit card transactions...keep a running balance...check that every withdrawal and deposit is listed on the monthly bank statement...compare the dollar amount of all cleared checks against those that are listed on the statement...add any interest paid and subtract all fees. If nothing feels wildly out of line, you should be able to trust the bank's arithmetic and accept the statement's closing balance as correct.

Source: *Making the Most of Your Money: Smart Ways to Create Wealth and Plan Your Finances in the '90s* by financial columnist Jane Bryant Quinn, Simon & Schuster, 1230 Avenue of the Americas, New York 10020.

5

Banking

Credit Card Companies' Tricks

Beware of credit-card companies' promotional promises to make up the difference if credit-card holders find an item they've purchased at a lower price.

Main problem:

Consumers must put together a lot of paperwork to get a refund, we hear from Gerri Detweiler of Bankcard Holders of America in Herndon, Virginia.

Clothing catch:

You may find a coat you bought last month at a lower price, but Citicorp requires a printed advertisement listing the specific item—and that's very hard to find.

Electronics catch:

Major electronic retailers get unique model numbers from manufacturers to prevent price shopping—even if you see your new VCR advertised for less, chances are it will have a different model number.

How To Get Lower Rates

Don't wait for your credit card company to lower your rates. If you want lower rates now, call customer service at the bank that issued your present card.

Some banks have another card program—even a gold card—that offers lower rates…but isn't being widely publicized. If you have trouble getting information, threaten to switch to another card issuer. Or order BHA's latest Fair Deal List*—a list of banks with the lowest card rates and cards with no annual fees.

*Fair Deal List, Bankcard Holders of America, 560 Herndon Parkway, Suite 120, Herndon, Virginia 22070. 800-553-8025.

Source: Gerri Detweiler, Bankcard Holders of American (BHA).

If Your Bank Fails...Or Merges—Self-Defense Strategies

In the recent past, there have been an unprecedented number of failures and mergers. Customers of the hundreds of banks and thrifts that went out of business usually wound up with a new institution handling their banking affairs...and an entirely new set of rules and regulations with which to contend.

A total of 534 commercial banks and 307 thrifts merged in 1991. On top of that, 29 private bank mergers—ones not assisted by the government—were completed. The largest of these private-sector deals were the combination of NCNB (Charlotte, North Carolina) and C&S/Sovran (Norfolk, Virginia)...Chemical Bank and Manufacturers Hanover in New York...Wachovia (North Carolina) and South Carolina National...Norwest Corp. (Minneapolis) and the United Bank of Colorado...and Banc One Corp.'s (Ohio) acquisition of four banks in Ohio from PN Financial Corp. in Pittsburgh.

Regardless of the circumstances surrounding the merger or failure, customers whose banks are taken over may face changes in account numbers, services, fees and charges, interest rates and federal deposit insurance coverage.

What to expect:

• At least some chaos. Deposits may be credited to the wrong account, loan payments may be lost and checks for use at the new institution may be sent to the wrong address.

Self-defense: Immediately open all mail that you get from both your new and old banks. Read it all carefully. Typically, there will be a blizzard of mailings telling customers what is in store as a result of the merger. Often, there are handouts at branches, with answers to the most commonly asked questions.

• Announcements of changes in service. Don't delay in checking over your monthly statement. It may contain announcements of forthcoming changes that can affect your account—increases in monthly service fees or hikes in the minimum account size you must maintain in order to escape such fees.

• Interest rate changes. If the merger takes place to save a troubled institution, and one bank acquires the assets of another, the acquiring bank has the right to lower interest rates on certificates of deposit (CDs). There's no requirement that the acquiring bank pay even a passbook rate of interest. Theoretically, it could reduce the interest rate to zero. That, however, is highly unlikely, since the idea behind such mergers is to gain customers, not drive them away.

Many acquiring banks, though, have reduced the rates that the old banks paid on CDs, often to drive away "hot" money of customers who chased across the country for the highest rates on such investments. But if a new bank decides to lower the rate on an existing CD issued by the old bank, it must give you 14 days in which to withdraw that money without penalty. So it's especially important to read all mail from the new bank, in order to give yourself some time to scout for new investments.

• Confusion regarding account ownership. Gather together all the paperwork on accounts maintained at the old bank. Reason: You may need to prove you are a bona fide depositor and that you own the accounts in question. Very often after a merger, the supporting paperwork showing who owns what accounts is mislaid. This can create a big problem for customers who need to get their hands on their money, but can't readily prove the accounts are theirs.

Crucial documents to save—or get copies of—include signature cards (which show how an account is registered) for checking accounts...and CD agreements (which show the same thing, as well as the term and rate).

Do it now:

Obtain and file crucial paperwork now, even if you have no reason to believe that your bank is about to be acquired. It's much simpler to request documents while a bank is operating normally, than it is to ferret them out while the bank is in the process of reorganization.

• Change direct deposit instructions if your

bank is the one that is being acquired. Otherwise, direct deposits such as Social Security benefits, your paycheck and interest payments on Treasury securities you purchased directly from the US government may be sent to the old bank, and then returned because the account has been closed. Depending upon the new bank's administrative policies, it may be necessary for you to establish these direct deposit agreements with the Social Security Administration and your company from scratch, as if you had never before made such arrangements.

• Change automatic payment instructions. Often, people have payments for regularly recurring items such as a home mortgage, car and health insurance automatically withdrawn from their bank accounts each month. If your old account is closed, you have to give the necessary instructions to your new bank in order for these automatic payments to continue.

• Know how federal deposit insurance works in the case of mergers. The rule is that customers who have deposits at both merging banks receive dual protection for six months after the merger takes place. In the case of CDs, the dual coverage continues until the first maturity date after the end of this six-month grace period.

Example: You have a $75,000 CD at Bank A and another $75,000 CD at Bank B. The entire $150,000 would be covered by the Federal Deposit Insurance Corporation until six months after the merger is completed, or the maturity date of the CDs, whichever is later. If both the CDs matured during the six-month grace period and were rolled over into new CDs of the same term and dollar amount, both CDs would remain fully insured. But if the term or dollar amounts of the new CDs were different from the original CDs, then dual coverage would last only through the six-month grace period. Beyond six months, FDIC insurance covers only up to $100,000 of money in your name at any one bank.

• Expect a new account number and new checks—if your bank is the one being acquired. The new bank will want to eliminate any duplicate account numbers. And—since account numbers usually include the branch number—the account number may need to be changed if your old branch is closed. Typically, banks issue new checks after a merger to reflect a new bank name and account number. But they usually permit customers to use existing checks for a period of time, though that may be as brief as 30 days if the old bank was closed because of insolvency. Check numbers usually start where the old ones left off.

• Expect a new automated teller machine (ATM) card if your old bank is acquired. Your ATM card will be reissued with the name of the new bank. Your personal identification number will need to be changed because of new computer software. If the two merging institutions are part of the same ATM network, fees for transactions at the old bank's machines usually are waived even before the new cards are issued.

Your bank credit card also will be reissued with a new bank name if the bank that issued the card is taken over. If the merging banks have different fee and rate structures, they must agree on the new fees and interest rate for the card.

Source: Robert K. Heady, publisher of the *Bank Rate Monitor*, a newsletter that follows trends in the banking industry, Box 088888, North Palm Beach, Florida 33408.

Frequent Switching Traps

Does it pay to switch credit cards every time you see a better deal on the annual fees? Does frequent switching affect your credit rating?

It pays to switch once—to a no-annual-fee card. There are many available, including some (like those from Texas-based USAA) that also offer low interest rates. Avoid cards that offer no fee for the first year only—after that, they have no advantages.

Officially, frequent switching does not hurt your credit rating, but why draw extra unwanted attention to your credit history with switches?

Important: Close accounts you no longer want by sending a certified letter to the issuer stating that you want the account closed—by customer request. This protects you against records saying your account was shut off. Accounts not formally closed may be carried in your credit history as still available for use, leading some issuers to reject you for new accounts because you have too much available credit already.

Source: Mary Beth Butler, Bankcard Holders of America, 560 Herndon Pkwy., Suite 120, Herndon, Virginia 22070.

Everything You Need To Know About Credit Cards

Most people carry around a wallet full of credit cards, but few give any thought to these powerful pieces of plastic after they say, *Charge it.*

Questions to consider: Are you getting the best deal for your money on your credit card? How do you guarantee that your rights as a consumer will be protected if there's a problem with your bill? Should you sign up with a credit card registration service as protection against theft or misuse of your cards?

• Travel and entertainment (T&E) cards (like American Express and Diners Club), are not issued by banks, and the card issuer requires monthly payment in full of all charges.

• Bank cards (such as Visa and MasterCard) essentially provide access to small, generally unsecured, personal loans that are repaid, with interest, over time. Because bank cards are really just personal loans granted by a bank, it pays to shop around for the best terms, just as you would for a mortgage or home equity loan.

About 6,000 different banks around the US issue Visa and MasterCard. Unlike American Express, which is one big company, Visa and MasterCard are more like franchise organizations that license agents—in this case, banks—to issue cards. Each bank is then free to develop its own annual fees, interest rates and additional charges (late charges, bounced check charges and cash advance charges), as well as its own package of useful extras (travel assistance or credit card registration, for exam-

ple). A bank can even set its own acceptance standards. If you've been turned down by an individual bank, feel free to take your business elsewhere.

Shopping for a bank card is really shopping for a bank. Potential pitfalls: Don't be lured into applying for a particular card because the issuing bank promises you a great package of extras. That's like choosing a savings institution because they give you a four-slice toaster.

Some consumers will decide to apply for a card issued by a bank in their town, thinking, *If there's a problem with the bill, I want to be able to walk in and talk to someone.* But under federal law, if you have any disputes about your bill, you must put your complaint in writing or you completely lose your rights to withhold payment without penalty. So it doesn't make much sense to choose a local bank for the walk-in convenience. But you should also be wary of the big banks that tout a flashy array of cardholder services—24-hour toll-free customer-service hotlines, for example. It's easy to get lost in the crowd at one of these megabanks.

Key: Focus on the financial terms—interest rates, annual fees and other charges. Bankcard Holders of America publishes a list (updated quarterly) of the best deals in bank cards—those with annual interest rates of 16.4% and below.

Current interest rates on bank cards range from a low of 10.5% to an awesome 24%. Most people pay about 18.8%.

About two-thirds of consumers use the revolving credit option with their credit cards. So, for most people, the interest rate is the biggest bank card cost factor.

If you don't carry a balance over from month to month, it's best to get one of the "free," no-annual-fee cards. They are listed in another of the Bankcard Holders' quarterly updates.

Pick a safe bank:

Many consumers have been concerned about whether a particular credit card issuing bank is a "safe," financially stable institution. You might think that you don't have to worry about that issue because, as a credit card holder, you owe the bank money, they don't owe you.

Trap: Your account may be sold. And credit cards are not like any other type of bank loan. A fixed interest rate does not always mean a fixed rate in the credit card business. A bank—your current bank or a new bank that buys your account—can raise its credit card interest rate at any time, to whatever level is legal in the state in which its credit card operations are located. All it has to do is give you 15 days advance written notice. Then the bank can apply the new rate to your outstanding balance, as well as to new charges.*

To err is human, but to fix a credit card billing error can seem to require divine intervention. In reality, laws can usually rectify the situation—if you know the laws.

The federal Fair Credit Billing Act specifies that, to assert a billing error, you must state your complaint to the credit card issuer, in writing, within 60 days of the postmark date of the statement on which the disputed charge first appeared.

Problem: Most people call their bank's customer service representative, who makes a note of the complaint and promises that someone will look into the matter. But if the card issuer can't get reimbursement from the merchant, or if there's some other problem, they can come back to you three months later and inform you that you're responsible for the charge after all. By then, it's too late to exercise your right to dispute the charge.

Self-defense: Complain to the bank—or other card issuer—promptly, and in writing. It's particularly important if you think you're dealing with a questionable merchant, or if you can't get a credit slip from the merchant immediately, or if a large dollar amount is in dispute, or if you anticipate any kind of problem. You may find that if you contact the merchant and not the card issuer, the merchant will promise to rectify the error—but then not do it. By the time you find out, it's too late to dispute the charge properly. If you call first, follow up the call with a letter summarizing

*Exception: In the state of Delaware, under Delaware law, consumers have 30 days to decline acceptance of the new terms. If they then stop using the credit card, they can pay off the existing balance at the old rate.

the discussion. Important:

• Send your letter by certified mail, with a return receipt requested.

• Include your name (as it appears on your credit card), your current mailing address, and credit card account number.

• Identify the type of error that you're disputing, the dollar amount, the merchant and the date of the billing error.

• Send the letter to the address listed on your statement for billing errors and inquiries. This is probably a different location than the address to which your payments are sent.

Within 30 days of receiving your letter, card issuers must inform you, in writing, that they are either still investigating the dispute, or that they have resolved the matter.

They are obligated to tell you, in writing, the way in which a dispute has been resolved. During an investigation, you may withhold payment of the disputed amount and any related finance charges—without penalty.

The card issuer must, within 90 days, either correct the error, or provide you with a full written explanation that no billing error has occurred.

Trap: During an investigation, the disputed amount is "frozen" against your credit limit, so if it's a large amount, it will leave a dent in your credit line.

Credit card services typically keep records of all your credit card accounts. If your cards are lost or stolen, you call the registration service and the service notifies all your credit card issuers. Some of these services promote themselves by claiming to "insure" you against loss—but they really don't provide much insurance because, under federal law, you're not liable for that much money even if your card is stolen and used fraudulently.

Self-defense: If you decide to register your credit cards with a service, make sure that the company you're dealing with is reputable. Be sure that the service has a toll-free telephone access number, preferably with international access, and that they'll accept collect international calls.

Generally, these services are not recommended—unless they are offered free or at very low cost from the bank or company that issued your credit card.

A credit card issuer can cancel your credit card at will—at any time—for any reason.

These seemingly arbitrary cancellations are happening more and more frequently nowadays, as credit grantors are closely scrutinizing their current customers.

When your card comes up for renewal, most banks do a full credit analysis. If you're not as good a credit risk now as you were when you applied for the card, the creditor can lower your credit limit, freeze your line of credit or revoke your card privileges altogether.

Travelers beware: Many credit card companies are cutting back on free car rental insurance coverage...so check with your issuer before you rent.

Also: When you check into a hotel or rent a car, the merchant will—completely legally—put a "hold" on your credit card for the estimated amount of the rental or the stay, so that there's money available (for them) when you check out. But these holds can remain on your account for as long as two weeks. If you're traveling for an extended period of time, you could easily freeze up your entire credit line.

Solution: Use two different cards when you travel—one for hotels and car rentals, one for important purchases or emergencies.

Source: Gerri Detweiler, education coordinator for Bankcard Holders of America, 560 Herndon Pkwy., Suite 120, Herndon, VA 22070.

Spotting A Forged Check

• See if the check has perforations on one side. (A false check often has four smooth sides.)

• The code numbers printed on a legitimate check reflect no light. They are printed in magnetic ink, which is dull.

• The numbers in the upper right-hand corner of the check indicate the age of the account. Be suspicious of those that are numbered 101-150 or 1001-1050 (the starting numbers).

Source: Frank W. Abagnale, once a master forger and now a consultant to banks and retailers, writing in *Real Estate Today*.

How To Protect Yourself From Banks' Services

Banks are offering an avalanche of "new" services that are just old services—repackaged. And they are charging you for them.

Charges for some bank services have gone up 400% since the banking industry's deregulation in the mid-1980s.

How your bank may be squeezing you...

• Controlled dispersement services—your ability to transfer money electronically to cover checks. This used to require nothing more than a call to your bank. Now many banks charge customers $1 or more for these off-site transactions.

• Overdraft service. In the good old days, you could call your bank and ask to be notified if a check came in that your funds couldn't cover. The bank would then give you a chance to deposit money that day to cover the check. Now, overdraft services cost consumers a hefty service fee—plus, if you have overdraft "protection," interest on the "borrowed" funds.

• Automatic Teller Machines (ATMs) used to be a free service—but now many banks charge 50 cents to $1 for each transaction.

• Calling in for balances—and a record of checks cashed. Once you could call your friendly teller for this service, free of charge—but it may now be costly.

• Home-equity lines of credit are just repackaged second mortgages ...with a bundle of additional service fees tacked on.

Self-defense

When you shop for a bank, compare the fees on new services. Go with the bank that has the lowest fees for the services you use most...and stay away from the routine use of ATMs.

Don't immediately opt for the checking and savings account packages that have a lot of services attached.

If you write only a few checks a month, ask the bank for its low-cost, minimum standard checking account. And if you're a student, disabled or a senior citizen, ask for a service-charge-free checking account. Most banks make these available, although few promote this service.

Get to know your banker

If you know your banker, go to the bank and ask him/her to phone you to let you know when an overdraft occurs—instead of paying for an overdraft "service." And if you know your banker, you are much more likely to get a loan…be able to negotiate service charges, fees and loan interest rates…or get a dispute with the bank solved quickly and favorably.

You should know at least one teller, a loan officer and a vice president at your bank. These are the people who can solve virtually every banking problem you encounter. I call this preventive maintenance.

Source: Ed F. Mrkvicka, Jr., author of *The Bank Book: How to Revoke Your Bank's License to Steal*, Harper-Collins, 10 E. 53 Street, New York 10022, or 800-331-3761. He is also publisher of *Money Insider*, a financial newsletter for consumers, Reliance Enterprises, Inc., Box 413, Marengo, Illinois 60152.

Credit-Card Protection

Avoid being charged for goods or services you didn't buy by scribbling over the shaded sections labeled "delayed charges" and "revised total" when you sign credit-card slips. Often, unscrupulous merchants will add charges there, hoping the customer won't notice the discrepancy on the bill. By scribbling over these areas on each slip, you deter such acts of theft.

How To Keep Your Friendly Banker From Robbing You Blind

In 1976, a one-time bank teller—Edward Mrkvicka—after seven years in banking, became president of an Illinois national bank.

He resigned from his job five years later, convinced that the banking industry was per-

vaded by deception and greed, and that it victimized those who could afford it least—average American families. Now a financial consultant, Mrkvicka counsels people on how to revoke their banks' license to steal…

If you are a person of average means and assets, your bank will rob you of well over $100,000 during your lifetime. You will pay more than you should for your mortgages, credit cards and other loans. You will be cheated out of a fair return on your savings and bank IRA deposits. And along the way, you will be outrageously overcharged in fees and penalties for every service your bank provides.

Bankers are not your friends.

Bankers are, in fact, your worst financial enemies. The community banks—which once weighed a loan applicant's character above his collateral—are being squeezed out by a handful of big banks. These huge institutions cater to major corporate accounts and are scarcely regulated by the government, which depends on their financing to keep it afloat. The banks' attitude toward small customers is simple—our way or the highway.

Basic rules:

• Do business with one of the smaller banks in your market area, where you will have most leverage in negotiating more favorable terms.

• Comparison-shop each banking service among at least three institutions. After you find the best deal, negotiate for even better terms.

Example: After locating the best interest rate for your $10,000 savings deposit, you tell the bank officer: "I'm assuming we can work something out for a no-fee checking account." Your assumption will be right—but only if you ask.

Forget about finding a one-stop financial supermarket. You may wind up at Bank A for a checking account, at Bank B for a savings account, and at Bank C for a mortgage. Anyway, banks do not value your loyalty. They value only your money—and the more of it they can take from you, the better they like it.

The mortgage is the largest investment most people ever make—and the one where banks take greatest advantage. Most people decide on a mortgage based on whether they can afford the monthly payments. They rarely consider—nor do banks openly disclose—that at prevailing interest rates, homeowners repay about four dollars for every dollar they borrow over the standard 29- or 30-year term. In other words, a $100,000 mortgage will cost them about $400,000.

Advice: Accelerate your payments against the mortgage's outstanding principal. A negligible increase in your monthly payment—perhaps 4%*—can save you 25% or more of the amount you ultimately repay the bank, and shorten your obligation to 20 years or less. While some experts advise keeping the longer term for its tax advantages, this is a big mistake for the great majority of consumers. Even if you are in the 28% tax bracket, every dollar of unnecessary interest will still cost you 72¢ after taxes—money you could be investing for your own benefit, rather than the bank's.

Other mortgage scams:

• The adjustable-rate mortgage (ARM) represents the banking industry at its worst. It is a blatant marketing gimmick—complete with the deceptive come-on of an initial "discounted" rate—that fleeces the most vulnerable and over-extended. The ARM was created to ensure that banks might skim the absolute maximum from their borrowers, no matter where interest rates head. The risk is virtually all yours. (It is also possible, of course, that interest rates will fall—but since bankers control the rates, rates will always fall more slowly than they rise.)

Unfortunately, the prime interest rate will tend to increase in reverse proportion to our economy's health. In other words, your mortgage payment soars just when it is most likely that you may lose your job or business. Even if you hold steady, there's a fair chance you won't be able to afford the larger payments. Consider: If your ARM is based at 10% interest and then rises to 13%, your interest costs have actually risen by 30%—not the innocuous-sounding "three percentage points" advertised by your bank. On a $100,000 mortgage, that could translate to several hundred dollars

*Because that goes to pay off the principal.

more a month—a prescription for foreclosure.

Advice: Stick to a fixed-term mortgage, unless you are certain you will be selling your house before your ARM interest rate can substantially increase.

• Negative amortization mortgages are special ARMs which allow for fixed monthly payments regardless of interest-rate fluctuations. What most customers don't understand (and what most bankers fail to make clear) is that the bank may be siphoning their equity into its profit center. If the mortgage rate rises, the difference between what you pay each month and what you owe is assessed against a balloon payment, usually due in five years. At the end of the balloon, you may actually owe more than when you took out the loan. Aside from pocketing your interest payments, the bank now owns a substantial portion of your down payment.

Worst case: When you need to refinance the loan after paying off the balloon, your increased mortgage needs may exceed the property's appraised value. After the banks turn you down, you may have no option except to sell the house—at a loss.

Advice: Avoid this one at all costs.

• Reverse mortgages, recently in vogue, are supposed to enable people (mainly the elderly) to stay in their homes when they are no longer able to afford upkeep expenses. The borrower receives a monthly check from the lender, either for a set term or until the borrower dies. The loan balance plus interest is repaid by the sale of the house.

This new mortgage vehicle is very popular these days. In most cases, however, it is a gigantic rip-off. After 30 years of monthly mortgage payments, the homeowner trades in all that equity for five or 10 years of moderate income.

Example: If you took a 10% reverse mortgage on a mortgage-free home worth $125,000, you could get approximately $5,000 up front —most of which will be swallowed by various closing fees and points. You then get a monthly check of $1,175 for five years. At the end of the loan you would owe $100,000. You may also be out on the street (since your house would be sold to pay the bank), and your income would simultaneously be reduced by the amount of the reverse-mortgage payments.

An "open-term" reverse mortgage allows for permanent residence until death, but it is available only on premium homes in excellent condition. And if something unexpected happens to the elderly homeowners, the bank has hit a bonanza.

Example: An elderly couple takes out an open-term reverse mortgage which returns $450 a month on $100,000 equity. Three years later the husband dies, and the invalid wife is forced to move to a nursing home. She now owes $16,200, plus interest, not to mention the thousands of dollars in closing fees she and her husband paid up-front. Since her mortgage is unassumable (a common hidden feature), she (or her heirs) must either pay off the loan or sell the house. Kicker: In many of these mortgages, the bank gets to keep an appreciation beyond the original property appraisal—in this case, about $20,000.

Alternative: Parents might sell their home to their children and remain there without worry, while the kids benefit from tax advantages—and the property's appreciation.

• Home equity credit lines represent new packaging for a dog-eared product—the second mortgage. While they remain tax-deductible, that advantage is quickly wiped out by fees for the application, credit check, appraisal and closing, among others. For every dollar you save in taxes (versus an unsecured personal loan, for example), you may pay the bank two dollars in fees.

Since your home equity is your least liquid asset, you should save it for true emergencies. Any other purpose (to finance a car or home improvement, for example) represents an unacceptable risk...if you default on the loan, after all, you could be faced with foreclosure.

Source: Edward F. Mrkvicka is president of Reliance Enterprises, a national financial-consulting firm in Marengo, Illinois, and publisher of *Inside Financial* newsletter. He is also author of *The Bank Book: How to Revoke Your Bank's "License to Steal"—and Save Up to $100,000*, published by Harper & Row.

Shrewd Banking

Anyone can use a bank's night deposit box at any time of day or night to beat the long lines. It's fast, simple...and the bank mails you a deposit verification. Unless you deposit large parcels—bundles of checks, for example—you don't even need a key. Night depositories at most banks work like a mail slot. Drawback: Most banks don't post night depository transactions into an account until the next business day. Caution: Deposit only items with restricted endorsements—never, ever deposit cash.

Source: Edward F. Mrkvicka, Jr., Reliance Enterprises, Inc., Box 413, Marengo, Illinois 60152.

Beware Of Your Bank

Just because your bank now offers a broader range of financial services, it doesn't mean you should use them. Problem: When banks fail, it's the consumer and taxpayer who pay the bill—since our US Treasury ultimately backs the FDIC. Overworked regulators aren't ready—or able—to oversee banks that offer non-traditional services. Lacking in-house expertise in more complex investment vehicles, more banks could fail—and that means a greater drain on the FDIC and taxpayers. Bottom line: Stick with banks for traditional banking services, and look elsewhere for investment expertise.

Source: Edward F. Mrkvicka, Jr., Reliance Enterprises, Inc., Box 413, Marengo, Illinois 60152.

How Two-Paycheck Couples Can Make Their Money Work As Hard As They Do

Most working couples fail to exploit their financial clout. It gets lost in the hassle of everyday living.

A two-earner couple can raise capital much more easily than a one-earner…and capitalize on that additional borrowing power—even gamble on one of them starting a business. What you can do:

• Take your joint earning power seriously. If you are jointly bringing home $100,000 (or $50,000), you are more than mere wage earners. Managing your money is a business.

• Start now. Two-earner couples typically talk themselves into a "tomorrow" attitude about starting to save and invest. Few take the time to compute the enormous sums they will need to buy a home, rear children, have a comfortable retirement, etc.

Guideline: Newlyweds should save at least 5% of their joint income and gradually increase the amount to 20% during peak earning years.

• Set goals. But make them flexible enough to enable you to deal with new situations— the arrival of a baby, the purchase of a home, a promotion, etc.

• Keep the lines of communication open about how to handle money. That way you can resolve differences and negotiate changes necessary to meet changed conditions. No matter how in love you are, no two people are going to agree completely about money. Make time for making money:

Juggling job, home and family doesn't leave much time for financial management. Helpful: Transfer your combined knowledge of the business world to family finances. Modify the reports, forms, controls and filing systems you use at work to serve your needs at home.

• Get organized. Until you hack through the jumble, you can't tackle the real business of money management—investing.

• Set up a portion of your home as an office —with enough work space for each of you.

• Buy a filing cabinet for investment publications, articles and prospectuses, and for your bookkeeping records.

• Use in and out baskets. Pay bills when received and balance checkbooks monthly.

• Set up a "tickler" file to alert you to matters requiring action. Start with 12 file folders, one for each month, with the current month

in front. Behind the current month's file, add 31-day files. File documents or projects according to the day you must start work on them, not by the deadline. At the end of each week, transfer the now-empty day files to the next month and start over.

• Open a single joint bank account. It cuts down on paperwork and administrative fees. The fewer accounts of any kind, in fact, the better…cuts down opportunities for errors.

Keep enough in the checking account for day-to-day expenses and avoid bank charges.

Automatically transfer any excess funds to a joint money-market account with a higher interest rate. Use your money market account to pay large bills and hold savings while you decide where to invest them.

If you want to have some money separate from your spouse, pool the bulk of your incomes and put the rest in separate accounts. Do not use these accounts to pay for tax-deductible expenses unless you intend to file separate returns. You would have too many trails to follow at tax time.

• Cut back on credit cards. Carry only a few credit cards in your individual names. One spouse should be the "primary" cardholder on Mastercard, for instance, and the other spouse the "primary" Visa cardholder. You will save time, checks, postage and membership fees.

• Keep good records. The driving force behind record keeping is taxes. You cannot intelligently spend, invest or plan without being aware of tax implications.

Sort your income and expenses in folders labeled by categories behind subject dividers. Each of you will file cancelled checks written on your separate accounts. One of you will be responsible for filing the joint accounts.

Keep current on filing. You will always know where you stand. And tax time will be a snap.

At regular intervals, summarize these records, preferably on a computer. Financial software packages save time in tracking your assets and help in controlling spending—essential for successful investing. Recommended:

• Quicken.

• Andrew Tobias' Managing Your Money.

• WealthBuilder.

• Staple cancelled checks and their related receipts together. Don't pay cash for tax-deductible expenses but if you must, get a receipt. Use a separate credit card for business travel and/or entertaining. There's no reason to spend time separating business from personal expenses. The monthly total will be the amount deductible.

• Delegate and rotate responsibility so that you both gain experience in all aspects of finance. In the event of disability, death, overtime or out-of-town meetings, either partner should be able to carry on. This also prevents one person from getting stuck with boring chores or losing sight of the overall financial picture.

You can divide tasks equally, then switch jobs every six months. Or one spouse can take charge completely for six months at a stretch. This latter arrangement may be the best approach if one of you is in a seasonal business or travels extensively at certain times of the year.

Consider a tradeoff if one of you is constantly traveling. The wandering spouse can assume three or four big tasks, such as preparing the tax return or studying investment prospectuses—perfect hotel reading.

Splitting authority is a great time-saver. You don't have to do everything in tandem. After a joint initial visit with an attorney, accountant or stockbroker, only one of you need go thereafter except in matters of great importance.

• Discuss financial goals and share decisions. Schedule periodic meetings to assess your financial status, confer about problems and review plans for the future. Make an appointment if you have to. Reserve a table at your favorite quiet restaurant, bring your documents and go over the scheduled topics as you would at any business dinner.

• Form an investment club with your spouse. Decide what types of investments are needed to meet your goals, then divide the work.

Example: One spouse can research and select stock funds while the other does the same for bond funds. Or you might each agree to pick one stock and one bond fund.

Compare results. Analyze why one outper-

formed the other and learn together.

As you get your financial affairs under control you can branch out from easy, no-fuss investments like CDs and money-market funds into more diverse and potentially more profitable ventures.

Work efficiently:

It's not enough to carve out time. You must also use it effectively.

• Batch related activities. Write all your checks on the first Sunday of the month, for example, then drop them into your tickler file by mailing date.

• Make a list of tasks that need to be done. Then work through the list, crossing off each job as it is completed. Update the list daily or weekly.

• Be decisive. Plan the research…carry it out…see if more research is desirable…move ahead. Don't procrastinate.

Source: Tax attorney Mary L. Sprouse. She is the author of *Sprouse's Two-Earner Money Book*, Viking Penguin, 375 Hudson St., New York 10014.

Financial Planning Secrets

If you're in your thirties or forties—and certainly if you're in your fifties and haven't accumulated much in savings—you've already lost valuable time and opportunities.

Wealth-building in the 1990s will be much more difficult than it was in the 1980s.

Weaknesses in the US economy, including record low profit margins and an enormous federal deficit that shows no sign of being cut, still overwhelm its strengths. Individual tax rates are likely to go up, too, after a decade of relatively low rates on higher incomes.

Even the cash input of a second income in two-income families is not enough to make most middle-class couples confident about meeting college expenses for their children and providing for their own retirement.

And with the recent recession, many people in once-secure jobs in middle management, education and government services have suddenly found themselves out of jobs paying more than $80,000 a year, facing the prospect that they will have to settle—at best —for $40,000-$50,000 jobs.

The good life:

Short of winning the lottery or coming into a surprise inheritance, there's no sure and easy way to leap over these hurdles. But there is a sure and steady course to follow to enjoy a comfortable life-style, a secure retirement— and even to leave your heirs well provided for.

• Save often and early. Once your household income reaches $50,000 a year, you must set aside 10% of your after-tax income—or about $300 a month—for investment. Don't start your savings drive by figuring out a family budget to calculate how much you can afford to set aside. Make the monthly $300 check out to the fund or other savings vehicle you select just as you make out the mortgage check. No ifs, ands, or buts. And no backtracking. If some (real) emergency comes along, borrow from yourself as if you borrowed from the bank, and pay yourself back on a regular schedule.

There's no easy alternative to this discipline. If you can't commit yourself to saving 10% of your after-tax income on a regular basis, you will never save much at all. Regular saving is the essential first step to accumulating wealth.

Starting to save early is more important than an investment with an outstanding rate of return. You would wind up with more money at 65, for instance, if you saved $300 a month for the five years from age 25 through 29 and kept these savings earning 15% a year...than if you saved $300 per month for every year from age 30 through 65, investing it at the same 15%.

• Use the current tax laws to your advantage. Choose forms of investment where the tax code works for you, not against you. Since the 1986 Tax Reform, this has become more difficult. For practical purposes, most tax shelters are dead. Beware—because salespeople still try to sell them.

Still available: Tax-deferred accounts for your savings that can help you avoid the trap of giving about one-third of every dollar in investment income back to the government.

Incentive: Starting at age 25, every $1 you invest on a tax-deferred basis during your working life at 12% will be worth $4 invested on an after-tax basis.

Main tax-deferred techniques to use for your investments...

• Individual Retirement Accounts (IRAs)... the most familiar tax-deferred accounts, but also the least flexible. Your contributions are smaller than with other tax-deferred accounts (maximum $2,000 a year for an individual... $2,250 for a joint return) and the annual contribution is only deductible if you're not covered by a company pension plan. They are a good start, however.

• 401(k) and SEP plans...can be funded by you or by both you and your employer. The maximum allowable tax-deferred annual contribution you can make has been moved up with inflation, starting with $7,000 in 1987 to $8,475 in 1991. This maximum does not include employer's contribution, which is allowable up to $30,000.

• Self-employment retirement plans (Keoghs)...make owning your own business the only substantial tax shelter left. Providing your income is high enough (at least $150,000), you can save up to $30,000 per year on a taxdeferred basis in conventional money-purchase and profit-sharing Keoghs. And for those who begin to earn substantial self-employed income in their later years, a defined-benefit Keogh enables you to put aside considerably more.

• Annuities...also permit you to build up your savings on a tax-deferred basis. The insurance companies and investment firms that sell annuities charge sales commissions, management fees and other expenses, so the question becomes whether the annuity is worth it. (Paying the fees is probably not worth it if the money is invested in bonds, which over the long run earn less than stock investments.)

Variable annuities are probably the best choice for most of those who are buyers of annuities.

Helpful: Pick one by examining the past performance record of the investment manager, or the investment performance of mutual funds or other investment products handled by the management group. Steer away from a variable annuity heavily invested in small company stocks, but do pick one oriented toward growth.

• Real estate is still a good investment over the long term. Don't spend more than 20% of your pre-tax income for total housing costs (mortgage payments, real estate taxes, home insurance, utilities). But, within that guideline, carry as big a mortgage as you can. With a mortgage rate of 10% and a standard 20% down payment, you can afford to buy a home worth about 2.5 times your income at the time of the original mortgage. In many cases, rent payments and mortgage payments are about equal for the same amount of living space. But for many people, putting money into a home is one of the best ways to "save" because of leverage (only 10%–20% down payment) and the deductibility of mortgage interest.

Advantage: Despite the current downturn in real estate values in much of the country, real estate values have generally kept up with increases in family income—both increasing at an average rate of 7% a year—over the long term. If you buy a house for $125,000 with a $100,000 mortgage and 10 years later it is worth $250,000, you have $25,000 in equity. The sensible move at that point might be to get a $100,000 home-equity mortgage and invest the proceeds in the stock market—preferably in a tax-deferred account such as 401(k) or Keogh.

• Consider shifting from term life insurance to whole life insurance between 40–50 years of age if it appears likely by then that you will accumulate enough assets to be hit by the substantial 55% estate tax.

The conventional argument against "investing" in life insurance is that your cash accumulation is severely diluted by sales commissions, operating costs and the insurance companies' less-than-great investment performance records.

But the life insurance industry survived the slaughter of tax shelters by the Tax Reform Act of 1986 almost intact. So buildup of assets in life insurance is tax-deferred. Death benefits are exempt from income tax. And, with proper planning, death benefits can also be exempted from estate tax.

After considering the about one-third bite on your incremental earnings from federal income tax, state taxes and the 55% estate tax, your post-tax return on a 12% investment in securities might be well less than the 8% or less you earn on a whole life insurance policy.

Source: Michael K. Evans, PhD, author of *How to Make Your Shrinking Salary Support You in Style for the Rest of Your Life*, 201 E. 50 St., New York 10022, and chairman and president of Evans Economics, Inc., and Evans Investment Advisors, Box 25303, Washington, DC 20007.

Get The Best Loan Deal You Possibly Can

Getting a car loan or a personal loan is simple. But to get the best possible terms, you need to know a few things that your banker isn't going to tell you...

1. Get a copy of your credit report. Go to your local credit bureau—you can find it in the Yellow Pages. Alternative: Call your bank to get the phone number of the credit agency it uses.

Check your credit report to make sure the information is accurate.

Beware: An estimated 40% of all credit reports contain inaccurate information that may prevent you from getting a loan.

If there is negative, but accurate, information on the credit report, such as a payment you refused to make (because an item you bought was a lemon and the company wouldn't take it back), bring it to the attention of the loan officer. Being "up front" about it will show you to be a responsible and honest prospective client.

2. Shop by phone. Call a minimum of three banks in your area and request to speak to a loan officer. Ask him/her to enumerate the fees associated with the type of loan you need as well as the interest rates being

offered. Compare the costs of all three. Include credit unions and your local savings and loan institution in your survey.

3. Sit down with a loan officer and structure the loan you want—once you've found the institution with the most favorable rates. Warning: Quite often the loan vehicle the bank offers is not the least expensive option available.

Example: Many banks use an installment loan vehicle that is based on an add-on interest-rate installment plan. This means you're paying interest on the total of the loan (say $10,000) every month rather than paying interest on the declining principal. This is called a front-end loaded loan and is not a good deal for you.

Best: Ask for a simple interest, single-payment note that allows for monthly payments or an installment loan calculated on a simple interest basis. This loan vehicle charges interest only on the remaining amount of the principal you're paying off.

4. Negotiate a better position. Push to get a point—or at least a half point—shaved off the interest to be paid on the loan. Bargaining chips:

• If you've been with the bank for a long time, you can reason with your loan officer that you've given them steady business and should get something a little better than the guy who just walks in off the street.

• If you're at a new bank, offer to let them handle a Certificate of Deposit for you, or tell them you'd be willing to move your checking account to their bank to get a better loan deal.

• An excellent credit rating is also a bargaining point—that's worth a lot to a bank. You are the kind of customer whose business a bank wants.

Look to shave off loan fees, such as application fees, credit-check fees, document or secretarial fees, lawyer's fees, title search fees, etc.—not just points on the interest of the loan. If you are negotiating a loan with many up-front fees, such as a home-equity line of credit, negotiate with the bank to waive a few of these fees.

You stand a much better chance of getting a better deal if you are negotiating with a small institution than you would if you were negotiating with a large bank. A smaller bank will work harder for your business.

5. Calculate the total cost of the loan. You should know exactly how much the loan will cost you in fees and interest over the life of the loan. A bank, for example, that has a higher fee structure, but a slightly lower interest rate, may look more expensive at first glance. But if you calculate out a loan from another bank that has very low fees and higher interest rates, it may turn out that the former bank's loan is actually cheaper than the low-fee/high-interest combination.

Source: Ed F. Mrkvicka, Jr., author of *The Bank Book: How to Revoke Your Bank's License to Steal*, Harper-Collins, 10 E. 53 St., New York 10022. He is also publisher of *Money Insider,* a financial newsletter for consumers, Reliance Enterprises, Inc., Box 413, Marengo, Illinois 60152.

6

Smart Tax Moves

Loopholes For The Lucky Taxpayers With Sideline Incomes

More and more people moonlight, consult...and have set up sideline businesses. The tax advantages of having a business of your own, even if it's only a sideline, are significant.

Opportunities:

• Report income and expenses on Schedule C of Form 1040. There's a big advantage in doing this. Business expenses, such as transportation costs, are deductible in full on Schedule C. They are not subject to the 2%-of-Adjusted-Gross-Income limitation that applies when the same expenses are taken on Schedule A of the 1040.

If you get a commission, report it on Schedule C, even if you have no business expenses to write off against it. Reason: If the income qualifies as self-employment income, you can use some of it to set up a Keogh plan.

• Have bigger pension plans. The amount of money employees can put into tax-favored retirement plans is relatively modest. If they qualify under the new deduction rules, they can put $2,000 a year into Individual Retirement Accounts (IRAs) and deduct it, and put that and about $8,000 a year into 401(k) plans, if their companies have such a plan.

But people who have sideline businesses can build bigger retirement nest eggs. They can open Keogh plans and SEPs (Simplified Employee Pension plans), which have more generous contribution and deduction limits. You can put up to $30,000 a year into a Keogh or SEP, or 13.043% of your earned income, whichever is less.

Super Keoghs: There's a kind of Keogh, called a defined benefit Keogh, where contributions are determined actuarially. You can contribute to—and deduct from—this kind of Keogh, an amount that will provide you with a retirement benefit of over $100,000 a year.

Loophole: Contributions to IRAs must be made by April 15 to be deductible on the prior year's return. But contributions to Keoghs and SEPs can be made after April 15, until the extended due date of your return, provided the plans were set up by the deadlines imposed by the Tax Code—December 31 for Keoghs and April 15 for SEPs.

• Depreciate business equipment. Depreciation deductions on equipment, such as a personal computer, shelter some of your income from tax. Instead of taking depreciation deductions, you may, under Section 179 of the Tax Code, write off up to $10,000 worth of business equipment in the year of purchase.

• Hire your children. A child who works in his parent's sideline business can earn up to $3,400 in 1991 without owing any federal income tax. The salary is deductible by the business. An additional $2,000 of the child's salary would escape tax if it was put into an IRA.

Loophole: If your business is unincorporated, you don't have to pay Social Security tax on wages paid to a child who is under 18.

• Deduct advertising expenses. These are deductible along with all other ordinary and necessary business expenses.

Example: A freelance computer consultant is drumming up business among his neighbors. He decides to sponsor the Little League team his child plays on. The cost of his sponsorship is a deductible business expense—it's advertising.

• Deduct home office expenses. If you work out of your home and it is the main place of business of your sideline business, you can deduct a portion of your expenses—insurance, utilities, rent, etc.—as home office expenses.

• Maximize your interest deductions. When you borrow money to put into an unincorporated business, the interest you pay is fully deductible as business interest on Schedule C. If you borrow money on your credit card to put into the business, the interest is business interest, not personal interest, and is fully deductible.

Compare: If you borrow money to invest in an incorporated business, the interest is only deductible as investment interest, subject to investment-interest limitations. These limit your interest deductions to the amount of investment income you have for the year.

• Hire independent contractors. When you hire people who are self-employed, as you are in your capacity as the owner of a sideline business, they may be considered "independent contractors" for withholding-tax purposes, rather than employees. Benefit: You don't have to withhold income tax or pay the employer's portion of Social Security tax for independent contractors.

The key test for determining whether someone who performs services for you is an employee or independent contractor is this: Do you control what will be done and how it will be done? If you do, the person is an employee. If you don't exercise control over the methodology of services, the person is an independent contractor.

• Minimize Social Security taxes. When both spouses work in the business, and one spouse has a full-time, high-paying job, that spouse should be listed as the sole owner of the business. Business income paid to that spouse will not be subject to self-employment tax if the spouse pays the maximum Social Security tax on his salary from his job. (For 1991, the maximum amount of salary that Social Security tax is taken from is $53,400. However, the 1.45% Medicare hospital insurance tax is taken from salary up to $125,000.)

Compare: If the business was in the name of the spouse who did not have a full-time job, that spouse would have to pay self-employment tax on up to $53,400 (or Medicare hospital insurance tax up to $125,000) of business income.

• Write off your losses. If your deductions for the year are more than your income, your net loss can be used to offset other income.

Caution: Certain deductions can't be used to create a loss. These include home office deductions and the expensing deduction under Section 179.

• Minimize estimated tax payments. If you have sideline income, you're required to make quarterly estimated tax payments to the government. You'll be penalized by the IRS if your payments fall short in any quarter.

Loophole: You can avoid making estimated payments on your sideline income by increasing the amount of tax that is withheld from your salary. You do not have to make estimated tax payments if your withholding for the year equals 90% of the total tax shown on this year's return, or 100% of the tax you paid last year.

Loophole: If you receive most of your income late in the year, use what is called the annualized income installment method to figure your quarterly estimated payments. This will allow you to pay the bulk of your estimated tax after you've received the bulk of your income. To calculate your payments, use the annualized income installment worksheet in Form 2210, *Underpayment of Estimated Tax by Individuals and Fiduciaries.*

Source: Edward Mendlowitz, partner, Mendlowitz Weitsen, CPAs, Two Pennsylvania Plaza, New York 10121. Mr. Mendlowitz is the author of several books, including *Aggressive Tax Strategies*, Macmillan Publishing Co., 866 Third Ave., New York 10022.

Interest Deductions: New Traps And Opportunities

Tax reform imposed strict limits on interest deductions, breaking interest payments into five distinct categories, each with its own separate and complex rules.

Interest payments that don't fit into any of the categories that are given special treatment under tax reform (i.e., mortgage interest, business interest, investment interest, passive activity interest) are considered personal interest and are not deductible.

Interest charges that you might not think of as "personal" interest are included in this dramatic phaseout of deductibility. Surprises and very helpful solutions:

Interest paid on a car loan by an employee who uses the car for business is personal interest, even if the car is used solely for business. The same rule applies to interest paid on the financing of any other type of property that an employee might use for business, such as a personal computer.

Loophole: Have the company buy the car (or other property) that you use for business. A corporation's interest costs are 100% deductible as business interest. To square things up, the company can charge you for personal use or reduce your salary accordingly. (You will be taxed to the extent you use the car for personal purposes.)

Interest paid for borrowing against life insurance policies is personal interest.

Loophole: Pay off the existing loan, take out a new one, and use the newly borrowed money to buy stock or other investments. Since the deductibility of interest depends on what you spend the borrowed money on, your interest payments will now be investment interest, deductible up to the amount of your net investment income for the year.

Interest on loans from your employer is also considered personal interest.

Loophole: To increase your interest deduction, borrow from the company pension plan. Use your house as security for the loan. Use the proceeds to pay back the loan from the company. Interest on the pension-plan loan will be fully deductible home mortgage interest, since it's secured by your house—it's the same as a home-equity loan. (Check with your tax adviser as there are limitations on your right to borrow from pension plans.)

Interest on credit-card balances, car loans, and other consumer loans is personal interest.

Loophole: If you have large credit-card balances, consider taking out a home-equity loan and using the proceeds to pay the credit-card companies. Interest on home-equity loans (up to $100,000) secured by your home or vacation home is fully deductible mortgage interest, regardless of what you spend the money on.

If you borrow money from your margin account and use the money for personal purposes (for instance, to take a vacation), the interest is personal interest. But if you use the money to buy stock, the interest is investment interest (fully deductible up to the amount of your investment income for the year).

Loophole: To get full deductions for interest on money borrowed for personal use, sell some of the stock you currently own, use the proceeds to take your vacation, and buy the stock back on margin. Your margin interest charges will be fully deductible investment interest.

Caution: Keep records that clearly show where borrowed money came from, what it was spent on, and all interest payments you make.

Rental property. Mortgage interest on a "passive activity," such as a house you rent out, can't be deducted separately. It's part of the overall expense of the property and part of any annual rental loss. If your Adjusted Gross Income (AGI) is under $100,000, you can deduct up to $25,000 of loss against your other income. You can get a partial loss deduction if your AGI is between $100,000 and $150,000, but you are not entitled to a deduction if your AGI is over $150,000.

Loophole: Suspended losses from passive activities (e.g., those you can't use because your AGI is too high) can be carried forward to future years. And you will be able to deduct them when you eventually sell the property.

Co-op apartments. If you give stock in the co-op corporation to a bank as collateral for a loan, your interest payments are fully deductible mortgage interest.

Home buyers: Get as big a mortgage as possible when you buy. The Revenue Act of 1987 imposed new limits on interest deductions for mortgages taken out after October 13, 1987. Interest is fully deductible on mortgages of up to $1 million spent to acquire, construct, or substantially improve a principal or second residence.

But if you need to borrow further, through refinancing, second mortgages, or home-equity loans, interest will be fully deductible on only $100,000 additional. Since interest on additional borrowing is so severely restricted, it's wise to take out as large a mortgage as you can when you buy a house, especially if you know you'll be needing money in the future, e.g., for your children's college education.

Source: Edward Mendlowitz, partner, Mendlowitz Weitsen, CPAs, 2 Penn Plaza, New York 10121.

Commuting Costs Can Be Deductible

Most commuting expenses aren't deductible. But if a person works at least two jobs in the same day, the cost of traveling from the first job to the second job is deductible as a business expense to the extent that when added to all your other business expenses, they exceed 2% of your adjusted gross income. (You still can't deduct travel from home to your first job or from your second job back home.)

Similarly, customer visits made on your way to work are partially tax deductible. The deductible portion: The distance between the customer's place of business and your office.

Neglected Medical Deductions

• You can deduct medical bills paid for another person, provided that you paid more than half that person's support in either the year the bills were run up or the year they were paid. A similar rule applies to married couples. You can deduct bills paid now for a former spouse, so long as you were married when the bills were incurred.

• A transplant donor can deduct surgical, hospital, and laboratory costs and transportation expenses. So can a prospective donor, even if found to be unacceptable. If the recipient pays the expenses, the recipient gets the deduction.

• Removing lead-based paint and covering areas within a child's reach with wallboard to help prevent and cure further lead poisoning are deductible expenses.

• A clarinet and lessons are deductible medical expenses when prescribed to cure teeth defects.

• A hypoglycemia patient was put on a special diet requiring six to eight small, high-protein meals daily. The Tax Court allowed a deduction of 30% of her grocery bills—the amount spent in excess of the cost of her normal diet.

How To Use Company Cash To Build Your Home

Here's a way to take cash out of your corporation without paying tax on it...and build or buy your dream home.

Loophole: Give the corporation a first mortgage on the home.

As long as you dot your "i"s and cross your "t"s you can nail down substantial tax deductions by letting your corporation finance your home. The interest you pay on up to $1 million of mortgage debt will be fully tax deductible home-mortgage interest.

Guidelines:

• Be sure the corporation charges market-rate interest on the loan.

• Document the loan with a promissory note.

• Record the mortgage at the courthouse.

• Adhere strictly to the payment schedule called for in the note.

• Correctly classify the loan and your subsequent repayments on the corporate books.

If you carefully follow these guidelines, you can dip into the company till and avoid paying any tax personally.

Source: Irving L. Blackman, partner, Blackman Kallick Bartelstein, CPAs, 300 S. Riverside Plaza, Chicago 60606.

Paying Tax On Inheritance

My mother died and left an amount of money that is to be paid to me on a monthly basis over several years. Why do I have to pay tax on these payments when a lump-sum bequest would have been tax free? [A.H., Greenville, Texas]

Inheritances payable in three or fewer installments are income tax free to the recipient. However, when inherited property is distributed over a period of time, part of each payment may be taxed.

Distributions such as yours are deemed to come first from the estate's taxable income, to the extent that there is any. The estate does not pay tax on the income that is distributed to you.

Source: David S. Rhine, partner, BDO Seidman, 15 Columbus Circle, New York 10023.

Statute of Limitations Rules

How is the three-year statute of limitations measured on a return, from its due date or the date it is filed? And, what if there is an IRS-approved filing extension? [S.C., McLean, Virginia]

The limitation period runs from the later of the due date or the actual filing date. Thus, if you file early, the period will run from April 15, even though you filed before that date. If you file after April 15, the limitation period will run from the actual filing date, whether you have an extension or not.

Source: Randy Bruce Blaustein, Esq., partner, Blaustein, Greenberg & Co., 155 E. 31, New York 10016.

Municipal Bond Trap

Bond prices have risen sharply due to the recent dramatic drop in interest rates. But when considering whether to take profits on bonds you own, remember that only the interest paid on tax-exempt bonds is tax-free. A profit earned from an increase in a bond's value is a taxable capital gain when the increase in value results from a change in market conditions—such as a decline in interest rates.

Computer Limitations

The IRS's out-of-date computers record only about 40% of the information taxpayers put on their returns. It takes a large amount of labor to take data off of a return and enter it into the computer. IRS workers do it by hand now. The agency's computers won't become more effective until new systems are installed...and that could be a long time off.

How To Reduce Property Taxes

When most people complain about taxes, they tend to think in terms of federal income taxes. Yet property taxes are the stiffest of all, and rising faster than any other type of levy. In some areas of the country, they have sky-rocketed by nearly 50% in the last five years. And—according to the headlines—they'll be going up further...fast.

Many Americans are overpaying their property taxes—needlessly. When faced with an enormous property tax bill, homeowners generally take a defeatist attitude. They think there is nothing they can do about it. Nothing could be further from the truth.

For about 60% of American homeowners, there is sufficient evidence to warrant a tax reduction.

There are a wide variety of reasons to justify a tax cut.

Examples: There could be arithmetic errors in the records of the local taxing authority...or you could be taxed for a two-story house when in fact you own a one-story residence...or your residence may be listed as 10 years old when in fact it is twice that age...or the dimensions of your land may be overstated...or you may not have been given a special exemption to which you are entitled, such as a veteran's exemption...or property values may have declined significantly in your area.

It makes sense to complain about your property taxes when you can demonstrate that you have been wrongfully overcharged. More than half of the homeowners who do protest their assessments get them reduced...according to the International Associ-

ation of Assessing Officers, an organization dedicated to property valuation for assessment purposes.

It isn't quite as easy as walking into the tax assessor's office, informing the official that you think your taxes are high and expecting a reduction on the spot.

You must take the time to collect the necessary information that will support your case.

Next, you need to present your appeal in an organized, convincing fashion that will leave the tax officials little choice but to agree with your contention that your tax bill is incorrect.

This approach will take some time—generally between six and 10 hours of research and writing. But the time you spend will be well worth your effort. In addition to reducing your tax bill for the tax year in question, you'll be reducing your property taxes for years to come, since future tax bills are based upon past records.

Step one: Obtain what is called the tax list. This document, which is available in the local tax assessor's office, is simply a list of property owners in your area. It lists blocks and lot numbers or property identification numbers, assessed values of the properties...and what their property taxes are.

Next step: Obtain your own property record card. This document, also available in the tax assessor's office, is the assessor's official worksheet that is used to determine the assessed value of your property. It contains information that is unique to your property—the dimensions of the house and lot, list of unique features, etc.—as well as a top-view drawing of the residence with dimensions.

Usually, it's simple to obtain a copy of your property record card. But, in a few states, these cards are not considered public records and assessors are not required to furnish you with a copy until a week to 10 days before a formal appeal. This policy may put you in the position of having to file an appeal before knowing all the facts. And, if the assessor decides to go by the letter of the law, you may not even be allowed to photocopy the card when you do get your hands on it.

Self-defense: Take carefully handwritten notes on the information you need from the card while you are still in the assessor's office.

Regardless of whether you get a photocopy of the property record card, or have to transcribe it by hand, you should scrutinize it carefully. Often, there are many errors in these records. Most common:

• The dimensions of your land are wrong. You may own 1½ acres, but you are being taxed on two acres.

• The dimensions of buildings or improvements are wrong. If your house is rectangular, the length on one side may be listed as 20 feet, while the length on the opposite side is given as 25 feet. Or you may have a 1,800 sq. ft. house and are being taxed for a 2,500 sq. ft. house.

• The description of the building is wrong. Your house may be listed as being made of brick when it is less expensive frame construction.

• The description of your land is wrong. Perhaps the description includes part of your neighbor's land and you are wrongfully being taxed on it.

• Finished areas of your house are listed incorrectly. Your record may indicate that your basement is completely paneled, with an acoustical ceiling and hardwood floors, when in fact it is unfinished.

• The grade and quality of improvements are wrong. Perhaps you put gravel stones on your driveway, but you're being charged for a paved drive.

• The depreciation factor—the assessor's opinion of the condition of your house—is wrong compared with houses whose condition is similar to yours.

You may find enough errors on your property card to justify a meeting with the assessor on those mistakes alone.

Is your house being assessed at a higher value than "comparable properties"? These are properties that are similar to your own residence in location, age, design, size and construction. Goal: Unearth data that will support a lower assessed value for your property.

Example: If you can show that a property comparable to yours is assessed at only $120,000 while your house is assessed at $145,000, you have solid grounds for an appeal.

Ideal: Have your house compared with a twin of your own house that was sold during the current tax year. This establishes the comparable's "market value"—the best indicator of the property's true worth. If you live in a development, for example, the ideal comparable would be the house next door that is identical to yours. To find a comparable:

• Begin by looking for comparables in your neighborhood—within a few blocks of your home rather than across town. Then, compare similar styles.

• Compare such items as square footage of living area, number of bathrooms and bedrooms, whether the houses have air conditioning, fireplaces or unfinished basements, garage capacity, etc.

Since it's unlikely that another house is completely identical to yours, you probably will have to make adjustments.

• After you gather information on three comparable properties—and take photos of them if possible—you must come up with an adjusted value for your property and the three others. You then take the square footage for your house and the comparables, divide by each property's adjusted value and come up with adjusted value per square foot for each house. This gives you the basis on which to compare the assessments on all the properties. Presumably, your research will indicate that your house has been assessed at a higher value than the three comparable properties.

When presenting your case, remember the rules of successful negotiating:

• Let the assessor make the first offer.

• Never say yes too quickly.

• Don't be vague about what value is acceptable. Suggesting—and supporting—a specific assessed value for your property is essential. Without your input, the assessor's own conclusion may not be satisfactory.

Bear in mind that determining the value of a property is partially subjective. It is an opinion that is supported by facts—but there can be a difference of opinion about those facts. So, to avoid disappointment, recognize that you may not get total agreement from the assessor about the value you are proposing.

Though it's possible to take your appeal to a local review board or to court, you may wish to accept a reasonable compromise offer. It is better to accept a slightly higher valuation than to risk a worse outcome.

Source: R. Harry Koenig, owner of King Associates, a Chester, NJ, tax-consulting firm. He is the author of *How to Lower Your Property Taxes,* Fireside/Simon & Schuster, 1230 Ave. of the Americas, New York 10022.

Tax Loopholes For Hobbies

Most people have a hobby of one kind or another that they pursue for enjoyment.
Opportunity:

If the hobby is set up with taxes in mind, the government will subsidize some of the costs.

For tax purposes, there are two kinds of hobbies—those where you collect things, and those that are more active, such as photography, painting and weekend farming.

• General rule for hobbies that involve collecting: Gains on the sale of items in your collection are taxable. Losses can be offset only against the gains from the sale of items in your collection.

Loophole I: If you take big gains in one year, remember to also take some losses that year. Use the losses to offset the gains.

Loophole II: Suppose you want to keep your collection intact, and you also want to sell loss items to offset gain items. You can repurchase the items you sold, but you must wait 31 days before doing so. Your losses will be deductible as long as you avoid the wash sale rule by waiting 31 days.

Loophole III: Take advantage of tax-free swaps. Tax on any gain will be deferred if you trade items in your collection for other collectible items.

Loophole IV: Change your status from hobbyist to investor so you can take deductions for your losses.

• How to maintain investor status for your collection. There are three tax categories of collectors—hobbyist, investor and dealer. Tax differences:

Hobbyist: When you sell items in your collection, the gains are taxable. Losses can be written off against gains, but otherwise they're not deductible. The stamp hobbyist can't take stamps he sold at a loss and apply them against the stock he sold at a gain.

Investor: Profits are capital gains. Losses qualify as capital losses and can be used to offset other types of capital gains, such as gains on the sale of stock. If your losses exceed your gains, they are deductible against your other income, subject to the $3,000 per year limit, until they are used up.

In addition, your investment expenses are deductible. These include insurance, investment advisory fees and travel costs, safe-deposit-box rent, subscriptions to collectors' journals, appraisal fees and depreciation on safes and other security systems.

Dealer: Profits are taxable income. Losses are deductible as ordinary business losses.

For most collectors, the best category to be in is investor. Whether or not you're an investor is a question of intention and facts. Things you can do to maintain investor status:

• Make necessary sales. If you never sell items from your collection, you're a hobbyist. As an investor, though, you would sell when items in your collection don't meet your investment needs or goals.

• Buy investor grade items—such as stamps and coins that are sold in two grades—collector and investor—depending on their condition. Buy items that you expect to appreciate in value.

• Keep detailed records. If you do this, you're obviously not just a hobbyist. The extent of the detail may be the deciding factor in whether an item is bought for hobby or investment purposes.

• Be well informed about this field. Subscribe to trade journals and publications. Buy auction house catalogues and follow the trends.

Caution: To be an investor—don't make sales at the retail level, and don't advertise in trade journals. If you do, you might be considered a dealer.

If you want to be treated as a dealer, you should open a separate bank account, register a trade name, obtain a resale certificate, be listed as a dealer in trade publications and join a trade society.

You may be able to operate your hobby as a business. If that is the case, your expenses are deductible and any losses you incur can be used to offset other income. Key: You have the intention of making a profit.

But if the activity is not carried on for profit, your deductions are limited and no loss is allowed to offset other income.

Factors the IRS considers in determining whether an activity is carried on for profit include...

• The time and effort you put into the activity indicate whether you intend to make it profitable.

• You carry on the activity in a businesslike manner.

• You are depending on income from the activity for your livelihood.

• Your losses from the activity are due to circumstances beyond your control or are normal in the start-up phase of your type of business.

• You change your methods of operation in an attempt to improve the profitability of the activity.

• You, or your advisors, have the knowledge needed to carry on the activity as a successful business.

• You have been successful in making a profit in similar activities in the past.

• The activity makes a profit in some years.

• You can expect to make a future profit from the appreciation of the assets used in the activity.

An activity is presumed to be carried on for profit if it produced a profit in at least three of the last five tax years (two out of the last seven years for activities that consist primarily of breeding, training, showing or racing horses).

If you are just starting out in an activity and you do not yet have three years of profit, you can take advantage of this presumption at a later time.

Loophole: File IRS Form 5213, *Election to Postpone Determination as to Whether the Presumption That an Activity is Engaged in for Profit Applies.* Filing this form postpones any determination that your activity is not carried on for profit until five (or seven) years have passed since you first started the activity.

Impact: The IRS will not question whether your activity is engaged in for profit until three or five years are up. It will not question your deductions relating to the activity.

If you have the choice of receiving a valuable collection either as a gift or an inheritance, it's best to take it as an inheritance. You'll pay less capital gains tax when you ultimately sell the collection.

Reason: When you inherit property, the basis, or tax cost, is stepped up to its value on the date of the donor's death. But when you take property by gift, your basis is the basis of the person who gave you the property, which is usually its cost to that person.

Source: Edward Mendlowitz, partner, Mendlowitz Weitsen, CPAs, Two Pennsylvania Plaza, New York 10121. Mr. Mendlowitz is the author of several books, including *Aggressive Tax Strategies,* Macmillan Publishing Co., 866 Third Ave., New York 10022.

Pros And Cons Of Tax-Deferred Annuities

Tax-deferred annuities are an increasingly popular investment. And now they are aggressively being marketed by the insurance companies that sell them.

But while annuities provide tax-saving opportunities, there are traps for investors as well. How they work

There are two kinds of tax-deferred annuities—fixed and variable.

• Fixed annuities: Provide a set investment return, which is determined by the return the insurance company earns on its investments.

Catch: The return on a fixed annuity may be guaranteed for a period of time (typically from one to five years), but it is not fixed for the life of the annuity. The return will vary with the insurer's financial performance.

• Variable annuities: In effect, these are mutual funds run by insurance companies. You select your own investments, and can change investments as you go along. Your return depends on your investment results.

With either type of annuity, you can withdraw your investment balance either in a single lump sum, or through payments made over a period of years.

However, with a variable annuity, you withdraw annuity "units"—the equivalent of mutual fund shares. If you withdraw your investment over a period of years, the value of these units may rise or fall, affecting your cash payout.

Tax advantages

The main advantage of an annuity is that investment earnings compound on a tax-free basis as long as the money remains in the policy. Other advantages:

• You do not have to start making withdrawals at age 70½, as you would with an IRA or other retirement plan. Thus, money can stay invested in the annuity and earn tax-deferred interest for a longer period of time.

• You can make contributions to an annuity after the 70½ age limit set on IRAs and other kinds of plans.

Variable annuities also provide what could be a major tax advantage for mutual fund investors. They do not have to pay gains tax when they switch from one fund investment to another, as long as the money stays in the annuity. Thus, aggressive investors who try to time the market and frequently switch among various investment options may cut their tax bills significantly if they invest through a variable annuity.

Traps

Annuities hold traps for investors as well. The first mistake many annuity investors make is to overestimate the value of the tax deferral they get—if money is kept in an annuity for less than 10 years, the tax deferral may be the equivalent of less than 1% of yield. This is important because an annuity may pay less than other available investments.

Example: A fixed annuity generally pays less than a taxable bond fund, and variable annuities typically impose annual charges of up to 2% of investment assets. That charge is more than that imposed by the average no-load mutual fund.

In order for the value of tax deferral to outweigh these costs, money must usually be held in an annuity for 20 years. This condition would be met, for example, if after a 10-year investment, annuity funds were withdrawn over a 20-year period, thereby providing a 20-year average investment period.

More annuity drawbacks…

• A 10% early-withdrawal penalty applies to funds taken out of an annuity before age 59½.

• Most annuities impose surrender fees if you cash them in early. Typically, these start at 7% during the first year, decline 1% annually and are eliminated after the seventh year. Details vary from policy to policy.

• Some policies impose other kinds of fees, such as "deferred sales charges," which are charged to your investment over a period of years.

Carefully check any annuity contract for all charges and expenses before buying, and be sure to consider how they will affect the net return compared with other investments.

Inheritance trap:

Many people buy annuities with the financial goal of saving money that they intend to pass to the next generation—while keeping the money accessible in case they need it. But there's a trap here. The increase in an annuity's value due to tax-deferred earnings becomes a taxable gain at death.

A better investment for many people in this situation is life insurance, which also provides tax-deferred status for investment earnings left in the policy but provides a tax-free death benefit. Even if an annuity provides a higher investment return than a life-insurance policy, the insurance may provide a much higher net return after taxes.

Annuities and life insurance are both extremely complicated investments. The policies must be examined in detail to be sure you are getting the best deal.

Helpful: The National Insurance Consumers Organization's *How to Save Money on Life Insurance.* It compares various types of annuity and insurance programs from insurance companies. To order, write: NICO, 121 North Payne St., Alexandria, Virginia 22314.

Source: James H. Hunt is a director of the National Insurance Consumers Organization, 121 North Payne St., Alexandria, Virginia 22314.

How The Estate Tax Rules Can Fool You

The worst mistake that an individual can make about the tax treatment of estates is to assume it is now so generous that estate planning is hardly necessary.

Married individuals can leave all their financial holdings to their spouse free of any estate tax. This sounds like a bonanza, but unless a careful plan is drawn up, the overall tax burden on a married couple could wind up being more than it should be.

The unlimited marital deduction gives a couple a free tax ride in the first estate. But it can have very negative tax consequences when the surviving spouse dies. Reason: Property that passes tax-free in the first estate must be included in the surviving spouse's taxable estate. Assuming the survivor dies without dissipating the estate, that second estate will be subject to tax on the full inherited amount plus its appreciated value (unless the spouse remarries and leaves everything to that surviving spouse). Possible impact: A greater overall tax on the spouse's combined estates.

Source: Sanford J. Schlesinger, partner, Goldschmidt, Fredericks & Oshatz, New York City, and adjunct professor of law, New York Law School.

How To Cut Corporate Real Estate Taxes

Tax Reform generally toughened up the tax rules concerning business real estate—for example, by lengthening the period over which the cost of a building may be recovered through depreciation.

Yet many companies are overlooking tax-cutting opportunities that still do exist. With planning, companies can significantly cut or defer the tax bill on business real estate. Here's what businesses need to know now...

The first step to take toward cutting the company's tax bill is to make a careful allocation of a property's overall cost to land, buildings and personal property. Key:

• Land is not depreciable, so the portion of the cost allocated to land will produce no tax benefit through depreciation deductions.

• Buildings are depreciable, but Tax Reform established recovery periods of 28½ years for residential real estate, and 31½ years for other business real estate. As a result, earlier annual deductions are smaller than they were under pre-Tax Reform rules, and the difference is recovered over a longer period.

• Personal property can be depreciated over a much shorter period—typically seven years. It is sometimes even shorter—producing a much quicker recovery of the cost of the property. Thus, the portion of cost allocated to personal property will produce the largest tax benefit.

Generally an item qualifies as personal property if it is movable and reusable, even if it probably never will be moved. Examples of personal property range from movable office partitions to manufacturing equipment and emergency generators.

Surprising items may qualify as personal property. For example, foundations that are reinforced to support heavy equipment may be treated as part of the equipment rather than part of the building. Similarly, plumbing and electrical lines that are installed specifically to support equipment may be depreciated in the equipment category.

Trap: Contractors may provide cost breakdowns by type of expenditure (piping, wiring) rather than by depreciation category. But it is the depreciation category breakdown that is needed to maximize tax benefits.

When building, improving or modifying a property, realize that there is often a choice as to whether an item will qualify as personal or real property.

Example: The company may choose to

install permanent walls or movable partitions. Similarly, lighting fixtures, retail counters, lobby guard stations and many other items may be installed on a permanent or movable basis.

Examine improvements made on land separate from a building…fences, roads, parking lots, exterior lighting, billboards, landscaping, etc. If the price of these items is allocated to the cost of the land, it will produce no depreciation deductions. But if their price can be properly allocated to the building or other special depreciation categories, deductions may be saved.

Caution: There are many gray areas among asset definitions, and many exceptions to the standard recovery periods. So it may be beneficial to hire a consultant in this field to perform an allocation that will produce the most tax benefit and, perhaps, uncover unexpected deductions.

Value allocations made for different items of property can have major tax impact in areas other than depreciation.

•Local taxes. Many states and localities impose transfer tax when real estate is sold. Typically, the tax applies only to the real property involved, not the personal property. Again, a higher allocation of price to personal property will cut the tax bill.

•Alternative Minimum Tax (AMT). The AMT is a special tax computation that all corporations must work through. It is designed to keep profitable companies from largely eliminating their tax bills through the use of tax deductions such as accelerated depreciation, loss carry-forwards, etc. The company owes the tax computed under AMT rules if that amount is larger than the tax computed under normal rules.

Trap: Under AMT rules, the real estate depreciation period is generally 40 years, which is even longer than the standard periods prescribed by Tax Reform. This further spreads out the annual depreciation deductions that result from the price allocated to a building.

Passive losses generally aren't deductible against ordinary income under Tax Reform rules. As part of the attack on tax shelters, Tax Reform decreed that tax losses derived from rental real estate (for example, through depreciation deductions) are passive. Exceptions:

•A closely held regular corporation (C corporation) can deduct passive losses against regular trade or business income. Thus, a family business, for example, may still benefit from old-style tax-shelter type arrangements that the business invests in at the corporate (rather than personal) level.

•The IRS has ruled that an S corporation or partnership that has passive losses amounting to 20% or less of gross income can deduct such losses against its trade or business income. Thus, owners of businesses that include rental real estate activities can still get some benefit from passive losses on their personal returns.

State tax rules can vary greatly from federal rules.

Example: New York's transfer tax is based on gross sale price, while federal tax is based on gain derived from a sale. So a sale may be taxable in New York without resulting in a tax on the federal return.

A common trap in states with transfer taxes is that the buyer will agree to pay the transfer tax owed by the seller. But such payments have been held by local authorities to be extra consideration to the seller, which increases the sale price—and the tax due. If the buyer pays the increased tax, that again increases the price and tax…and so forth. Better: The parties should estimate what the transfer tax will be and include it in an adjusted sales price.

Installment sales were restricted for most uses by Tax Reform, but are still a valuable tool when planning real estate transfers. When an installment sale is used, the seller's gain is taxed proportionately as payments are received, over more than one year. Thus, gain may be deferred until a later year when the company expects to be in a lower tax bracket. Caution: Any recaptured depreciation is recognized as income in the year of sale, even though no cash may have been received.

Shared-appreciation mortgages are an increasingly popular financing device. In exchange for receiving a lower interest rate on a loan used to finance a property acquisition, the company gives the lender a share in the future appreciation in the property's value.

Tax point: Since appreciation share is being given to the lender in lieu of interest, it should be deductible as interest. Be sure the loan agreement covers this point and provides a method for valuing the share. Note: This method of financing may not be as attractive as in recent years because the amount of appreciation expected is not as great as in the past 10 "boom" years.

Points paid on a loan used to finance a building other than a personal residence are not deductible immediately, but must be amortized. Do not make the mistake of deducting them over the life of the building. Deduct them instead over the life of the loan, which will usually be shorter.

Like-kind exchanges can be used to indefinitely postpone tax on the gain that results when the company disposes of a property. Instead of selling the property, the company exchanges it for another piece of business real estate. Taxable gain is not recognized until the replacement property is disposed of…but that property can be exchanged, too. Exchanges involving several parties are possible, and the company can use a broker to find a replacement property and arrange an exchange.

Source: Jacob Weichholz, director of tax of the New York Metropolitan Office of Ernst & Young, specializing in taxation of closely held businesses, and Ronald J. Sacco, senior tax manager of the Metropolitan Office, specializing in real estate, 787 Seventh Ave., New York 10019.

How To Deduct Nondeductible Expenses

The tax law imposes strict limits on personal deductions. But creative tax planners have found ways to get around these limits. With a little careful planning, you can turn nondeductible expenses into tax deductions.

• Interest deductions. Interest on personal debt is no longer deductible. This includes interest on car loans, college loans, credit cards, revolving charge accounts, installment purchases and late-paid taxes. But interest on home-equity loans of up to $100,000 remains fully deductible.

Loophole: Take out a home-equity loan on your first or second home and use the proceeds to pay off personal debt. Your interest payments will then be deductible. You will have converted nondeductible personal interest payments into deductible mortgage interest.

• Hire your kids. Instead of paying your child a nondeductible allowance, put him/her to work as a bona fide employee in your business. The wages are a deductible business expense.

Loophole: If your business is unincorporated, you don't have to pay Social Security tax on wages paid to a child who is under 18.

• Buy a vacation home. It can be a source of personal pleasure and valuable tax breaks. When you rent a vacation home to strangers for fewer than 15 days, the rental income is tax-free. This is one of the few instances in the Tax Code where income is considered nontaxable. You are not even required to report it on your tax return. Nevertheless, you are still entitled to full deductions for mortgage interest and property taxes.

When you rent your vacation home to others for 15 days or more, the income you receive is taxable. But expenses related to the property rental (including depreciation) are deductible, subject to certain limitations depending on the number of days you personally use the place. To get the full deduction, you yourself cannot use the place for more than the greater of 14 days or 10% of the number of days it is rented to others.

Loophole: Days spent fixing or maintaining the house do not count as personal use.

• Medical expenses of dependents. Even though you may not be able to claim a personal exemption for your contribution to the support of a relative because he/she had a gross income of $2,150 or more, you can still deduct any medical expenses that you pay on your relative's behalf. Key: You must provide more than one-half of the relative's support.

Loophole: Instead of giving your relative cash to pay medical bills, pay the bills yourself. This may give you a deduction.

If you are the one who is claiming a dependency exemption for a parent under a multiple-support agreement (Form 2120) with other relatives, you should also pay the dependent's medical expenses. Reason: In determining qualification for the exemption, the payment of medical expenses is treated as part of the dependent's support. The payment is also deductible as a medical expense.

Impact:

You get a double tax benefit for the same payment, a dependency exemption and a tax deduction.

Another way to get a double benefit is to make a charitable contribution on your parent's behalf. The payment is included in calculating support, and you get a charitable deduction for it.

• Hobby losses. Expenses of activities that are primarily sport, hobby or recreation are not deductible. In order to convert these non-deductible expenses into allowable deductions, the activity must be changed to an activity carried on for the production or collection of income. This is not hard to do if you keep good records. Factors that the IRS considers include…

• The businesslike nature of the taxpayer's records.

• The extent of the knowledge and expertise of the taxpayer and the manner in which he/she uses them in the activity.

• The history of prior income or losses connected with the activity.

• The taxpayer's success in conducting other types of activities.

• Employee business-expense deductions. As an employee, you can deduct unreimbursed expenses for business-related travel, transportation, meals, entertainment and gifts.

Trap:

Most unreimbursed employee business expenses fall under the category of "miscellaneous itemized deductions" and, as such, can only be deducted to the extent that, in total, they exceed 2% of your Adjusted Gross Income (AGI). If your expenses don't come up to this floor, you get no deduction for them.

Loophole I: Have your employer reduce your salary by the amount you normally spend on business expenses during the year — say, $1,000. Then have your employer reimburse you directly for the $1,000 of expenses. Impact: You no longer have to worry about the 2% floor. You get a deduction for the full $1,000 of expenses through the salary reduction. Caution: The salary reduction may affect your pension contributions.

Important:

Be sure to adequately account for the expenses to your employer. If you don't, you could be required to pick up the entire amount of the reimbursement as ordinary income.

Loophole II (for anyone who is physically or mentally handicapped): Impairment-related work expenses are not subject to the 2%-of-AGI limit on miscellaneous itemized deductions.

Loophole III: Beat the 2% floor on the deductibility of employee business expenses by filing Schedule C (Profit or Loss From Business), where there is no such limitation. In order to qualify for reporting your expenses on Schedule C, you must fit into one of the following categories…

• Self-employed individual or independent contractor.

• Statutory employee. This is a category of worker that includes full-time life-insurance salespeople, certain agents and commission drivers and certain home-workers. Statutory employees are entitled to file Schedule C even though Social Security tax has been withheld from their paychecks and they have been issued W-2 forms.

• Qualified performing artist. To qualify in this category, a taxpayer must have performed services in the performing arts for at least two performances in the tax year…and had performing-arts-related business expenses in excess of 10% of his/her performing-arts gross income…and had an AGI of $16,000 or less. (Performing-arts expenses can be deducted even though deductions are not itemized.)

• Passive losses. Tax Reform produced the "passive loss rules" that generally limit the deductibility of losses from passive activities to the amount of income derived from such activities. Passive activities are defined as activities involving the conduct of a trade or business in which the taxpayer does not materially participate.

Accordingly, you can avoid the disallowance of losses if you "materially" participate in the otherwise passive activity. Material participation in a trade or business activity means satisfying any one of a variety of tests.

Example: If you participated in the activity for more than 500 hours during the year, the passive-loss rules would not apply to that activity.

Strategy: To prove material participation, keep an appointment book, calendar or narrative summary in which you record a listing of all of the services you performed.

Loophole I: New IRS regulations for self-charged interest permit the matching of interest income (normally portfolio income) directly against passive losses to the extent that the loss includes self-interest charged through the entity by the S corporation shareholder or partner.

Loophole II: Amended returns can be filed to claim a refund going back to all open years from 1987 on.

• Small business losses. If you're operating a business as a regular corporation, any losses you suffer when you sell your stock in the company are usually treated as capital losses, deductible only against capital gains and up to $3,000 a year of ordinary income. Losses on the sale of Section 1244 stock are deductible in full against ordinary income.

Limits: $100,000 a year on a joint return ($50,000 a year if you are single).

To qualify under Section 1244, the corporation must have capital of $1 million or less. It must operate as a business. And the stock must have been issued for money or property.

Source: Edward Mendlowitz, partner, Mendlowitz Weitsen, CPAs, Two Pennsylvania Plaza, New York 10121. Mr. Mendlowitz is the author of several books, including *Aggressive Tax Strategies*, Macmillan Publishing Company, 866 Third Ave., New York 10022.

There Are IRS Abuses... And Ways To Protect Yourself

The most common and most dangerous IRS abuses—and what to do to protect yourself...

• Beware: Property seizure. You may receive a surprise notice that the IRS is taking steps to seize your house or bank account, or put a levy on your salary.

Self-defense: Contact an IRS Revenue Officer immediately by responding to the reply address given on the notice of levy or seizure. Find out what the problem is and what the IRS wants.

Urgent: If seizure seems imminent, immediately file IRS Form 911, *Taxpayer Assistance Order,* either in person or by mail, with the Problem Resolution Office in the IRS district in which you live. This automatically puts a temporary stay on the seizure process and gives you a chance to have your case reviewed. Use the stay to get expert advice.

• Beware: You're read your rights. IRS Special Agents show up at your home or office, read you a Miranda warning—and indicate that you have violated a law. Danger: Special Agents are criminal investigators. They're serious—anything you say to them can be held against you.

Self-defense: Explain to the agents that you don't want to say anything until you've contacted your lawyer. Then immediately contact your lawyer to get a referral to an attorney who handles criminal tax matters.

Do not rely on your bookkeeper or accountant to handle the problem. First of all, they're not qualified to give legal advice. Second, they may be under investigation, too—and if they are, their interests may not coincide with yours.

• Beware: Mystery penalties. The IRS sends you a bill for tax penalties you don't understand.

Self-defense: Do not ignore the bill. Look at the letter the IRS sent you to find the address or phone number to call for more information. Then contact the IRS to get an explanation of the penalties. Be sure that you get a full explanation and truly understand what's happened.

If it turns out that you do owe a penalty, it pays to argue that the penalty should be abated because "reasonable cause" existed for the error you made.

The IRS can waive penalties when a taxpayer has a plausible explanation for why rules weren't followed exactly—sometimes even in seemingly extreme circumstances.

Recent case: A couple filed their tax return three years late and with $30,000 of taxes due. Court: No lateness penalties. The husband had been ill and the wife knew nothing about taxes. Thus, their late filing had a reasonable cause.

Samuel T. Isaac, ED Ky., No. 89-146.

• Beware: Hostile auditor. You may feel that an IRS auditor is taking completely unreasonable positions while examining your return.

Self-defense: Request a conference with the auditor's group manager. The manager is likely to be much more experienced than the auditor and is also responsible for seeing that cases are handled fairly and expeditiously. He/she can provide a helpful second opinion.

If meeting with the group manager doesn't work, ask for a conference with the IRS Appeals Division. Why: While auditors are supposed to enforce the letter of the law, appeals officers work to settle cases in a practical manner. They can consider "hazards of litigation"—the strength of the IRS case, what it is worth, and what it could cost to pursue it. An appeals officer is likely to see through an unreasonable auditor's determination.

• Beware: Taxing tax-free income. The IRS may try to tax your tax-free income. This often happens, for example, when a person takes a distribution from a retirement plan (such as a company 401(k) plan, Keogh or IRA) and rolls it over into another plan. The individual knows the distribution is tax-free, so he doesn't bother to include it on his tax return. But the IRS gets a 1099 reporting the payout from the trustee of the plan making the distribution. It doesn't know there's been a rollover, so it taxes the money.

Self-defense: Include an explanation on your tax return whenever you receive a 1099 reporting to tax-exempt income. Include copies of any documentation that proves the income really is tax-exempt, such as receipts showing a rollover has been completed.

• Beware: Miscredited tax payments. The IRS may lose your tax payment—or they may apply it to the wrong account. You find out when you get a surprise tax bill.

Self-defense: First, make it as easy as possible for the IRS to apply your payment correctly. Be sure that on the check you pay with you write your taxpayer ID number, the tax year the payment is for and the type of tax involved (Form 1040 income tax, Form 1040 ES estimated taxes, etc.) Also use IRS pre-printed coupons and vouchers whenever possible to facilitate processing, and IRS-supplied return envelopes or mailing labels to be sure that payments go to the right address.

If your tax payment is lost anyway, reply to the IRS tax bill with a copy of your canceled check, along with a cover letter detailing when and how the tax was paid. It takes time for the IRS to correct its computer records, so don't worry if you get another dunning notice or two. But do respond to the notices with copies of the explanation you have already provided.

• Beware: Bad advice. We all turn to an IRS agent for advice sooner or later. The problem is that if the advice turns out to be bad, you can't rely on it unless you've gotten it in writing. And the IRS is very unlikely to agree to give you any advice in writing, especially if you're making a telephone inquiry.

Self-defense: Whenever you get tax advice from the IRS, ask for the legal authority behind the advice. Have the IRS agent tell you the section number of the Tax Code or the name and page number of the IRS publication that supports his/her opinion.

• Beware: The notice you never get. You may suddenly find yourself being dunned for a tax bill you never heard of—and being told you've missed the deadline to appeal or take your case to Tax Court.

What's happened: Perhaps sometime in the past few years you moved. Now the IRS is

challenging some items on an old tax return. It sent all its tax notices to the old address shown on that return. You never got the notices, so you lost your case by default.
Self-defense:

Write a letter to the IRS district director asking for reconsideration of your case. Detail the hardship you face and show how you could have answered the tax assessment on the merits if you had been given a chance. The district director can reopen your case if fairness demands it and he/she concludes that you were not at fault.

If the IRS refuses to reopen your case, you can still contest the tax bill in US District Court. But first you must pay the disputed tax and sue for a refund.

Future self-defense: You can prevent this from happening in the first place by filing the new IRS Form 8822, which gives the IRS official notice of your change of address when you move.

• Beware: Lost-in-the-mail nightmare. The IRS loses your return or other important tax papers, then claims it never received them. You don't find out until deadlines have passed and it's too late to do anything about it.

Self-defense: Always send important documents to the IRS by certified mail with a return-receipt requested. It's the only form of proof of delivery to the IRS that's accepted. Neither the IRS nor the Tax Court is required to accept receipts provided by private messengers or express-mail services.

• Beware: Missing/seized refund. The IRS may lose your refund check, delay it through misprocessing or intercept it and apply it against some other bill it says you owe.

Self-defense: Don't let the IRS hold your money. Adjust payroll withholding and estimated taxes so that you don't overpay your taxes during the year. Even if you get your refund back with no trouble, it amounts to an interest-free loan that you provided to the IRS during the year.

• Beware: Erroneous refund. The IRS sends you a large refund that you're sure is a mistake. You're afraid that if you cash it, eventually the IRS will come after you for the refund and interest.

Self-defense: Don't cash the refund check. Send it back to the IRS with a request for an explanation of it. If they again state that the refund is yours and give you a correct reason why, you can cash it.

• Beware: The impossible problem. Sometimes a problem that ought to be simple to solve never goes away. Maybe a refund that the IRS admits is due to you simply never arrives. Or a miscredited tax payment never gets straightened out in spite of your repeated attempts to do so.

Self-defense: Contact the IRS Problems Resolution Office (PRO). The PRO has the authority to cut through IRS red tape to solve taxpayer problems in an expeditious manner.

Requirement: You must have tried to resolve the problem at least twice on your own through normal channels, and have proof that you have done so—such as copies of letters sent to the IRS.

The PRO can be located through the government listings in your phone book.

Source: Randy Bruce Blaustein, Esq., partner, Blaustein, Greenberg & Co., 155 E. 31 St., Suite 15L, New York 10016.

Your Real Estate Taxes Can Be Much Lower

Many people pay too much in property taxes year after year without ever realizing it or questioning the system. Yet it is fairly easy to get property taxes reduced.

Statistics show that more than 60% of homeowners who challenge assessments succeed. Our own firm's success rate on behalf of clients varies from 70% up to 100% in some counties.

No lawyer is needed to challenge an assessment, and there's no fee. All you have to do is make the effort.

The savings you reap can become huge over time. Not only do you cut your tax bill every year, but your savings grow each year as property taxes go up on a percentage basis in line with inflation. And by lowering your tax rate, you increase your home's resale value.

The big trap:

The key to cutting your tax bill is understanding how the system works. The big trap is that many people believe their homes are assessed at bargain rates. That's because assessed value is typically only a percentage of market value. Thus, a house with a $200,000 market value may be assessed at only $100,000, and the owner may think he's/she's getting a bargain tax rate.

What most people don't know is that property tax is computed by multiplying assessed value by an "equalization ratio" that is determined by the state. If the ratio on a $200,000 house assessed at $100,000 is 2.5, the owner is being taxed on a house value of $250,000 without even knowing it.

Equalization ratios are determined by the state and are applied countywide or throughout a tax district. The ratios are increased periodically to keep track with inflation and market transactions. But the fixed ratio often can easily be shown to be inappropriate for a particular property. If you can change your equalization ratio, you can cut your tax bill.

Steps to take:

• Analyze your current assessment. Call your local tax assessment office and ask what equalization ratio is used to make the adjustment. Your tax bill may show an assessment at $100,000, but if the multiplier used is 2, then your assessment is really for $200,000. A challenge should be made if your home is actually worth less than $200,000.

• Justify your opinion of market value. Your opinion that the tax assessment is too high is probably right. Tax assessors usually base their assessment on the cost of replacing your home plus the land.

More accurate: A comparison of actual sales of similar homes in your area. This will produce a more realistic (and lower) valuation of your home. Sales prices and information about houses sold are a matter of public record at your local deed-recording office.

Write all the information down in an organized format to be presented to the tax assessor. Don't forget to include adjustments for differences between your home's value and a recent local sale due to conditions, location, date of sale, amount of living space, etc.

• Research other assessments. Your property should be assessed at about the same rate as comparable homes in your neighborhood. If yours is higher, you are entitled to a reduction. Get information about other assessments at the assessor's office. (Your neighbors will never know.) All you need to find is three or four homes very similar to yours that are assessed at a lower value.

• Challenge the opinion of the tax assessor. Tax assessments are based on the market value of your land and the buildings on that land, in the opinion of the tax assessor. Yet tax assessors rarely have any kind of professional training in this area. Even professionals in the real estate business reach different opinions when valuing property.

Compare any recent professional appraisals of your home with the assessor's. If you recently purchased your home, you paid your bank to perform an appraisal before it lent you the money. Call your lending officer and ask for a copy of that appraisal. If it's lower than the tax assessor's opinion, use it to show that you've been overassessed.

• Hire your own appraiser. Tell the appraiser that you need it for a real-estate reduction appeal. Shop around and get quotes from several appraisers. The cost is usually small compared with the amount of tax you will save, especially since a reduced assessment will stay in effect for several years.

• Look for the lowest value. Use anything you can to explain why your property's value is lower than what the tax assessor determined it to be. Put yourself in the place of a buyer who is trying to justify why you should lower the selling price of your home.

Examples: Water in the basement, radon or general deterioration in the condition of your home since the last assessment was made.

• Look at the assessor's worksheet. Go to the tax-assessment office and ask to see the worksheet that the assessor used to value your property. You have the right to see this document. Check to see if the assessor properly describes your home, land, zoning and public services. Check that the number of bathrooms and garages are listed correctly.

• Review property descriptions for mechanical errors. Check to make sure the dimensions of the house were measured correctly and that the correct mathematics was used in calculating the number of square feet.

• Look for clerical errors. The amount of the assessment on the worksheet should be the same as the amount on your tax bill.

• Check to make sure personal property wasn't included. Personal property is anything that is easily movable and is not fixed to the land. Example: A shed that is not permanently affixed to your real estate. Items that can be removed relatively easily are considered personal property and are not subject to real estate taxation.

• Calmly present your facts. Go to the assessor's office and tell him/her what reduction you want and why. The assessor will probably make an adjustment if you have a good case. If the tax assessor doesn't agree to reduce your assessment, ask for a hearing with the local board of review. These boards have been established to give an impartial opinion. If the board decides against you, you can take your case to a court of law.

Source: Howard J. Udell is president of Property Tax Reduction Services, Inc., 2647 Russell St., Allentown, Pennsylvania 18104.

The 12 Best Ways To Cut Your Taxes

Taxes are one component in a personal financial plan. Some of the best ways to save taxes:

1. Start with an overall personal financial game plan that includes, as well as taxes, investments, insurance, education, employee benefits and retirement needs. Only when you have the big picture of your financial goals will tax-saving strategies make sense. In many cases, taxes are only a consequence of key financial planning decisions.

2. Review your Alternative Minimum Tax exposure. The time to do this is at the beginning of the year, not the end. Your tax strategies (and personal financial planning) will be altered considerably if you are close to, or in, the AMT. See your tax adviser if you have substantial itemized deductions, large charitable gifts of appreciated property, or incentive stock options, among other things. You could be an AMT target.

3. Make contributions to retirement plans now. The sooner in the year you contribute, the better. The money you put in the plan compounds, and it compounds on a tax-deferred basis.

Caution: Be sure this is money that you don't need before you retire. You'll be penalized if you withdraw money from your plan before you reach the age of 59½.

4. Contribute the maximum amount of salary to your company's 401(k) plan. It's especially important to do this if your employer makes matching contributions to the plan. (Many employers match employee contributions by putting in, say, 50 cents for every dollar that the employee contributes to the plan.) Matching contributions are an immediate, substantial benefit to you. Other benefits:

• Tax is deferred on the money you put into the plan.

• The money builds up in the plan on a tax-deferred basis.

• Many 401(k) plans allow participants to borrow against their accounts.

5. Review your W-2 withholding. Consider readjusting the amount of tax withheld from your pay in light of changes in either your family or your financial situation. Don't give the IRS more than you need to early in the year. Aim: To come out even with the government on April 15, 1994.

6. Defer tax on interest income. Buy one-year-or-less Treasury bills or Certificates of Deposit that come due in January, 1994. This will shift almost a full year's interest income into 1994. Reason: Interest on these investments is not taxable until they come due.

Caution: To defer income with Certificates of Deposit, the interest must not be credited to your account or made available for withdrawal until the CDs reach maturity.

Money saver: Buy your T-bills directly from the Federal Reserve. (Contact your regional branch of the Federal Reserve Bank for more information.) This will save you the commission that banks and brokerage firms charge when you buy T-bills from them.

7. Entertain business contacts at home this year. Many people simply don't know that they can deduct 80% of the cost of all business meals that they prepare and serve in their own home. It must, of course, be a legitimate business meal and you should be sure to keep an accurate record of all the people that you entertained, the business discussions that took place, etc.

8. Review your debt strategy. The deduction for personal interest is dead as of 1991. But home mortgage interest, business interest, and investment interest remain deductible within certain limits. Now is the time to review your debt strategy. Clean up your personal debt and use home mortgage, business, and investment interest deductions to your best advantage.

Home mortgages: Interest on up to $1 million of home acquisition debt is fully deductible as well as interest on up to $100,000 of home-equity debt.

9. Use gifts to lower taxes. Families should devise tax-sheltered ways to finance children's education costs. Gifts can be used to do this. Parents (or grandparents) can give up to $10,000 a year to each of their children, free of federal gift tax. The figure is $20,000 a year if a husband and wife make the gift jointly.

These gifts can be used to shift income from your highly taxed return to your child's low tax bracket. As long as your child is 14 or over, the earnings on assets you put in his name are taxed at his/her bracket, not yours.

10. Pay tuition directly to a college or university. Parents or grandparents can give a child more than $10,000 a year by paying the child's tuition bills directly, rather than giving the money to the child. Such payments are free of federal gift tax, over and above $10,000/$20,000 annual amounts. The only qualification is that the money must go directly to the educational institution.

11. Make gifts to elderly parents. An annual gift-giving program also makes sense if you are supporting your parents. If your parents are in a lower tax bracket, you'll save on taxes by transferring income-producing assets to them.

Make the gift at the beginning of the year and you'll be able to shift a whole year's income. The same limits apply here—you are allowed to give up to $10,000/$20,000 to each parent each year free of federal gift tax.

Another way that you can make additional tax-free gifts to your parents is by paying their medical expenses directly to their health-care provider. The same wrinkle that applies to directly paid educational expenses also works for directly paid medical expenses.

12. Learn something about taxes and personal finance. Take the time to read books about personal taxes, investments, and retirement planning. Consider forming a financial plan.

While you're reading, take the time to think about the things that you like to do the most in life. Read books and other publications about your hobby and think of ways of turning that interest into a sideline business.

When you establish a legitimate business of your own, even if it's just a sideline business, some previously non-deductible expenses become tax deductible business expenses on Schedule C of Form 1040.

Source: George E.L. Barbee, executive director, personal financial services, Price Waterhouse, 51 Sawyer Rd., Waltham, Massachusetts 02154.

The Biggest Mistakes Taxpayers Make At IRS Audits...And How To Avoid Them

Audits are a part of life. They are neither something to be feared—nor something to be offended by. If you've prepared a correct and accurate return, an audit is going to reveal that.

Common mistakes people make at audits:

• Mistake: Being too defensive. Some taxpayers are so defensive at an audit that they seem to deny the government's right to ask them questions about their return. This attitude only leads to trouble. It can cause the examiner to think that there must be something wrong on the return. His natural response will be to ask more probing questions than he otherwise would, and to go more deeply into things. That's the last thing you want.

The right attitude to have at an audit: Be cooperative and forthcoming. Avoid showing hostility and fear.

• Mistake: Volunteering information. In your effort to be cooperative and forthcoming, you must remember never to volunteer information. Answer only the questions that are asked…nothing more.

And…produce only those records that you've been asked to produce. The IRS will inform you in the audit notice what items are being investigated on your return. If the agent brings up any items other than what you expected, explain that you don't have them with you since they were not relevant to the audit notice. Ask the agent if the audit could be adjourned until such time as you can produce the additional records.

• Mistake: Trying to handle technical issues yourself. Know your limits. If the audit involves nothing more than providing proof for your deductions, you can probably handle it yourself.

But if technical or legal issues are involved, particularly if you had to seek advice in the first place for the treatment on your return, you should be represented at the audit by an experienced tax professional. The problem with doing it yourself is that you won't be equipped to field specific technical questions the auditor will ask.

• Mistake: Not preparing ahead of time. Taxpayers who show up unprepared run the risk that the agent will interpret the lack of preparation to mean that there is something wrong on the return.

Helpful: Bring an adding-machine tape and a worksheet that show how you arrived at the figures you claimed on your return.

If you're missing a significant number of cancelled checks, you should prepare for this in advance by getting corroborating evidence for the expenses.

Example: If you've made a contribution to a charity and you don't have the cancelled check, you should try to get a statement or a receipt from the charity indicating that you made the contribution. Another way to approach this is to see if your bank keeps photocopies of cancelled checks.

• Mistake: Not asking for relief under the IRS's repetitive audit procedure. If you've been audited in either of the last two years on a particular item and the audit resulted in no change in your tax bill, you can request that you not be audited on that same issue again.

Self-defense: As soon as you receive your audit notice, write to the IRS to claim an exemption under the Repetitive Audit Program. Enclose a copy of your audit notice and "no change letter" from the previous audit.

• Mistake: Not reviewing your rights. Along with your audit notice, you should be sent a copy of IRS Publication 1, Your Rights as a Taxpayer. Read this pamphlet carefully, so that you know your rights. Remember, you're dealing with someone—a revenue agent or tax auditor—who does audits every day.

• Mistake: Not drawing attention to items you could have deducted but didn't. If you come across deductions you're entitled to, but failed to take, you should bring them to the IRS's attention. Use these items to offset any deficiencies the IRS finds during the audit. Some people actually wind up getting refunds as a result of an audit.

• Mistake: Not trying to talk the auditor out of penalties. Penalties may be brought up by the agent during the audit. These penalties are really judgment calls on the agent's part. They don't have to impose them. You should make every effort to convince the agent that the penalty shouldn't be applied.

• Mistake: Not asking to speak to the auditor's manager when you can't reach an agreement with the auditor about adjustments to your tax bill. The Internal Revenue Manual requires that whenever there's an unagreed case, the IRS manager should offer to speak to the taxpayer to try and resolve the matter.

It's a good idea, though, for the taxpayer to initiate the meeting...if the IRS doesn't.

Source: Marvin Michelman, specialist in IRS practice and procedure, Deloitte & Touche, One World Trade Center, New York 10048. He held various positions with the IRS for 19 years, including senior regional analyst for examinations.

Fine Points Of Tax Law

• An individual reimbursed by his company for the business use of his car at a rate greater than the IRS standard mileage allowance must include the excess as income. He can then deduct the excess as a business expense, if he has substantiation that will satisfy the IRS.

IRS Letter Rulings 8003119 and 8004052.

• Recording serial number of stocks might help reduce your taxable gain. It proves to the IRS when, and for how much, the stock was purchased. If the share's price went up, sales of those shares that cost the most produce the lowest taxable gain. But if the taxpayer can't prove which shares he's selling, the IRS computes the gain on a straight first-in, first-out basis.

Kluger Associates, Inc., et al. v. Comm'r., 2d Cir., 3/17/80.

• Silver lining to an unhappy land investment: IRS considers land a long-term capital investment. Buyers can write off losses in full against capital gains and up to $3,000 per year, against their regular income. If you bought an undeveloped lot from a shady land-sales company, it may pay to finish paying it off, sell at any loss, and take the tax deductions.

• An employee who relocates because of a job transfer loses the right to deduct moving expenses if he doesn't work in the new location for at least 39 weeks. Exception: The 39-week requirement is waived if the employee loses his job for reasons beyond his control or is retrans-

ferred to another location by his employer.

• If your employer reimburses or pays your moving expenses, take allowable tax deductions and report the reimbursement as additional income. Important: Check to see whether your employer reported the reimbursement as wages on your Form W-2. If so, don't report it again.

• Moving expenses paid by landlord. Landlords seeking to persuade tenants to move often agree to pay part or all the tenants' moving costs. Tax trap: The landlord's payment is fully includible in the taxpayer's income. But the expenses reimbursed are not deductible. Reason: The move isn't connected to a change in employment. This is one of the conditions to be met before moving expenses can be deducted.

IRS Letter Ruling 8104100.

• If the doctor orders you to take a vacation, and says it's medically necessary, it may be deductible. One case: Doctor wouldn't permit the executive to go to Europe unless he took his wife along, since she was specially trained to deal with his heart illness. The wife's travel expenses were allowed as a medical deduction.

• If the check you mail to the IRS should bounce, you can sometimes avoid interest and late-payment charges. Just be sure to send in a new check within 10 days after the IRS notifies you that the original check was not honored. Enclose a detailed explanation of the circumstances beyond your control that caused the check to bounce. If the circumstances were not beyond your control, you are stuck with the extra charges.

Internal Revenue Manual, P-2-8; P-2-16.

• IRS can search your safe-deposit box: (1) If you refuse to pay taxes due. (2) If the auditor thinks you are hiding assets. The IRS can force open the box if you won't supply the key.

• IRS usually will not try to collect back taxes by levying against current Social Security benefits, veteran's benefits, GI Bill awards, and similar payments, even though it has the authority to do so. Exception: Flagrant or aggravated cases of neglect or refusal to pay.

Internal Revenue Manual, P-5-30.

• If an IRS agent calls: Find out if the person is a Revenue Agent or a Special Agent. (The agents are required to identify themselves.) Exercise extreme caution if it's a Special Agent. They are assigned to suspected fraud cases. Call your lawyer at once.

• Proof that a car was used for business purposes: Keep a simple log in a 3- x 5-inch notebook, listing the date, beginning and ending mileage, and purpose of each tax-deductible trip. Separate pages for business, medical, charitable, and moving-expense mileage simplify preparation of the tax return.

• Deductible costs of business driving include payments to injured pedestrians. A recent decision: Accidents by drivers are inseparable incidents of driving a car. Costs incurred as a result of such an incident are just as much a part of overall business expenses as the cost of fuel and maintenance. *Dancer et al. v. Comm'r., 73 T.C. No. 88.*

• Casualty losses. Damage or loss of home or personal property entitle you to a casualty deduction, but not to the amount of the replacement cost. You can only claim the lower of either (1) the actual cost or (2) the fair market value immediately preceding the loss. In either case, you can only deduct that part of your loss that exceeds 10% of your adjusted gross income and the first $100 of each loss is not deductible. *Gay et al. v. Comm'r., T.C. Memo 1980-19.*

Retirement Tax-Planning Loopholes

The key to a successful and happy retirement is that you have enough money to satisfy your wants and needs.

Fortunately, there are a good number of tax loopholes that will help you accomplish this goal. But there are traps to avoid, too.
Pension plans:

• The amounts you receive as distributions from your company pension or profit-sharing plan are generally fully taxable.

Loophole: If you contributed to the pension plan with some of your own after-tax dollars, that contribution is not taxable when you take it out. Obligatory contributions to your employer's pension plan and voluntary nondeductible contributions to an IRA are not taxable when you withdraw them. (But 401(k) contributions, which are made with pre-tax dollars, are taxable when you take them out.)*

Important: Keep careful track of the amounts you contribute to a pension plan.

• Lump-sum distributions from pension and profit-sharing plans qualify for special tax breaks…

Rollover loophole: You can roll the money over into an IRA and postpone paying taxes until you take the money out of the IRA.

1936 loophole: If you were born before 1936, you can choose to treat a portion of the taxable part of a lump-sum distribution as a long-term capital gain taxable at a 20% rate. Also, you may elect to use tax-favored ten-year averaging for the ordinary income part of the distribution. This can further reduce the tax you pay.

59½ loophole: Regardless of when you were born, as long as you're at least 59½ years old, your lump-sum distribution qualifies for five-year averaging. You may end up paying a very low rate on the distribution.

• Don't miss the deadline for beginning to take money out of your IRA and pension or profit-sharing plan. Distributions from the plan must begin by April 1 of the year following the year in which you become age 70½.

Trap: If you miss the deadline, you'll be charged a 50% penalty tax on the amount you should have withdrawn, but didn't.

• Avoid penalties on excess distributions from your pension plans. You'll be charged a 15% penalty tax to the extent your annual distributions from all your plans exceed $150,000—or to the extent that you get a lump-sum distribution that exceeds $750,000. If you made a grandfather election on your 1987 or 1988 return, you might be exempt

---

*Special loophole: Pensions from certain governmental agencies are not subject to state income tax. Check with your tax advisor.

from the 15% penalty tax on part of your excess distribution.

Grandfather election loophole: Review with your tax advisor the way the election was made. You may be able to change the method of making withdrawals and, thereby, reduce the penalty.

Social Security:

Up to 50% of your Social Security benefits are taxable, depending on your total income. The calculation for taxing Social Security benefits includes tax exempt interest you've earned from municipal bonds.

Taxable bonds loophole: You may be better off owning taxable bonds rather than tax exempt ones since taxable bonds pay a higher interest rate.

Social Security benefits are based on your income. It's important to check periodically on your earnings record with the Social Security Administration. Errors more than three years old are hard to correct. If you catch a mistake early on, you'll be able to fix it.

To check: Fill out and mail to the Social Security Administration Form SSA-7004-PC, Request for Earnings and Benefits Estimate Statement.

Other loopholes:

Squeeze the maximum tax benefit from your home.

Home loophole: If you're 55 or older, you don't have to pay tax on the first $125,000 of profit on the sale of your home. This is a once-in-a-lifetime exclusion. Married individuals are entitled to only one exclusion per couple.

It's not a good idea from a tax standpoint to give the family home to your intended beneficiaries before you die. Reason: The recipients take over your tax basis in the property, which is generally its cost. When the recipients sell the property they will pay income tax on the full appreciation in value since you bought the property.

Inheritance loophole: Let your beneficiaries inherit the family home. They will receive it at its stepped-up, date-of-death value, and income tax will be forgiven on the appreciation. This same loophole applies to other appreciated property. For instance, instead of selling

stock and giving your children the proceeds, give them cash and let them inherit the stock.

A way to reduce your taxable estate is to make annual gifts to family members. You can give up to $10,000 a year to each of any number of recipients ($20,000 a year if your spouse joins in the gift) without having to pay federal gift tax.

Gift loophole: In addition to $10,000 or $20,000 amounts, you can also make gift-tax-free gifts for education expenses. To qualify a payment as a tax-free gift, however, you must make it directly to the college or other institution.

There are two ways to make gifts to children and still control the use of the money. Set up a trust for the children or a custodial account under the Uniform Gifts to Minors Act.

Trap: Don't make yourself the trustee or custodian of these accounts. If you do that, the assets will be taxed in your estate when you die.

• Life insurance. Premium payments on life insurance are not tax deductible, and any proceeds that are eventually paid out are not considered taxable income. Many senior citizens have fully paid-up life insurance policies from which they receive dividends. They get 1099s from the insurance company for these dividends.

Insurance loophole: The dividends are not taxable until the cumulative amount of dividends received exceeds the total amount of premiums paid by the policy holder.

Source: Edward Mendlowitz, partner, Mendlowitz Weitsen, CPAs, Two Pennsylvania Plaza, New York 10121. Mr. Mendlowitz is the author of several books, including *Aggressive Tax Strategies*, Macmillan Publishing Company, 866 Third Ave., New York 10022.

Beware Of Telephone Conversations Being Monitored

Telephone conversations on cordless phones can be monitored by Internal Revenue Service investigators seeking evidence of criminal fraud, according to an advisory to agents. The official policy is that investigators do not need a warrant before such eavesdropping. Court permission is still required for tapping wired phone conversations.

Source: Revision to Sec. 9389.61(9). IRS manual.

Motheraid

A son paid his mother's medical expenses with money he withdrew from her bank account under a power of attorney. The IRS disallowed the son's deduction for these expenses, saying the money was really the mother's. But the Court of Appeals allowed the deduction. The money was legally his—a gift from his mother to him.

Source: *John M. Ruch,* CA-5, 82-4463.

Tax-Free Living

A family self-incorporated and transferred its assets—including house, car and equipment used in the family business (a farm)—to the new company. The family then entered into an employment contract with the company, which required family members to live in their former house because their presence was required at all hours to run the business. The company agreed to pay the family's living expenses, including food and lodging. The family took the payments tax-free because the arrangement benefited their employer, and the company deducted its expenses. IRS ruling: The arrangement is proper even if it was adopted with the explicit intention of avoiding taxes.

Source: *Letter Ruling* 9134003.

Payment-Extension Secret

The form no one at the IRS talks about is Form 1127. That's the form you file when you can't pay your taxes on time. It's called *Application for Extension of Time for Payment of Tax,* and it gives you up to six months from the due date to pay the tax you owe. Problem: You must be able to show that you can't borrow money to pay your tax bill except under terms that would cause severe loss and hardship. Note: Though late-payment penalties are excused when you're granted an extension, you still owe the IRS interest on late-paid tax.

Source: Ms. X, a former IRS agent who is still well connected.

What The IRS Knows About You

The IRS gets information from third parties and matches this information to you through its computers. Stay one step ahead by being extra careful to report on your tax return what the IRS already knows about you. (You should receive from the third parties copies of all the information they send to the IRS.) What the IRS knows and how:

Your income. The IRS knows, of course, if you have been paid over $600. The payer must report this payment to the IRS on Form 1099-MISC, *Statement for Recipients of Miscellaneous Income.* Included in this category:

- Free-lance income.
- Rent or royalty payments.
- Prizes and awards that are not for services rendered.
- Payments made by medical and health-care insurers to a doctor or other supplier of medical services under an insurance program.
- Attorney's and accountant's fees for professional services.
- Witness or expert fees paid by a lawyer during a legal proceeding.
- Payments made to entertainers for their services.

Your wages. And the IRS knows from your W-2 Form exactly how much you earned in regular income, bonuses, vacation allowances, severance pay, moving-expense payments and travel allowances. Your W-2 must be attached to your return.

Interest income. The IRS knows if you've been paid any interest. Banks and financial institutions must report these payments to the IRS on Form 1099-INT, *Statement for Recipients of Interest Income*. Trap: Some interest income is reported to the IRS even though you haven't received it yet. It must be reported as part of your income.

Dividend income. The IRS knows if you received over $10 in money, stock, capital-gain distributions or property from a corporation. The corporation must report these payments to the IRS on Form 1099-DIV, *Statement for Recipients of Dividends and Distributions*. Important: Make sure the report agrees with your records.

Tax-refund income. The IRS knows about tax refunds you receive. State and local governments must report such payments of over $10 on Form 1099-G, *Statement for Recipients of Certain Government Payments*. Important exception: If you didn't claim the state and local taxes that you paid as itemized deductions on your federal return, you don't have to report these refunds as income. If you receive a Form 1099-G, analyze it carefully to see whether you must include it in income or if you qualify under this exception.

Gambling winnings. The IRS knows about money you won from horse racing, dog racing, jai alai, lotteries, raffles, drawings, Bingo, slot machines and Keno. It's all reported to the IRS on Form W-2G, *Statement for Recipients of Certain Gambling Winnings*. The general rule: Payments of $600 or more must be reported by the payer. Exceptions: Bingo payments of $1,200 or more and Keno payments of $1,500 or more will be reported.

Deduct Your Parents' Medical Costs

You may be supporting your parents by giving them money regularly to pay their bills, including medical expenses.

Suppose you're paying medical expenses for them and also providing half their support, but you can't claim them as dependents because their gross income exceeds IRS limits. You may be able to deduct your parents' medical expenses. The key is for you to pay these expenses directly. Of course, the amount you are allowed to deduct is subject to the limitations on your own medical-expense deductions.

Source: *New Tax Traps/New Opportunities* by Edward Mendlowitz, Boardroom Special Report, Springfield, NJ 07041.

Uncharitable Charities

Generous people who donate to charities like to think they're helping a philanthropic cause and people in need. Very often this is not the case! However, many times the only cause being helped is the charity itself—or its officers.

Problem: There are no federal guidelines specifying the amount of funds charities must channel toward their cause.

As long as some of the money raised goes to the charities' cause, the organization can still call itself a charity. Because of "creative" accounting practices used by charities and professional fund-raisers, it is often difficult for donors to assess how well a particular charity is performing.

Background: According to the standards developed by the Council of Better Business Bureaus, each charity must apply at least half of all income to its particular activities. Fund-raising activities should not absorb more than 35 percent of the contributions received by the charity.

Because of incompetence or outright fraud, many charities flout these guidelines.

To protect yourself: Before donating to a charity, contact the local Better Business Bureau or the state charities registration office in your area. In addition, it is important to obtain the following information:

• The percentage of funds raised are donated which actually go to the cause.

• Examples of how the charity has benefited the cause over the past years. If they tell you what they plan to do…Remember, big plans for the future do not count!

Personal Interest And Mortgage Interest

To get the greatest tax benefit for your interest costs, you'll have to know how to handle each interest charge.

Personal interest includes charges incurred on credit cards, car loans, personal loans and the like. Until 1987, personal interest was generally deductible, but the new tax law is phasing out this deduction. In 1991, the deduction was eliminated completely.

Interest paid on a mortgage on your primary residence or a second home (as defined in the new law) is deductible. Limit on deduction: $1 million of mortgage debt on the original purchase plus capital improvements.

There is also a way to get around the deduction limit on personal interest. Someone who has partially paid off the mortgage on his/her home may obtain a home-equity loan and use the cash obtained to make personal purchases (items such as a car, boat, new furniture, etc.). Since the interest paid on the refinancing is deductible, the homeowner in effect gets an interest deduction for a personal loan.

Limit: The interest deduction on a home-equity loan is limited. The amount of a new loan incurred after October 13, 1987, must not exceed the fair market value of the home up to a limit of $100,000.

Example:

A taxpayer bought a house 20 years ago for $80,000. He later spent another $25,000 adding an extra room and other improvements to the house. The house has also appreciated in value by $40,000 so that it's now worth $145,000 on the market. The remaining mortgage debt is $40,000.

Based on these facts, the taxpayer will be able to deduct all the interest on a home-equity loan of up to $100,000. The new loan doesn't exceed fair market value ($145,000) less acquisition debt ($40,000).

Planning point:

• Many homeowners are careless about keeping records concerning the cost of home improvements. But now these records are important. If your records aren't complete and up-to-date, pull them together now.

• If you own more than one second home, you can deduct only interest that's paid on one of them. But you get to choose which home you'll claim a deduction for, and you can change your designation each year (for example, if you increase the interest paid on one home by refinancing it).

Source: Jerry Williford, partner, Grant Thornton, 2800 Citicorp Center, Houston, TX 77002.

7

Investment Savvy

How To Buy Into Mutual Funds That Are Impossible To Buy Into

Some of the most successful no-load mutual funds are impossible for small investors to buy.

Reason: They require prohibitively high minimum investments—up to $500,000.

The back door:

By going through a discount brokerage that maintains a master account with such funds, you can often bypass the large minimum that would be imposed if you were to go directly to the fund.

Although these funds require a large amount of money to open the account, most allow investors to deposit far smaller amounts of money after that.

Because many discount brokerages maintain omnibus accounts with no-load mutual funds, new shareholders buying into the funds through a discount brokerage are treated as if their investments were subsequent investments.

Example: The Gabelli Asset Fund, run by renowned stockpicker Mario Gabelli, has a $25,000 initial minimum.

Since subsequent investments can be as modest as $250, small investors can gain access fairly easily by going through a discount brokerage.

Even though the funds may not impose a minimum for subsequent investments, discount brokerages generally set their own minimum transaction fees.

And of course you must pay the transaction fee on such trades, even though they involve no-load funds. Our transaction fee on trades of less than $50,000 is $20 plus .002 ($\frac{2}{10}$ of 1%) of the principal.

Source: Jack White, president of Jack White & Co., 9191 Towne Center Dr., Suite 220, San Diego 92122. Tel. 800-233-3411. One of the first discount brokerages, it pioneered the concept of secondary trading in mutual funds.

Best Time To Buy US Savings Bonds

Buy US Savings Bonds at the end of the month. Reason: No matter when the bond is purchased, interest is credited from the first day of that month...so you get most of the month's interest for free.

Source: *The Super Saver: Fundamental Strategies for Building Wealth* by Janet Lowe, Dearborn Financial Publishing, 520 N. Dearborn St., Chicago 60610.

Caution And Quality In Investments

People who depend on the income from their investments to maintain their standard of living are now panicking over the low rates. What can they expect?

Interest rates are the lowest they have been since the 1970s—it's important for income-oriented investors to put that into perspective. The inflation rate is way down, too. In the days when investors were getting double-digit rates on their Certificates of Deposit (CDs), the inflation rate was very high.

For your cash reserve—money that you might need over the next six months or a year—a money market fund or short-term CD is still your best choice no matter how unhappy you are with the low rate it pays. If you are in the 28% tax bracket or higher, you might consider one of the tax-free money market funds.

What do you recommend for longer-term investing?

We believe that rates will bottom out this year and start rising again—gradually.

Conservative investors who might be tempted to put their money into 10-year maturity bonds now for the extra yield may well find themselves whiplashed if they need the cash in five years or so and have to sell those bonds before maturity. If interest rates have gone up by then, they will suffer a loss on the value of their bonds.

I am concerned that the relatively unsophisticated investors who have been chiefly in CDs and government bonds don't understand this risk.

Isn't there any safe way for a conservative investor to get a higher yield?

There are some comparatively safe ways to get higher income—but they involve risk.

For that reason, we don't think conservative investors should be tempted to put their money into 20-year maturity bonds now for the extra yield. They would do better buying a managed bond fund where the professional manager follows interest rate trends carefully and buys and sells bonds in the portfolio accordingly.

To further minimize risk, look for a bond fund with an average maturity of less than 20 years. And make sure the bonds are rated A or better.

Using these criteria, you can now find bond funds with an average maturity of 5½ years that yield a 7% taxable return—or a municipal bond fund offering 5½% tax-free. While that yield is not exciting, it's better than what you can get at the bank.

There are bond funds yielding more than that, however.

Recently, I checked out a municipal bond fund that paid 7¼%. But the bonds in its portfolio had a 20-year average maturity. Less than one-third of its portfolio was in A-or-better rated bonds. That's too high a risk in my view.

There's some worry that we might see some problems with municipal bonds this year or next. Many municipalities have been coasting along, postponing maintenance on basic systems, because they don't have the tax base to do more than that. That's a potentially dangerous situation.

This is clearly the time to look for quality and be more cautious.

What about utility stocks, which usually pay high dividends?

You have to be cautious here, too. Some utility stocks pay much higher yields than others. But you may find that the higher-yield utility is paying all of its earnings out in dividends—earning $1.50 a share and paying a dividend of $1.50 a share. With 100% dividend coverage, there is nothing left to build the company. And if the utility's earnings go down, the dividend is vulnerable.

So it's better to buy a lower-yielding utility stock with better dividend coverage. For instance, the dividend is only 75% of earnings. With that cushion, there's more likelihood that the dividend can be maintained.

Economic and tax policy are such unsettling factors in this year's election politics. How can investors best cope with that news?

Just don't get upset about the posturing and the proposals for tax law changes. There's absolutely no sense in making investments on the basis of what might happen.

Do you mean buying annuities, for instance, because the tax-deferral feature might be eliminated?

Exactly. It just becomes an excuse to sell something to somebody. I'm not a big fan of annuities anyway.

Why don't you like annuities?

Well, variable annuities have done very well for many people. But I'm convinced that taxes will be higher in the future than they are now. Right now, taxes are at a historical low. So I don't see much sense in accumulating money while taxes are low and taking it out when taxes are higher. Generally, I favor paying taxes as you go. Own the investment outright rather than face future tax liability.

The management fees on annuities are considerably higher than those on mutual funds because with mutual funds there are no mortality charges. Even though an annuity may not have an up-front sales charge, the higher carrying fees may reduce profits over time.

Source: Alexandra Armstrong, CFP, chairman of the financial advisory firm Armstrong, Welch & MacIntyre, Inc., 1155 Connecticut Ave. NW, Washington, DC 20036.

Stock Smarts

Dilemma: I inherited and sold some stock that had gone far up in value since my parents bought it many years ago. Do I have to report the same taxable gain that my parents would have had if they had sold it? [R.M., Andover, Massachusetts]

Solution: No. Your basis in the stock is its value on the date of death of the previous owner, and your gain or loss on the stock is figured from that date.

Thus, if the stock had fallen somewhat in that time, you could even claim a deductible capital loss while cashing in the large profit your parents had earned by holding the shares.

You Can Create Your Own Mutual Fund

Between 75% and 80% of all equity mutual funds fail to outperform either the Dow Jones Industrial Average or the S&P 500. Why pay for such mediocrity?

Alternative: Create and manage your own mutual fund by building an investment portfolio of common stocks from between five and eight different companies. That might not seem like a lot, but a five-stock portfolio reduces risk by 77%, eight stocks decreases it by 86%. Surprising: Adding more companies to the mix reduces risk almost imperceptibly.
Simple steps:

• Choose your stocks. Buy shares only in high quality companies that are financially sound. That's not as hard as it seems. Most people can name at least eight companies that have been around for decades and that make products they trust and provide services they value.

Example: When my daughter was 10, she invested $4,000 in eight companies she picked herself. Her choices: PepsiCo (she likes Pizza Hut, which PepsiCo owns), Chrysler (we owned a jeep), Xerox (she had used the copying machine in my office), Duke Power (our local utility), BellSouth (our local phone company), McDonald's and Coca-Cola (she knows they're good companies) and NationsBank (a rapidly growing, North Carolina-based bank). Good choices all.

Other strategies: Choose from among the Dow Jones 30 industrials, from "100 Timely

Stocks" listed weekly in *The Value Line Investment Survey* (available at most libraries), or simply pick eight market leaders.

Examples: Eastman Kodak (film), Exxon (oil), Merck (drugs).

Or, look in America's Finest Companies,* an annual list of 425 publicly traded stocks (from among more than 15,000) with at least 10 straight years of higher earnings or dividends per share.

• Diversify. Reduce risk by buying companies from different industries.

Examples: Duke Power (utility), First Union (bank), IBM (computers), Food Line (grocery chain) and Nucor (specialty steel manufacturer).

• Buy equal dollar amounts of each stock. Example: If you're investing in an IRA, buy $400 worth of each of five stocks.

Money-saver: Since you're doing all the research yourself, purchase shares through a discount brokerage house.

• Hold the stocks for a period of time—a quarter, six months, a year. At the end of that period, take all the money you've accumulated for additional investment, add any cash dividends from your holdings and buy enough new shares of your five (or eight) stocks until you again have equal dollar amounts in each.

Note: You'll be buying more shares of the portfolio laggards, fewer of the pacesetters in order to get the benefits of dollar-cost averaging.

Result: Over time, the average price you pay will be lower than the average price of the stock.

• Continue to diversify, but only to a point. By the time your portfolio reaches $15,000 to $20,000, you should have 10 companies. Adding any more companies, however, no longer reduces your risk, making additional diversification unnecessary.

*Available from The Financial Training Group, 300 East Blvd., B-4, Charlotte, North Carolina 28203.

Source: Bill Staton, author of *60-Minute Investing*, The Financial Training Group, 300 East Blvd., B-4, Charlotte, North Carolina 28203. He offers financial skills training to companies and associations throughout the country.

Value Averaging

Even though the dreams of winning big through the use of timing strategies are very common—few investors succeed by this method.

Instead of buying low and selling high, individual investors usually are trapped into joining the prevailing psychology of the market and doing just the opposite.

Of course, it takes a lot of courage and conviction to buy into the stock market when it's in a downturn.

But most seasoned investors have learned —through painful experience—that the worst time to buy stocks is when everyone is proclaiming the immortality of a current bull market.

Individual investors need a disciplined approach to help them avoid the herd mentality that often leaves their ill-timed investments trailing the market averages.

To the rescue: Formula strategies—passive guidelines that signal when to move money into or out of the stock market.

Aim: To navigate through the twisty, bumpy investment highway on "cruise control"—avoiding the excessive stop-and-go tendencies that seem to leave your investments in all the wrong places.

Formula strategies are automatic and mechanical—the very antithesis of the emotional involvement that can skew market timing decisions.

Formula strategy options:

Passive formula investing is designed not so much to ensure that you beat the market, but that you ride out its roller-coaster course and end up with the proper reward for the risks you've taken. Strategy options:

• Dollar-cost averaging. With this popular formula strategy, you invest the same amount of money at regular intervals every month or quarter—for example, regardless of stock price fluctuations. When prices go down, your money purchases more shares of a stock or mutual fund...and when prices go up, it purchases fewer shares. Fact: Your average cost per share always ends up being less than the average price of the shares over that period.

Bonus: Sticking to this steady investment formula means that you avoid the nervous selling during market panics that leaves so many individual investors on the sidelines during the inevitable upturns that follow down markets.

• Value averaging. This new strategy takes the averaging concept one step further, by focusing on the value of your investment rather than the cost.

Under this approach, instead of investing a set amount of, say, $100 each month or $300 each quarter, you set an investment objective of increasing the value of your portfolio by $100 a month or $300 a quarter. At the end of the given time period, depending on the current value of your portfolio, you either invest or divest whatever amount is needed to bring the value of your portfolio to the desired level.

If your stocks have decreased in value since the previous period, you may have to put in more than the $100 or $300 to "replace" the lost value. But if they have increased in value, you can put in less than the usual amount— perhaps even selling some shares—because capital gains will have furnished some of your "required" increase in value.

Result: By reducing your investment and taking profits off the table when stock prices are high, you will achieve an even lower average cost per share than you'd get with dollar-cost averaging. That generally means a higher rate of return on your long-term investment program.

Easy implementation:

The ideal way to implement value averaging is through the use of no-load mutual funds, preferably in an IRA or some other tax-deferred account.

Index funds, which are designed to match some market index, such as the Standard & Poor's 500, are particularly suitable because they offer broad diversification with very low management fees and expense ratios compared with other types of funds.

Note: I don't recommend value averaging with individual stocks. Reason: You could wind up pumping more and more money into a company whose stock price is declining because it is truly a poor investment and may even go bankrupt.

Value-averaging example:

Here's how an actual value-averaging program would work if you started at the end of January 1993 with a monthly value goal of $1,000. Owning no stock, you would have started by purchasing $1,000 worth of a no-load stock mutual fund. If the fund shares were trading at $4.64 a share, you would have needed to buy 215.5 shares to purchase $1,000 worth.

At the end of February, if the share value of the fund had dropped to $4.38, you would have to purchase 241.2 more shares (spending $1,056 that month) to make the value of your holdings increase to $2,000.

At the end of March, if the share price increases to $4.56, you would need to invest only $917.60 to bring the value of your holdings up to your $3,000 target.

These figures are taken from an actual mutual fund that I tracked for 24 months. During that time, the fund's highest value reached $7.47. Its lowest point was $2.99. It started the period at $4.64 and ended the period at $5.06. The average price per share during the 24 months was $5.10.

Comparison: Buying the shares using traditional dollar-cost averaging and investing a fixed $1,000 per month could have lowered your average cost per share to $4.85. But by using value averaging, the net average cost was only $4.07. That cost advantage can improve your return dramatically.

Quarterly system:

Though the above example uses monthly changes in portfolio values, many investors may not want to recalculate the value of their holdings every month. You can simplify the technique by investing quarterly, with no adverse effect on your performance.

Then it would really take only four phone calls a year to apply the value-averaging strategy.

Drawback: By its very nature, value averaging can't be totally automatic like fixed dollar investing. You do have to to sit down once every set period and compare the actual value of your portfolio with your targeted value so you know how much you need to invest. But you can make the process almost automatic by investing a regular amount monthly in your fund family's money market fund.

Then, after you've calculated the quarterly "required" investment under value averaging, you can make a telephone transfer from the money fund to the equity fund. Similarly, when shares are sold, the proceeds can be moved over into the money market fund to be reinvested later.

Don't panic:

There will be times when value averaging results in a big cash buildup as you sell shares whose value far exceeds your predetermined value target. Don't be afraid to let that cash sit in the money market fund. There will be times when you will need the money to shore up the portfolio's value after a big market drop. That's what value averaging is all about.

Example: After the October 1987 stock market crash, you would have needed to invest large extra amounts to meet your value goal the next month. That money would have come from the other half of value averaging— the cash you set aside earlier in 1987 when market prices went wild and your strategy told you to sell a lot of "excess," high-priced shares to bring your portfolio down to your predetermined value goal.

On average, the stock market keeps on growing every year. If your targets don't allow for that growth, after several years you'll find that—on average—you're taking money out each period instead of putting money in. That's not the point of an investment program. Depending on what interest rates are doing and the relative attractiveness of stocks versus other investments like Treasury bonds, over time, the stock market can be expected to provide returns of at least 1% a month, on average.

So, instead of a straight-line value target (option A), consider option B as a way to increase your target value by leaving room for market growth. You'll eventually end up with a much bigger nest egg.

Option A: Advance your target value a flat $100 a month. It will go to $200, $300…to $10,000 in month 100, and $10,100 in month 101.

Option B: Increase your target value by 1% each month, plus the $100. It will go from $100, to $201, to $303…to $17,048 in month 100, and $17,318 in month 101.

Source: Michael E. Edleson, assistant professor of finance at Harvard University's Graduate School of Business Administration. He is the author of *Value Averaging*, International Publishing Corp., 625 N. Michigan Ave., Chicago 60611.

A New Opportunity In Government-Only Funds

One government-only fund doesn't declare a daily dividend: *The Treasury Bill Portfolio of the Permanent Portfolio Family of Funds.**

Instead, share prices increase in value and investors pay little or no tax on the increase. Its 4.44% 30-day total return may seem low, but in terms of spendable money, the fund is more than competitive. Advantages:

• Turning ordinary income into capital gains. When you redeem shares, the increase in value is a capital gain that can be offset by capital losses.

• Tax avoidance. Most of the money you withdraw is counted as a return of capital. You pay taxes only on the increase in value of shares you redeem.

• Tax deferral. You choose when to withdraw money and can put it off indefinitely, meanwhile piling up totally tax-free earnings. It's actually a lot like an IRA account without the early-withdrawal penalty.

• Stepped-up cost basis for heirs. Ideal for senior citizens who don't need income but want the solidity of a money-market investment. They pay no taxes during their lifetime on increases in the value of unredeemed shares and the tax basis for their heirs is market value at the time of death.

The fund enjoys all these advantages be-
*Permanent Portfolio Family of Funds, 207 Jefferson Square, Austin, Texas 78731. 800-531-5142. No load. Minimum initial investment: $1,000. One-time setup fee: $35. Dividends exempt in some states.

cause its legal form is a corporation and re-demptions count in meeting the 90%-distribu-tion rule. As long as some investors withdraw enough money to equal the required amount, there are no taxable dividends.

The fund has been in existence three years and it's unlikely there will be a significant per-share distribution in any given year. There was a 27% per-share distribution in 1991, on earnings of about 6%, which means that 73% of the total return was still tax deferred.

Source: William E. Donoghue, publisher of *Donoghue's MoneyLetter* and the audiocassette advisory service, Donoghue's MoneyTalk. For free *MoneyLetter* sample: Call 800-445-5900.

Secrets Of Safe Investing

It's an interesting challenge for individuals to have their money work aggressively for them. And any investor who follows these 10 simple rules will be rewarded with security and reasonable growth...

• Have a sufficient cash reserve. Too many people invest everything at once and then sud-denly need $5,000 and have to sell something, often at an awkward time. Before starting to invest, set aside a cash reserve of six months' living expenses so that unexpected financial problems won't force you to disturb your investments. This cushion is especially neces-sary given today's uncertain job situation.

• Think long-term. Don't go after the hot mutual fund of the month. Always evaluate the five- or 10-year record of a fund because that will encompass both up and down mar-kets. While, historically, the best returns have come from the stock market, you must invest over a long period. There will be ups and downs, so don't get rattled by every drop in the market.

Market corrections can offer great opportu-nities to pick up bargains that will make you rich in the future. Consider what happened to investors who became discouraged by the 1990 stock market when the Standard & Poor's 500 lost 3.2%. For 1991, the S&P 500 was up 24.25%. Those who pulled out of the market at the end of 1990 missed that big 1991 move.

• Diversify between kinds of investments... and within investment categories. It's elemen-tary—but never put too many eggs in one basket. When stocks did badly in 1990, bond-holders were happy because bonds did well. When domestic stocks are off, international stocks may be doing well.

Don't concentrate your holdings in any one area, industry or company—even the com-pany for which you work.

Important: Count the company stock in your pension plan.

• Strive for the right balance between cate-gories. This will shift according to what the economy is doing.

Right now, for a safe portfolio that will pre-serve principal and still offer growth without much downside risk, we're recommending an asset distribution of...

• 45% stocks (good quality individual growth stocks or mutual funds with good long-term records)

• 30% bonds (US government and top-quality corporates, not junk bonds, despite their high-sounding yields)

• 15% real estate (for long-term apprecia-tion only) and

• 10% cash or money-market funds.

You should also strive for balance within an individual stock portfolio. If you have $100,000, for example, divide it equally among eight different stocks. Some will perform better than others, and that helps to contain your downside risk.

• Invest systematically. If you invest a fixed amount on a regular basis, you will come out ahead of the sporadic or impulse investor.

Reason: It's impossible to consistently pre-dict, short-run, whether stock market prices will go up or down.

Thus, if you have $10,000 to invest, it's much smarter to put it into the market in six equal installments over the next six months than to put it all in today and hope that the market isn't topping out.

Again, looking at 1991, you might wish you had invested all $10,000 in January, since the market went up for the first 10 months of the year.

But January was exactly the time when pessimism was extreme. Chances are you would not have put any money in the stock market then unless you had a long-term systematic investment plan. Regular investment also allows you to dollar-average stock purchases, buying fewer shares when prices are high and more shares when prices are low. This reduces your average cost over time.

• Investigate before investing. An old wisdom, but I'm still surprised how many people will buy something from some stranger who calls up on the telephone. Even if it's your long-time broker who calls to sell you a solid 10-year tax-free bond yielding 6½%, it's essential to investigate.

A client recently called to ask me to check just such a bond...it turned out that it was actually a 30-year bond that was noncallable for 10 years...hardly the same thing as a bond maturing in 10 years. Always know what you are buying.

• Educate yourself. In most cases when people lose money on something, it's because they didn't ask the right questions. You won't know the answers, but if you make an effort to inform yourself you'll know what questions to ask and you'll be a better investor.

• Review investments regularly. Even if your portfolio has been invested for maximum safety, you can't just forget about it. Review all investments at least every six months, and preferably monthly.

• Get professional advice. We spend all of our time keeping up with the fast-changing financial market. It is more than a full-time job in today's complex financial world. You may not want to delegate full discretion to a financial adviser, but now and then pay the fee to have a consultation and get some expert ideas.

• Don't procrastinate. Don't wait until tomorrow to start saving money. If you start today with a serious investment program, you will be able to meet your financial goals...and that could include getting rich.

Source: Alexandra Armstrong, CFP, chairman of Armstrong, Welch & MacIntyre, Inc., financial advisers, 1155 Connecticut Ave. NW, Suite 250, Washington DC 20036.

How To Market-Proof Your Mutual Fund Investments

There's no such thing as risk-free investing.

There is, however, a way that risk-averse people can invest and still sleep well at night. Secret: Maximize the diversification of your investments by using a carefully honed group of all-weather stock and bond mutual funds to create a balanced portfolio that can withstand the inevitable ups and downs of the financial markets. The idea is to practice defensive investing...to minimize losses rather than to maximize gains.

As an investment adviser to FundTrust, which manages six multifunds—funds that invest as shares in mutual funds—we've developed expertise in investing funds. We focus on the "tortoises"—funds that are slow but steady performers—rather than the "hares"... mercurial funds that may be among the top 10 performers in one period, but in the basement the next.

The three "P"s:

My investment strategy is built on the three "P"s...

• Performance—finding funds with good, consistent long-term track records.

• People—evaluating a fund's management to see who is running the fund and whether the person responsible for the fund's good performance is still at the helm.

• Process—evaluating a fund's investment style to identify its operating strategy and particular area of expertise.

Our non-traditional approach of focusing on tortoises will become increasingly popular in the 1990s, especially if this decade turns out to be as treacherous as investment professionals forecast. By using the techniques outlined below to screen out flash-in-the-pan performers, and by then focusing on the management and investment style of the remaining funds, you'll be launched upon an investment program that will enable you to win without losing.

To successfully follow my investment philosophy, you must be willing to forgo the gratification of seeing the mutual funds you own appear at the top of all those lists of front-runners that perennially appear in the business press.

We've found that the funds that are able to deliver consistent performance rarely, if ever, gravitate to the top of the lists. More typically, they deliver median-plus performance and are often found in the 35th to 50th percentile —meaning that 35% to 50% of similar funds in their peer group outperform them in a given period.

Flip side: These funds rarely sink to the bottom of the list. If they consistently wind up in the 80th or 90th percentile, we weed them out. How to pick the tortoises:

In order to qualify as a tortoise fund, a candidate must have ranked in the top half of the fund universe in each of the last three years. Three years is a long enough period to discern if a fund has staying power, but not so long that it will knock out every candidate. These criteria may seem very modest, but the result is that they winnow out 90% to 95% of all mutual funds from further consideration. So rather than having to deal with a universe of 1800 or so funds, we usually work with 100 to 150 for our FundTrust series of six different mutual fund portfolios.

Next, we narrow our list of prospective funds even further by concentrating on the other two Ps: People and Process. In looking at people, we subscribe to the proposition that the manager makes the fund, not vice versa. We wholeheartedly believe in the star system. Reason: The good results of most funds can be ascribed to the talents of a single individual.

Best-known star managers: Peter Lynch (former head of Magellan), John Neff of Windsor, Mario Gabelli of Gabelli Asset and John Templeton of the Templeton funds.

While we do own a few funds that are managed by committee, most of the funds on our buy list are managed by individuals. And when those individuals leave, we've found that it's extremely difficult for the management company to find an equally adept replacement. Before we buy a fund, we want answers to the following questions....

• Who's running the fund now, and how long has that person been there? (We particularly avoid funds that have a revolving door of top managers.)

• Is the individual who's responsible for the fund's good performance still around?

• Is that person supported by a good internal research staff?

• Are most of the investment ideas that eventually appear in the fund's portfolio generated by outside brokerage research?

Evaluating process:

In our evaluating process, we focus on a fund's investment style. This should not be confused with a fund's objective. It's wrong, for example, to say a fund's investment style is one of "aggressive growth." That's its investment goal.

A fund's investment style should tell you how the fund intends to reach that goal. Does it plan to invest in emerging growth stocks, or in some other area, such as cyclicals, turnaround situations, small-cap stocks or high-tech stocks?

You want to know what techniques a fund manager employs to ferret out these investment opportunities. Does the fund use earnings screens, dividend screens, stocks trading at a fraction or multiple of market ratios?

Goal: To own a variety of funds with a variety of investment styles, so you'll be better able to smooth out market cycles.

Not all styles work in all market environments. Even tortoises will have bad quarters …and bad years. There will be times, for instance, when value stocks outperform growth stocks, and vice versa. By owning funds with both investment styles, you will have diversified to the point where some part of your portfolio will always be working for you.

Once you've identified some potential funds that have passed the three Ps, run the following final acid test. Compare their 10 largest holdings—which typically account for 25%–50% of a fund's assets—against one another. The idea here is to only own funds with distinctive holdings, and to discard funds with significant overlaps.

Example: You've honed in on five aggressive growth funds. Write up a master list of the 10 largest holdings. The optimum would be that you come up with 50 different stocks (five funds times 10 stocks per fund). While there are no hard and fast rules, I believe that overlap of more than 25% (12–13 names appearing more than once) would indicate that you have not done a good job defining process. What you believe are five different investment styles may in reality be no more than two or three.

My picks:

The following are six equity funds that have made it past all our screens for performance, people and process. They represent the two largest holdings within each FundTrust equity portfolio.* Performance figures are on a total return basis (assuming reinvestment of dividends and capital gains) for the 12-month period ended April 30, 1992.

FundTrust Aggressive Growth:

• New York Venture Fund. Up 15.4%. Load: 4.75%. Minimum initial investment: $1,000.

Venture Advisers, 124 E. Marcy St., Santa Fe 87501. 800-279-0279.

• Penn Mutual Fund. Up 15.9%. No load. Minimum initial investment: $2,000.

Quest Advisory Corp., 1414 Avenue of the Americas, New York 10019. 800-221-4268.

FundTrust Growth:

• AIM-Charter Fund. Up 15%. Load: 5.5%. Minimum initial investment: $500.

AIM Advisors, 11 Greenway Plaza, Houston 77046. 800-347-1919.

• Vanguard World US Growth. Up 17.7%. No load. Minimum initial investment: $3,000.

Lincoln Capital Management, Vanguard Financial Center, Box 2600, Valley Forge, Pennsylvania 19482. 800-662-7447.

FundTrust Growth & Income:

• T. Rowe Price Equity Income. Up 17.8%. No load. Minimum initial investment: $2,500.

T. Rowe Price Associates, 100 E. Pratt St., Baltimore 21202. 800-638-5660.

• Washington Mutual Fund. Up 14%. Load: 5.75%. Minimum initial investment: $250.

*FundTrust Management, 522 Fifth Ave., Suite 1600, New York 10036, 800-638-1896, manages six separate mutual fund portfolios that achieve their objectives by investing in shares of other mutual funds. Maximum sales charge: 1.5%. Minimum initial investment: $1,000.

American Fund, 333 S. Hope St., Los Angeles 90071. 800-421-0180.

Source: Michael D. Hirsch, president of M.D. Hirsch Investment Management, a New York investment advisory firm that manages private accounts and serves as investment adviser to the six different portfolios of FundTrust mutual funds. As former chief investment officer of Republic National Bank, he pioneered the concept of multifund investing. His book is *The Mutual Fund Wealth Builder*, HarperBusiness, 10 E. 53 St., New York 10022.

The Investment Mistakes That Too Many People Make

As an investment counselor who has been practicing for decades, I've probably witnessed just about every possible investor mistake.

Here are the most common mistakes that investors tend to make on their own, before they finally seek professional advice…

• Mistake: Chasing yield. Many investors are particularly vulnerable to such behavior these days, with bank CDs only paying about 3.5%. In their quest for higher rates, these investors are stretching out their maturities longer and longer.

Trap: When interest rates start to rise, the market value of these long-term investments will plummet. And their total return* will fall as a result. Instead of focusing on current yield, you should structure your entire portfolio—which includes cash, plus stocks, bonds and mutual funds—so that it produces the total return you need.

• Mistake: Failing to diversify your portfolio. It's important to divide up your portfolio into different asset classes that move in opposite directions from each other. That way, if one or two of the asset classes in your portfolio move down, the chances are that the others are moving up.

In our firm, we work with 22 different asset classes, but the individual investor can diversify with just five or 10.

The most common asset classes are cash

*Rate of return plus appreciation—or depreciation.

and cash-equivalents, such as money funds, bank CDs and Treasury bills...domestic and international stocks...domestic and international bonds...real estate...and gold and foreign currency. You can further diversify in the stock area by dividing investments into large-capitalization, medium-cap and small-cap stocks. In the fixed-income area, you can divide investments into different maturities, ranging from short- to long-term, and along the quality spectrum ranging from government bonds to AAA-rated corporate bonds to junk bonds.

• Mistake: Not understanding the trade-off between risk and return. People now—as always—want to get something for nothing. But to get bigger returns on your investments, you have to be willing to assume more risk.

Problem: Most people don't quantify how much risk they're willing to accept. You should select a tolerable range of returns.

Example: In nine out of every 10 years, your rate of return on stocks—based on past performance of the Standard & Poor's index of 500 stocks—would have ranged from minus 15%/yr. to plus 37%/yr. If the performance of an individual stock falls within your allowable range, it's okay. Otherwise, bail out. Select a mutual fund or—better yet—buy an index fund.

A properly diversified portfolio might be expected to earn between –5%/yr. and 14%/yr. in nine out of 10 years. The performance of your overall portfolio, and whether it falls within your allowable range of return, is far, far more important than the performance of the individual securities or asset classes.

• Mistake: Not using dollar-cost or value-averaging. About 80% of individual investors are in cash or cash-equivalents. And when they decide to venture into stocks, they either want to do it all at once, or to go much too slowly.

A much better approach is to dollar-cost average—invest a set amount of money on a regular basis, say once a month. This way, you smooth out market fluctuations and usually wind up purchasing at a lower cost per share than if you bought all at once.

Value-averaging* is a variation in which you invest whatever amount is needed to make the value of your investments increase by some preset amount each period. If you've decided to try the stock market, I usually suggest averaging into the market over a period of six to 12 months, with a two-year investment period the outside maximum.

Example: If your goal is to invest 24% of your entire $1-million portfolio in large-cap domestic stocks...that's $240,000. Buy $20,000/month over 12 months, or $10,000/month over 24 months.

• Mistake: Letting the tax tail wag the dog. All too often, doting grandparents want to minimize hefty estate taxes by setting up a generation-skipping trust naming their grandchildren as beneficiaries.

Problem: Young people who inherit enormous amounts of money very often tend to be enfeebled—rather than empowered—by their wealth. Oftentimes, they suffer from low self-esteem and are unable to support themselves through regular employment.

• Mistake: Giving too much to children through custodial accounts. Gifts made to children under the Uniform Gifts to Minors Act (UGMA) or its newer relative, the Uniform Transfers to Minors Act (UTMA) are alright... up to a point. That point is where the income produced by the assets transferred to a child equals the amount of unearned income that the child can have before he/she becomes subject to the "Kiddie Tax."

At current interest rates, that means you should only put between $10,000 and $15,000 into a custodial account. Any gifts above that level should be transferred to a "minor's trust."

With UGMA or UTMA accounts, the assets in the account automatically become your child's property when he/she reaches the age of majority, which is 18 or 21—depending upon state laws. If, at that point, the child wants to take the money and give it to a cult group or buy a Ferrari instead of going to college, the parents are powerless. But with a trust, the parents remain in control.

When establishing the trust, parents can

*Value averaging is explained in greater detail in the April 30, 1992 issue of Bottom Line/Personal.

specify how and when to distribute interest and principal from the trust. Also, if a parent dies before the child reaches the age of majority, the assets in a properly drafted trust do not become part of the parent's taxable estate the way that they would with a custodial account. Nor can trust assets be attached by creditors, or by a spouse in the event of divorce.

A healthier route is to provide your children (or grandchildren) with sufficient funds for college and graduate school, and then give them enough to purchase a first house or start up a business. After that, they should be on their own. And if you're still worried about estate taxes, then bequeath the rest of your assets to charity.

• **Mistake: Poor record-keeping.** It's amazing how often people come in to my office with their financial affairs in a state of total chaos.

I've had first-time clients who came in with huge portfolios—but were totally befuddled when I asked them how much they paid for each of their holdings. They didn't know the basis (tax cost) of the securities in their portfolios. This information is vital because it de-termines the profit (or loss) and, thus, the amount of capital gains tax you must pay to the IRS if you sell.

If you're in this predicament, you may have to hire an accountant to unravel the truth. Then resolve that you or your investment counselor will keep good records from here on out, especially if you are reinvesting dividends from stocks or mutual funds.

• **Mistake: Looking for the Guru.** By concentrating on short-term performance results, you wind up choosing yesterday's guru. The probability is that that guru will wind up being tomorrow's average performer or—even worse—tomorrow's loser.

A much better approach, particularly with mutual funds, is to purchase index funds, which mirror a broad segment of the market. They are the lowest-expense, lowest-risk way to represent a particular asset class in your portfolio.

Source: Gary Greenbaum, a fee-only financial and investment counselor with Greenbaum and Associates, Inc., 496 Kinderkamack Rd., Oradell, New Jersey 07649. The company's high-tech asset-allocation investment strategy is designed to help clients meet financial objectives with reduced risk and lower cost.

8

Insurance

How To Bring Some Sanity To The Insurance World

Nothing can be more infuriating than spending hours grappling with medical bills and insurance claim forms, only to have the claim rejected weeks later.

Unfortunately, now, insurance companies are seizing every opportunity to deny claims in their attempt to hold onto their money for as long as they can. The aim of consumers should be to get their claims paid…get them paid promptly…and get them paid fully.

But these days, you have to be a savvy consumer who knows just how to play the game in order to accomplish those seemingly simple goals.

Here are some suggestions, gleaned from my decades of experience in dealing with insurance companies, for how you can beat them at their own tricky games…

•Know your policy. All too often, people just don't know what their policy covers. Take the case of parents of a one-year-old who submit bills for their toddler's ear infections, inoculations and other "well baby" care. The policy pays for treatment of the ear infections, but denies payment for the other care, saying it only provides well baby care for the first six months of the child's life. Instead of simply accepting the denial, the parents should check their policy. A growing number of plans now provide such coverage until the child reaches the age of two, and some will provide it until the child reaches the age of five or six.

• Keep a log of your claims. A growing number of companies are using every flimsy excuse in the book to delay paying a claim. They'll say they never received it, that they received it without any medical bills attached, or minus your signature. Don't assume that no news from the company is good news. Keep track of the date you submitted the claim and the amounts involved. And always keep copies of your bills in case the company says the claim was lost in the mail. That way, you can resubmit the claim with a minimum of hassle.

• Contact the insurance company if you're not paid within four weeks. Thirty days from the time you mail in a claim is a reasonable turnaround time for payment of a routine medical expense. By contacting the company after that time, you'll know whether there are any administrative problems with the claim… and let the company know that you won't stand for unreasonable delays. If you still don't receive payment, then follow up again in two weeks asking when the claim will be paid. Try to get a commitment as to when the claim will be paid. Also get the name of the person you spoke with. Note: More extensive procedures, such as a heart transplant, may take longer for a company to process.

• Beware of coding mistakes. A common problem arises with the five-digit procedure (or CPT) codes that reflect the treatment you receive from a doctor. It's not unusual for an insurance company clerk to enter an incorrect CPT number into the computer. Result: You are reimbursed the wrong amount, or even denied coverage. One way to spot this is to compare the insurer's code (if it is shown on the statement of benefits form) with the code on the doctor's bill and make sure they match. But some insurance companies don't divulge these codes, and may instead say something like "diagnosis does not cover that procedure." This language should alert you to call the company and ask that it provide the codes for the procedures performed and the codes for the procedures actually reimbursed.

• Beware of down-coding. If multiple procedures are performed at the same office visit, a company may mistakenly assume that less was involved than actually was the case.

Example: You visit a dermatologist to have five moles removed. The company might reimburse for the cost of having only one mole removed. Solution: Compare your doctor's bills with the insurance payment to be sure the company considered all the charges for treatment rendered at that visit.

• Beware of a lowering of what had been considered a "customary and reasonable" fee. Typically, companies will only pay the prevailing fee in your area for a given procedure. But sometimes a company will unilaterally decide to cut what had been considered customary and reasonable…and thus reimburse you less. If you've been undergoing the same procedure for a while—say, you get regular allergy shots—you will instantly know whether a company is trying to shave its reimbursements, and you can complain.

If it's a non-routine surgical procedure—say, removal of your gallbladder—you may have to do some research before you go ahead with the treatment. Ask your physician what he will charge, and then call a few other doctors to find out their fee schedules. As long as your physician is in line with his peers, you shouldn't have a problem. But if his fee is much higher, you might tell him that your company will pay only the prevailing fee…and ask him whether he is willing to accept the insurance company reimbursement as payment in full. If not, you may have to cough up the extra money yourself, or find another surgeon.

• Beware of a denial because a treatment is considered "experimental." Some insurers refuse payment for bone marrow transplants, routinely used for patients with leukemia and melanoma. They maintain the treatment is experimental. In such cases, it may be necessary to go to court in order to get the insurer to pay up. There's often a two-year lag between the time the medical community starts using a new procedure and when the insurance company agrees to cover it. Sometimes your doctor can shorten that span by interceding on your behalf and presenting an insurer with medical testimony and literature that attests to the efficacy of a particular procedure.

• Don't take no for an answer. If you feel the company made a mistake in processing your claim, by all means call and complain. If the person with whom you speak dismisses your arguments, ask for a review of your claim. Typically, a review is handled by someone other than a claims clerk and should take no more than four weeks. Often, just having a second opinion will resolve the problem—since many of these decisions are arbitrary judgments.

When you call your company, always keep notes on the date and time you called, with whom you spoke, the telephone number at which you reached the person and what transpired during the conversation. This will allow you to keep tabs on the progress of your claim.

Example: If you haven't received payment for a strep throat culture, your notes should indicate whether Mr. Smith said he would get back to you in 48 hours, or whether he asked you to provide a more detailed bill with a diagnosis. If Mr. Smith fails to contact you within the agreed-upon time, you should again contact the company, this time by writing to his supervisor.

• Go to court if necessary. If, after all your efforts, a company still resists paying a legitimate claim, it may be prudent to take legal action. For smaller claims, you can sue in small claims court and act as your own attorney. For larger claims, consult a lawyer or independent claims adviser. Often, simply the notice of a court action is enough to spur a company to settle.

Source: Greta Tatken, director, Claims Recovery, 10119 Walnut Road Court, Burke, Virginia 22015. The firm intercedes with insurance companies on behalf of patients and physicians who have difficulties getting claims paid.

Where Are The Best Insurance Buys?

Best life insurance buys are from insurers that many consumers have never even heard of. The insurers don't advertise widely and don't use commissioned salespersons. They pass those savings on to buyers. USAA and Ameritas are the life insurers in this category that offer a full line of products nationally on a no- or very low-commission basis. Both

companies have strong financial ratings. USAA Life: 800-531-8000...Ameritas Life: 800-552-3553.

Source: Taking the Bite Out of Insurance by James H. Hunt, former State Commissioner of Banking and Insurance for Vermont, published by the National Insurance Consumer Organization, 121 N. Payne St., Alexandria, Virginia 22314.

How To Get Government Aid

Given the skyrocketing costs of medical care and health insurance, it is particularly important to make sure you receive the benefits you're entitled to...and to minimize the expenses for which you are liable.

The primary federal health-care programs are Medicare*...and Medicaid—for the needy.

Other government programs, for which fewer people are eligible, include Veterans Administration (VA) benefits and Supplemental Security Income (SSI), which assists the low-income aged, the blind and the severely disabled.

Medicare and Medicaid aren't charity programs. They are tax-funded insurance programs you have paid annual premiums for—through Social Security—and that you are entitled to. Most beneficiaries of Medicaid, which now covers half of the US nursing-home population, have paid premiums for most of their working lives.

Even with an employer-provided health insurance plan—and we recommend you keep any plan you have—you should enroll in Medicare Part A (hospital insurance), when you turn 65...and purchase Part B (doctor insurance) within three months of your 65th birthday. Otherwise you will have to pay an additional 10% premium for every year you wait. Enrolling keeps that cost to your employer down and maximizes the benefits of your existing plan.

*Insurance companies listed in a alphabetical order. Each has more than $2 billion in assets.

Medicare was never intended to cover all of its beneficiaries' health costs. Everyone's share is rising. Today, the elderly spend up to 20% of their income on health care, even with Medicare. The Medicare premium rises every year, and in 1988, the Part B section rose a staggering 35%—and is still rising.

Money-saving solutions: Make the most of Medicare. Make sure you have supplemental private insurance (medigap coverage)…and try to keep all medical costs as low as possible. How to get the most from Medicare:

Maximize your coverage by tuning into Medicare's best-kept secrets…

• Doctors' fees are very negotiable. A doctor who accepts Medicare assignments agrees to accept the fee that it pays for the procedure or treatments provided, and handles the paperwork. You remain responsible for your deductible and 20% co-payment.

Only 40% of doctors accept assignments for all of their Medicare patients. But 70% accept assignments for some of their patients or for some services. So it is up to you to persuade your doctor to accept Medicare assignments on all of your bills.

Helpful approach: "I believe that Medicare pays a fair rate, and I hope you will respect my request, as I cannot afford more than the 20% co-payment. However, if you do not accept assignments, perhaps you could refer me to another practitioner who does." Doctors do not like to lose clients. Most people who take the trouble to negotiate assignments are successful.

• You never have to pay more than the Maximum Allowable Actual Charge (MAAC) for any service, even if your doctor does not take assignments.

Medicare has set a maximum fee (MAAC) for all services that doctors who do not take assignments may charge Medicare patients. To find out a specific MAAC, call the Medicare carrier in your area. If your doctor bills you for more than the MAAC, neither you nor your insurance company has to pay the difference.

Example: Your doctor charges $3,000 for a procedure. Medicare pays $2,000 for the same procedure, and has set the MAAC at $2,500.

Medicare will pay 80% of the $2,000 "reasonable cost," or $1,600. If your doctor accepts assignments, you would only have to pay the 20% co-payment, or $400. If the doctor does not take assignments, you must pay the difference between $1,600 and the $2,500 MAAC, or $900, and the doctor must absorb the other $500. But if you haven't bothered to check the MAAC, you may be billed for the full $3,000, less Medicare's $1,600, and unknowingly pay the $1,400 difference.

• The fact that Medicare refuses payment does not necessarily mean that you must pay. You are not responsible for any medical bill that you could not reasonably have been expected to know wasn't covered. You must be informed in writing from an official source, such as a Medicare notice or pamphlet, that a service isn't covered. If your doctor tells you something is covered by Medicare and it isn't, then the doctor—neither you nor your insurer—is responsible.

• You cannot be discharged from the hospital before you are medically able to go. You cannot be discharged because your Medicare payments or "DRG" (Diagnosis-Related Group system) days have been used up. When you are admitted to the hospital, you will be issued a form outlining your rights as a Medicare patient. If you think you are being discharged too soon, request a review by your state's PRO (Peer Review Organization), a group of doctors who review Medicare cases. The PRO will decide if your Medicare coverage can be extended, based on medical necessity.

Shopping for medigap insurance:

Employer-provided retiree health insurance is usually as good as the available high-option medigap policies, and often better. But more than five million older Americans are paying an unnecessary, duplicative insurance that they mistakenly believe supplements their Medicare coverage. If you have an employer-sponsored plan, you may not need more coverage. If you do not, consider supplemental insurance. What to look for:

The federal government certifies medigap policies as meeting minimum standards for Medicare supplemental insurance if the company requests it. To check on an individual policy, call your state insurance office.

Under Part A, supplemental policies are required to cover $78.50 per day co-insurance for care in a skilled nursing facility through the 100th day, when Medicare stops paying. A generous policy will provide coverage past the 100th day.

Under Part B, supplemental policies must pay the 20% co-payment not covered by Medicare, but only up to $5,000 total, and only after you have paid the $100 deductible and the first $100 of co-payment.

Key: A good policy will cover doctors' fees in excess of Medicare-approved amounts.

It is against the law for a policy that calls itself a Medicare supplement to exclude any preexisting conditions for more than six months.

Choose a policy that has a stop-loss provision, or ask your agent to add a rider (usually for a small extra fee).

Make sure the policy is automatically adjusted to increases in Medicare deductibles or co-payments.

Saving on out-of-pocket expenses:

You can minimize your co-payments and keep premiums down by trying to keep your medical expenses as low as possible.

• Take advantage of low-cost or free health services offered by counties, organizations or health fairs.

Examples: Inoculations, screenings.

• Make sure you are aware of your health plan's limits and exclusions.

Example: Number of chiropractic visits.

• Shop around for prescription prices, and buy generic drugs when possible.

• Guard against unnecessary or excessive testing. Many physicians have adopted new, costly tests while continuing to administer the old ones—often less expensive, and as effective.

• Avoid hospitalization and surgery unless absolutely necessary. Avoid for-profit hospitals—they're up to 23% more costly. Avoid weekend admission.

• Bring your own food, vitamins and drugs.

• Specify in writing that surgery or invasive procedures must be done by the person you are paying, i.e., your fully-trained physician, not a resident or intern.

• Keep track of all bills and services while hospitalized.

Common errors to check for: Type of room…number of days (look for an extra day on checkout day)…tests actually received, medications actually taken, physician's visits that actually occurred, as opposed to routinely billed.

Source: Charles B. Inlander, president of the People's Medical Society, a nonprofit consumers' health organization, 462 Walnut St., Allentown, Pennsylvania 18102. 800-624-8773. His book, co-authored with Karla Morales, is *Getting the Most for Your Medical Dollar,* Pantheon, 201 E. 50 St., New York 10022.

Strongest US Insurance Companies

Company Name*	State	Safety Rating
Combined Ins. of America	NC	B+
Commonwealth Life	KY	B+
Continental Assurance	IL	A−
First Colony Life	VA	B+
Hartford Life	CT	A−
Jefferson-Pilot Life	NC	A+
Liberty National Life	AL	B+
Lincoln National Life	IN	B+
Massachusetts Mutual Life	MA	B+
Metropolitan Life	NY	B+
Nat'l Home Life Assurance	MO	B+
New York Life	NY	B+
Northwestern Mutual Life	WI	B+
State Farm Life	IL	A+
United Ins. of America	IL	A+
Unum Life Ins. of America	ME	B+

The weakest insurers

Anchor National Life	CA	D+
Equitable Life Assurance	NY	D+
Equitable Variable Life	NY	D+
Executive Life Insurance	NY	E−
Fidelity Bankers Life	VA	D+
First Capital Life	CA	D+
Kemper Investors Life	IL	D+

Monarch Life	MA	D+
Pruco Life	AZ	D+
Tandem Insurance Group	IL	D
Union Labor Life	MD	D+

Source: Martin D. Weiss.

How To Find Health Insurance If You Don't Have A Company Policy

If you or your spouse changes jobs, move to another state or become self-employed, there's a good chance that you and your family may be left without health insurance. That could be a nightmare today as medical costs continue to skyrocket.

Though not widely known, there are places to find coverage. If you and everyone in your family are under 40 and in perfect health, you can probably call Blue Cross/Blue Shield and get coverage without delay. The process becomes harder, however, if you are over 40...and in less than excellent health.

Smart strategy

• Buy an interim medical policy. Though rarely advertised, many insurance companies write policies for up to 12 months. These typically have deductibles of at least $500 and often lack the generous benefits commonly attached to company policies.

But interim coverage is usually very affordable. A middle-aged person in good health, for example, can expect to pay $100–$150 a month for an interim medical policy.

Where to find interim coverage: Ask your life insurance company if it offers interim coverage. Many companies do, and there are also specialty insurance carriers in the business. If your life insurance company doesn't sell interim medical policies, call the state insurance commission for names of companies that do.

Limitation: Though most interim carriers say their policies can't be extended once they expire, many actually will extend them, especially if you haven't filed a claim during the initial period.

• Contact local health-maintenance organizations. In general, HMOs provide health care that is as good as or better than what most company policies provide.

The problem is that in many areas, HMOs screen applicants before accepting them. Then they either reject those who have serious health problems or exclude the problems from coverage.

Example: Someone with a serious heart condition might be accepted, but coverage wouldn't extend to their heart problems.

But don't give up on HMOs, even if you have a serious medical problem. Opportunity: Many HMOs, and occasionally Blue Cross/Blue Shield, have an "open season" for one or two weeks a year. At this time they accept virtually all applicants without subjecting them to a physical. If you have doubts about being accepted on the basis of an exam, wait for an open season (often advertised in newspapers and on television).

• Consider a separate policy for an existing medical condition. If one member of your family has a kidney problem, for instance, look for a general policy or an HMO to cover all but that ailment. Then buy a separate policy to cover dialysis or whatever else is needed for the kidney condition. The premiums, while high, might be less than what you'd have to pay if the condition worsened.

You can find special high-risk carriers through state insurance commissions.

• State uninsurable plans. Twenty states, including most of the predominantly industrialized ones, have plans to insure people who can't get coverage elsewhere. Rates, however, are usually up to 50% higher than what carriers normally charge.

Advantage: These plans accept nearly everyone, regardless of existing medical conditions. This may actually make the coverage cheap for people who have ailments that are expensive to treat.

• Join an association that offers health insurance. Many fraternal and professional organizations—as well as some clubs, alumni associations and civic groups—sell health insurance to their members. Coverage can sometimes be bought even without taking a physical.

Caution: Look at the policies carefully. A few are excellent, but others can be expensive—and coverage minimal.

To find out which organizations you might consider joining, consult the Encyclopedia of Associations, available in nearly all public libraries. By looking up any of your special interests in the index, you'll find a list of organizations involved with that field.

Then phone the groups to find out if health insurance is one of the benefits they offer. In general, nationwide organizations are more likely to offer health insurance than are local groups.

Source: Robert J. Hunter, director, National Insurance Consumers Association, 121 N. Payne St., Alexandria, Virginia 22314.

The Best Home Insurance Is Usually The Cheapest

One of the quickest ways to put money in your pocket is simply to review your home-insurance policy.

Chances are, minor adjustments in coverage will save you hundreds of dollars a year. And in the event of disaster, having the right home coverage will probably protect the biggest assets you own.

According to the latest estimates, 80% of the country's homeowners are not buying the right home-insurance coverage.

Finding the best companies:

Some storm victims in South Carolina are still waiting for their insurance settlements months after Hurricane Hugo struck. The situation is similar in California, long after last year's earthquake.

But don't think horror stories like these happen just to victims of front-page disasters. Each year thousands of people whose homes are hit by fire, flood, wind or theft are dismayed to discover that...

• They're not fully covered for the loss.
• They are covered, but they have huge expenditures before the insurance company finally settles.

Ironically, the best insurance companies are often the cheapest. Usual reason: They sell directly to homeowners without using agents. This eliminates agents' fees—and often speeds up settlements.

Companies consistently rated high in customer satisfaction: Amica Mutual, Erie Insurance Exchange, State Farm and USAA.

Those often ranked low: Several of the largest and most well-known insurers.

If you have doubts about a company, check with people in your neighborhood who have put in a claim. Be wary of an agent who won't put you in touch with homeowners who have filed claims. Some state insurance commissions also have complaint data on insurance companies. Helpful:

• The September 1989 issue of *Consumer Reports,* available in libraries.
• *The Buyer's Guide to Insurance* (available for $3 postpaid with a stamped business-size envelope from The National Insurance Consumer Organization, 121 N. Payne St., Alexandria, Virginia 22314, 703-549-8050).
• Price data from insurance regulators in an increasing number of states.
• Information issued by the Insurance Information Institute (110 William St., New York 10038, 212-669-9200).

The over-insuring trap:

The prospect of having inadequate coverage scares some homeowners so much that they overinsure. Examples:

• Insuring a house for its current market value. This might sound like a good idea, but it's foolish because even serious disasters rarely destroy the full value of a home. The market value, for instance, includes the price of the lot and the foundation. These are likely to survive anything short of an engulfing earthquake or nuclear explosion.

Even if a $200,000 house is completely destroyed by fire, a policy will pay, at most, around $160,000, assuming the lot is worth about $35,000 and the foundation $5,000. The difference between premiums on policies that provide $160,000 and $200,000 in coverage can easily be more than $200 a year.

• Buying a low-deductible policy. Again, this only sounds sensible. In fact, premiums are about 40% lower on a $1,000-deductible policy than on $100-deductible coverage. With savings like that, it clearly makes sense for most families to assume a $1,000 risk, especially if they put the savings into an interest-bearing account.

Families with low-deductible policies are often reluctant to file small claims anyway. And for good reason. Insurance companies are more likely to cancel a policy after paying several small claims than after paying one large claim.

The underinsuring trap:

Many people think they're completely insured once they make an inventory of everything in the house and have it all written into their policy. What they overlook: Insuring for replacement cost instead of market value.

Example: If a sofa that you bought for $500 10 years ago is destroyed, a standard policy is likely to pay only about $200 for the depreciated couch. But if you're insured with a replacement policy, it might pay you $1,000 to buy today's comparable sofa.

The difference between premiums on standard and replacement policies runs only 10%–15%—but replacement costs can actually run much higher.

Even the best policies don't cover homes for flood and earthquake damage. That coverage must be bought separately. Trap: Outside of a few obvious areas, homeowners often don't know when they're vulnerable to floods or earthquakes.

Helpful: Federal maps show flood and earthquake risks for homes in every part of the country. They're available through city and county governments.

Source: J. Robert Hunter is president of the National Insurance Consumer Organization, 121 N. Payne St., Alexandria, Virginia 22314.

What Would You Do If The Feds Closed All Weak Insurance Companies Next Week ??

Imagine that one day in the coming year you are tuned in to your favorite news program and a government official comes on and announces, "Effective immediately, all life insurance cash value is frozen. There will be no new life insurance policy loans, policy surrenders or transfers from weak life insurers to strong life insurers until further notice."

If that scenario seems a bit harsh, you should consider the fact that according to the latest research, 1,897,212 Americans' cash value is already locked into their policies in failed life insurance companies. In total, there are over 5,950,422 ordinary and group life insurance, annuities and group health policies in failed life and health insurers.

Not what you bargained for:

This means that these policyholders cannot borrow money from their life insurance policies for uninsured medical emergencies, their children's tuition, buying new homes or just having a "cushion" to fall back on during a recession.

It means that they cannot shift their life insurance policies to a stronger insurer that's more likely to be able to keep its promises of safety and security.

It means that they cannot shift their annuity to a stronger insurance company or higher-paying annuity.

It means that they cannot get at important cash reserves—unless they die, because death benefits will be paid then.

Why would a life insurance holiday be necessary?

Many institutional investors who have large amounts of money invested in insurance companies are concerned about the problems life insurance companies are having now. Result: These institutional investors are reevaluating their investments and may pull out. If the big boys take 100 cents on the dollar out of the insurance companies' capital pool, that could mean less than 100 cents on the dollar for you. State insurance commissioners are ready to take regulatory action to make sure that the institutional money stays with the life insurers.

Warning: Because of the limitations on some state guaranty funds, some policyholders may not be covered in full, or ever.
Prudent diversification could start a run:

This is the time of the year when many pension and retirement savings plans—including corporate 401(k), nonprofit organizations' 403(b) and small-business Keogh plans—reevaluate their Guaranteed Investment Contract (GIC) investments.

One insider told me a story of a $100 million GIC with a household-name insurance company that is switching from that insurer because of safety concerns.

GICs are essentially insurance company IOUs that are fully "guaranteed" only by the issuing company, and not necessarily by a third party. Because the fate of failed Executive Life's GIC-holders is still up in the air (it is unlikely those GIC-holders will get paid 100 cents on the dollar), many institutional investors are prudently shifting from one-company GICs to diversified pools of GICs for their plans.

Not placing all of their eggs in one basket is a wise choice not only for institutional investors but also for millions of other investors.
Liquidity is the issue:

The risk many life insurers are facing is not necessarily bankruptcy but liquidity. The growth of the life insurance industry has slowed down and in the past year has turned negative.

A negative growth rate means that new cash flows are no longer available to pay off policyholders and GIC holders who wish to shift to a stronger insurer. The next choice is to sell off assets. While many have substantial holdings of highly liquid securities, once that buffer is gone the insurers will have to dip into relatively illiquid holdings of junk bonds, commercial mortgages and real estate, most of which are "underwater."

To be forced to sell in this market means to realize, in many cases, capital losses. Realizing enough capital losses could wipe out the insurance company's capital. Wiping out capital could drive the insurance company to insolvency or bankruptcy. Next: Sooner rather than later, the regulators will take over.

You can understand why the cash flows from new business in a growing company are a high priority for life insurers.

It was an institutional "run on the bank," not the lines of consumers at their front door, that caused New Jersey regulators to take over Mutual Benefit Life, an old-line insurer viewed by the industry as strong.
How would it happen?

Currently, life insurance solvency regulation is the responsibility of the states rather than the federal government. As regulation currently stands, an insurance holiday would take a unanimous statement by all state regulators. While it is unlikely that such a resolution could occur soon, the March 1992 meeting of the National Association of Insurance Commissioners in Seattle could provide a forum for such a resolution without tipping off the industry.

The second possibility could come at the federal level. According to a respected insurance and securities lawyer, state insurance regulation was made possible by a specific exemption that Congress could reverse, and place the life insurance industry under the regulation of the SEC or a federal insurance czar.

Stranger things have happened. A few months ago I testified before my state's senate committee on insurance and depository institutions. I predicted national regulation and a national life insurance holiday, and the senators agreed with me.
What can you do?

The first step to protecting yourself from the threat of a national life insurance holiday is to find out if you are at risk. How to take action: Investigate how your life insurer stands up to demanding analysis by ratings companies.
Rating the rating services:

The first rating service referred to brokers is often A.M. Best & Co. But consider that Executive Life, First Capital, Fidelity Bankers, Monarch Life and Mutual Benefit Life, the five biggest life insurance failures to date, had A.M. Best ratings of A(w), A-, A+(c), A+(c) and A+, respectively, on June 1, 1990—and a year later they had all been taken over by state regulators. Don't trust A.M. Best ratings blindly.

Weiss Research rated Executive Life, First Capital and Fidelity Bankers "D"—or "weak."

Monarch Life, which was taken over by regulators to prevent its parent from raiding its assets to make up for huge real estate losses, was rated by Weiss as a C+.

Mutual Benefit Life, which was taken over by regulators to prevent a "run on the bank" and was technically still solvent at the time, was also a C+.

You can call Weiss Research (800-289-9222) and get a rating on the life insurance companies that hold your policies. The cost is as low as $15 per company.* If your insurers are rated "C-" or below, seriously consider taking action.

If they are "C," you need to keep an eye on them.

With a "B" or "A," you are all right.

You may want to call your insurer and ask them for their ratings by Standard and Poor's, Moody's, and Duff and Phelps.

Few insurers acknowledge Weiss. Weiss's ratings, which are on an "A" to "F" range, are just not good marketing fodder. Insurance companies like to be rated on an "A" to "B" scale.

Your action plan:

If you have concerns about the safety of your insurer and find it has a Weiss Safety Rating of "C-" or below, you have basically three choices…

• If you are uninsurable—and cannot get new life insurance from another life insurance company—it is probably prudent to borrow as much of the cash value of your policy as possible. A bird in the hand is worth two in President Bush's—assuming a federal regulatory takeover. The interest on the loan will probably be competitive, although not deductible. You can minimize the cost by investing in a safe-harbor investment such as United Services Government Securities Savings Fund (800-US FUNDS)—a "safer than money-in-the-bank" state income tax-free government money fund.

• If you are insurable—look into shifting your policy, using IRS Form 1035, to transfer to a stronger life insurer after consulting with your adviser. Your broker should be very helpful in arranging such a transfer since it will generate him/her a new commission from a new company.

Your decision may trigger surrender charges forfeited to your current weak insurer. However, if you use the 1035 form, there will be no tax consequences.

• You could do nothing. Before making this decision, you should fully understand the coverage of your state guaranty fund. Let's use Executive Life as an example.

If your insurer fails—as Executive Life has done—and the state insurance commissioner issues an order of liquidation (something the California insurance commissioner has not yet done), the state guaranty association can then assess the healthy insurers to bail out the policyholders of the failed company (up to the limits of that coverage).

In the case of Executive Life, the current estimate is that in the liquidation proceedings, the policyholders will receive only 72 cents on the dollar and the state guaranty funds will make up the balance—up to their limits.

You need to call your state insurance commissioner and see how much that will mean to you if you are an Executive Life policyholder. Most state funds "guarantee" only up to $100,000 per policyholder. So if you have more, you might not get back all your money.

This is a good time to project how your state's guaranty-fund limits apply to your life insurance policies.

Of course, if you stick with strong life insurers like State Farm, Prudential and Metropolitan Life, you can avoid this whole mess.

Now is the time for action—I suspect we have at least a few months before any real immediate threat of a national life insurance holiday presents itself, but events have a tendency to unroll quickly these days.

With some luck, this threat may pass. And if you follow my advice, you will sleep better and increase the probability that your life insurer will be fully capable of keeping its promises.

Source: Bill Donoghue is the publisher of Donoghue's *Moneytalk,* a new audiocassette advisory service.

Insurance Traps That Can Effectively Cancel Your Insurance Coverage

Exclusions are the clauses usually placed at the back of insurance policies that cancel out the coverage promised at the front. Most claims denials are based on exclusions. Many policyholders are unaware of them until their claim is turned down.

According to law, exclusions clauses must be plain, clear and conspicuous—or they may not hold up in court. But insurance policies are tricky. Some exclusions are not identified specifically in the exclusions section, but are instead camouflaged as narrow definitions, conditions or limitations inserted elsewhere in the policy.

Important: Review your policies, especially exclusions, with your insurance agent. If you are unhappy, ask if an additional premium or a different policy would provide the coverage you need.

Here are the most common exclusions traps to watch for…

Auto exclusions:

• New-car exclusion. If you already have auto insurance and you buy a new or second car, many policies will automatically cover it for 30 days.

Trap: Some policies may only cover a new car for less than 30 days. If you have an accident after that limited period, you could be in trouble.

• Members of the household exclusion. If you occasionally allow another person to drive your car, that person is generally covered as a "permissive user."

Trap: If the borrower is a member of your household, coverage is excluded unless the person is listed on the policy and an additional premium is paid.

Example: An adult child or parent who resides with you.

• Own-car exclusion. If you are in an accident while driving someone else's uninsured car, most policies will cover you.

Trap: If you own the vehicle and it's not listed on your policy, you won't be covered.

Example: You own an old pickup truck or an antique car that you've been restoring.

Camouflaged exclusion: Limit of liability. Many people think they are fully covered if they are sued by people they have injured in an accident.

Trap: Most policies limit liability coverage to $15,000 per injured party—and $30,000 per accident. Your personal assets are at risk for the balance if the damaged party is awarded a greater amount.

Remedy: You can usually increase your liability coverage to $100,000, $300,000 or more for surprisingly little extra dollars in premiums.

Camouflaged exclusion: Uninsured motorist protection. Coverage for you or your passengers if injured by an uninsured motorist is usually fixed at $15,000/$30,000. Again, you can usually buy better protection for yourself at low cost.

Camouflaged exclusion: Geographical range. Most auto policies are valid only in the continental US. Check your own coverage if you are planning to drive your car in Canada, Alaska or Mexico. You may not be insured outside the US on your policy.

Recommended: Rent a car and/or buy short-term coverage if you are planning to drive outside the US.

Homeowner's exclusions:

As a consumer lawyer, I am always outraged by typical homeowner's policies that are advertised as "All-Risk Policies" but exclude almost every risk. Exclusions are not consistent in every company and on every policy, however. Important traps to watch for…

• Trap: Water-damage exclusion. Many homeowner's policies exclude coverage for any kind of water damage, not just damages sustained in a flood or hurricane.

Beware: Water damage is very common and can be extensive. Most people assume they are covered if their roof leaks during a normal rainstorm, ruining a carpet or wood floor. But many policies specifically exclude damages resulting from roof leaks, swimming pool leaks, water that backs up through a sewer or drain, surface water overflow, etc.

Solution: If water damage is a substantial risk in your area, shop for the broadest available form of water coverage.

• Trap: Contractor/third-party negligence exclusion. Be wary of policies that exclude damages caused by negligent construction. There are policies that cover this.

Example: If your roof leaks and damages your carpet, you may be able to get coverage for the carpet by proving that the leak was caused by negligent construction.

• Trap: Earth-movement exclusion—another large problem area, especially in California. This exclusion applies not just to earthquake damage, for which a policyholder can buy extra coverage, but also to any damages that result from earth settling.

Beware: If your home is built on a landfill, hillside or site that's likely to settle, you may find that cracks in your driveway, foundation, patio or pool aren't covered.

• Trap: Mechanical-breakdown exclusion. Excludes damages caused by the failure of mechanical equipment.

Beware: If you have an electrical fire due to a malfunction of your heat pump or other mechanical device, your insurer may refuse to cover you.

• Trap: Home-office exclusion. If you operate a business from your home, or if you use your personal computer, camera or other equipment primarily for business purposes, a loss may be excluded or the amount you can recover may be limited.

• Trap: Wear and tear, aging or deterioration. Using this exclusion, an insurer can claim that damages to your home were caused by your own negligence in failing to keep up repairs or anticipate a breakdown.

• Trap: Vandalism or malicious mischief is commonly excluded if your home has been vacant for 30 days.

Caution: Arrange to have someone "house sit" if you plan to be away from home for any length of time.

Also commonly excluded are damages from…dry rot or mold…contamination or hazardous gases…smog or smoke…insects, rodents, birds or domestic animals.

Caution: Check your policy if these risks are substantial for your property.
Camouflaged exclusions:

• Replacement vs. actual cash value. Many policyholders are dismayed to learn that their stolen color TV is only covered for its actual cash value (depreciated to about $45) rather than its replacement value.

Recommended: Check the coverage on your personal possessions.

• Basis for deductible. Recent hurricane and earthquake victims in South Carolina and California have understood the deductibles on their homeowner's policies to be based on the total amount of damages.

Example: For $10,000 sustained in property damage, they expected to pay a 10% deductible, or $1,000, and to be compensated for 90%, or $9,000.

Big trap: Some insurers have tried to claim that the deductible was based on the total insured value of the property.

Example: On a home insured for $100,000, the deductible would be $10,000 and the homeowner would collect nothing! Good news: These cases are being decided in the homeowner's favor in court.

Source: William M. Shernoff, a specialist in consumer claims against insurance companies, and the author of *How to Make Insurance Companies Pay Your Claims* (1990), Hastings House, New York, $9.95. His Claremont, California, law firm, Shernoff, Bidart & Darras, has a staff of insurance analysts who will answer questions regarding insurance coverage and disputes. Policyholders can call 714-621-4935.

Insurance Traps: Buyers Beware

Don't buy life insurance from television or mail-order advertisements. No matter how much you trust their paid shills—such as Dick Van Dyke and Ed Asner—it is a rip-off.

Serious drawbacks: These companies accept anyone who applies—no matter how high the risk—and charge a monthly fee about twice what other insurers charge per $1,000 of life insurance coverage. Major trap: You don't receive any coverage until you've made at least two years of monthly payments. If you die before that, your estate receives only the premiums you've paid—without interest.

Much ado about very little: One of the policies we reviewed paid out only $1,900 after two years. After age 55, the payout dropped annually.

Example: If the insured dies between the ages of 75 and 80, the estate receives only $200.

Exception: Some university alumni insurance programs are less expensive...and are legitimate.

Source: Robert Hunter, president of the National Insurance Consumer Organization, 121 N. Payne St., Alexandria, VA 22314.

Collecting More On Your Company Health Policy

Health insurance policies are not etched in stone. There are contractual provisions in the insurance policy that are negotiable.

Most companies give health insurance to engender goodwill among employees. Many problems in collecting the maximum due you are a result of incompetence or negligence on the part of the administrators who handle insurance benefits. They may be too busy or unaware of how to get more for you.

Here are three ways to improve your ability to collect:

Know the insurance contract and all its provisions. Be aware that everything is negotiable. Example: Home health care by someone other than a registered or practical nurse is not covered in the policy. Contractually nothing needs to be said, but administratively an alternate source of home health care could be covered. It is really a question of negotiation.

Have the company's insurance broker help negotiate with the insurer. He is the one who is making the money from selling your company the policy. He also has more leverage than you do with the insurance company. If he is unwilling to help, encourage your company to switch to a more cooperative broker.

Set up a liaison. The individual in your company who is in charge of claims should have a good working relationship with the insurance company. Reason: If the settlement is too low or doesn't fully cover your needs, the claims person at your firm can make a better settlement. After all, the insurance company is selling policies.

Strategy: If your claims person is uncertain whether you can get more compensation for an ailment or treatment, ask for permission to contact the broker. The broker should know the terms of your contract and be familiar with the people at the insurance company. He should have an idea of how to get the claim paid, especially if it's a legitimate claim but a trifle unusual.

To increase your benefits, take advantage of situations in which both you and your spouse are covered at your jobs by group insurance policies.

Example: You both have Blue Cross to cover hospitalization and, in addition, you both have major medical. Typically, the major medical has a $100 deductible. The insurance company will pick up 80% of the next $2,000 and 100% thereafter. However, if both you and your spouse coordinate your policies, you could wind up using each other's policy to pay the remaining 20% of the $2,000.

Don't expect to make a profit by having several insurance policies. Years ago many health insurance policies were not coordinated and it was possible to get duplicate payments. Today all plans are coordinated so you can't get duplicate payments.

Trying to make specifically unallowable treatments allowable: This is between the doctor and you. For instance, if you want to claim cosmetic surgery necessary for health reasons, consult your doctor. If he won't go along with it, you won't get anywhere with the insurance broker, the personnel at your office or the insurance company.

If you're stuck with a flawed company policy and find that you have huge deductibles and other uncovered expenses, take out a personal policy that coordinates with the company's.

Source: Leonard Stern, president, Leonard B. Stern & Co., an insurance consulting and brokerage firm, 305 Madison Ave., New York 10017.

Questions About Health Insurance and Life Insurance

The National Insurance Consumer Helpline (800-942-4242) operates from 8:00 AM to 8:00 PM. Eastern time, Monday through Friday, as a toll-free source of answers to various insurance questions.

Although people's insurance needs differ, some questions to the Helpline come up again and again.

Most frequently asked questions lately:

How do I figure out if an insurance company is reliable and solvent?

Many companies investigate and report on insurance firms' finances. The big four raters: A. M. Best (Oldwick, New Jersey)...Duff & Phelps (Chicago)... Moody's Investor Service and Standard & Poor's (both New York City). These companies' reports are available in many library reference sections.

Other information sources: Your state insurance department (it requires yearly financial reports from the companies it licenses—but it doesn't provide ratings)...the companies themselves (call or write to the home office for a copy of the most recent annual report).

Note: Since rapid changes in the economy can quickly render reports obsolete, the companies are now updating them much more frequently than they did in the past.

What is COBRA?

COBRA is the federal continuation-of-benefits requirement for most organizations with 20 or more employees. It lets you keep group health insurance with your former company for up to 18 months (36 months for certain qualified dependents). You must pay the full price of the insurance.

Limitation: COBRA does not help if the company goes out of business, since COBRA ties you to the employer's group plan, not to a particular insurance company.

What do I do when my insurance company refuses to repay me because it says my doctor overcharged me?

Most coverage levels are based on what doctors in a particular geographic area charge for a service. Check with other doctors—if yours is out of line, ask for a fee reduction. But if other doctors also seem to charge more than the insurance company is willing to pay, appeal the reimbursement by writing a letter listing the doctors you contacted and the amounts they quoted to you.

Will I still get good medical care if my employer switches to a Health Maintenance Organization and requires me to see only HMO doctors?

HMOs help keep costs down by using internists, pediatricians and general practitioners as "gatekeepers" to determine whether or not you need to see a high-cost specialist. This does not keep you from getting top-quality medical care, but it does represent a change in traditional ways of selecting doctors. Advantages: Lower out-of-pocket costs...no deductibles... no cost for regular checkups and other preventive care.

What is the basic difference among types of life insurance?

Term insurance simply protects your family for a specified—and finite—period of time. It only pays death benefits if you die during this period. At each renewal, the benefit remains the same...but your premium increases. Whole-life insurance protects you for as long as you live. Premiums do not increase year-to-year but are averaged out over your lifetime. Whole-life provides an investment—cash value—as well. You can cancel the policy and receive a lump-sum payment. You only pay taxes on this amount if the cash value—plus any dividends you received—exceeds the sum of premiums you have already paid.

In the past, whole, or traditional, life was the only type with a cash-value component. Today there are others: Modified life, limited-payment life and single-premium whole life. Other alternatives with cash-value options: Universal, variable and current-assumption whole life. An insurance agent can explain the detailed differences and help determine which type is best for you.

How do annuities work?

An annuity is basically the opposite of life insurance. Instead of being designed to pay when an insured person dies, an annuity is designed to pay benefits for as long as a person lives. Annuities are usually set up as retirement plans. Depending on your contract, the insurance company provides you with a regular income (monthly checks) for as long as you live. Your choice would be either an immediate annuity, bought by retirees and payable starting now…or a deferred annuity, where you deposit money into an interest-bearing account, for your payments to start at some specified future date.

What are accelerated death benefits?

This new form of payout is already being offered by more than 100 companies. It allows 25% to 100% of life-insurance benefits to be paid while the insured is still living. These living benefits are paid in connection with terminal or catastrophic illness or a need for long-term care or confinement to a nursing home. As living benefits are paid, however, the payments received upon the policyholder's death are correspondingly reduced.

Warning: Tax treatment of these benefits is unclear. Life-insurance payments are generally not taxable, but the IRS has not yet ruled on benefits paid while the insured is still alive.

What if someone dies and their policy can't be found?

For missing policies, send a self-addressed, stamped envelope to the American Council of Life Insurance, 1001 Pennsylvania Ave. NW, Washington, DC 20004, and ask for a policy search form. A search takes three months—or more—after you submit the form.

What if a policy was issued by a company that I cannot locate?

Simply call the toll-free National Insurance Consumer Helpline. Within a few weeks, you will receive a reply from the ACLI, which maintains a list of companies that have merged, changed names, or gone out of business.

Source: Melanie K. Marsh, manager, consumer affairs, Health Insurance Association of America, and Arlene Lilly, manager, public information, American Council on Life Insurance, both in Washington, DC. The two organizations, with the Insurance Information Institute, are the principal sponsors of the National Insurance Consumer Helpline. Tel.: 800-942-4242.

What To Do About Preexisting Medical Conditions

For many people suffering from heart disease, cancer, diabetes and other chronic medical conditions, obtaining health insurance is difficult or even impossible. Insurance firms just don't want to assume the financial risk of covering such people, and no law forces them to do so.

At one time only serious ailments were grounds for refusal of coverage…but no more.

Insurers now refuse coverage even for minor problems, such as mild hypertension or depression—in some cases even for trivial things such as having once sought psychological counseling. Sadly, federal regulations governing the insurance industry are notoriously spotty…and state regulations are not much better.

Scandalous: In many parts of the country, state insurance agencies are staffed by former insurance-company executives—hardly an unbiased group.

While such problems defy easy solutions, certain steps do bring you some protection…

• Hold on to your existing health insurance. If you're covered by an employer's health plan but are considering switching jobs, determine in advance whether you're eligible for coverage under the new employer's plan.

137

Some insurers refuse coverage for any pre-existing condition. Some accept persons with preexisting conditions, but only if they've been managing without treatment for a specified length of time. Others accept such people but will not honor any claims for that condition made within the first year of coverage.

Bottom line: Get the terms of your prospective employer's insurance plan in writing before you quit. If you're not guaranteed adequate coverage in advance, you may want to hold on to your current job.

If your employer switches insurers, the new insurer is required by law to accept all employees for coverage. If you quit or get fired, federal law dictates that you can keep your existing health plan for 18 months.

• Be honest about your health. Hiding a preexisting medical condition when applying for coverage is fraudulent and foolish. Even if doing so did enable you to get coverage, it might mean big problems later on.

Reason: Insurers scour applications at the time of the first significant claim. If even a hint of dishonesty is found, the claim is usually denied…and the coverage dropped.

• Don't let yourself be mistreated. Some insurers mistreat their policyholders, confident that few people have the wherewithal to fight shabby treatment. Don't let them get away with it. If you've been unfairly denied coverage, or if your insurer fails to honor a legitimate claim, you have many potential allies—local media, elected officials, the state insurance commissioner, etc.

Some states now publish a list of health insurers—and many of them publicize complaints against these carriers. A few now publish rankings of health insurers, from "good" to "bad."

• Go to court. If all else fails, find a lawyer experienced in health-insurance issues. If your case has merit, the lawyer may suggest a lawsuit.

Good news: In many cases, insurers will pay up at the very hint of a suit.

An insurer that loses such a "bad faith" lawsuit is liable not only for the amount of the claim but also for potentially astronomical damages.

Few insurers are eager to risk losing a $1 million judgment over a $20,000 claim. Insurers also fear the negative publicity that could be generated by media coverage of such a lawsuit.

Source: William M. Shernoff, a senior partner with the law firm of Shernoff, Bidart & Darras, Claremont, California. Shernoff, whose firm has represented thousands of consumers seeking settlements from insurance companies, is the author of several books on insurance fraud, including *How to Make Insurance Companies Pay Your Claims* and *Payment Refused: How to Combat Unfair Insurance Practices*, both published by Hastings House, 141 Halstead Ave., Mamaroneck, New York 10543.

Yard-Sale Insurance

If someone gets hurt while picking through the items you are selling, your homeowner's policy will usually protect you. But if you hold sales regularly, you may need separate liability insurance to cover them as a business event. Recommended: Ask your insurance agent if you are covered before holding a sale.

Source: Insurance Information Institute, 110 William St., New York 10038.

How Much Insurance Is Enough?

Many successful people who make sure that their investment portfolios are reasonably balanced, and who steer their careers and personal lives skillfully between risk and opportunity, nevertheless make completely inappropriate choices when they buy insurance. Reason: They don't want to think much about the risks—death, disability, major illness, infirmity—they have to insure against.

Insurance premiums are now becoming a major item in many household budgets. A middle-class family that tries to cover itself with insurance for everything that could possibly go wrong could easily wind up spending $5,000 to $10,000 a year in insurance premiums…and wind up with little to save and invest toward retirement.

Twin risks:

To avoid the twin dangers of being overly or inadequately insured…

• Make a list of what you and your family's areas of risk really are…and prioritize them.

• Consider what stopgaps you can call on to cover some of these risks—aside from insurance.

Examples: If only one spouse works, is the other spouse employable if the salary-earner becomes disabled or dies? How much of current income or savings could reasonably be used to meet an expensive medical emergency—before health insurance takes up the rest?

• Be realistic about how much you can afford to spend for insurance—and still be able to save for college expenses, retirement or other needs.

Priorities and trade-offs:

Now review your risk areas, set priorities—and be prepared to make trade-offs. Basic insurance strategy: Insure yourself against events that could really blow you out of the water—not against every little thing that could go wrong.

• Disability insurance. A middle-aged person is five times more likely to be disabled and unable to work than to die. Covering yourself and your family against this risk is a high priority.

If you have company-paid disability coverage, ask for information that explains what your benefits would be. Important to know:

• What is the company's policy on paid sick leave—how long are you likely to remain on full salary?

• What percentage of your salary will your disability benefit amount to? (The maximum is usually about 70%.)

• Is there a gap between the end of paid sick leave and the start of disability payments? How long? (Some disability plans don't kick in until 6 to 12 months after the onset of disability.)

• Can you supplement the disability coverage your company provides by buying additional coverage at group rates? Gaps to consider filling: Starting disability sooner. Increasing the payout to at least 60% of salary.

Helpful: Update your knowledge on company coverage at least once a year. Companies have been shaving benefits as their insurance expenses skyrocket.

Buying disability coverage as an individual if you have no company coverage is expensive, but it is essential for most people who depend on their earnings.

If you are currently employed where you have coverage, but anticipate leaving to start your own business, start shopping now for individual coverage so you fully understand what your expenses may be.

• Life insurance. The most common insurance mistake is relying too heavily on life insurance and neglecting to cover other risks (disability, medical expenses) or needs (retirement income).

This lopsided situation often results from the practice of providing company life-insurance benefits as multiples—two, three or more—of employees' annual salaries. The size of that benefit gives many families a false sense of security.

Calculate how much life insurance is needed—and how sufficient the company's benefits are. The life-insurance needs of a single provider with a young family are more substantial than those of dual-income couples, older individuals with grown children or those with no dependents. If there is a real gap in coverage, the economical way to supplement is to pay for additional coverage at the group rate—a benefit that many companies usually make available to employees.

• Health and dental insurance. Less than a decade ago, most employed people never gave a thought to this expense because so many companies paid the entire cost. But in recent years, as health-insurance premiums have gone up 10%–15% a year, companies are making employees more responsible for sharing the cost.

Face reality: You and your children are going to have to be more self-reliant about health expenses. Count on these insurance premiums being a substantial part of your family budget.

Sensible strategy for health insurance you buy for you and your family: Pay for runny noses and insure against surgery. Make a reasonable assessment of how much you can afford to pay, out-of-pocket and out of savings, to meet run-of-the-mill doctor-visit and prescription charges. Use that sum as your deductible to reduce your premium expense. What to look for in company coverage:

• If both spouses are working and covered by company-sponsored health insurance, know which one is the most generous in providing overall benefits—or benefits to children or other dependents. Use that policy. In the past, couples often abused double coverage and made claims for the same medical expense under both policies, turning the insurance into a money-making device. Computerized systems have virtually eliminated that practice. You have to lie now in order to be paid twice for the same procedure. Don't do it.

• Know the age at which your children fall out of family coverage under company plans. Be sure to provide individual coverage for them.

While your children are in college, the school will usually charge you for health insurance. Often that insurance has a fairly low cap—$20,000 or so. Helpful: If your child is not covered by your family plan, consider supplemental insurance with a $20,000 deductible. It's cheap and it covers your child—and your pocketbook—in the event of a medical catastrophe.

Don't waste your money on specialized medical insurance—for cancer care, for instance.

• Long-term care. Companies are just beginning to offer plans covering nursing-home, extended hospital-stay and other long-term care, but it is far from common. Some company plans cover employees, their spouses, their parents and in-laws—but employees pay the premiums.

Most long-term-care plans are less than five years old, with little experience. They differ greatly in what they cover. Some, for instance, don't cover home care. Others require a stay in a hospital before the individual qualifies for custodial-care coverage.

Don't buy this insurance impulsively—but stay alert to developments and keep assessing your potential needs. Prepare a long-term total financial plan. Insurance is just one facet of an overall game plan.

Beware: Don't count on Social Security, Medicare, Medicaid or your kids to meet your needs as you become elderly.

Source: George E.L. Barbee, executive director, Client Services, Price Waterhouse, 1251 Avenue of the Americas, New York 10020. He is a contributor to the firm's books on retirement, taxes and investing.

Selling Your Life Insurance Benefits

Life insurance benefits can be sold for cash—before you die? About a dozen companies have been formed nationwide to buy benefits from persons who are terminally ill. How: The policy owner names the company as beneficiary in exchange for an immediate cash payment, typically 55% to 80% of the benefit. In effect, the insured borrows against the future benefit to meet cash needs. Danger: Unscrupulous buyers of benefits could set terms that exploit the insured's unfortunate position. To meet this problem, California has just adopted rules requiring buyers of benefits to be licensed by the state.

Source: John Garamendi, California state insurance commissioner, quoted in *Medical Economics*, 5 Paragon Dr., Montvale, New Jersey 07465.

Term Insurance Opportunities & Traps

Trading in your low-cost yearly renewable term insurance* policy for traditional whole-life coverage with premiums that may initially cost five times as much may not be as outlandish as it sounds. Reason: Even though term is the cheapest approach for people in
*Term insurance is renewed each year, year after year, but builds no cash value.

their twenties and thirties, the premiums increase steadily year after year, so that by the time you reach age 50 or so, buying permanent insurance that creates cash equity (cash value) could cost you less over the rest of your lifetime.

How much insurance do you need?

Most people need enough capital to generate 80% of their current income should they die—which can come from income-producing assets they already own, as well as from life-insurance proceeds.

Example: If you are earning $100,000 a year, you'll need at least $1 million in assets to produce an $80,000 a year income at current rates of earnings.

You probably would not need a policy for the entire $1 million if some of your earnings would be replaced by a group life-insurance policy at work—and Social Security benefits for your survivors. You should also consider the earnings power of stocks, bonds, Treasury securities, bank certificates of deposit and other securities. Nonincome-producing assets, such as your house, would not be included.

Older folks who have already accumulated sizable assets and people with salaries over $250,000 or so don't need to replace as much of their income with life insurance. A replacement goal of 70%–75% of current earnings is probably sufficient.

Compare insurance costs:

Do a numerical analysis of the costs of term and permanent insurance to figure out whether you can afford to buy a cash-value policy, such as whole life, universal life or variable life.

Initially, the costs of term are almost always lower. That's because the premiums start out at very modest levels but increase steadily and at a much sharper rate as you age.

Permanent insurance, by contrast, has an annual premium that is higher than the cost of term insurance initially but remains the same for the duration of the policy, regardless of how old you are, as long as you make regular payments. Therefore, permanent insurance can be less expensive than term insurance in the long run.

Furthermore, part of the premium is invested in a tax-deductible account that you can borrow against. Term policies have no such cash buildup.

Example: A 40-year-old man with two children earns $50,000 a year and needs $250,000 in coverage. His first-year cost for a $250,000 term policy is $330 and, because the man's premiums for term will rise annually, his costs for the first five years of coverage will total $1,962.

A comparable permanent policy has an annual cost of $950, or a total expenditure of $4,750 for the first five years. But by the end of five years, the permanent policy will also have accumulated a cash value of $1,750, reducing his net cost to $3,000. This is still roughly $1,000 more than the cost of term, so for someone who's probably spending every penny that he's earning, term is clearly the best option.

Later on, however, when this man's earning power has increased and he has more discretionary income, he may want to convert his term policy to permanent coverage.

When to switch:

Consider switching from term to permanent coverage when you are saving at least 10% of your income and living on what's left—rather than paying your expenses first and then saving what's left.

For most people, this point typically occurs around age 50, when they've bought all the furniture they'll ever need and the kids have all graduated from college. This also happens to be the time when the cost of term insurance starts increasing at a faster and faster rate.

Example: A client of mine, a 52-year-old businessman, recently compared the costs of a $250,000 policy. The first-year cost of term was $565. By the end of 10 years, his total cost would be $14,703, with an accumulated cash value of zero.

The annual premium for a permanent policy would be $3,438. By the end of 10 years, the premiums would amount to $34,380. But the cash value of the policy would grow to $28,432, reducing its net cost to about $6,000.

Since he had already educated his children and had the necessary income to pay the higher annual premiums, he opted for the permanent coverage.

Caution: Don't convert unless you plan to keep the new policy for at least 10 years, and preferably longer. It takes that long for the cash-value account, which is yielding about 7%–8% at current rates, to exceed the policy's up-front expenses.

If you develop health problems, converting to permanent life insurance from term insurance makes particular sense. Reason: You shouldn't have to pass a medical exam as you typically would if you were buying a new policy from another company. This means that even if you develop a serious illness such as cancer or diabetes after taking out your term insurance, you will generally be permitted to convert it to permanent coverage despite your illness.

Picking a term policy:

If, despite the long-term cost advantages of permanent insurance, you decide to buy term initially…

• Make sure the insurance company is financially sound and likely to be around years from now. If you later develop health problems and are rejected by other carriers, you may be stuck with your original—and now dangerous—company.

• Make sure the policy has a good conversion option that does not have any medical restrictions. Ask your agent to show you how you would be able to convert your term policy to the best permanent policy—not just any cash-value policy—that your insurance company now offers. Otherwise, converting may not be worth the additional outlay down the road.

Source: Stephen C. Shaw, a partner in the insurance firm of Jenkins, Reeves & Shaw, 3730 Mt. Diablo Blvd., Suite 220, Lafayette, California 94549, and president-elect of the National Association of Life Underwriters, the national trade association of more than 140,000 life- and health-insurance agents.

Beware of Nursing-Home Insurance

Nursing-home insurance isn't a good buy for most people. Problems: Premiums are high…they're often not deductible…and coverage may be inadequate. Also—since it only insures a policyholder for one year following payment of premiums—it's a bad deal for people under 60 because it's unlikely they'll end up in a nursing home within a year. The policies are best primarily for those aged 65 to 75, with lots of disposable income, who feel that peace of mind is more important than a good investment decision.

Source: Robert Freedman, attorney, Freedman & Fish, a law firm specializing in elder law, trusts and estates, 260 Madison Ave., New York 10016.

Insurance Limit

An insurance company does not have to defend an insured party who refuses to cooperate in the investigation of an accident. So if an individual takes the Fifth Amendment rather than cooperate with the insurer's investigation—to assure that no personal criminal liability results—insurance protection is forfeited.

Source: *Aetna Casualty v. State Farm,* US District Court, W. Dist. of Pennsylvania, No. 90-535.

Property Insurance Trap

Employee vandalism and arson are not covered by the standard language in many company property insurance and employee fidelity policies, according to recent court decisions. Check with the company's insurance broker to see if coverage protects against employee wrongdoing. Ask for a written, plain-English, "yes or no" answer.

Source: Stanley Hartman, publisher, *The General Ledger,* 6001 Montrose Rd., Rockville, Maryland 20852.

Disability Coverage

Best: Your personal insurance coverage, supplemented by employer group coverage—

not the other way around. Employer plans are usually short-term, not transferable to a new company, and the benefits are taxable. That's not so when you pay for your own coverage. Don't rely on Social Security for disability pay. Benefits are limited and partially taxable, and you must be totally and permanently disabled to collect.

Source: *Query*, American Society of CLU & ChFC, 270 Bryn Mawr Ave., Bryn Mawr, Pennsylvania 19010.

Insurance—Tricks And Traps

A wave of concern about insurance-industry solvency is prompting many people to investigate switching annuity contracts or life-insurance policies to companies they perceive to be unquestionably healthy.

While there are situations in which it may be advantageous to switch policies, in general, there is no need for concern. Most states have guaranty funds (similar to the FDIC) that protect these investments.

Depending on the type of policy you have, switching may cost far more in lost interest and surrender fees than the low risk of staying put.

Bigger problem: Policyholders have lost a great deal of money to deceptions and scams involving unnecessary replacement of their existing policies.

Life insurance switching:

• Term life insurance. Switching a term-life policy is as straightforward as exchanging an auto or homeowner's policy. It is advantageous if you find a better deal. Most people are competent to judge whether a new rate compares favorably with their old rate and encounter no significant problems switching policies.

• Cash-value policies. The worth of an individual cash-value policy is far more complicated and difficult to assess. It has a dual purpose. The policy serves as a death protection—and a savings plan. Furthermore, insur-ance agents are not trained to analyze these policies.

General rule: If you own an older policy that is paying dividends (and most do), it is best not to change. If you feel you need it, buy additional coverage rather than a replacement policy. Be very wary if you are approached to trade in an old policy for new, broader coverage.

Trap: Unscrupulous agents routinely "rip off" clients by persuading them to cash in their older, relatively high-yielding cash-value policies for lower-yielding new ones. This is usually a ploy to boost sales commissions.

When it may be useful to switch: If your policy doesn't pay dividends. In a close call, it may tip the balance if you are now a non-smoker and you bought a policy before the early 1980s, when insurance companies began to make the distinction.

Most damaging time to switch: After the first two to three years, when surrender penalties are at the maximum. But there is likely to be some kind of surrender penalty for the first 10 to 15 years. Also: Switching to a new policy will activate new suicide and con-testability clauses.

If you do decide to switch, both life insur-ance and annuities can be exchanged by tax-free transfer. (The succeeding company will ask you to fill out a "1035 Exchange" form.)

But if you cash in your policy, you will have to pay taxes on any gain, as well as on recent single-premium life policies and most annuities, and there's a 10% penalty if you are younger than age 59½.

Annuities:

It is generally not possible to terminate an annuity contract once it has begun to pay. Of those not in payout:

• Annuities beyond the surrender charge period. It may be wise to switch annuities if you are no longer liable for a surrender penalty (that's usually after seven or eight years) and the interest rates are significantly better elsewhere.

Downside: With a new policy, you incur a new surrender charge period.

• Annuities within a surrender charge period. The current yield is composed of two elements...the interest rate being paid now...added to the decline each year in the amount of the surrender charge.

Example: If the annuity is currently paying 8%, and the surrender charge goes down by 1% per year, the current yield is the sum of the two, or 9%. Therefore, it would be foolish to switch to a company paying 8.5%.

Before considering a switch, ask the new company for its track record on interest credit. Do rates remain favorable? Are policyholders treated fairly and consistently?
One of the best deals around:

Compare any policy you are looking at with the life-insurance annuity products offered by USAA Life (a subsidiary of United Services Automobile Association, headquartered in San Antonio, Texas). It sells life insurance and annuities that are available to the general public.

Because USAA does not pay agents or brokers, it can offer a better deal than most companies. One advantage is low surrender charges—for example, 4% on annuities—that disappear after two years. USAA is a highly rated, efficiently run company with a good record on annuities.

Source: James Hunt, life insurance actuary, former state insurance commissioner and director of the National Insurance Consumer Organization, 121 N. Payne St., Alexandria, Virginia 22314.

The Biggest Business Insurance Mistakes Can Be Avoided

Because most top managers aren't insurance experts, companies often find out the hard way that they're uninsured...or underinsured. This costly risk can, however, be eliminated by checking this list of common business insurance mistakes...

• Mistake: Not keeping up-to-date records on replacement costs for all plants, machinery and equipment. Guesswork isn't good enough if equipment is damaged and an insurance claim is filed. The insurance company will want to see detailed documentation for the values the company reports.

• Mistake: Not having enough business-interruption coverage. Companies usually underestimate the true length of business interruption after a loss.

Example: It may take two years to rebuild, order and install new equipment and reopen operations. Yet it may take much longer to operate at full capacity. Be careful when making this calculation.

Added trap: The formula used by insurance companies to calculate business interruption differs from that used by accountants. It is extremely rigid because it is the same for all companies regardless of their industry. The company should have an insurance expert explain the requirements of the formula. Failure to do so could result in inadequate coverage.

• Mistake: Not valuing finished goods at selling price. Most manufacturers are adequately insured for the value of their raw materials or work-in-progress inventories. But many companies err by insuring their finished goods inventories at replacement cost instead of selling price. The only way to guarantee coverage of the full price, including normal markup in the event of a loss, is to insure at the selling price.

• Mistake: Failure to use "blanket" insurance. Companies with more than one location should take advantage of what is called blanket insurance. If the company has one factory valued at $5 million and one at $3 million, it could buy blanket coverage for $8 million. If either factory was lost, the company would be covered, even for losses well above their stated value.

Example: If the $3 million factory had a $4 million loss because it had just received a $1 million shipment of inventory, for example, the company would be fully covered, instead of losing a million dollars as it would if the factory were insured individually.

• Mistake: Not disarming the coinsurance clause. This is a valuable, usually overlooked, option to increasing insurance coverage for almost nothing.

How it works: Normally, insurance companies will pay 100% of all commercial claims up to policy limits, providing the company has insured at least 80% of its values. But if the company covers less—say, 60% of the value—it will be penalized. In that case, the insurance company will pay % of any claim. Instead, the company can get a co-insurance waiver clause to waive the 80% requirement by meeting the insurance company's requirement of filing annual reports on the value of the company's insured assets, and paying a nominal waiver fee. In that case, partial losses filed will be covered at 100%.

Example: With the 80% coinsurance clause on a policy covering 60% of a $1 million factory, a claim for a $100,000 loss will be covered at $75,000 (% of $100,000). But if the company gets the co-insurance waiver clause, it would get the entire $100,000 back.

• Mistake: Inadequately insuring computer systems. Though the system may be adequately insured when it comes to replacement costs of hardware, software and the reconstruction of records, the key to protection involves proper backup, off-site storage of data and provision for alternate data processing operations.

• Mistake: Paying insufficient attention to workers' compensation. Companies are either passive about workers' comp—relying on the insurance company to handle everything—or aggressive, treating employees with suspicion and creating an adversarial environment. Neither approach helps to control either losses or costs.

Best: Institute the company's own loss-control policies, procedures and training and establish an effective claims-management program adapted to its own needs.

• Mistake: Misunderstanding deductibles and self-insurance. The purpose of insurance is to protect against unexpected losses.

When expected losses are also covered, the insurer charges for the amount of expected loss plus overhead and profit.

It is far more cost-effective not to insure expected losses, such as damage to company-owned automobiles. Among other cost savings, the company has the use of premium dollars until there's an accident.

Strategy: Protect against unexpected or catastrophic losses with insurance policies that have high deductibles. The amount of the deductible should be based on how much the company can afford to self-insure on smaller or expected losses.

• Mistake: Carrying inadequate catastrophic liability coverage. Most companies are underinsured when it comes to liability limits. The key here is to have ample umbrella liability coverage, especially if the company is involved with certain types of exposures such as trucks, large auto fleets, high-rise buildings, high-traffic customer areas, product liability, construction or liquor sales.

Don't overlook potential costs for legal defense either. While most umbrella liability-insurance policies do provide reimbursement for these often costly legal expenses, there are limits. The best approach is to have defense costs in addition to the policy's limit so you will have coverage for defense costs in addition to the limits of the policy.

Source: Joseph H. Albert, J. H. Albert International Insurance Advisors, Inc., 72 River Park, Needham Heights, Massachusetts 02194. A leading independent insurance advisory firm, it specializes in risk management, loss control and claims-management services. It does not sell insurance.

Business Insurance

Though property and casualty insurance premiums are still declining, history indicates that with little warning, business insurance could become harder to get and more expensive.

The last time prices turned up sharply was in 1987, so the industry's traditional three-year cycle suggests that a change in trend is overdue and companies should waste no time in preparing for it. Recent warning signs…

• Higher premiums are starting to creep into policies for the petrochemical, utility and offshore oil industries.

• Aviation, marine and officers' and directors' liability coverage are also rising.

• Workers' compensation costs continue to rise by double digits.

• With so many catastrophes occurring worldwide, the huge London insurance market has significantly raised rates for catastrophe insurance.

Problem: Insurance companies generally lose money on insurance underwriting, but make money on their investments. That's getting harder to do in the current low-interest-rate environment.

And, since the public is unusually sensitive to insurer insolvency right now, there's a danger that companies may understate the amount of money they would need to reserve to make future loan payments. This is called under-reserving. It has the effect of making an insurance company's financial condition look better than it actually is—by overstating profitability and surplus.

Reality: At some point, insurers will have to increase their reserves to cover losses. Then their financial strength will deteriorate... bringing on a tough new cycle of higher rates and restricted coverage.

Self-defense: Keep track of insurance company ratings from the leading independent rating services. Do business only with insurers that are in the top rating category of at least two such firms.

Beyond ratings:

• Lock into an insurance renewal deal early. By getting a written renewal commitment from the insurer well in advance of the actual renewal date, the company avoids rate fluctuations that may take place before that date.

• Change from an annual to a three-year policy. Some insurers, anxious to cement client relationships, will offer rate guarantees for three years...or sometimes longer. Even insurers that won't commit rate guarantees will offer multiyear policies in which premium rates are up for review each year. Often the insurer's underwriting department neglects to do this annual review and the policy stays at the original rate for several years.

• Amend policies to provide 90 days' advance notice of cancellation, nonrenewal or material change. This should be enough time to replace coverage, if needed, and it discourages the insurer from making unilateral changes in your policy.

• Prepare detailed specifications that put the company in the best light. The more an underwriter knows about your business, your company's loss-control program and its claims-management procedures, the more willing it will be to negotiate. Get professional help if necessary to present the right detailed information. When an underwriter gets a good, positive first impression about a company, insurance costs will be lower.

• Review loss records for accuracy. Insurance companies set aside loss reserves based on what they think their liability will be.

Recommended: Have a claims professional review your company's actual losses and compare them with the insurer's loss reserves for your company at the end of a policy year. Mistakes often occur and reserves can be too high based on the facts of the individual claim. Reduction of the insurance company's reserve will help you get lower premiums. Especially in a hard market, a good loss record can be your trump card for negotiating a premium reduction.

Workers' compensation:

Virtually every company is struggling with rising workers' compensation insurance, which keeps going up no matter what the rest of the insurance market does. Some of the biggest insurers are reducing their writing of this coverage or cutting it out altogether. Despite various legislative proposals in a number of states, no rate relief is in sight.

Best defense: Adopt your own loss-management program to reduce accidents and manage claims that do occur efficiently. Don't treat injured workers like demons. They've been injured on the job, after all, and they're worried about providing for their families. Treat them with courtesy and respect. This includes getting them prompt medical care at a local medical facility that specializes in sports or industrial medicine. Reason: Such facilities are geared to getting people back into action as quickly as possible, not sending them to bed for weeks. Avoid emergency rooms, which are overcrowded and terribly expensive.

Have supervisors accompany injured workers to get medical help. Assure workers that the company will provide a job for them as soon as they're able to work. In fact, if someone has hurt his/her right hand, shift him to a job where he can temporarily, for instance, answer phones with his left hand.

Bottom line: Studies show that using workers productively and getting them back on full income instead of giving them a disability check improves their self-image and helps them get better faster.

Loss-management programs such as these pay off because insurance premiums are directly determined by the company's loss experience.

In addition, the company may be able to save by self-insuring many of its losses. The ultimate loss-sensitive program, of course, is self-insurance, and this may be an alternative for bigger companies or those that operate in low-risk businesses.

Source: Joseph H. Albert, J. H. Albert International Insurance Advisors, Inc., 72 River Park, Needham Heights, Massachusetts 02194. A leading independent insurance advisory firm, it specializes in risk management, loss control and claims-management services. It does not sell insurance.

How To Deal With Claims Insurance Companies Are Delaying... Reducing...Refusing

While about 90% of insurance claims are handled smoothly and routinely, millions of unjustly rejected claims, though a small percentage of the total, are costing consumers billions of dollars. Encouraging: Most policyholders who dispute claims denials either win their case or improve their settlement.

Trap: The larger your claim, the more likely it is to be delayed, reduced or denied.

The person with the power to pay, settle or refuse your claim is the claims adjuster. Problem: Some adjusters may be looking for reasons not to pay legitimate claims.

If your claim is unfairly denied: First question the decision with a call to the adjuster handling the claim. Then contest it in writing—write first to the adjuster who handles the claim. Refer your complaint to the department's supervisor if necessary.

For best results: Assemble as much documentation as possible and submit it to support your position.

If you are still unsatisfied, contact your state department of insurance.

If you don't get a response, see a qualified trial attorney.

Here are the areas that most frequently turn into insurance nightmares. When filing these claims, you must be especially aggressive in dealing with your insurer.

Property claims:

• Fire: Fire-insurance claims, both residential and business, have become a fertile area for delays and refusals.

Common tactics by insurers: Arson accusations...disputed fine-print clauses...disputed appraised valuations.

Strategy: Property insurance companies know that delays in paying catastrophic claims leave victims open to further losses, and even bankruptcy. Result: Policyholders are forced to settle for less than their due.

• Hurricane, earthquake, tornado damage: With the exception of arson, the delaying tactics used are often the same as with fire damage. In addition, after filing a claim many policyholders are shocked to find that their property insurer has calculated the deductible based on the value of the policy—not on the damage incurred.

Reason: Consumers are accustomed to the deductible system used in medical insurance policies.

Example: The company pays 80% of a medical bill, the policyholder pays 20%. So a homeowner with $20,000 in storm damage expects to pay $4,000 and have the insurance cover $16,000. The homeowner is outraged when his/her claim is refused on the grounds that the home was insured for $200,000, therefore the deductible is $40,000—and nothing is paid.

147

Self-defense: Read your policy carefully. If necessary, buy a new policy with a fixed deductible. Courts have held that where insurance-policy language is unclear, it will be interpreted in favor of policyholders, or that the "reasonable expectations" of the policyholder will prevail. Recent disaster victims have filed suits in California and the Carolinas based on these rulings.

Life insurance claims:

Double indemnity: One would expect no problem with policies designed to pay at the time of a person's death, since the fact of death is rarely in question. Exception: Policies that agree to pay double in case of accidental death.

Common tactics: The insurer claims the death was not accidental. They may try to prove that the deceased committed suicide, or caused his/her own death due to alcohol or drug abuse. Self-defense: Be prepared to argue this with police reports, hospital records and an attorney's threat to sue the insurer.

Medical claims:

This is the area in which policyholders encounter the worst and most frequent insurance nightmares.

• Cancer: Most health-insurance policies provide for cancer surgery, radiation and chemotherapy.

Biggest problem area: Bone-marrow transplants, long considered by doctors to be standard effective treatment for patients who need more aggressive therapy when the first round has failed.

Common tactic: Insurers claim the procedure is still "experimental" and therefore not covered. Most alternative therapies are also refused on the grounds of being "unproven."

• AIDS or other catastrophic illness: The more costly or long-term the anticipated treatment, the more likely it is that your insurer will deny your claim or cancel your policy, shifting the burden of care to the public.

Common tactics: The insurer claims you have a "preexisting condition," or that the medications and treatment prescribed are unproven and experimental. Often, if you have been insured as part of a group policy, the insurance company cancels the group,

leaving you uninsurable elsewhere.

• Long-term progressive illness: If the condition is long-term, serious and/or deteriorating, you are likely to have frequent claims refused.

Examples: Coma victims, patients with multiple sclerosis, Alzheimer's disease.

Common tactic: The insurer claims the victim requires "custodial" rather than "medical" care.

• Work-related disability: Any ongoing claim is likely to be flagged for cancellation or reduction.

Common tactics: The insurer offers a flat settlement if the disabled person agrees to give up rights to collect under the terms of his/her policy. The insurer accuses the person of malingering and tries to prove that he/she is not really disabled.

Problem: You are disabled if you are unable to perform the type of work you are qualified to do. But an insurer may claim that you can work if you can function just minimally. Example: A roofer who is confined to a wheelchair following an accident is clearly disabled. Yet an insurer may claim that he is mobile and therefore able to work.

• Nursing-home or rehabilitative care: Many insurance policies exclude "long-term" or "custodial care." But patients receiving medical care in a facility that meets the definition of a hospital may be covered.

Common tactic: The insurance company claims that care is not medical but custodial, or that the facility is not a "hospital."

• Minor claims: Insurance companies make enormous profits by refusing to pay small sums to legitimate claimants.

Caution: Check your insurance policy and follow up on any discrepancies you find if a small part of a larger claim is refused. Don't be lazy, and don't settle for less than you are due.

While a complex or costly claim is far more likely to be reduced than a modest one, filing a small claim is no guarantee that it will be paid.

Example: Several years ago, I had a client who sued his insurance company over a $48 unpaid claim. During the trial, a pattern of fraud perpetrated against policyholders was revealed. Result: The jury ordered the insurer to pay $4.5 million in punitive damages.

Source: William M. Shernoff, specialist in consumer claims against insurance companies, and the author of *How to Make Insurance Companies Pay Your Claims*, Hastings House, 141 Halstead Ave., Mamaroneck, New York 10543. His Claremont, California, law firm, Shernoff, Bidart & Darras, has a staff of insurance analysts who will answer questions regarding insurance coverage, disputes and ERISA.

Life-Insurance Avoidance Strategies

Don't buy cash-value life insurance unless you are already making maximum deductible contributions to IRA, Keogh and 401(k) retirement accounts. Reason: While you get a tax deferral for investment earnings on the cash-value portion of an insurance policy, you get no tax deduction for the life insurance premiums.

In contrast, a retirement savings account provides both tax deferral for investment earnings and deductions for your contributions.

Strategy: If your insurance and long-term savings budget are limited to the maximum allowable deductible deposit and you need insurance protection, buy low-cost term insurance and place what you save on premiums in a tax-deductible retirement account. After making full use of such accounts, invest in cash-value life insurance.

Caution: Qualified plans have a pre-age-59½ withdrawal penalty tax, while withdrawals from cash-value insurance are not subject to this tax.

Source: Howard B. Klein, Klein, McGorry & Klein, Ltd., insurance consultants and brokers, 111 W. 57 St., New York 10019.

When To Sue Your Insurance Company

Policyholders pay insurance premiums for good faith protection against financial loss, and insurance companies are obligated to show good faith in their dealings with policyholders by delivering what has been paid for.

A policyholder who acts in bad faith by filing a false insurance claim is guilty of fraud and can go to prison.

Unfortunately, an insurer who tries to defraud a policyholder by refusing to pay a legitimate claim is not criminally prosecuted. The policyholder's only recourse is a civil suit to prove the company has acted in bad faith. What is bad faith?

"Bad faith," in the context of insurance, can be simply defined as "the unreasonable refusal on the part of an insurer to promptly pay a valid claim."

Bad faith practices on the part of an insurance company include:

• Failure to conduct an adequate investigation.

• Unreasonable delay in processing the claim.

• Inadequate payment for the claim filed.

• Conscious disregard for the rights of a policyholder.

Your right to sue:

If your insurance company has acted in bad faith, you are entitled to sue for the full amount of benefits due, plus damages for emotional distress and any economic loss you suffer due to the company's refusal to pay your claim. If the insurer's conduct has been particularly unscrupulous, you may also be awarded punitive damages, the purpose of which is to punish the company and encourage it to behave more responsibly in the future.

Case histories:

Here are a few of the bad faith lawsuits I have tried or been involved with over the years.

• Mike Egan, a roofer, fell off a ladder and severely injured his back. Surgery was unsuccessful, and Mr. Egan's doctors declared him totally disabled. His disability insurance policy promised to pay $200 a month for life if he was disabled by an accident. The insurance company paid the benefits for a few months, then suddenly stopped. Reason: It claimed the disability was caused by "sickness" rather than an accident, knowing full well that the sickness benefits lasted only three months. The company never consulted Mr. Egan's doctors. Result: The jury awarded Mr. Egan the benefits due under his policy, plus $78,000 for mental suffering, plus a record-setting punitive damage judgment that was later reduced when the company agreed to a settlement.

• The co-owners of a small auto-parts store in Bishop, California, were wiped out one winter night when an explosion and ensuing fire destroyed their business. Their insurance company refused to pay any benefits, accusing the two partners of arson—even though the men were never suspected or questioned by police or fire officials and no charges were filed. The insurance company publicized the accusations, and the businessmen and their families were forced to leave their small town.

One of the partners later suffered a stroke his doctors attributed to the stress of the fire and the trial. In court, the accidental cause of the explosion was proved to be a faulty butane heater. Result: The jury found that the insurance company had acted in bad faith by ignoring its responsibility to make an adequate investigation. The case was eventually settled for over $750,000.

Note: The attorney who tried this case called it a "typical fire case." Accusations of arson are a common delaying tactic that insurance companies use against fire victims.

• Mary Frazier lost her 23-year-old husband in a tragic drowning accident. His employee benefits included a $12,000 double-indemnity life insurance policy, under which she was due to receive a double benefit in case of accidental death. The company paid the first $12,000 but refused to pay the second $12,000. Reason: The company determined that her husband had committed suicide. Furthermore, it was revealed in court that the company had instructed its supposedly impartial investigators to find a motive for suicide, though none existed. The Fraziers were happily married, enjoying their first child and were very religious. And there were witnesses to the accident. Result: The widow was awarded the benefit due, plus $150,000 for emotional distress, plus $8 million in punitive damages. The latter was reduced to $2 million on appeal, and eventually disallowed because California's two-year statute of limitations for punitive damages had expired before the suit was filed. Lesson: State laws vary, but it is always best to act promptly if you feel you have suffered damages due to an insurer's bad faith.

When to sue your insurance company:

Before filing a lawsuit against your insurance company...complete these steps:

• Write letters of complaint.

• Provide necessary documentation.

• Complain to your state insurance commission.

• Have your attorney write a letter.

Schedule a conference with a trial attorney who is experienced with insurance cases and is willing to take cases on a contingency basis. Most will offer a free consultation during which they will evaluate your documentation and complaint. For a referral: Check with the Association of Trial Lawyers of America, 800-424-2725, or contact the trial lawyer organization.

If your insurer offers you a settlement: Unless you believe the settlement is fair, particularly if you've suffered damages, do not sign a release accepting the offer before discussing it with your attorney.

When not to sue your insurance company:

If you live in a state with poor consumer-protection laws...

Only about half of US state insurance commissions have bad faith laws, but all states have consumer-protection laws that apply to the insurance industry. Problem: Some are weaker than others.

Examples: There are some states that don't allow policyholders to recover attorneys' fees. Washington does not allow for punitive damages, while other states have capped them. Solution: It's sometimes possible to sue in the insurer's home state.

If you have health insurance through your employer...

If your health-insurance policy is governed by the provisions of ERISA (Employee Retirement Income Security Act), you can only sue to recover benefits due—not for damages.

Problem: Few, if any, attorneys are willing to take on such a case. Solution: Look for an individual or group health plan not provided by your employer. Encourage lawmakers to close the loophole in ERISA that preempts state consumer laws regulating insurance. Don't sleep on your rights:

The "bad faith" lawsuit is the consumer's most powerful weapon in a battle with an insurance company, and the one most feared by the insurance industry.

Proof: The industry spends millions trying to convince the public and lawmakers that an explosion of litigation and high damage awards are to blame for skyrocketing insurance premiums...that the public's ability to collect damages should be capped, their rights to sue limited and attorneys' contingency fees banned.

Facts: The number of lawsuits in the US, per capita, has not risen in 33 years...the mean jury award of $8,000 has stayed nearly constant since 1959...a contingency arrangement is often the only way a less-than-wealthy person can gain access to our nation's courtrooms.

Bottom line: Don't take your rights for granted.

Source: William M. Shernoff, the author of *How to Make Insurance Companies Pay Your Claims* (1990), Hastings House, New York. His Claremont, California, law firm, Shernoff, Bidart & Darras, has a staff of insurance analysts who will answer questions regarding insurance coverage, disputes and ERISA.

How To Buy Medigap Insurance

Medicare pays only about 50% of the health-care expenses a recipient incurs. The balance, or gap, must be picked up by the recipient. Or, it can be insured by a health-insurance policy called a "Medigap," which takes over where Medicare leaves off.

Cost: $40 to $120 per month—depending on the age of the policyholder and the scope of the benefits.

Before buying Medigap insurance:

• See what other coverage is available. Many employers offer medical coverage to retirees—sometimes you pay for it, sometimes you don't. This insurance will cover hospitalization, drugs and doctors' fees, making a Medigap policy unnecessary. Continued coverage under an employer's plan, where the retiree pays the premiums, may seem expensive, but it can be a very good deal—and cheaper than a Medigap policy.

Another possibility is coverage under your spouse's medical plan.

• Review your cash flow. You may have a sufficient amount of money coming in to pay for a reasonable level of medical expenses, in which case it may not be worth it to buy a comprehensive Medigap policy. You need insurance to cover catastrophic illness and long-term hospitalization. On the other hand, if your cash flow is tight, it would make sense to purchase a Medigap policy, for all cases.

• Understand what Medicare does and doesn't pay for. This determines the "gap" and tells you what a good Medigap policy should cover. Bottom line: A good Medigap policy will pay almost all costs not picked up by Medicare.

Main categories of benefits:

• Hospital benefits. You pay the first $628 of hospital costs. After that deductible amount, Medicare pays all the costs for the first 60 days of hospitalization each year. For the next 30 days of hospitalization, you pay $157 a day and Medicare pays the remainder. In addition, you have a lifetime reserve of 60 days of hospitalization, of which you pay $314 a day and Medicare pays the rest.

A good Medigap policy will cover all the costs of hospitalization that are not reimbursed by Medicare, including hospitalization costs when Medicare runs out.

• Skilled nursing benefits. Following a hospital stay of at least three days, Medicare pays the full cost of skilled nursing care for the first 20 days. All costs over $78.50 are covered for the next 80 days.

A good Medigap policy will pay the $78.50 deductible and some of the cost of nursing care beyond 100 days.

Caution: For complete nursing-home coverage, you need an additional policy called a long-term-care policy.

• Doctor's bills, lab tests, etc. Medicare pays 80% of covered expenses that are not directly related to hospital confinement, after a $100 annual deductible amount. However, Medicare pays only 80% of what it recognizes as an allowable charge. Your doctor may charge $250, while Medicare only recognizes $200 and will pay only 80% of $200.

Some Medigap policies pick up only the 20% that Medicare doesn't pay. Other policies will pay up to 80% of charges that are considered by the insurer to be reasonable and customary for your area.

Point: Doctors are encouraged to accept Medicare as payment in full for their charges. Most don't. But if your doctor is among those who do, you might not need Medigap coverage for anything more than the 20% of the Medicare allowable fee that Medicare doesn't pay.

• Prescription drugs. Medicare pays for drugs you're given while you're in the hospital. But it does not pay for prescription drugs when you're out of the hospital. A good Medigap policy will pick up the cost of prescription drugs.

Other considerations:

• Know what's going to be and what's not going to be covered. Most insurance policies won't cover preexisting conditions. They won't cover you if you've had treatment for a condition in the three or so months before you took out the policy. (This exclusion is usually dropped after you've held the policy for some months.)

Note: If you're in good health, it does not make sense to pay extra for a policy with a reduced preexisting-condition restriction.

• Medigap policies will soon be easier to buy. The federal government has stepped in to protect buyers of Medigap policies. The government's insurance commissioners have selected nine types of Medigap policies that will soon be the only ones insurance companies can sell. This will make it easier for consumers to compare one company's policy against another.

Currently there are thousands of policies on the market with almost meaningless distinctions. Many confused consumers have been sold unnecessary, duplicative policies.

Source: John M. Walbridge, senior vice president, Hay/Huggins Co., Inc., benefits consultants, 1271 Avenue of the Americas, New York 10020.

Mail-Order Insurance Danger

Many insurance policies sold by mail are heavy on exclusions for preexisting conditions...deny a higher percentage of claims than traditional insurance companies...pay for only a small portion of a typical hospital stay...cover accidents but not illnesses...lure new members with unusually low introductory premiums, but then quickly jack up the rates...are not licensed in every state and may leave you without adequate protection if there's a dispute.

Source: *The New York Times Book of Personal Finance* by Leonard Sloane, financial columnist, Times Books, 201 E. 50 St., New York 10022.

9

Career Success

Age-Discrimination Laws

Age-discrimination laws can be circumvented with employment contracts. A federal court approved the firing of a man who had an employment contract that expired on his 70th birthday. The man was kept on for six more months, without a contract, then let go.

Court:

The action did not constitute mandatory retirement, which is illegal, but merely the legal termination of the services of someone whose contract had expired.

Source: *Harrington v. Aetna-Bearing,* USCD Noll, 1/30.

Popularity Secrets

Be more popular at work by helping colleagues...doing favors when you can...being pleasant—smiling and saying a few nice words when appropriate.

Also helpful:

Don't annoy others when they are working...or contribute to the rumor mill. Benefit: Popularity pays off—people root for co-workers they like.

Source: Robert Half, chairman, Robert Half International, recruiters, 2884 Sand Hill Rd., Menlo Park, California 94025.

How Safe Is Your Pension?

More and more people are discovering—to their horror—that they can't rely solely on their company's defined-benefit pension plan for retirement security. Some companies have even terminated plans.

And sometimes plans fail because of a company's financial problems or problems with an insurance company that provided a Guaranteed Income Contract.

Better Job Hunting

Wait a full week before responding to a help-wanted ad. Reason: Respond immediately and your letter will arrive with many others—and may not get the attention it deserves. Also: Employers are often discouraged by the quality of the initial wave of applicants and watch eagerly for someone really good to apply. Don't worry that you'll somehow miss the boat by waiting. The hiring process typically takes weeks…and frequently months.

Source: *Fast Track to the Best Job: How to Launch a Successful Career Right Out of College by Bruce* J. Bloom, Blazer Books, Box 1153, Scarsdale, New York 10583.

Better Networking

Arrive 15 minutes early for meetings…approach events as if you are the host rather than a guest—take the initiative to introduce yourself…carry a large stack of business cards… get a card from every contact that you make… have a pen or pencil handy to make notes on cards you get…talk sincerely with a few people instead of rushing madly from person to person…follow up the next day with a phone call to anyone who has expressed interest.

Source: *Getting Business to Come to You* by self-employment consultant Paul Edwards, Jeremy P. Tarcher, Inc., 5858 Wilshire Blvd., Los Angeles 90036.

Pushing Employees Too Hard Backfires

In tough times, when employees are afraid of losing their jobs, many bosses exploit them, knowing that they'll be willing to work harder to stay employed. Trap: Pressing employees to *just do it* invites dishonesty. Reason: Pressure generated from the message *Just get it done, or else* can cause rules to be bent, data to be fabricated and reports to be buried—all in the interest of getting quick

results. Prevention: Set realistic goals, provide reasonable time, support and resources and ask all employees to speak up if the expectations are unfair.

Source: Barbara Ley Toffler, partner, Resources for Responsible Management, Boston consultants, writing in *The New York Times*.

Keeping Employees Happy Has Extra Benefits

Instead of looking for ways to cut costs by eliminating workers, inventive plant managers are finding ways to use workers more efficiently. This improves employee morale, thereby increasing the quality of the products—keeping customers happy.

Source: Charles R. Day, editor, *Industry Week,* 1100 Superior Ave., Cleveland 44114.

Hiring Basic

The best candidate for a job is often someone who already works for the company—who is well-known and well-respected…or someone who left under favorable circumstances (accepted early retirement, went to work for a subsidiary or joint venture partner, etc.).

Source: Robert Half, Robert Half International, Box 3000, Menlo Park, California 94026.

One-On-One Training Schedule

Allow at least one hour for each training session. Never go beyond two hours. It's best to work in an uncluttered place. Important: No interruptions. Best times: Ask a "morning person" to come in half an hour early and spend one full hour at the beginning of the day in training. Have a "late day" person stay half an hour after regular quitting time. And, be sure training starts punctually—to allow for a full hour's interaction.

Source: *Training for Non-Trainers: A Do-It-Yourself Guide for Managers,* by Carolyn Nilson, PhD, trainer, Amacom, 135 W. 50 St., New York 10020.

Networking Power

Managers who excel at their work are often the least well connected. Result: When they need a favor, or are looking for a job, they have trouble. By contrast, managers who spend time getting to know others in their companies, their industries and their communities are usually the ones with the most resources to draw upon when they are in need. Secret: Volunteer work is also helpful in networking. Volunteer to help with the community newspaper or in the school system.

Source: Gilda Carle, PhD, InterChange Communications, training consultants, 117 DeHaven Dr., Yonkers, New York 10703.

How Your Company Can Get Tax Benefits

Business insurance is a big opportunity area for tax savings. A well-designed program of life insurance, health insurance and other key insurance policies can cut corporate taxes…while it benefits all of the company's managers and employees. Areas to look at…

Tax avoidance strategies:

At a time when businesses must get the most for every dollar, it doesn't make sense for companies to pay insurance premiums on policies that will pay big benefits to the IRS. Yet that's just what many companies are doing.

While life insurance proceeds are income-tax free, they are subject to estate tax at rates of up to 55%. So the IRS may collect more than half of the proceeds paid out under an executive's group term coverage.

Many executives neglect to think of how

estate taxes can reduce their insurance benefits. Common mistakes:

•They believe that the $600,000 estate tax exemption will protect them. But even executives who are cash-poor may be well over the $600,000 limit when they total up their home equity.

•Married executives assume that insurance proceeds will pass to a spouse tax-free due to the estate tax marital deduction. However, this won't be the case if the spouse dies with the executive in an accident, or if the executive divorces or outlives the spouse. And even when policy proceeds do pass to a spouse tax-free, they will be taxed when the spouse dies.

Smart companies help themselves and their employees to get the most from group-term coverage by providing estate tax planning advice as part of the insurance program.

Key: Employees can be instructed on how to set up an irrevocable life insurance trust to hold an insurance policy for the benefit of family members. Three years after an executive's insurance coverage is transferred to the trust, policy proceeds become excludable from his/her taxable estate.

Opportunity: By providing planning advice to those receiving group insurance, the company may as much as double the benefits that employees keep—while effectively halving the premium cost for each dollar of benefits.

Off-balance-sheet compensation:

Another benefit a company can provide for its own benefit as well as an executive's is split-dollar life insurance.

How it works: A whole-life insurance policy on the executive's life is purchased. The policy proceeds will be paid to the executive's family—but the company retains the right to recover the premiums it has paid if the executive dies. Benefits:

•The company can use its accumulated value in the policy to pay future benefits to the executive, perhaps in the form of supplemental retirement payments.

•The company gets off-balance-sheet treatment for the supplemental retirement benefit given to the executive. Other unfunded compensation obligations create a liability on the balance sheet. But every $1 of premiums paid on a split-dollar policy creates a $1 asset of value on the balance sheet.

As with term insurance, the executive may give away his/her interest in a split-dollar policy, or assign it to an insurance trust to avoid estate taxes.

Buybacks:

Private businesses almost always need life insurance to finance the purchase of shares of owners who die or leave the business, and to fund future estate taxes due on the value of the business when an owner dies.

The way such insurance arrangements are set up can have a major impact on their after-tax cost.

Buyback agreements: When a company has more than one owner, there are two ways of using insurance to provide the money needed to buy back the shares of any owner who dies...

•The company can buy insurance on the life of each owner.

•The owners can insure each other.

In each case, 100% of the company will pass to the surviving owners—but there's a big tax difference.

Example: A company now worth $2 million was built from scratch by two owners with equal shares. One of the owners dies. The company buys the deceased owner's share for $1 million. The surviving owner then sells the business. His taxable gain will be $2 million—the business's value minus his original investment in it.

By contrast, if each of the two owners instead buys a $1 million policy on the other, the surviving owner will acquire a $1 million cost basis in the deceased owner's stock when he uses the policy proceeds to buy it. His gain on a subsequent sale of the business will be only $1 million, because his purchase of the shares increases his investment in the company by $1 million. Result: $1 million of taxable gain is avoided.

Because of this tax advantage, owners are usually better off owning insurance on each other personally, rather than having the company own it, when the number of shareholders is small enough to make it practical.

Of course, owners must pay for insurance they buy on each other. But the company can increase their compensation accordingly—as long as it remains reasonable.

The company's deduction for compensation will roughly offset the income tax on the extra pay, resulting in little or no total extra cost.

Estate taxes: The Tax Code gives private companies two breaks which help finance estate taxes due on the value of the business when an owner dies.

•Section 6166: Allows estate taxes to be deferred for four years—with only interest due in that period—and then the taxes can be paid in 10 annual installments with interest.

•Section 303: Allows a company to redeem stock to pay estate tax. The money received from the company is favorably taxed as proceeds from a sale, rather than as a dividend, reducing the tax due.

Mistake: Thinking these tax breaks eliminate the need to have insurance to pay estate taxes. Both impose cash-flow costs on the company (to pay interest or finance the redemption) at a time of crisis—when the key executive must be replaced.

Recommended: For a sole owner, the best idea is to use an insurance trust. The insurance policy proceeds can be used to finance estate taxes. Although the trust is outside the owner's estate, it can lend money to the estate or actually purchase the stock from the estate. Place money in the trust and have that trust buy an insurance policy. This will keep the policy proceeds out of the owner's estate even if the owner dies immediately.

If the owner buys the policy and donates it to the trust, policy proceeds will be taxed back to his estate—if he dies within three years.

Liability and disability:

Life insurance is usually the primary focus of a company's insurance programs, but liability and disability insurance for the owners and key executives may actually be of more immediate importance for many businesses.

Key: Executives in their prime typically face less risk of dying in the coming year than they do of becoming disabled and/ or becoming a party to a liability lawsuit. In either case, the result for the company can be a disaster.

Liability trap: Anyone can be in an auto accident—but highly paid executives and company owners are much more likely to be sued by accident victims because their high pay and accumulated assets make them a tempting target for plaintiff's lawyers who work on a contingency fee basis.

The typical auto insurance policy provides $100,000/$300,000 liability coverage—that is, $300,000 per accident, and $100,000 per individual plaintiff. And that's just not enough in these days of spiraling health costs and skyrocketing court damage awards. Dangers:

•A business owner who loses a lawsuit for more than his insurance coverage may lose his interest in the business. The other owners are then confronted with either an unwanted partner, or the task of raising the money to buy the new partner out.

•A key executive who is sued for more than his coverage will be distracted from his job by more important worries—protecting his home and life savings. This can only hurt his business performance.

Fortunately, there's a simple solution to the liability problem. All liability insurers offer "excess liability insurance" in million dollar increments at low cost—for example, the cost is about $200 per year for the first million dollars in high-cost New York.

The company should require all owners and key executives to have adequate excess liability insurance. Even better, it can buy it for them. The cost is slight and is deductible as a business expense. The trouble avoided may be enormous.

Source: Thomas J. Hakala, CPA, JD, tax partner, KPMG Peat Marwick, 345 Park Ave., New York 10154.

The Simple Secrets Of Quality Improvement

It's easy to jump on the quality band-wagon—and announce to the world that the company considers quality its #1 Priority. Unfortunately, getting impressive results is much harder than making costly mistakes in the quest for quality. I've identified eight common mistakes US companies make with great regularity…

Mistake: Failing to select a quality-improvement program tailored to the company's unique needs, culture and experience. This happens when a top executive tries to introduce a well-known quality improvement program simply because so many other companies use it.

Problem: No single quality improvement program fits every company. Good results require a good fit. Examples:

•Ford and Deming in the early 1980s. Ford determined that to manufacture better cars, it had to have parts which consistently met specifications. Since Deming's focus is on reducing production process variations, the partnership worked well.

•Caterpillar got good results by adopting a quality program from the Juran Institute. Caterpillar has an engineering-oriented culture. They emphasize the development of meticulous plans. Juran develops planned approaches to quality. That partnership worked.

•Johnson & Johnson has a strong sales and marketing culture, so they worked well with a top-level consulting firm that urges companies to rally the troops around the banner of zero defects.

Mistake: Delegating responsibility for implementing a quality-improvement program. If a chief executive does this, it sends the wrong message to the workforce. Worse: Lower-level executives don't have the perspective and clout needed to make a quality improvement program take hold in a large company.

Mistake: Failing to manage quality improvement as an integral component of the company's vital interests. When it is a particular executive's program, not a company program, the entire concept of quality becomes an ego matter—not a critical company issue.

Result: Inadequate motivation for quality improvement.

Better: The most successful companies embrace quality improvement as essential for satisfying customers and securing competitive advantages. While there will surely be debate on the most effective ways to improve quality, the mission of improving quality will endure regardless of who is in the chief executive suite.

Mistake: Pursuing quality improvement procedures rather than substance. Florida Power & Light several years ago set its sights on winning the Deming Prize. This required elaborate documentation of quality improvement.

The company did achieve significant gains...reducing power outages, etc. And, customer satisfaction improved. FPL won the Deming Prize, but the company became so preoccupied with statistical methods and the formal data collection that it developed a whole new bureaucracy that slowed down the company's overall operations. That bureaucracy has since been dismantled. Other companies have had similar experiences in pursuing the Baldrige Award.

Better: Quality improvement as an approach to achieving strategic results. The program must be implemented in the context of hard cost and efficiency goals.

Mistake: Failing to provide quality improvement teams adequate guidance. Result: Anarchy. Executives err when they let teams do their own thing. Hundreds of people go off in different directions, accomplishing little. This happened for a while at General Motors.

Mistake: Focusing on complaints as the primary measure of customer satisfaction. In many companies, customer service is driven by complaints. Customers receive little attention unless they complain. This is misguided for two reasons...

First: Many customers who don't complain become quietly angry because they're neglected. When their patience is exhausted, they switch to a competitor.

Second: Complaints are generally a poor gauge of performance. They don't reveal what really contributes to customer satisfaction.

Better: Managers and front-line employees must plan their time so they can stay in touch with all customers. This enables them to address problems before they lose business and to focus on the sources of customer satisfaction, not dissatisfaction.

Mistake: Limiting market research to current customers. This can be misleading, because most current customers are at least partially satisfied with a company's performance, or else they would have already switched to competitors. Managers can easily become complacent.

Better: Survey former customers to find out why they left. Survey customers of competitors to see why they prefer another company. They'll offer some bad news, which is probably why their views are commonly overlooked. But the result should be to stimulate corrective action while there's still time.

Mistake: Making uninformed assumptions about the kinds of quality improvement customers want. Detroit automakers long assumed that when American customers talked about quality, they meant more features. Detroit added features, and millions of American customers bought Japanese cars. Years passed before Detroit executives figured out that what Americans wanted was reliability.

Research pays: A bank assumed customers wanted less waiting in line, so it took steps to cut waiting time about 50% to five minutes. Some customers actually became more dissatisfied. A lot of senior citizens liked waiting in line, because it was an opportunity for socializing. What they wanted was less paperwork to get bank services.

Quality can mean many things. Survey customers to find out what they want most, so quality improvement efforts will be focused properly.

Source: David Garvin, Robert and Jane Cizik Professor of Business Administration, Harvard Business School, Soldiers Field, Boston 02163.

All About Authority

A company's management style—the habits and techniques used by managers to exercise authority—are usually the main causes of serious productivity and morale problems.

But management style is often the last cause acknowledged by top management when trying to diagnose problems.

Symptoms of misuse of authority:

• Workers become frustrated and productivity drops.

• Disputes erupt among previously friendly employees.

• Absenteeism rises.

• Turnover rate increases.

Worse: Employees sabotage operations. Examples: Workers in fast-food restaurants who flip hamburgers on the floor…auto workers who put their own "signature" defects on cars.

Where managers go wrong:

There are three main ways authority is misused by managers…

• The autonomous boss. Many businesses fall into the trap of putting one manager in control of so many subordinates that they rarely have access to the boss when they need it.

These managers typically operate in their own world. Though they might be fair and even gregarious by nature, their tight schedules leave little time to solve unexpected problems, let alone to build trust among the staff. They seldom visit the shop floor or white-collar work areas. They work behind closed doors.

In this situation, employees become frustrated because they can't get close enough to the boss to figure out what motivates him/her…what he/she expects from them…and what his/her reasons are for those expectations.

Workers might not like the reasons, but they still need to know them. Otherwise, they begin taking less and less responsibility. It's just too risky.

Some workers who have an autonomous boss will try to learn more about their boss by working the rumor mill. But that often backfires, if only because what they learn may be incorrect or out of date.

• The authority hoarder. Other companies concentrate authority in a small group of executives, but try to disperse responsibility throughout a larger group of middle managers and their subordinates.

Example: A manager gives several subordinates responsibility for completing a task. But the manager denies them the authority to purchase needed supplies or hire competent workers to assist them. Instead, the manager hoards that authority.

Especially vulnerable: Companies where sales depend heavily on the boss's personal relationship with customers…and entrepreneurial businesses where a few executives retain authority long after the company has grown to the point where authority can be dispersed.

On paper, keeping authority at a high level might look like an effective bureaucratic structure. But it doesn't always work in practice. Reasons:

• When employees begin new tasks, they rarely know exactly what resources they'll need. It's difficult for workers to perform tasks smoothly if they must constantly interrupt it by going to a boss for authority.

• Bosses who don't dispense authority along with responsibility waste their own time on decisions they could more easily delegate.

In the end, subordinates begin shirking responsibility because they don't have the authority to take action.

• The credit-hogging boss. Every time a subordinate comes up with a good idea, some bosses take the credit and give no recognition to the subordinate. Often, this type of boss is also quick to blame the subordinates when mistakes are actually the boss's fault.

In some companies, that type of behavior has gone on for so long that it has become part of the management style. In those cases, bosses are even open and frank about appropriating credit.

When credit-hogging has become part of the corporate culture, employees may tolerate it for a surprisingly long time. But eventually they'll want responsibility of their own. When they're unable to get it, their frustration leads to disputes, productivity declines, etc.

Preventing the problems:

The challenge for top management is to

create an environment where managers do not want to, or at least, cannot exercise the destructive habits described above. Effective preventive measures...

• Clearly communicate the company's management rules and values—in one-on-one meetings—to every manager and subordinate. When rules and limitations are vague, managers take the opportunity to hoard credit or deny authority, even when what they do is against company policy. The responsibility of superiors is to eliminate this opportunity by instilling the values of cooperation, coaching and personal growth in everyone.

• The CEO should monitor the total performance of managers. Often, top executives look only at managers' results, not at how they achieved them. A closer look, for instance, may show that the CEO's own demands on managers' time prevent the managers from being accessible to subordinates.

• Instruct managers to give subordinates reasons for their actions. Aim: To prevent any sense of arbitrary action on the part of managers.

• Let managers be seen more often—even if it's not possible to give them more time to be accessible. Even office design matters. Giving managers offices with glass doors, for example, makes authority more visible and makes it seem less distant.

• Have managers list the times they've given credit to a subordinate. If the occasions are few, tell managers their own evaluations will be based in part on how well they share credit. Management training courses may be useful.

Caution:

If the CEO is a credit-hoarder, it may be impossible to change the bureaucratic style unless the CEO is willing to change.

• Judge job applicants on how well they would fit into a constructive management style. Unfortunately, interviewers often talk to applicants about wages and benefits, but avoid questions about the management style they've worked in.

Applicants who are used to substantial authority, for instance, may not do well as subordinates in a bureaucracy where they

have little. Or managers accustomed to spending time with their staff may not last long in a company where their time is taken up with other duties.

Source: Dr. Howell S. Baum, a specialist in organizational behavior and professor of urban studies and planning, University of Maryland, College Park 20742. Baum is the author of *Invisible Bureaucracy,* Oxford University Press, 200 Madison Ave., New York 10016, and *Organizational Membership,* State University of New York Press, State University Plaza, Albany, New York 12246.

Provide A Line To The Top

Every employee should have a way to communicate with top management, either anonymously or personally, through an accepted procedure that avoids going through a supervisor or outside channels. Example: A suggestion box that is regularly read only by top management. Advantages: Employees are more likely to blow the whistle on wrongdoing in the company, participate in crime- or drug-prevention programs and report employee theft. Key: Employees must trust management to take action on their behalf.

Source: Rick Crandall, PhD, editor, *Executive Edge,* Box 37, Corte Madera, California 94976.

Leadership Development

Many companies have gotten good at hiring managers with growth potential and ambition. But beyond setting minimum performance goals, few do anything to help managers learn the skills needed to develop into higher-level leaders.

Solution: Stimulate learning by giving these talented managers intense challenges, such as special projects or turnarounds. Make sure constant, effective coaching of potential leaders is always available. Consider setting up a special executive development staff of senior officers and/or outside consultants to make sure managers with strong growth potential get the opportunities, training, feedback and criticism needed for steady, significant improvement.

Source: Morgan McCall Jr., Center for Effective Organizations, quoted in *Behavioral Sciences,* 45 Whitney Rd., Mahwah, New Jersey 07430.

Incentives Go A Long Way

Incentives can hold key managers during a restructuring—making it less likely that they will leave just when their expertise is most needed to smooth a tough transition. Helpful: Special awards for executives who play a role in the sale of their units…retention bonuses for employees who stay during restructuring.

Source: David Swinford, executive compensation specialist, William M. Mercer, Inc., 1166 Ave. of the Americas, New York 10036, quoted in *CompFlash,* 135 W. 50 St., New York 10020.

Discrimination Complications

Physical fitness tests of job applicants can be illegal if they discriminate against women—psychologically. In a case, the judge admitted that sawmill jobs required strength and endurance, but nonetheless found the testing, which disqualified a lot more women than men, was unacceptable because women waiting to take the test *were treated in ways that caused tension and anxiety.*

Source: *EEOC v. Simpson Timber,* USDC Wash., 1/7.

How To Settle A Labor Dispute

Settling a labor dispute without going through formal arbitration procedures is con-

sidered by the National Labor Relations Board to be a legal outcome—as long as both sides make concessions—even if individual employees aren't happy with the deal. A court decision upholds the Board policy.

Source: *Plumbers and Pipefitters v. NLRB,* USCA DC, 2/11.

Sexual Harassment

In a sexual harassment case, the concept of a "reasonable woman" test has replaced the "reasonable person" test, which was considered male-biased. A court ruling said courts must focus on the female victim and judge if harassment is conduct that a "reasonable woman" would consider sufficiently severe or pervasive to *alter the conditions of employment and create an abusive working environment.*

Source: *Ellison v. Brady,* CA 9,1991, 54 FEP Cases 1346, reported in T*he Webb Report,* 4044 NE 58 St., Seattle 98105.

Executive Protection

When three workers were killed in a tunnel explosion, OSHA brought criminal charges against the company and the executive who was project manager. He protested. Court of Appeals: OSHA can only penalize "employers"—defined as companies and their officers and directors, not lower-level managers. Since the project manager was not an "employer," charges against him were dismissed.

Source: *U.S. v. Patrick J. Doig,* CA-7, No. 91-1394.

To Boost Performance

Two groups of people confronted the same problem—how to make the best use of a limited resource. One group received a lecture from an expert explaining how to approach the problem. The other group only received the facts, and was asked to develop an approach on its own. Result: The second group produced far superior performance. This experiment, which was conducted during World War II, remains a classic today. It points out that group participation in decision-making is not a "kinder, gentler" way to manage—but a way to get results.

Source: Experiment by anthropologist Margaret Mead, cited in *On Achieving Excellence*, 555 Hamilton Ave., Palo Alto, California 94301.

Innovative Rewards

For a high-performing employee: Lunch with a top manager...company president phones a personal "thank you"...a letter to the employee's family praising a recent accomplishment...a modest gift relating to the employee's hobby...award high-performers a three-day weekend...take a group of them to lunch. Key: Make rewards unique, frequent and fun.

Source: Dr. Ken Blanchard, management consultant, writing in *Personal Selling Power*, 1127 International Pkwy., Fredericksburg, Virginia 22405.

How To Retain Your Best Employees

Even in tough economic times, when employees hold on to their jobs because their options are limited, the people who do leave are too often the company's most valuable ones. To retain those top employees, follow this acronym—R.E.T.A.I.N.S.

• Respect all employees. Avoid criticizing them in public...but don't hesitate to praise them in the presence of others.

• Empower talented employees who can handle authority well. Good people need challenges. And they deserve the authority to take responsibility for their actions. Some of their decisions will be wrong. But making

wrong decisions is better than being forbidden to make decisions at all. That kind of restriction is the quickest way to lose talented employees.

• Team players are often the best performers. Build teams, and give them leaders who show clear talent in managing cooperative groups.

• Acknowledge outstanding performance by promoting from within. A strong incentive for good people to look elsewhere is created when outsiders are hired despite the fact that more than enough qualified talent is available inside the company.

• Ideas and innovation are important to talented employees. Never discourage or dismiss creative thinking by talented employees. Doing so will force them to find receptive ears elsewhere.

• Never say, *never*. Top performers will quit if too many restrictions are put on them.

• Salary and benefits must stay competitive. Be sensitive to the fact that exceptional medical benefits are often more important to a valuable employee than a bigger paycheck.

Source: Robert Half, Robert Half International, Box 3000, Menlo Park, California 94026.

Improve Job Security Policies

To eliminate employee fears of being fired unfairly, employers are developing company discipline and grievance procedures, whether or not they are working with a union contract. Aim: Increased employee satisfaction, reduced likelihood of union problems or wrongful discharge suits.

Recommended:

Adopt a system of progressive disciplinary actions that is consistent throughout the company. Train supervisors to document and counsel problem employees. Develop an internal arbitration system.

Source: Mark McQueen, attorney, Berens & Tate, writing in *Laborwatch*, 10050 Regency Circle, Omaha, Nebraska 68114.

Laughing On The Job

Ninety-six percent of executives believe that people with a sense of humor do better at their jobs than those with little or none. Reasons: People who laugh frequently tend to be good communicators, team players and stress-relievers.

Source: Robert Half, Robert Half International, Box 3000, Menlo Park, California 94026.

College Campus Smarts

Use a college campus as the site of a company training program. During summer months and holidays, colleges have an abundance of unused classroom space, and often dormitory space as well. The facilities are, of course, designed for teaching and learning. They are likely to be more convenient than using the company's own premises, and much less expensive than renting space in a hotel or a commercial meetings facility.

Source: Dennis Stostad, director of education and training, State Farm Insurance, Austin, Texas, quoted in *Creative Training Techniques,* 50 S. Ninth St., Minneapolis 55402.

How To Solve The Problem Of Problem Employees

Even at well-run companies such as Stew Leonard's, Delta Airlines and Wal-Mart, talented managers stumble on the job of identifying and dealing with employees who are strong in certain areas—but have major personality problems that hurt the company.

I've done extensive research and consulting in this area. In the process, I've learned that managers are greatly helped by first understanding the major categories of problem employees. These are...

•Failure Avoiders. Though almost every organization has a group of people who could be characterized as failure avoiders, they are usually very hard to detect.

Reason: They tend to be loyal, hard-working and well-liked because they don't represent a threat to others. They avoid confrontation—even to the point of failing to offer constructive criticism to their associates. In meetings, they'll answer direct questions, but won't take the initiative to offer anything innovative. When they disagree or if a subject is controversial, they don't speak up. Instead of thinking in terms of success and failure, they think only about failure and how to avoid it.

Failure avoiders are rarely found in top management because they're careful to insulate themselves from becoming victims of the Peter Principle—being promoted to their level of incompetence. But they can be a menace as middle managers because they'll make only safe decisions, instead of facing risks that the company really needs to take. Their decisions (by default) leave the company following paths of inertia which can put the entire organization at risk over the long-term.

Example: Not making needed personnel changes. Failure avoiders dislike change because it represents uncertainty and the threat of failure. Decisions to terminate, add or move people all spell bad news to them.

Solution: Don't always tell them exactly what to do or expect them to do only what they're told. That encourages failure avoiders. When delegating to them, make them accept and commit to responsibilities in front of their peers. Keep them in positions where the objectives have been well-defined—the work of today. Keep them away from the cutting edge work of tomorrow where subjective and creative decisions need to be made about the future.

•Mavericks. Companies need innovators, but they don't always need mavericks. Businesses are organized to enable people to do things as a group working together that they would not do as individuals. There are many examples of star performers in the sports field who aren't real assets because they aren't team players. Though mavericks can make

163

significant contributions in the right jobs, they are menaces if not controlled.

Example: When I was CEO of a computer services company, my best programmer was a maverick. He worked only on what interested him and wouldn't keep records of how he spent his time. We finally let him go—unfortunately the only viable action to take with most mavericks. He ended up in freelance contract programming, which was where he belonged—not in an organization.

•Those on the road to obsolescence. Most managers spend a disproportionate amount of time trying to decide what to do with employees who are marginal— not doing well enough to promote or poorly enough to let go. Like a dull, persistent headache, keeping marginal performers makes managers uncomfortable because they represent a problem without a clear-cut solution.

Main problem with these people: High costs in counterproductive time...lost customers...sales that should have been made but weren't...declining morale among productive workers who can't understand why the company tolerates such dullards.

Solution: Ask yourself if you'd be happy if an employee quit. If the answer is yes—for a long-time employee—try putting the person in a different position...downgrade his/her present job...take some action like retraining or restructuring the job to help make the person more productive.

For newer hires, simply admit a mistake was made and terminate them. In my experience, most workers would happily accept a lateral transfer or even a demotion rather than face termination.

Special problem: CEOs, and even founders of companies, can eventually become obsolete. The time came with one of my own companies when I found myself beginning to cling too much to the past and avoiding innovative risks. Fortunately I was able to turn over the running of the company to others and pursue other interests before I became a menace to the company.

Solution: All managers should ask themselves, *Who in my organizational group (including myself) is susceptible to becoming obsolete because of changes taking place either outside or inside the organization? What steps can I take to give my associates and me a fair chance of remaining productive?*

•Egomaniacs in the executive suite can be either liabilities or assets. As assets, their determination, persistence and drive can provide much-needed strength and leadership (even against overwhelming odds) when a company is in turmoil.

As liabilities, they tend to be autocratic, giving only lip service to participative management. They display poor human relations skills. They may obsessively pursue objectives far beyond the point at which they should be altered or abandoned. They strive to be irreplaceable. Because of these tendencies, they're such poor role models that they cause organizations to lose many of their best people.

Solutions: Recognize the problem and watch for closet egomaniacs who don't show their true colors until they've been promoted several times. Encourage a policy of participative management through regular meetings. Promote the importance of open communication among team members by setting the example. The more top managers tell their subordinates, the more you'll receive in return. Ask associates for their opinions without telegraphing your own. Don't punish the bearer of bad news. Admit your own mistakes and encourage others to do the same...and learn from them.

•Those who can't get along with others. When employees fight with each other, it's usually about who has a certain responsibility.

Solution: Clarify company policies ... develop better descriptions of job responsibilities...clarify authority. When conflicts occur, approach the people with the mindset that conflicts will not be tolerated and will be resolved for the good of overall performance. If conflicts arise between people who answer to different managers but must work together, such as sales and production people, their respective managers should agree on a position, then meet with the antagonists and issue an ultimatum that if they can't learn to work in harmony, their jobs will be in jeopardy.

Source: Everett T. Suters, Atlanta-based businessman, consultant, speaker and author of several books, one of which is *The Unnatural Act of Management,* Harper-Business, 10 E. 53 St., New York 10022.

How To Stay On The Critical Cutting Edge Of New-Product Development

Brilliant engineers and designers are obviously essential to any company trying to stay on the cutting edge of new-product development.

But if these high-paid professionals are mismanaged, or undermanaged, by top management, there's no chance that the best results will emerge.

What top management is responsible for:

•Planning: Determining who is going to do what in the new-product development process and setting milestones for measuring progress.

•Anticipating contingencies: Putting the collective experience and skills of the company to work figuring out what could go wrong as a new product is developed, how problems can be corrected and what criteria to use to kill a project.

Making maximum use of resources:

Effective management of new-product development requires making the best use of the company's resources…and recognizing when the company may have to go outside to supplement its capacities. Keys:

•People resources. A common mistake is to assign people to a new-product development team because they are available. But it rarely pays to use only the available talent. Important: Find the best talent for a specific new-product assignment.

Common problem: Managers of marketing, manufacturing, finance or other functions put "available" people on the development team but then replace them when another assignment turns up within their own lines of authority. Or they keep a tight rein on the team members so that they never consider the work of the development team a priority.

In addition to putting the most talented innovators on the team, assign someone from every company function that will eventually be involved in producing, financing and selling the new product—at the beginning. Include those involved with regulators or with environmental issues. Or, at least, make sure to set up timely communications among these functions.

•Technical resources. It's essential to use these effectively. Typical technical traps that can be avoided…

1.Mismanaging skills. The new product needs a particular skill or technology the company lacks—such as operation of an electronic measuring device. Rather than look outside for that skill, the company assigns an existing employee to bring himself/herself up to date on the subject—rarely the best way to come up with a solution.

2.Underestimating the competition. Gather competitive technical intelligence on an ongoing basis. Use the trade media and professional associations. Rather than assembling a grab-bag of information, review it thoughtfully…strategically. At least twice a year, write down an estimate of what the next year's competition will look like at the technical level. What will the standards be? Is the company compatible? What new features are likely to be introduced?

Marketing plans:

Screen all new-product concepts in their early stages to be sure the company has the resources to support the best ones on the market. As the product is being developed—and its specifications change—be sure it is not likely to damage the company's reputation in the market.

Goal: No surprises. As technologies and markets advance, as specifications for the product change, as the development team discovers what is technically feasible and estimates costs, make sure the people in the company who will have to live with the product when it's produced and sold know what's happening. Ensure that they have a way to respond quickly if they spot a problem.

Things you don't want employees saying later: *We didn't know about this specification. We can't make it that way now. It will take us six months to tool up to do it. Can you change the design so it will be easier and cheaper for us to make?*

The high cost of failure:

Innovators can dream. But managers must be realistic about new products. Plan for success and failure. No company can succeed with each effort. And a major failure in the marketplace can seriously hurt a company internally.

Set milestones—and stick to them—so senior management can make realistic go/no-go decisions along the line. If the product is so changed from its initial concept because of limits encountered by the development team, it may no longer be attractive to the market. Or its cost-benefit ratio can get so out of line that nobody will buy it.

A key part of management success in new-product development is knowing when to kill an idea before it gets too far along. Helpful: Enough new alternate opportunities.

Source: Stephen E. Rudolph, vice president and managing director, product technology, Arthur D. Little, Inc., Acorn Park, Cambridge, Massachusetts 02140.

Cost-Cutting Checklist: The Important Basics

Companies have gotten very good at cutting costs by cutting payrolls. This relieves financial pressure for the short term.

But few businesses have begun to take advantage of the many, important continuous ways to make big cuts, without sacrificing quality or efficiency. Here are eight of the most often overlooked cost-cutting opportunities today...

•Speed up decision-making. Time and business opportunities are wasted when decisions must be referred up the corporate lad-

der and back down again—over several weeks...or months. Savings can be realized by having decisions made at the lowest possible level.

Top executives should give the company's customer service representatives clear guidelines for making decisions, then stay out of the way unless problems require intervention.

•Simplify systems. The more complex a system, the more people are driven to pursue wasteful practices. To minimize costly set-up time, companies frequently adopt "batch processing" which means that individual customers are served only after an entire batch of orders is processed. Unfinished inventory piles up until people further down the line are ready to handle it. Better: Constantly look for ways to streamline systems.

Example: General Motors streamlined its set-up procedures for certain metal-stamping machines from 12 hours to 18 minutes.

•Cut out useless paperwork. Businesses think they're doing this, but they rarely go far enough. Almost all executives routinely get reports they never use. Sometimes these reports are generated for internal political reasons. Sometimes it's because no one has questioned their rationale.

Regardless of the reason, such reports waste the time of the people who produce, copy, distribute and dispose of them. When a report becomes clearly useless—get rid of it for good.

•Organize and manage meetings more productively. Many meetings perform functions that are better handled on a one-to-one basis. In addition, meeting agendas often don't make clear how people should prepare.

Finally, meetings commonly start late. If a 12-person meeting starts just 10 minutes late, already two person-hours have been wasted. Because late starts tend to mean late finishes, it's likely that other people will then be wasting time waiting around for subsequent appointments.

•Eliminate useless committees. Large companies are especially prone to setting up committees whenever it seems "appropriate" to do so. Sometimes the committees never should have existed, because they didn't add value for customers. In other cases, committees had a legitimate purpose when they were formed, but then they continue to chew up the time of participants long after their mission has been fulfilled. Either way, they should be disbanded.

•Reduce wasted space. Savings from lower-rent office space are often cancelled out by losses due to inefficient building layout. When the design of building systems, the location of columns, wiring for telecommunications, etc. are inappropriate, long-term losses are inevitable.

Solutions: Waste can be cut by moving to a building with a more efficient layout. Space can also sometimes be used more effectively.

Example: Since files tend to occupy a lot of space, throw out everything that isn't required for legal reasons or that almost certainly won't be used again.

•Reduce the need to move materials. Just-in-time operations have come a long way in the US, but not far enough. High inventory levels and inadequate planning still force many companies to put materials in places where they shouldn't be. Consequently, they must be moved one or more times before actually being used.

One Japanese car maker had a key supplier locate immediately next door, and punched a hole in the factory wall, so materials could be moved the shortest possible distance as needed.

•Cut inventory—even further. Because of unreliable quality, companies order more inventory to make sure of having enough usable material. That incurs higher costs, and inspection of incoming material. Eliminate this type of excess by setting higher quality standards, being more selective among suppliers and helping suppliers upgrade their quality and performance.

For the most part, these eight kinds of waste are best identified by lower level people. Top executives, surveys repeatedly show, know about fewer than 10% of all the problems in their companies.

And if supervisors and rank-and-file employees uncover wasteful processes they have been involved with, don't criticize them for the waste—applaud them for getting rid of it.

Source: Richard C. Whiteley, vice-chairman, Forum Corporation, management consultants, One Exchange Place, Boston 02109, and author of *The Customer-Driven Company,* Addison-Wesley, Rte. 128, Reading, Massachusetts 01867.

How To Avoid Laying Off Workers

In many cases, shutting a plant, or eliminating an entire division—along with its employees—is essential to the company's survival.

But in at least as many cases, there is a less unpleasant alternative—offering employees a period of unpaid vacation, with the promise of being asked back to work in the future.

How a company uses non-paid leave depends on individual circumstances. If times are really tough and it must shut down production at several facilities, it might require many weeks of mandatory unpaid vacation. That is probably the least popular type of unpaid leave, and some efforts run into union resistance.

In other cases, a slow period may be easily survived by offering voluntary unpaid leave to a group of employees, knowing that not all will accept the offer.

Advantages of unpaid leave over layoffs…

•Stronger competitive position. This is an important plus because most companies' worst fear is losing ground to the competition while their company is in turmoil during a layoff process.

•Better financial condition. Downsizing costs money—severance, benefits, rehiring and retraining. Much of this expense can be avoided by using unpaid leave.

•Greater continuity. Companies that use unpaid leave can usually maintain research and development programs and continue to introduce new products or services because they keep the same team in place, though at reduced hours, instead of having to retrain a new team after a layoff period.

The most powerful positive result of using non-paid vacation time to avoid layoffs is the message it sends to employees— *We care about you…we're trying to find an alternative to layoffs.*

Downside: The only drawback of unpaid leave that we've discovered is the risk that some valuable employees may want or need to earn full pay. If other full-time job opportunities are available in the area, the company may lose those employees. Management can consult with these individuals and suggest that they take on free-lance work, or help a spouse find work—so the employees are able to stay with the company and maintain their income level.

Source: Virginia M. Lord, senior vice president, Right Associates, a consulting firm specializing in human resources and career management, 1818 Market St., Philadelphia 19103.

Ways To Reduce Workplace Injuries

Traditionally, the main type of common workplace injuries were slips, trips and falls in factories. And serious physical injuries are still commonly associated with industrial jobs where the range of accidents involve broken bones, eye trauma, hearing loss and respiratory problems. Now, however the fastest-growing category of workplace injuries originates in the office…

•Cumulative trauma disorder. Long-term occupational injury or illness caused by repetitive motion or long-term exposure to computer screens or other conditions involving flawed ergonomics.

•Occupational stress. In a substantial portion of workers' compensation cases, a stressful work environment apparently contributed to chronic pain, ringing in the ears, nervous breakdowns, depression, strokes and heart attacks.

Fighting back:

Regardless of the type of workplace injury, careful planning and disciplined management can control the cost spiral associated with it. Steps to take:

•Carefully screen employees based on the kinds of stress they will encounter. Whether the stresses involve working around explosive materials or dealing with difficult customers, disorders often arise because of a mismatch between the person and unavoidable job conditions. This results either in accidents due to inadequate skills, or stress-related disability due to the strains associated with being the wrong person for the job. To minimize the likelihood of such a mismatch, many companies use psychological testing techniques during the hiring process.

•Define department manager responsibility for safety. They should be responsible for seeing to it that all employees comply with safety procedures, making adjustments to such procedures when necessary and allocating the necessary budget.

•Define second-line supervisor responsibility. They should be responsible for assuring compliance and reviewing the effectiveness of safety programs.

•Define first-line supervisor responsibility. They should be responsible for seeing that…

1. *Right-to-Know* posters are clearly displayed.

2. Written copies of the safety program are available for all employees.

3. Employees are informed about the written program and their right to review.

4. Employees are informed about procedures for new products.

5. Reporting is initiated when necessary.

6. Appropriate chemical evaluations are conducted.

7. Employees have time for training and maintaining training records.

•Restructure the workplace safety department. It should…

1. Maintain company's safety program.

2. Inform management of changes in laws and policies.

3. Provide technical assistance.

4. Maintain a master file of all safety procedures.

5. Interpret safety procedures.

6. Conduct new evaluations of potential hazards.

7. Communicate with manufacturers.

•Educate employees. Key areas of training: Reading warning labels...reviewing safety procedures...following precautions for handling hazardous materials...attending scheduled meetings about workplace hazards.

Caution:

Don't simply hand out materials for people to read, because many employees can't read. Find out if they can. If not, have someone read to them the material about workplace hazards. Get an explicit acknowledgement that employees understand what potential hazards exist and how to work safely.

•Train management. Managers must be alert to subtle signals that a safety problem may exist.

Example: Data entry workers who take frequent breaks, massage their wrists or frequently do neck gyrations to loosen up could indicate that a workstation isn't ergonomically engineered. Minor adjustments of lighting, chair height or monitor angle almost always resolve the situation. Ignored, it can result in serious disability for an employee and a health claim against the company.

Important:

Train managers to be especially alert for symptoms after employees have been on the job for six or seven hours. Notice whether anyone seems to be making bad decisions which might be related to prolonged stress.

•Improve workplace warning signs. OSHA regulations require that specific language be used for a wide range of known hazardous workplace conditions. Keep signs simple. Some surveys show that more than a third of Americans can't read above a fourth-grade level. If English isn't the native language for a significant number of employees, use bilingual material.

Visual symbols can help, but they have drawbacks, too. Because 30% of males over age 40 are color-blind, they could miss the symbolic meaning of certain colors.

•Remove barriers to communication about hazards.

Trap:

The conventional system whereby departments are rewarded for a good safety record, and supervisors can be penalized for a high rate of reported injuries is dangerous. Reason: Since a hazard report, in effect, means indicting someone, many employees hesitate to file one. Other employees want to suppress reports that could blemish their department's safety record and reduce prospects of winning a safety award. The federal government puts additional pressure on companies to keep reported workplace hazards low.

Solution:

Encourage employees to share their experiences at regular meetings. Many employees are more open in a group than in a one-on-one meeting with a supervisor. Contractors should be included in the information exchange process. Essential: Make it clear that reports about workplace hazards won't be used as the basis for retribution against anyone in the company.

Probe employees about potential hazards, such as faulty or missing equipment, missing labels, inadequate communication procedures, poor equipment maintenance procedures, etc.

Key:

OSHA investigations of workplace injuries reveal that employees often know about a potential hazard but are discouraged from reporting it.

While the initial effect of full disclosure could be an increase in reported workplace injuries, managers must keep in mind that this probably doesn't mean injuries are increasing. It means the actual extent of injuries is becoming known for the first time. With the information, future injuries can then be prevented.

The benefits of full disclosure should become apparent over time as underlying workplace hazards are mitigated.

Source: Philip E. Ulmer, The American Society of Safety Engineers, and Health and Safety Advisor, ARCOAlaska, Inc., Box 100360, Anchorage 99510.

Mistakes Companies Make In Team Training

•Mistake: Offering sensitivity training instead of skills training. Team leaders sometimes concentrate on trying to get new team members to know and like each other, while giving lower priority to the team's goals. Reality: Teams need focus first—on external issues, such as customer service, quality or cost reduction. When their efforts result in success, the success builds self-esteem, thereby equipping the team members to confidently and comfortably get to know each other better.

•Mistake: Confusing the building of knowledge with the building of skills. It's wonderful to offer new teams courses and guidebooks on how to perform new skills. But too much time in the classroom and too little on hands-on, trial-and-error practice is a common mistake.

•Mistake: Trying to get training done fast…and cheaply. Ineffective training is a waste of money—no matter how little time it takes. Alternating training with on-the-job practice is the best strategy for teams. That means spreading training over longer periods—giving all team members ample opportunity to learn.

•Mistake: Not checking out outside training suppliers. Don't buy any training without thorough documentation from the vendor of the effectiveness of its programs… and without consulting customers that have already used the vendor.

Source: William C. Byham, PhD, president, Development Dimensions International, human resources training and development consultants, 1225 Washington Pike, Bridgeville, Pennsylvania 15017.

Secrets Of Much More Effective Coaching

Encouraging managers to become coaches—instead of just order-giving bosses —has become the goal of more and more top executives in recent years.

Here's how the most successful companies have helped their managers make the change from old-style top-down bossing to coaching…

The first step is to define a manager not just as a person who gets the work out, but as someone who helps the staff grow and improve. To accomplish this, managers become coaches who…

•Teach workers how to solve problems.

•Tutor them in new skills.

•Encourage them to develop new abilities on their own.

Comparison: Under the old, *I'm-the-boss-and-I-give-the-orders* system, the boss would simply jump in and take up the slack of workers when their productivity slumped. Later, the boss would punish workers for slacking off.

Trap: Managers were sidetracked from other duties, and subordinates had reason to think the boss would rescue them whenever they got behind in the job. It wouldn't take long before they were always behind schedule. And the reprimanding left employees demoralized.

Now, under the new system, if production slips, a coaching manager finds out the cause of the problem. The manager gives staff members more tools, if that's what they need. Or if they're weak in certain skills, he/she takes responsibility for improving them. Finally, the manager teaches them how to anticipate similar problems…and avoid them.

Long-term payoff: Fewer production problems and higher morale. As workers' skills improve, they develop a greater sense of pride in themselves and their jobs.

A manager/coach uses positive discipline instead of arbitrary punishment.

Example: A subordinate is late three times in one week. The manager first reminds the worker that he has an obligation to be on time each day and that he must pay a price if he's late again. Then the manager asks the worker, *What would motivate you to be on time?* The goal is to agree on a fair consequence for continued lateness. Once the manager and subordinate agree on it, the punishment is virtually always more effective than arbitrary discipline handed down by the manager. The punishment also runs much less risk of incurring resentment because the subordinate knows that he was the one who suggested the penalty…and that his actions resulted in it.

Making the change:

In the real world, of course, a company can't just announce that supervisors are now coaches and expect them to change their management style overnight. To begin the process…

•In addition to output goals, evaluate managers on the basis of how well they help their staffs grow.

Example: Apart from turning out 25 widgets a day, a manager might agree with her supervisor that she also upgrade job skills in at least half the staff members within, say, one year.

These skills might include mastering a higher-level computer program…learning a colleague's job (in order to take over when the colleague is out) or taking courses to enable promotion. At the end of the evaluation period, the manager must be able to demonstrate that each of the targeted staff members did actually upgrade the agreed-upon skills.

Managers shouldn't worry that newly skilled workers will be promoted out of their departments. A manager who is lucky enough to see that happen will have such a highly productive department that it can easily afford the slightly higher turnover.

•Offer training to managers who need help becoming coaches. Not all managers are natural coaches. Some will quickly understand their new role, others will need help. If a top executive is especially skilled in developing talent, consider putting him/her in charge of helping managers become coaches.

Many management training institutions offer courses that teach managers to take responsibility in this way. Among the best is the Center for Creative Leadership, Greensboro, North Carolina.

Also useful: Encourage managers to get involved in outside activities that require

them to nurture others. Example: Little League teams, Scouts, etc.

•Look for coaching ability as a criterion in hiring and promoting new managers. When you interview applicants, ask about their experiences in helping others learn—in or outside the office. Ask about successes and failures.

What to look for: Answers that demonstrate the applicant learned something from the experience…and enjoyed it.

•Reward supervisors for their success as coaches. In addition to monetary rewards, recognition from top management helps to promote a corporate culture that values coaching.

Source: Michael F. Murray, president, Creative Interchange Consultants International, a management training firm, 1018 Arlena Dr., Arlington, Texas 76012.

Have Employees Evaluate Supervisors

Having employees give regular, anonymous feedback to their supervisors is a useful management tool. Benefits:

•Helps supervisors focus on the needs of the employees who are, after all, their customers.

•Gives supervisors specific areas where they can change their behavior.

•Gives employees the sense that they are being listened to about how they're supervised.

There are traps:

Trap: Using the feeback too quickly for formal appraisal of supervisors. This makes the feedback system threatening to supervisors. The supervisors should be given the chance to improve, based on information they obtained from the feeback reports.

Trap: Making the appraisals public. This builds fear in the workplace. Supervisors will be afraid that they're being held up to ridicule.

Key: Nobody should see the feedback other than the supervisor, especially not the supervisor's boss. Disgruntled employees may be tempted to "get back" at their supervisors if they know the supervisor's boss will see the feedback reports.

Source: Dr. Frank Petrock, president, General Systems Consulting Group, management consultants specializing in team building, 6055 Jackson Rd., Ann Arbor, Michigan 48103.

How To Get Better Responses

If you fit the job that was advertised, send your resume and a cover letter outlining your qualifications. Send it immediately. Most job candidates procrastinate. Many believe that the delay is to their advantage…it isn't.

•Send the letter and the resume, unfolded, in a 9" x 12" envelope. Or, better yet, send it by one of the air courier services—even if it's local. (If you're sending it to a US Post Office Box, use their Express Mail service. The post office will not accept another courier's mail.)

•If you do not get a response in two weeks, mail another resume, but this time use a yellow highlighting marker to make your qualifications for the job stand out on the letter and resume. Handwrite on the letter words to this effect: *Here's another copy of the resume that I sent two weeks ago. I really fit the job, and would appreciate an interview.* If you didn't get a nod in the first place, persistence can't hurt.

•If, by the wording of a blind ad, you can make an educated guess that it was placed by one of just several companies—don't mail your first response to the box number. Instead, mail a letter, along with your resume, to the executive at each of those companies who would likely be your boss. Do not allude to the blind ad, and do not send a second letter to these people. Instead, in two weeks, send your cover letter and resume in response to the blind ad. There is a calculated risk because of the delay, but if you're lucky to hit on the company that ran the ad, you may very well get priority attention. Fringe

benefit: You may uncover a good job that was not advertised.

Source: Robert Half, founder, Robert Half International, Inc., Box 3000, Menlo Park, CA 94026.

Improved Productivity

A company can purchase the most technologically advanced manufacturing equipment in the world. But if the company lacks a carefully selected, well-trained and productive workforce, its capital investment will not be an asset. In fact, it could even become a liability.

It is urgent now for companies to recognize and reject the dangerous hiring techniques and ineffective training programs of the past. To be successful in such difficult economic times, companies need a whole new way of looking at hiring and training.

Important now: Carefully conceived, thorough hiring and training policies. Many foreign companies and some of the more progressive US companies have shown how valuable effective hiring and training can be.
New-style hiring:

Traditional hiring fails because the hiring decision is made narrowly, based only on past work experience— generally by the hiring manager alone or with a senior executive.

The judgment is often made hastily — within the first 15 minutes of an interview— based on the manager's gut reactions.

Result: Inadequate consideration is given to whether a candidate will be able to adjust to the company's culture and its expectations. Bad hiring decisions are made, leading to reduced productivity and increased costs.
Better way:

•Expand the interviewing process. Include a broad group of people the new recruit will have to work with, including peers and even outside suppliers or clients.

Goal: To learn how candidates are likely to fit into an increasingly team-oriented work environment…and how their skills and attitudes would complement the team.

• Seek candidates who are amenable to change. That's an important trait as companies face fast-changing competitive conditions.

• Put as much emphasis on personal skills as on technical skills. People hired primarily on the basis of their technical skills might not have the interpersonal skills or flexibility necessary to work as part of a team.

Those hired from competitors because of their familiarity with the company's line of business may have learned ways of working and managing that are incompatible with the way your company operates. Technical skills are often easier to teach than interpersonal skills.

Training strategies:

Even if companies do learn better recruiting techniques, they often fail to follow through with strong training. US companies spend much less on skills training compared to German and Japanese companies.

Instead, most US managers still believe on-the-job training is all that counts for the majority of workers. They refuse to do even introductory training in the belief that it helps the organization more to let people sink or swim and retain only those enterprising enough to figure out what needs to be done on their own.

Usual result: Great loss of productivity as qualified, but undertrained, individuals wander around trying to figure out how they fit into the job, taking time from co-workers in a haphazard effort to work effectively.

Newest training problems:

• Restructured companies are often so lean that managers and front-line workers are worried about their own job security and take no time to orient and train new recruits. Training by mentoring is a time-proven technique to create loyal, skilled workers. Few companies can be productive without encouraging it, but fewer and fewer managers offer it because of their own concerns.

• As earnings are squeezed, so are training budgets in most companies.

Training tactics for the 1990s:

• Don't limit training to teaching specific tasks and skills. For employees to cooperate in company efforts to continuously improve work processes, they must also learn how to ask the right questions and how to define, test and refine their ideas for doing the job better.

• Train teams. Individual training is important. But it's not enough as companies increasingly structure work processes around groups, rather than individuals.

• Provide retraining whenever technology changes. Effective policy: If workers take the training and fail, management undertakes to train them until they can perform well. But if workers refuse to retrain, then termination is a possibility.

• Encourage employees to take responsibility for their own training and for developing new skills. Introduce a system where they contract with their managers and supervisors to upgrade their abilities.

• Train managers in team-building. Most managers need training in the techniques of leading rather than issuing orders. Improving the technical skills of front-line workers can too easily be negated by managers who lack the "people" skills of involving everyone in making the company more productive.

Source: Charles Garfield, author of Second to None, published by Business One-Irwin, 1818 Ridge Rd., Homewood, Illinois 60430. Garfield is founder and head of a consulting organization, The Charles Garfield Group, 6114 LaSalle Ave., Oakland, California 94611, which has followed high achievers and successful firms for 25 years.

Beware Of Employee Handbooks

Mounting workplace regulations and new court rulings are making it trickier to write useful employee handbooks without running big legal risks. A carelessly worded handbook can...

• Unintentionally create binding employment contracts.

• Expose a company to anti-discrimination suits.

• Increase the company's vulnerability to stiff penalties for white-collar crimes.

Many states have broadened employee rights, and many cities are enacting workplace rules of their own. Where handbook rules are in dispute, more and more courts are ruling in favor of employees.

All this puts a burden on companies—even small ones—to write handbooks in such a way that they spell out workplace rules while at the same time avoiding sloppy wording that can land the company in legal trouble. Handbook essentials:

•Disclaimers. All handbooks should include statements saying that...

1. The company reserves the right to terminate employment at any time.

2. Nothing in the handbook should be construed as a contract of employment.

Without these statements, a company might find itself unable to fire a poorly performing employee who has somehow managed to adhere to every rule in the handbook.

•Description of benefits. Handbooks should explain the company policies for such benefits as vacations, holidays, sick leave, tuition refunds, jury duty leave (including a cap on duration of salary in case an employee is selected for a lengthy trial), bereavement and family leave, medical coverage and pension plans.

A handbook, however, shouldn't include more than a summary of medical and pension plans. Instead, it should refer employees to other printed material which the company can develop to describe the plans in detail.

Reason: Not going into detail keeps the handbooks to a manageable length and also avoids the necessity of rewriting each time there's a minor change.

•Description of compensation policies. Explain how often salaries are reviewed, but state that all raises and bonuses are made solely at the discretion of management.

•Expense reimbursement. Describe the reimbursement procedure for employees who incur expenses.

•Hours of work. State the length of the work week and when employees are eligible for overtime pay.

•Compliance with nondiscrimination laws. This section should state that the company intends to comply with all federal, state and local nondiscrimination laws, including, but not limited to, those prohibiting discrimination on the basis of age, sex, race, color, national origin, religion, creed, veteran status or disability, and that the same applies to all employees and applicants for employment. The policy also should include a statement prohibiting sexual harassment in the workplace.

It need not list all the categories of individuals protected by anti-discrimination laws. Reasons: The company may operate in several states that have differing discrimination statutes. Also, the handbook becomes misleading whenever a jurisdiction adds to the list of protected categories.

Example: Many jurisdictions are now amending employment discrimination laws to expressly prohibit bias on the basis of an employee's or job applicant's sexual preference. If a handbook lists other categories but isn't updated for this one, the company leaves itself open to litigation from an employee who can say the company did nothing to prevent discrimination because of sexual preference.

•Compliance with federal statutes governing the conduct of business. By telling employees what the company expects from them, it can help prevent violations of the law as well as bolster its case in court if the company is charged with failure to adhere to the statutes.

Though the handbook shouldn't attempt to list all of these rules, it's useful to include mention of laws against...

1. Doctoring financial data.

2. Violating export and customs laws.

3. Tax fraud.

4. Money laundering.

5. Criminal violation of federal safety and health laws.

6. Offering bribes and making false reports to the federal government.

State in the handbook that the company expects all affected employees to obey these laws and to participate in company training to assist them with compliance.

Important: Under new federal guidelines, companies that don't offer training programs informing employees about compliance with federal laws can face stiffer penalties in the event of a conviction. Statements in the handbook can help convince a court that the company has a compliance program and takes it seriously.

•Disciplinary policy. Describe work rules and the company's disciplinary policies, but only in broad terms.

Example: Explain that grounds for dismissal include, but aren't limited to, habitual absence or tardiness, failure to comply with company safety rules, etc. The key words here are *include, but aren't limited to.*

Being more specific—spelling out the number of absences, for instance—could prevent the company from firing a disagreeable, unproductive employee who has managed to stay just within the guidelines.

Exception: In certain businesses, work rules such as punctuality are especially important. For these companies, it does make sense to spell out rules in detail.

If the company has or requires a drug policy, it should also be described in this section. And, state again in this section of the handbook that the company reserves the right to terminate employment at any time for any reason. That reaffirms the company's right to fire a worker at the very first infraction of a significant rule.

If the company has a probationary period for new recruits, this should also be described in the handbook. If appropriate to the company's business, state that all employees are expected not to disclose confidential information.

Writing the best text:

If an outside attorney or benefits consultant writes the handbook, there's a risk that it won't accurately reflect the way the company does business. Moreover, employees and their supervisors may feel that rules are being imposed on them.

Better: Retain a lawyer experienced in employment law to suggest details of what the handbook should cover. Then let the personnel director, with input from appropriate departments, make the first draft. There are now sophisticated computer programs that can assist managers in this process.*

When the handbook is completed, the attorney can refine the language.

As laws and policies change, distribute supplements to the handbook. Plan to revise it about every two years.

*Examples: Personnel Policy Expert from Knowledge-Point, 1311 Clegg St., Petaluma, California 94952. Company Policy and Personnel Workbook from PSI Research, 300 North Valley Dr., Grants Pass, Oregon 97526.

Source: John P. Furfaro, employment law specialist, Skadden, Arps, Slate, Meagher & Flom, 919 Third Ave., New York 10022.

How To Avoid The Big Mistakes In Severance For Executives

Laying off managers is never easy, even when the company can afford to be generous with severance benefits. But, the last thing a company needs when it must dismiss a manager is a lawsuit or bad publicity. It's particularly troublesome if it's initiated because of a poorly designed or poorly executed severance package.

Biggest trap: Being forced to terminate managers suddenly—without a formal severance policy in place. That puts top management in the difficult position of having to create a severance offer at a time when it may not be thinking clearly.

Obviously, every dismissed executive's terms of dismissal are unique. That means the company must be prepared to tailor its severance deal to individual executive's needs. To make the negotiations run smoothly, though, it helps to have a formal severance policy in place as a starting point for negotiating details.

Added benefit: A formal severance policy helps the company attract and keep talented executives. Reason: They're less inclined to look for another job if they know they'll be taken care of in the event they are dismissed.

The severance policy:

•Provide for severance pay. Most terminated top executives are offered 12 to 24 months of their base pay. For middle-level executives, six to 12 months is usually adequate.

Important: Offer severance pay on the condition that executives sign, and comply with, non-compete agreements for a specified period. Then, instead of giving severance pay in a lump sum, simply continue paying executives as they've been paid, for the specified period. The company can monitor compliance with the non-compete agreement, and be prepared to discontinue severance payments if the agreement is violated.

•Arrange for payment of bonus money. Bonus amounts for the year termination occurs are usually forfeited. However, if an executive is dismissed in the middle of a 12-month bonus period, the company can offer to pay a pro-rated bonus amount based on what it would pay at the end of the full period.

Exception: When the executive is being dismissed for poor performance and doesn't deserve a bonus to begin with.

•Provide for continuation of health benefits. Most companies continue full medical and dental benefits for the term of the severance pay period.

•Provide secretarial services and office facilities. We recommend the company provide top executives with these services as a gesture of goodwill, to assist the executive in finding a satisfactory new position. It costs little and goes a long way to defuse bad feelings.

•Provide outplacement services. Offer to pay for the services of an independent recruiting firm to support the executive's job-hunting effort. This assistance may be provided for a set time period—such as the length of pay continuation—or up to a set dollar amount— such as 20% of the executive's base pay.

•Arrange for a company car. Executives who have been driving company cars should be offered the option of buying the car from the company at fair market value. This costs the company nothing and spares the executive the trouble of shopping for a new car.

•Work out retirement benefits. It may cause tax and ERISA problems for a company to provide additional benefits under qualified retirement plans, such as pensions and 401(k) accounts, after an employee's dismissal. Additional retirement benefits can be provided through a non-qualified retirement plan.

•Long-term incentives. If the company has a stock-option or restricted-share plan, where executives earn or can purchase shares, they may not have earned their full allotment at the time of dismissal. However, as an additional point of negotiation, the company can offer to replace a portion of the forfeited value to achieve a smooth transition.

Alternatively, the severance policy should contain a statement of the company's willingness to negotiate this issue.

Source: Robert Romanchek, executive compensation consultant, Hewitt Associates, 100 Half Day Rd., Lincolnshire, Illinois 60069.

Cutting Employee Personal Phone Calls

A certain amount of personal phone use by employees is unavoidable. But if left uncontrolled, some employees will make frequent, lengthy long-distance personal calls, while others will spend hours chatting with their friends across town. The cost is higher phone bills and lost productivity.

Recommended measures:

•Develop and distribute a formal phone-use policy. Reasonable guideline: Local calls to spouses or other close relatives of brief duration (under five minutes) are acceptable during business hours. Local calls for personal business are permissible, but only during lunch hour. Personal long-distance calls must be paid for by the employee.

•Install controls of company phone lines to block out unauthorized calling. Most modern business phone systems can be programmed to do this.

•Set up a system of authorization codes. For employees whose jobs require substantial long-distance calling, but without a clear area code pattern, provide authorization codes they can use to gain access to long-distance services.

•Set up a computerized call-monitoring system—and use it to consistently monitor employee calling patterns. Company phone systems generate detailed data on all phone calls made from the system's extensions. It's quite easy with a personal computer, and inexpensive software,* to organize this data in customized formats that best suit management's monitoring requirements. Examples:

1. Data on calls over 10 minutes within the hours of 9 am and 5 pm can be printed out on a daily, weekly or monthly basis.

2. All long-distance calls can be printed out weekly (to be checked for patterns of abuse for personal purposes).

3. All calls during lunch hours can be printed out by duration and phone number.

Include in the company's written phone policy a paragraph notifying employees that the phone system is monitored by computer and that any patterns of abuse will be investigated.

*There are over 100 such programs costing $395–$2,000. For reviews, refer to *Teleconnect Magazine's* Buyer's Guide, July 1991. 12 W. 21 St., New York 10017.

Source: Neil Sachnoff, president, TeleCom Clinic, telecommunications project management consultants, 469 Tenafly Rd., Englewood, New Jersey 07631, and is author of *Secrets of Installing a Telephone System.*

The Productive Powers Of Information Sharing

To promote improvement in productivity, efficiency and competitiveness, companies must learn the techniques of sharing knowledge and ideas—both within their organizations and with other companies.

Only when ideas and information begin to flow freely can companies make strong gains in new-product development, quality and productivity…

•To promote innovation: Share ideas—the insights, intuitions and experiences of employees and managers. Suggestion systems with attractive rewards for submitting good ideas are often highly effective.

•To enhance quality: Increase knowledge and understanding across workplace functions and promote learning across companies. This often requires restructuring departments and divisions to break down barriers between functions.

•To build productive teams: Managers must be sensitive to the complex pressures on employees with diverse lifestyles.

Accepting different opinions:

In each of these areas, open communication is the instrument of success. Promoting open, spontaneous communication is difficult, and the skills in promoting it must be practiced by top managers.

Challenge: To make intra- and inter-company communications work as an asset for all parties.

Sensitive communications: It's important to understand the cultural and bureaucratic contexts within which people in other companies, departments or divisions function. Ignoring these important realities is one of the major causes of communication breakdown in a business.

Example: British negotiators in a British-French deal have a hard time understanding why their French counterparts are often so slow in negotiations. They think it has to do with a French cultural need to establish personal relationships with their adversaries, while in reality French negotiators often lack the authority to make substantive decisions— and must stall until they can speak to their superiors.

Key: Better, much more thoughtful research, listening and questioning— to gain insight into important issues that can help facilitate cooperation.

Trap: Expecting people in the company as well as other companies to share their knowledge can force companies to expose their weaknesses. Reason: When communication is increased, an appetite for ever greater communication develops. It becomes like an addiction that requires ever greater input.

If left uncontrolled, such communication could cause the company's setbacks and vulnerabilities to become widely known—to the company's disadvantage.

Solution: Top management must set limits before beginning to promote openness—so the boundaries will be respected.

Source: Dr. Rosabeth Moss Kanter, professor at Harvard Business School and editor, *Harvard Business Review,* Soldiers Field, Boston 02163.

Here Come Worker Stress Claims

Years ago, workers' compensation claims for on-the-job stress were practically unheard of. Now, such claims are growing at a distressing rate. In trend-setting California, stress claims under workers' compensation were up 700% in the decade ended 1989.

The increase in total workers' compensation claims was only 25% during that period.

The cost to employers throughout the US in higher workers' comp insurance premiums—and lost workdays—will continue to escalate, unless steps are taken to control it now.

Reasons for the explosion of stress-related claims…

•Increased on-the-job pressures due to layoffs, and management efforts to trim ranks may trigger such claims by employees who feel threatened.

•In most states, stress claims under workers' compensation require minimal proof. A physician's certification that the worker experiences too much stress at work will often suffice.

•Health clinics have begun to advertise that they will examine employees to see if they qualify for filing such claims. That encourages employees to file for stress-related compensation.

Sequence of events:

Often, workers' comp claims for stress-related illness are legitimate.

Air controllers, hospital emergency room workers and others often experience severe physical reactions to too much job pressure. Unfortunately, even legitimate stress cases result in excessive time away from work—because the system permits this.

The typical sequence in a stress claim is for the worker to go out on sick leave, followed by short-term disability and, frequently, long-term disability. By the last stage, the employee may be nearly fully recovered.

Latest abuse: A high incidence of claims filed by workers who fear being fired because they have received poor performance evaluations or are on warning. Many workers can get a doctor to certify that they are suffering stress from the workplace, protecting themselves because they know that it's very difficult for the boss to fire them while on sick leave.

Advice: If a worker has had a poor performance review, keep the two issues—job performance and the validity of the stress claim—separate. To avoid discrimination traps, don't jump to the conclusion that a worker's claim of excessive on-the-job stress is related to the facts of poor job performance.

If firing becomes necessary, it will be important to prove that performance was the only reason—not absence due to stress.

When workers return from sick leave or disability leave, having gone through the stress claim procedure, don't treat them worse for having been absent.

Make sure that the company record demonstrates that management acted fairly while the disability claim was under review.

To cut down on stress-related claims:

•Require second opinions in all cases where an employee produces a physician's certificate that on-the-job stress led to disability. This is allowed by law.

•Determine if one or more stress claims coming from a single department warrant a review of working conditions in that department.

Guideline: If one employee in the department has an undisputed claim of disability caused by on-the-job stress, that is not proof that working conditions in the department are onerous. Physicians and the law recognize that vulnerability to stress is very individual—people react differently to the same set of circumstances.

•When hiring for jobs in which high stress is unavoidable, make it company policy to explain the job conditions and to ask applicants if they are prepared to cope. Screen for experience indicating an ability to handle stress without problems.

•If the company provides rehabilitation services to help employees with substance abuse or family problems, consider adding professional assistance to deal with on-the-job stress.

•In companies or departments where stress is inevitable or even likely, introduce opportunities to relax, to exercise, to participate in lunchtime seminars on how to deal with stress successfully.

Source: Herbert J. Levine and Jeffrey D. Wohl, partners, Orrick, Herrington & Sutcliffe, a law firm representing management in labor and employment litigation, 400 Sansome St., San Francisco 94111 and 599 Lexington Ave., New York 10022.

For More Effective Motivation

To motivate employees and keep them motivated, managers must do more than offer a share of the profits when business picks up. While sharing profits can be a powerful motivator, it's only one step in stimulating everyone in the company to operate at maximum potential.

To build your skills as a motivator, ask these four key questions…

Question #1: How do we recognize those who are motivated? And, how do we recognize those who aren't? Characteristics of motivated people…

•Express enthusiasm.
•Act energetic and productive.
•Remain energized long after others grow weary.
•Do whatever it takes to get the job done, even if it means working late hours and weekends.
•Love their jobs.
•Find creative ways of solving problems.

Question #2: How do we motivate those who aren't motivated? Some employees are impossible to motivate. Their nonproductive attitudes are so ingrained that no manager will change them. They may have to be terminated. But this is only a small minority of people. In most cases, lack of motivation is a management problem—and an opportunity.

First, assess whether the reason for lack of motivation is that people are doing things that create stress, displeasure or productivity problems.

Example: An associate in a consulting firm did fabulously in the firm's first five years because he brought in three strong clients, providing enough work to help get the consulting firm solidly into the black. But in the next few years, the business plateaued because no new clients were signing on. The associate was asked by the partners to spend most of his time developing new business. As time went on, his original clients began to complain because his work for them was suffering. His motivation was waning because he disliked hunting for new business.

Solution: The partners hired another associate who had talent in recruiting new clients. They delegated all of that responsibility to the new associate, freeing the other's time to get back to what truly motivated him—doing good work for his clients. Result: His motivation revived, and the firm began to grow, due to the successful efforts of the new associate.

Lesson: Unmotivated employees in the company are often suffering under mismatched responsibilities. Talk to them to find out exactly what they're doing that's dragging them down. Then, adjust their responsibilities to fit their talents.

Question #3: Does top management resist change…or relish it? This is a critical obstacle in many US companies. Most companies don't need revolutionizing. But they do need to improve. Companies that don't improve undermine their employees' motivation by letting them think mediocrity is acceptable.

Remaining open and eager to improve gives employees a sense of mission—and it fosters commitment by making them part of a growth-oriented organization. Steps to take:

•Commit to making changes every day that bring about incremental improvement in the way the business is run.

•Identify what the company does best, and concentrate improvement efforts there.

•Make sure that everyone in the company understands that rewards depend on doing things better…and better. Urge all employees—and customers—to suggest ways to improve operations. Then, act on the ideas that promise the most progress. Reward the originators with recognition, money or other appropriate awards.

Question #4: Are you motivating people in the right direction? Change for the sake of change is no good. Energizing people without the company's interests in mind is counterproductive.

Solution: While matching people's talents with job responsibilities, and pushing for constant improvement, remember what the company's goals are —and how job responsibilities relate to the company's growth and change.

Design incentive systems—bonuses, commissions, promotions, etc.—that reward people for accomplishments that directly conform with the company's goals.

Source: Craig Hickman, management consultant and president, Cannon Hickman Johnson, capital investment firm, 3944 North 450 West, Provo, Utah 84604. Hickman's book is *Practical Business Genius,* John Wiley & Sons, 605 Third Ave., New York 10158.

10

Retirement Planning

Early Retirement Programs Do Not Have To Backfire

The favorite method of companies that have downsized, or that plan to, is offering employees financial incentives to voluntarily leave the company earlier than they had planned to.

Problem: While such early retirement plans are, in theory, an effective way to avoid the pain of outright layoffs, they rarely accomplish what the company wants to accomplish—substantial reduction of unnecessary jobs.

Reasons for failure:

• Early retirement plans siphon off the most talented people at each level. That leaves less creative or less productive workers to help the company through difficult times.

Example: Eastman Kodak recently offered a plan that was open to all workers who had joined the company directly after college graduation. They could retire with full benefits at age 48. Not surprisingly, the plan (which cost Kodak $300 million in the third quarter of 1991 alone) drew twice the expected number of retirees. Some Wall Street analysts worried that this would seriously disrupt operations and lead to expensive retraining of remaining employees. Others predicted that Kodak might be forced to rehire some of those who had left, possibly at the cost of new incentives.

Shrewder reduction: Instead of blanket retirement offers, analyze the business to discover which departments or divisions are overstaffed or unprofitable. Then terminate the individuals whose contributions are not significant.

Often, this is the only way to get the cuts the company really needs—painful as they may be. Recognize that a needed change now, even if it temporarily depresses morale, can save jobs for the rest of the company's employees in the future.

• Getting too few volunteers because the offer is badly defined. Usually companies simply say...If you leave within the next 30

181

days, we'll give you credit for an additional five years' service on your retirement benefits.

Trap: Employees don't know exactly what that will mean.

Solution: Spell out retirement plan details with real numbers, explaining to employees exactly how much this will be worth to them in monthly income and how long they will have to work to achieve those extra benefits if they don't buy into the plan.

Important: Train supervisors in how to rate workers and have them face up to that responsibility honestly at least once a year. Aim: To get accurate reports on exactly whom to dismiss…and whom to keep. Once management has established who is essential to the operation, be prepared to offer them cash bonuses or career development incentives to stay on.

Key: Be sure to have legal counsel involved in this procedure from the start, because there's a danger that the company may be accused of age or sex discrimination. Make sure employees the company wants to retain get the message that they are wanted.

• Getting too few volunteers because the retirement offer is unattractive. While voluntary early retirement plans do avoid the discomfort of outright terminations, they're especially harmful if too few people accept them.

Solution: Don't make the offer if there's a chance it won't work and will have to be followed by a second or third offer. It prolongs and worsens morale and productivity problems. This happened at AT&T and Sears.

• Survivors are demoralized. Golden parachutes—highly generous cash and benefits deals for top executives—may be legal, but when they're offered in the midst of an unprofitable time for the company, they can be very bad for morale and for the health of the business.

Recommended: Use them judiciously—and on a one-year-only basis. Agreeing to lavishly compensate for 2, 5 or 10 years of doing nothing is robbing shareholders and surviving employees.

Source: Fred Schick, managing vice president of the Chicago office of Noble Lowndes, international employee benefits consultants, 525 W. Monroe St., Chicago 60661.

Retirement Plans… Cost Comparison

Traditional defined-benefit pension plans are more expensive to administer than defined-contribution retirement plans. Basic difference:

• Traditional pension plans give employees a guaranteed fixed benefit, typically calculated as a percentage of final or average pay.

• A defined-contribution plan—such as a profit-sharing plan—annually deposits a percentage of pay into a retirement account for each employee, and the size of the final benefit depends on how much money is saved by retirement.

Costs:

For 500 employees, the average annual administrative cost is $133 per worker for a pension plan and $85 per worker for a defined-contribution plan. For smaller companies, cost differences are much greater. With 15 employees, pension plans cost $455 per worker, and defined-contribution plans cost $228.

Source: Data from Hay/Huggins Co., benefits consultants, Philadelphia, cited in *Crain's New York Business*, 220 E. 42 St., New York 10017.

You Don't Have To Wait Until You've Retired To Lead The Life You've Always Wanted To Lead

So many of us spend our entire lives deferring our dreams and postponing our enjoyment of each moment, all the while thinking that tomorrow will be more fulfilling and less stressful. We fantasize about the day when we can finally enjoy everything we've worked so hard to gain.

But you don't have to wait until you're retired to lead the life you've always wanted. You can take the plunge now…give up your current less-than-satisfying way of life and embrace a new lifestyle that will allow you to fulfill your deepest interests and desires.

Making a radical change—say from working as a Wall Street lawyer to running a bed-and-breakfast in Vermont—usually requires some personal sacrifice, in terms of giving up many of the amenities you think of as necessities. The most common questions I receive about how to take your life off hold…and answers to them…

Why would you want to make big changes to an already good life? Because there is more to life than simply accumulating possessions. Because you have silenced your secret inner longings—whether it be to write a book, paint a painting, play an instrument, enjoy nature or simply meditate—long enough. As business gets tighter and tighter, many are finding it to be unbearable. For many people, there comes a point when they finally must give those secret longings a voice.

What happened that made you yourself heed your secret longings? The catalyst was when my partners in a company I had founded with them nine years earlier offered to buy me out. It was an amicable business divorce in which I either had to sell or buy them out. So my wife, an interior decorator, and I decided to sell the company, a "shopping service" that sent anonymous reporters into banks and other retail establishments to evaluate their customer-service shortcomings.

We had planned to relocate to a luxurious house in Austin, Texas, but when we ran into a minor glitch in obtaining the mortgage, we decided to chuck the whole thing, sell most of the possessions we had accumulated in 25 years of marriage and move into our tiny ski condominium in Breckenridge, Colorado. The mortgage problem was just the prod I needed to move to a much simpler, less acquisitive lifestyle. And it is a move I have never regretted.

Then problems—the forced buy-out of your interest in the company, and trouble in getting the mortgage you wanted—actually served as a positive force? Yes, in much the same way the loss of a job forces people to reevaluate the kind of life they have been living. Very often, people decide that they no longer want to pursue that lifestyle—working harder and harder to acquire more and more things—and opt for a major change.

Aren't there times when a move to a simpler, more laid-back lifestyle is not advisable? Yes, if you're the kind of person who just thrives on making your business grow. Such people get all the excitement and creativity they need from tending their business and giving up such an endeavor would probably make them very unhappy.

How do you decide if a radically different lifestyle is right for you? By giving yourself time to contemplate the new life you are considering. Start by taking long walks so your mind can wander and you can mull over the changes you are considering.

Write your autobiography as you'd like it to look when you're 90. This forces you to grapple with the issue of how you'd like to live your life. Do you want to see yourself as a corporate vice president with lavish tastes who had an enormous house in the best neighborhood, memberships in the most sought-after clubs and a collection of fancy cars in the driveway? Or would you rather see yourself as someone who spent lots of time with his family, took every opportunity to watch his grandchildrens' recitals and soccer games, enjoyed hiking and fishing and just talking with the neighbors? Preparing the autobiography is invaluable because it helps you discover your true mind-set.

Why is your mind-set important? Because the biggest obstacle to changing how you live is your mind-set—refusing to give up your old lifestyle. More than anything else, your mind-set determines what you find satisfying and fulfilling. If you have an acquisitive mind-set in putting great emphasis on having the finest clothes and home furnishings, you will have trouble adjusting to a less consumption-oriented lifestyle.

How do you know if your mind-set will allow you to be comfortable with a major change? By trying to visualize—in great detail—what your new lifestyle will be like. If, for example, you want to give up your present job as an insurance salesperson in a large metropolitan area and become a potter, you will probably have to move to a more rural area and scale back your living accommodations. While you're dressing for work in the morning in your 10' x 10' bathroom with two sinks and a Jacuzzi, imagine what it would be like dressing in a bathroom the size of a closet that needs new fixtures and a lot of repairs. Then, imagine what it would be like to forsake the plays and concerts you are so fond of and instead watch an old movie on the VCR or play cards around the kitchen table for the evening.

Is that enough? No. The next step is to make some trial runs of the new lifestyle from your present home base. If you're going to a cocktail party, for example, leave your fur coat and expensive jewelry at home and wear simple clothing that you've worn many times before. And leave the Mercedes in the garage and drive to the party in the beat-up old car you only use to get groceries.

Making these experimental cutbacks can be a huge emotional wrench, especially because you are changing your image in front of friends and acquaintances who have known the "old" you for many years. Some people find these trial runs so difficult that they no longer have the desire to make a major life-style change.

Is there any common trait among people who successfully make a big change in how they live and work? Yes, almost always these people have tremendous self-confidence. They look at life as a creative adventure and realize that regardless of what happens to them— whether it's a business setback or an unexpected illness—they have the ability to handle it.

Have you discovered any surprises that await people who have made such changes? Yes, the high—and ever-increasing—cost of living. Speaking personally, as someone who has made such a shift, I am astounded at how much it costs to live these days. Insurance costs, in particular, keep on rising for everything from your auto to your home and your health insurance policy. So you have to be willing to make more cutbacks than you ever dreamed necessary. For example, I recently boosted my insurance deductibles so I could continue to afford to carry coverage. The increased cost of living also pushed me to go back to my old line of work, and to resume organizing business seminars. But this points to a common mistake many people make.

What is that? Expecting not to have to work at all. You need to have a focus in your life, and a reason to get up in the morning. While some folks may be satisfied with looking ahead to their next golf or tennis game, many others need a more substantive goal. In fact, my experience shows that most people who make a big change in lifestyle eventually gravitate back to their old line of work. The big difference is that they do it on a smaller scale and are much less frenetic and stressed. This gives them the opportunity to spend time on the other things that matter to them as well, such as family, volunteer work and religious activities.

Source: Ted Dreier, speaker and seminar leader in the field of human improvement. His book, *Take Your Life Off Hold*, is available from him at Box 3880, Breckenridge, Colorado 80424.

A Cheaper, Happier Retirement

You can have a happy retirement even if it arrives sooner than you planned…even if you never got around to planning it. But without planning, your income will drop significantly —so you must study all of the options to make the most of your assets…and to cut expenses.

Lower living expenses:

Most people who are approaching retirement have substantial equity in their homes. If you sell and move to a lower-cost area, you can relieve many retirement financial pains— and if you're over 55, $125,000 of your capital gains is tax-exempt.

If you choose to stay where you are, you can still convert your equity into cash via a reverse mortgage—or via a sale-leaseback arrangement.

If the thought of moving doesn't faze you, investigate places with lower housing costs— including utilities—and lower local taxes and find those most compatible with your preferred lifestyle. Some may be quite close to home.

Example: My husband and I live in Turlock, California—two hours from the Bay area, but a house just like ours costs almost $400,000 more in San Francisco.

There are many relocation options. Many of the retirement communities are very lively, with wonderful options. They come in all forms—condos, rentals, home sharing...even living abroad.

Other expenses:

You can also drastically cut your spending on other goods and services. It can become a continuing "game"—checking out seasonal specials, flea markets, garage sales, factory outlets and classified ads. You can borrow or barter, do it yourself, take advantage of all kinds of coupons and senior discounts...and take advantage of the wide variety of freebies, too. Also...

Health: Health insurance and medical expenses are a major concern for retirees. A few alternative ways to save here include continuing employer-paid group plans, joining an HMO, choosing doctors who accept Medicare patients on assignment and making use of university optical and dental clinics.

Further, you can both save money and improve your general well-being if you plan and shop for inexpensive, nutritionally balanced meals.

Another low-cost way to improve health is by taking an aspirin every day. Studies indicate that this may prevent heart attacks and colon cancer. You can also reduce stress by making friends and having a pet.

Money making: Part of the extra time retirement makes available can be turned into cash by part-time employment—including home businesses.

Activities: A huge selection of high-quality leisure pursuits—from sports, hobbies and travel to educational and volunteer activities—can be pursued with little financial outlay.

Source: Diane Warner, the author of six nonfiction books presently on the market, including *How to Have a Great Retirement on a Limited Budget*, Writer's Digest Books, 1507 Dana Ave., Cincinnati 45207. She also conducts retirement seminars at northern California universities and is a member of the National Speakers Association.

How To Take Money Out Of Your IRA Or Pension

Many people think of their IRAs and other retirement funds as money in the bank. But when they try to make a withdrawal, they're surprised to run into severe restrictions imposed by the tax laws and enforced by heavy tax penalties.

There are, however, ways to escape the penalties...

Premature distributions:

The general rule is that distributions to people under age 59½ are subject to a 10% penalty—in addition to the regular income tax on the distribution. This rule applies to IRAs, Keogh plans, 401(k)s, most company pensions and tax-sheltered annuities.

Like most rules, however, this one has its exceptions...

• Exception: Annuity distributions. There's no penalty if you take the money as an annuity—a series of substantially equal periodic payments (made at least once a year) over your lifetime (or that of you and your beneficiary).

Limits: This method of distribution must continue for at least five years or until you reach age 59½, whichever is later. You can then switch to any distribution method you choose, including a lump-sum payout.

• Exception: Special cases. No penalty is charged on distributions that are made to...

• Support you in the event you become totally disabled.

• Settle a domestic relations court order—a property settlement, for instance.

• Cover medical expenses exceeding 7½% of your Adjusted Gross Income. Note: This is not allowed for IRAs.

What if you receive a lump-sum distribution because you change jobs...or lose your job...or your company goes out of business? If you're under 59½, this could mean a 10% penalty plus a whopping tax bill, since the pension money will push you into a higher tax bracket.

• Exception: Rollovers. To avoid this double disaster, you have 60 days in which to make a rollover of the money into another retirement fund. Options:

• Roll the money over to your new employer's pension plan (or a Keogh plan if you're self-employed), provided the plan accepts rollovers. You avoid the penalty and defer payment of tax. In addition, if you receive a lump-sum distribution from your new plan, after you reach age 59½, you may elect 5- or 10-year averaging, which can greatly cut the tax bite on the distribution. The way averaging works is that you assume that your income was received equally by five different persons (10 for 10-year averaging) in the current year and that each of these people had no other income.

• Roll the money over into an IRA. Again, you avoid the penalty and defer tax. The problem here is that an IRA can never qualify for averaging. But there is a way for you to preserve that option.

• Roll the money over into a temporary "conduit" IRA. Later on, you may be able to roll it over into a Keogh plan or a company pension, regaining the averaging option for a later lump-sum distribution. To qualify as a conduit, the IRA must be kept separate from your other IRAs. It must contain only the distribution from the other plan and accrued earnings. No additions are allowed.

Partial rollovers are allowed. If, for instance, you receive $100,000, you could keep $40,000, pay the tax and the penalty on it and roll over the $60,000 balance.

If you are over 59½, there's no 10% penalty on distribution. But you may still elect a rollover to defer taxes and continue tax-free accumulation.

Special rule on averaging. The special tax break called "averaging" greatly reduces the tax on lump-sum distributions. You may elect to use five-year averaging if you are at least 59½ when you receive the distribution.

If you were born before 1936, the 59½ requirement does not apply and you may elect to use 10-year averaging at 1986 income tax rates rather than 5-year averaging at current income tax rates.

Caution:

Averaging is a once-in-a-lifetime privilege. Once you avail yourself of it, you can't use it again, even if you continue to work and build up a new pension account. So even if you qualify, you may prefer to make a rollover and save the averaging option for possible future use.

Required distributions:

At age 70½, you must start making annual withdrawals from all your retirement funds—even if you haven't retired. (You don't have to take money from each IRA you own, but a minimum distribution must be figured for each one. Then, you can take all the money from one IRA if you wish.) The first distribution, for the year you reach 70½, may be delayed until the following April 1, but later withdrawals must be made by the end of each year.

The minimum withdrawal for each year is calculated from life-expectancy tables for you and your beneficiary.

Trap: Failure to comply with the minimum distribution rules carries a heavy penalty—50% of the amount you should have withdrawn but didn't.

Normally your company or your retirement plan trustees will take care of things for you. But you should be aware of the rule, just to make sure they don't slip up.

Problem: Some people routinely lop a few years off their age when they apply for a job. When they reach 70½, the employer's records show them as younger. Result: They don't receive the required distribution and become subject to the heavy penalty. If you're in this situation, go to your employer and get the records corrected.

Excess distributions:

If total distributions from your retirement accounts exceed $150,000 in any year ($750,000 for lump-sum distributions), you'll be charged a 15% penalty tax on the excess.

You can't even escape the penalty by dying. Your estate will be subject to the penalty if your retirement accounts exceed a certain amount, determined by a complex formula.

There are ways to avoid or minimize the tax, but they're complicated. If you're in danger, consult a tax professional.

Source: John Caplan, partner, Price Waterhouse, 153 E. 53 St., New York 10022, and Eric Raps, senior manager, Price Waterhouse, 1801 K St. NW, Washington, DC 20006.

Retirement Planning

One of the most important decisions you may make in your lifetime is where you will live after your retirement.

Despite the widespread belief that many people who retire move to a warm climate, the reality is that most people simply stay in the same place.

A recent survey conducted by the Harvard–MIT Joint Center for Housing Studies found that only 20% of those over age 55 had moved …and only an additional 5% were planning to move within five years.

For those over 65 years old, only 1% planned to move in the years ahead.

Conclusion:

The vast majority were content to stay in their existing homes.

It's also commonly thought that older people feel burdened by a house that is too large for their current needs. But surprisingly, very few survey respondents felt that their house was too large or that they had more space than they could use.

Yesterday vs. today:

These attitudes evolve from the time when people didn't live as long as they do now. In today's world, increasing longevity can have a major impact on how people approach the question of retirement housing. In the future, longevity may mean much greater changes in retirement lifestyles.

As life expectancies reach into the 80s and 90s, people will have to plan ahead and decide what they will do when they retire. That may not include staying in the same house they've always lived in. In the past, when people lived to be only about 60 years old, many worked right up until the time of their death.

Today, the average person can expect to live at least 20 to 25 years beyond actual retirement—if he/she retires at the traditional age of 62 to 65.

Reasons to move:

The best reason to move is that your current surroundings are unsatisfactory. Situations that might suggest the necessity of a move:

• Your home is too costly to maintain, especially if high mortgage payments cut into limited retirement income. Your house may need major repairs because of its age, or constant maintenance.

Warning:

A 7% inflation rate means that prices would quadruple in 20 years. Under these conditions, if you are now age 65 and have a comfortable $40,000 annual retirement income, you will be reduced to poverty-level purchasing power at age 85—if you have no inflation protection.

• The neighborhood is no longer safe—or friends have moved away.

• The design of the house limits accessibility. If the house has stairways or an inefficient floor plan, it may become a bigger problem as agility declines. If a wheelchair is needed, a stairway may make part of the home inaccessible altogether.

Choosing a new home:

When thinking about a move, the most important considerations are your personal needs and preferences.

You also have to consider what you are physically capable of doing…and your financial resources, now and in the future.

A home environment can be much more important during retirement than when you were working. A retiree will probably spend much more time in the home than before. Having pleasant surroundings, convenient shopping, recreational facilities and friends close by will become more important.

Other major factors:

• The amount of privacy desired in daily life.

• The type of lifestyle sought.

• Requirements for both interior and outdoor space.

• Safety and personal security.

• Design features that add convenience and utility.

Limited choices:

The widest array of housing choices are available for those who are independent—

187

those who don't depend on anyone else for care. As you lose independence—whether gradually or suddenly—choices become more limited.

A semiindependent person is someone who suffers some lack of mobility or other incapacity and requires assistance in the form of equipment or personnel.

The totally dependent person requires constant assistance—he/she needs help to perform basic life functions. For the totally dependent, housing choices are quite limited.

In some situations, if you choose one housing option, you may find that it sets you up for other contingencies.

Example:

In certain types of retirement housing, you can buy the option to be moved to a nursing home if that's needed. This makes it much easier than if you're just out in the public trying to get into a nursing home.

It's getting harder to get into good nursing homes because the demand is rising. But if your retirement community includes nursing-home care as an option, then you can move back and forth as you need.

Bottom line:

Your financial needs will not be uniform for the rest of your life. They will be composed of several stages. For this reason, financial planning is important, starting right now. As retirement approaches, it is prudent to reduce debts and gain financial flexibility.

Early retirement may involve a transitional period in which one spouse continues working, at least part-time. There is additional income, but there continue to be some work-related expenses.

The next period is one of complete retirement, meaning reduced income but lower expenses.

Finally, there may be a time of partial or complete infirmity that will require use of financial resources to their fullest.

Source: Jack Friedman, PhD, CPA, senior manager in the Roulac Group, Deloitte & Touche, Dallas, and Jack Harris, PhD, on the faculty of the Real Estate Center at Texas A & M University. They are the co-authors of *Keys to Buying a Retirement Home*, Barrons, 250 Wireless Blvd., Hauppauge, New York 11788.

How To Preserve Your Retirement Assets For The Benefit Of Your Children

High net worth individuals who have retired may not feel the need to withdraw the maximum amount of retirement income from their pensions. Instead, they may want to preserve a substantial portion of the retirement benefits for their children or other heirs.

Problem:

Without careful planning, not much will be left for the children after estate tax and income tax have been taken out.

There is a plan, however, for individuals who are insurable, which yields the same income to the retiree and spouse while greatly increasing the amount that the children ultimately get.

Typical scenario:

Jerry, who is 70 years old, has an IRA that has a current value of $1,000,000 and is generating about a 6.3% return. Jerry is currently drawing out the 6.3% as a taxable retirement benefit. The asset base of the IRA account is remaining intact, except for possible declines in market value.

At Jerry's death, the income will flow to his widow, Nancy, if she survives him, for her lifetime, with no estate tax ramifications. Jerry now pays—and later Nancy will pay—ordinary income tax on the benefits received. Since the assets are currently valued at approximately $1,000,000, the 6.3% income equates to roughly $63,000. After federal and state income taxes (New York, in this example), there would be $39,564 left.

At Nancy's death, estate tax (federal and New York) of 60% of the then value of the assets will be owed, leaving only $400,000 to pass on to the children. In addition, the children will be assessed income tax on the original $1,000,000 less a deduction for federal, but not state, estate tax paid. This will leave them with only $196,888 of the original $1,000,000—only 19.69%—assuming a 37.5% combined federal and state income tax rate.

Impact: Double taxation severely curtails the effective transfer of wealth to the younger generation.

Better way:

Jerry invests his IRA assets of $1,000,000 in a single-life annuity. The investment yields an annual income of $119,815, or $75,294 after the payment of income tax. This is a very substantial increase over the $39,564 of posttax income that would be available to Jerry and Nancy in the ordinary course of events.

At the same time he purchases an annuity, Jerry spends the $35,730 of excess posttax annuity income (the portion in excess of $39,564) on the first annual premium for an insurance policy on his life (to be purchased through a life insurance trust). That excess income, paid for 12 years, will purchase more than $1.1 million of insurance. After 12 premium payments, no additional premiums will be due if insurance company projections are met. At Jerry's death, the $1.1 million will be paid to the insurance trust.

If Nancy survives Jerry, then, under the terms of the life insurance trust, Nancy will receive the income from the proceeds. If the $1.1 million insurance proceeds are invested in tax-exempt municipal bonds yielding 6%, she will receive $66,000 in tax-free annual income.

At Nancy's death, the assets of the insurance trust will be distributed to the children free of both estate and income tax. Therefore, the net value to Jerry and Nancy's heirs from this plan would increase from $196,888 to $1.1 million with no net cost to either Jerry and Nancy or their children.

Summary:

Jerry will receive a greatly increased amount of posttax income over what he would have earned under the typical scenario arrangement. An income stream will continue to Nancy during her life through the insurance trust, if she survives Jerry. The children will enjoy a greatly enhanced inheritance at the death of the survivor of Jerry and Nancy.

Source: Stanley S. Weithorn, Esq., a tax attorney at both 525 University Ave., Palo Alto, California 94301, and 40 W. 57 St., New York 10019. Mr. Weithorn specializes in charitable tax planning and sophisticated estate planning.

The Biggest Traps In Retirement Planning

To make the most of your retirement years, start planning now. The earlier you start, the more you will be able to achieve.

Set goals:

The first mistake of retirement planning is not having goals. When you don't know what you want, you are unlikely to attain it. Helpful: Draw up a "dream list" for your retirement years. Consider…

• Where you will want to live.
• Your desired life-style.
• The income you will need.
• The specific steps required to turn as much of the list as possible into reality.

Goal-setting requires you to…

…take action. By having a goal of a certain amount of savings by a fixed date, you know how much you must save each year starting now. This also shows you how costly it is to delay saving, giving a greater incentive to start saving right away.

Example: Put away just $50 a month starting at age 25 and, assuming an average 5% after-tax annual return, you'll have $76,619 saved by age 65—at $100 a month, your nest egg will be $153,238. By contrast, put away the same $50 a month starting at age 55, and you'll have just $7,796 by age 65…$100 a month will yield only $15,593.

…be realistic. Everybody wants many things, but goal-setting makes you decide what's most important. Once you decide this, you can begin to assess how much money you're going to need. But more than finances are involved here. You're more likely to be happy in your retirement years if you've achieved what's important to you than if you've left your dreams too vague to be realized.

…be consistent. People typically want two things from their retirement investments— safety for their savings and big returns to fund a comfortable retirement life-style. But, of course, there's an inherent conflict here.

A sound investment plan designed to meet specific goals will make the most of the trade-off between risk and opportunity, and enable you to avoid the costly and common mistakes of investing either too riskily or with too much caution.

Example: You might invest in aggressive growth stocks while retirement is still years away, knowing that if the stock market falls there will be plenty of time for your portfolio to recover. Then, as retirement nears, you can shift money gradually into safer investments. With a specific financial target, you will know how much to shift each year to guarantee security. Excess funds can remain invested aggressively in the hope of hitting a financial "home run." The chance of big gains remains while risk is minimized.

Key: The target retirement date you set will have a big impact on planning strategies and the amount you must save each year.

Pick a date that is sooner rather than later. If you work beyond your planned retirement date, the extra income will simply make you even better off. But if you are forced to retire early, you will be glad to have planned for it. And it will always be pleasant to have the option of retiring early if you want to.

To avoid other common mistakes:

• Understand your company's retirement plan. Most people don't. Ask:

• How do benefits differ if you are terminated, take early retirement or leave at the normal retirement age?

• What would happen if you left the company today?

• Is there a vesting schedule that requires you to stay with the company a set number of years in order to receive full benefits?

• Will you receive a fixed pension with a dollar value you can estimate now? Or does the company have a profit-sharing plan under which its contribution to your account varies each year, making your final benefit an uncertain amount?

• Are plan benefits adjusted in line with inflation? Danger: If inflation continues at the 5% rate of recent years, a fixed pension will lose half its value in 14 years. You may need extra income.

• How and when will you get paid? Plan payouts may not occur until months after you retire. And if a company has more than one plan, they may make payouts at different times. This can drastically affect personal cash flow, so anticipate a retirement plan's red tape.

Warning: Beware of plan modifications. Many firms are cutting back retirement benefits to save costs. Employees must be notified when their retirement plan is modified, so pay attention and be sure you understand changes that affect you.

• Understand Social Security. Figure your expected benefit in advance. Helpful: Contact your local Social Security office and ask them to compute your expected benefit for you.

Big trap: Most people expect that they will receive their pension and Social Security. But many companies have "integrated" plans under which the designated pension amount includes Social Security—the company's contribution toward your pension is reduced by the amount of Social Security you receive. Find out whether your company's plan is integrated or not.

Social Security options: Some firms allow workers to retire early—before they are eligible to receive Social Security. Those companies increase early pension payments by the amount of the monthly Social Security that the retiree will ultimately receive. When Social Security payments start, pension payments are reduced accordingly. The result is an even flow of income to the employee that can facilitate early-retirement planning.

Consider taking Social Security benefits early, at age 62, instead of at age 65. While waiting until 65 provides a larger monthly benefit, you also miss three full years of payments in the meantime, and it can take many years of increased monthly payments to make up this difference.

If you work past retirement age, your benefits remain the same—they don't increase—so there's no monetary advantage in not taking them at 65.

• Make full use of company life insurance. Some companies have group policies that allow departing employees to convert their term insurance into whole life coverage without going through a physical examination. If your company offers this benefit, don't overlook it. If this benefit isn't offered, be aware that when you are older it may be more difficult to pass a required physical to get insurance. If you will need coverage then, take steps to secure it now (see below).

• Consider health insurance. Figure out in advance what the cost of insurance will be after you retire. Ask if your company provides retirement health benefits, and what are the plan limits. If you will have to pay for your own coverage, figure it in as a cost of retirement and start saving for it now.

Ask now about nursing home insurance and Medigap insurance for expenses not covered by Medicare, so that if the day comes in retirement that you need to obtain such coverage you will be familiar with it. Don't make the mistake of thinking, It won't happen to me.

• Protect yourself as a spouse. Ask: What are your rights under your spouse's retirement program? Has your spouse selected a survivorship option, so benefits will continue to be paid to you should he/she die first? Do you know where all necessary documents are located in the event your spouse dies or becomes incapacitated? What will happen to benefits in the event of divorce?

Note: Alimony is considered compensation, and can be used to make deductible IRA contributions.

Important: The worst time to make serious financial decisions is while experiencing the trauma of the loss of a spouse. Do financial planning beforehand so you will know what to do if or when the day comes.

• Diversify wealth. It's dangerous to keep all your wealth in one investment as retirement nears. Yet many people do so, especially sole proprietors and executives who keep their money in their own businesses.

Better: As retirement draws near, spread funds among several investments so that your retirement position won't be endangered by a loss suffered in any one area.

• Consider a lump-sum distribution. When you retire, it may be advantageous to take your benefit in the form of a lump-sum payment, rather than through annual pension or annuity payments. This gives you investment control over your money. A lump-sum distribution may be rolled over into an IRA tax-free if deposited within 60 days of receipt.

If you were born before 1936, the IRS provides a tax break for a lump-sum distribution in the form of income-averaging—treating it as if it were received over a period of years. The result is that much of the distribution avoids being taxed at top bracket rates. Technical rules apply, so consult with your tax adviser about making the right choices.

• Consider taking money out of an IRA before age 59½ without paying an early withdrawal penalty. This is possible if payouts are taken in the form of an annuity—that is, in even payments over your life expectancy.

• Do the paperwork. Make sure, for example, that all beneficiaries are properly designated or survivor benefits may not be paid out according to your wishes.

• Get qualified advice. Both investment advice and tax advice are absolute musts. Remember, you're planning your future and managing your life savings, so seek out the most qualified experts that you can find.

Source: Anna Polizzi-Keller, tax partner in the financial counseling and expatriate (citizens based outside the country of their citizenship) areas, Ernst & Young, 701 Market St., St Louis 63101.

Pension Traps And Annuity Opportunities

Before collecting checks from your company pension plan or a single-premium deferred annuity, it pays to investigate your options.

By choosing an immediate annuity, you may wind up with hundreds of dollars more per month in your pocket—at no additional risk.

An immediate annuity is an insurance contract that, in return for a one-time payment, starts paying a fixed sum for your lifetime or for some other period right away.

A single-life annuity, for example, pays the agreed-upon sum every month until the purchaser dies. The payment doesn't have to stop at the first death. It depends on the option you select: Joint and two-thirds survivor, joint and 50% survivor, and joint and 100% survivor. A joint-and-survivor annuity for a married couple, by contrast, pays one larger sum while both spouses are alive, and a lesser amount after the first spouse dies. Payments continue at the lower level during the lifetime of the surviving spouse and end only when that person dies.

Comparison shopping in the immediate annuity market can pay off quite nicely.

Example: Recently, I checked out rates—which are expressed as monthly income per $10,000 of premium—for a 65-year-old woman. For a $100,000 investment, the monthly income ranged from a high of $915 to a low of $716—a difference of almost $200, or about 28%.

Trap: Don't automatically go for the highest monthly income figure. Given all the turmoil in the insurance industry these days, and the recent failure of Executive Life, in the example above I decided to not even consider the seven companies paying the top rates because I had reservations about their soundness. Bear in mind that you are purchasing something that you intend to last for the rest of your life.

I wound up recommending my client purchase an annuity that ranked 20th out of 100. It was offered by Northwestern Mutual, the solid, conservative and well-run Minnesota company. The annuity provided monthly income of $839. The median income figure was $809 a month.

Two common situations in which investigating what you'd receive with an immediate annuity makes sense...

• When you're retiring from your company. Before you automatically accept the monthly pension check your company plan offers, ask if the plan permits a lump-sum distribution instead. Many, but not all, plans do.

See what you can get in monthly income by purchasing an immediate annuity with some of that money. You may be surprised to discover that you'll get a much larger payment with the annuity than with your company pension.

• When you're ready to start annuitizing, or receiving distributions, from a single-premium deferred annuity that you purchased years ago. Just because you purchased the annuity from Company A, don't assume that it now offers the best deal in terms of monthly income. You may do better by switching to Company B or C.

Caution: In either case, don't sink all your money into an immediate annuity all at once. You many be purchasing at a trough, and annuity rates may subsequently shoot up. I recommend that people purchase several contracts over time and that they not annuitize more than 50% of their total investable assets.

It's vital that you do your comparative shopping right at the point when you are ready to make your purchase.

Reason: The immediate annuity market is a very fluid one, and rates can fluctuate widely, even within a given company, depending upon the details of your individual situation.

Example: A particular company may post attractive payouts one month, but not the next. Or, it may be competitive at some ages but unattractive at others.

To check on the different rates offered by different companies, consult *Best's Retirement Income Guide.** It's published twice a year and available in many public libraries. The guide contains comparative information on many different types of annuities, both fixed and variable, offered by hundreds of different companies. To find out the annuity rate for an immediate annuity, you must consult the tables in the back, which give the monthly income you would receive if you paid a set sum to different insurance companies queried.

It's also possible to deal with a reputable broker who maintains a broad database of annuity rates paid by different companies. Sources:

• The Annuity Network, a subsidiary of the Laughlin group in Beaverton, Oregon (800-547-3257). The parent company evaluates the safety and stability of insurance companies. The Annuity Network works with about 300

*A.M. Best & Co., A.M. Best Red., Oldwich, NJ 08858.

insurance companies. The network is compensated on a commission basis from companies whose policies it sells.

• United States Annuities, Englishtown, New Jersey (800-872-6684). An insurance-brokerage and research firm that specializes in immediate annuities. It also works on a commission basis. The firm publishes the *Annuity Shopper,* a bi-monthly newsletter that compares different insurers' ratings, rates and charges. US Annuities, 98 Hoffman Rd., Englishtown, New Jersey 07726. Six issues. $45/yr.

Of course, there are some drawbacks to opting for an immediate annuity, rather than for your company pension. Rejecting your pension might be unwise, for example, if your company has a history of increasing its pension payouts from time to time in order to offset inflation. The annuity check you get the first month is the same amount you'll receive 20 years from now—assuming you're still alive to collect.

And—pensions are insured by the Pension Board Guaranty Corporation, while immediate annuities are only as good as the company that issues them.

Before you jump at the highest available rate, you should always very carefully investigate the issuing company's financial health.

Aim: To be reasonably sure it will be able to make those payouts as long as you live.

Caution: Some, but not all, insurers require annuity buyers to pay upfront policy fees or other charges, which can range from $150 to $500. And about 10 states impose premium taxes that amount to 1% to 3% of the amount invested.

Source: Glenn Daily, a fee-only insurance consultant and author of *The Individual Investor's Guide to Low-Load Insurance Products,* International Publishing Corp., 625 N. Michigan Ave., Suite 1920, Chicago 60611.

Seven Tools For Building Retirement Happiness

Americans are living longer, retiring earlier and saving less than they did a generation ago. This can cause serious financial problems in retirement unless you plan carefully—the sooner the better...

1. Set your retirement goals. What do you intend to do during retirement? How much money will you need?

2. Set a monthly amount that you are willing to invest for retirement.

3. Determine what investment vehicles you plan to use. Certificates of Deposit? Municipal bonds? Mutual funds? Real estate?

4. Make the monthly investment automatic. Have it taken out of your paycheck or your bank account automatically. You can make an arrangement with a mutual fund to take a monthly amount from your bank account.

5. Reposition current investments. Review your investments in terms of yield, safety, risk, etc. Do this now and on a regular basis—at least semiannually. Look on the investments as long-term, because you're investing for retirement.

6. Maximize 401(k) contributions annually. This year's maximum is $8,728. The contribution is deductible and the income is tax-deferred.

7. Put $2,000 a year into an IRA even if you don't get a tax deduction for the contribution. Take the money from other taxable retirement investments and put it into an IRA. Reason: The income the money earns is tax-deferred.

Source: Dan J. Hall, tax partner and director of personal financial services, San Francisco and Western Region, Coopers & Lybrand, 333 Market St., San Francisco 94105.

11

Preparing Your Estate

How To Keep Money In Your Family

Estate taxes are the highest taxes in America today. Estate tax rates go as high as 55%. When you take into account additional estate and generation-skipping transfer taxes, rates can run to over 80%.

While that's all quite bad—it could get even worse. Some Congressional leaders have advocated financing the cost of a new long-term health insurance plan with, among other things, a reduction in the current estate tax exemption amount to $200,000 (down from the current $600,000). For a couple's $2 million estate, this means $400,000 in additional taxes —a 25% increase.

Simply put, even individuals of moderate means need to address estate tax planning or forfeit a large portion of their hard-earned wealth to the government.

Tools for tax reduction:

The law provides certain tools for keeping taxes down. These include deductions for transfers to a spouse or charity, a unified credit which amounts to an exemption equivalent of $600,000 per person and an annual gift tax exclusion of $10,000 per donee ($20,000 if the gift is from you and your spouse). These tools must be used in strategic ways for optimum effectiveness.

Essentially all of estate planning for tax reduction can be boiled down to five categories in which the tools just mentioned are used:

- Wills and revocable trusts.
- Irrevocable trusts.
- Family limited partnerships.
- Charitable trusts.
- Private foundations.

Wills and revocable trusts:

All individuals—from those with moderate estates to the very wealthy—must select and combine the various categories for the greatest savings. Couples with combined estates up to $1.2 million can easily use wills and revocable trusts to ensure that the $600,000 exemption equivalent for each spouse is fully used.

195

Combined estates in excess of $1.2 million might want to consider additional strategies. Irrevocable trusts:

•Tax-free insurance trusts. Life insurance can be transferred to or bought by an irrevocable trust. The insured can gift the premiums to the trust tax-free—assuming so-called Crummey provisions have been included.

As long as the trust owns the policy (and any policy transfers were made more than three years prior to death), there is no estate tax on the proceeds. The heirs, presumably the grantor's children, receive those proceeds free from estate and income taxes.

What is more, the heirs can purchase assets from the estate to provide funds for the payment of estate tax on those other assets.

Wealth trust: Why should the wealthiest families in America be able to perpetuate their wealth from generation to generation while those with more modest estates cannot? In fact, families with assets of $1 million and more can enjoy the same strategies used by wealthier ones.

In the category of an irrevocable trust, the Wealth Trust is an arrangement that meets not only today's estate tax savings concerns but also offers protection from creditors and divorce for future generations. It is set up during the lifetime of an individual or couple ("grantor"). The gift to future generations is tax-free if under the $600,000 per donor amount (plus amounts shielded by the annual gift tax exclusion).

The Wealth Trust differs from other traditional trusts. Rather than being distributed outright to the grantor's children after the death of the grantor, it can continue to operate for several generations. If the grantor has grandchildren, or even great-grandchildren, each generation can be protected.

The trust can be funded with any type of asset. Life insurance can be used to provide liquidity for payment of estate taxes as discussed above.

The Wealth Trust has several objectives: It can be used to skip estate taxes for several generations while at the same time avoiding the very tax designed to prevent tax avoidance for multi-generational transfers—the generation-skipping transfer tax. It keeps property out of the hands of family members who might lose that property through creditor claims or in divorce settlements. It provides each family member with tailor-made benefits.

Benefits: The Wealth Trust can pay family members income for support and maintenance, medical and education costs, to buy homes and cars, and even to provide an effective line-of-credit on favorable terms.

Limits: To enjoy the advantages of a generation-skipping trust, a grantor can give no more than $1 million ($2 million in the case of a married couple). However, there is no limit on how large the trust can grow to. Good investments and modest needs of heirs can mean huge accumulations over the life of the trust.

At the end of the trust term, grandchildren or great-grandchildren may not need or want the vast sums built up in the trust fund. Typically, a grantor may limit the heir's interest to a dollar amount ($1 million, for example), or a percentage of trust assets. The balance of the trust property can be distributed to charity, or to a private foundation set up by the grantor or family members.

Trustees. The grantor's adult children can act as trustees along with an outsider (say, the grantor's attorney). It is advisable to use an outsider who knows the family and who is closer in age to the grantor's children than to the age of the grantor.

Family limited partnerships:

An owner of securities might want to transfer property tax-free but without using a trust.

Helpful: Create a family limited partnership with one general-partnership share and 99 limited-partnership shares. The title to the shares is changed to the name of that partnership. The owner retains the general partnership interest and, therefore, control over the property. Each year, he transfers a number of limited partnership shares to his children using the annual gift tax exclusion to avoid transfer tax. Ultimately, the owner will have transferred a sizable portion of his assets to his children, as well as any future appreciation.

Asset protection: The family limited partnership offers a key benefit over the traditional family partnership...asset protection for children. Since they receive only limited partnership interests, they are not as vulnerable to claims by partnership creditors.

Caution: New special valuation rules may affect transfers to family members. It is advisable to consult an experienced tax practitioner if this strategy is contemplated.
Charitable trusts:

A couple with highly appreciated assets can use a charitable remainder trust to avoid capital gains taxes, increase their income and at the same time benefit their favorite charity.

The charitable remainder trust can provide the couple with a life income. After their death, the proceeds go to a named charity. The couple receives a current deduction on income taxes. This is the value of the charity's interest figured according to IRS tables. The tax savings from the deduction can be used to buy life insurance for the children to replace the assets that will pass to the charity.

Caution: The trust must be carefully set up to meet IRS requirements in order to provide the intended benefits.
Private foundations:

Families with $2 million or more might consider using a private foundation to satisfy both charitable objectives and family income needs.

Private foundations must distribute at least 5% of their assets annually, plus usually an income tax, which amounts to 1% of the principal. A $2 million foundation would have to disburse $100,000 each year to recognized charities and $20,000 in taxes. If the foundation could earn 9% on its assets, then of the $180,000 in income, $60,000 would be available after charitable disbursements for expenses, including salaries for family members.
Special approach for retirement benefits:

Benefits from qualified plans can easily run to more than $1 million for business owners, executives and professionals. Yet the combination of regular and additional estate taxes can mean that heirs get only $300,000 of this amount after the government takes its due. Invested at 8%, this would give heirs $24,000 annually.

If, instead, the benefits were left to a private foundation, the $1 million at 8% would yield $80,000. Even after payment of $50,000 each year to worthy causes (5% of the foundation's assets), heirs who run the foundation would still be able to enjoy $30,000 a year, or $6,000 more than via a direct bequest. And there is the additional benefit of providing for charitable objectives.

Source: Andrew D. Westhem, chairman and managing partner, Wealth Transfer Planning Inc., 1925 Century Park East, Suite 2350, Los Angeles 90067. 800-423-4890. He is the author of *Winning the Wealth Game*, Dearborn Financial Publishing Co., 520 N. Dearborn St., Chicago 60610.

When Someone Close Is Very Ill

It may seem callous to even think about taxes when a loved one faces a life-threatening illness. But if tax planning is ignored at that point, assets carefully accumulated over a lifetime may be squandered unnecessarily. For many facing a final illness, dealing with these matters provides life-oriented focus that helps them to combat depression and achieve a sense of completion in seeing that their affairs are well ordered.

Some things to consider: Gifts by the patient. In many cases, estate taxes can be saved by making gifts to family members and other intended beneficiaries. An unlimited amount may be transferred tax-free provided no one person receives more than $10,000. The maximum tax-free gift per recipient can increase to $20,000 if the patient's spouse is still alive and consents to treat each gift as having been jointly made.

Under the old law, gifts made within three years of death were figured back into the taxable estate. The '81 tax act repealed this "contemplation-of-death" rule in most cases.

One major exception: The old rule still applies to gifts of life insurance. Gifts to the patient. This tactic may be useful when the patient doesn't have enough property to take full advantage of the estate tax exemption ($600,000 in 1987). Reason: Property that passes through a decedent's estate gets what's known as a stepped-up basis. That is, the person who inherits it is treated for income tax purposes as though he bought it and paid what it was worth on the date of death. (Or what it was worth six months after the date of death if the executor chooses this alternate date to set the value of the taxable estate.)

In most cases, it doesn't pay to use this tactic with property that will be bequeathed back to a spouse who gave it to the patient. Reason: Unless the gift was made more than a year before the date of death, stepped-up basis will be denied. But when the patient is expected to survive for substantially more than a year, this tactic can be quite useful.

Loss property. In general there is a tax disadvantage in inheriting property that is worth less than its original cost. Reason: Its tax basis is stepped down to its date-of-death value and the potential loss deduction is forfeited. If the patient has substantial income it might pay to sell the property and deduct the losses. But it doesn't pay to generate losses that are more than $3,000 in excess of the patient's capital gains. Reason: These excess losses can't be deducted currently, and there's likely to be no future years' income on which to deduct them. Alternative: Sell the loss property at its current value to a close family member. Result: The patient's loss on the sale is nondeductible, because the purchaser is a family member. But any future gains the family member realizes will be nontaxable to the extent of the previously disallowed loss.

Charitable gifts. In some cases, bequests to charitable organizations should be made before death. Benefit: Current income tax deductions. But it's important not to give too much away. This tactic may generate more deductions than the patient can use.

Flower bonds. Certain series of U.S. Treasury bonds can be purchased on the open market for substantially less than their full face value, because they pay very low interest. But if a decedent owns these so-called "flower bonds" on the date of death, they can be credited against the estate tax at their full face value.

Timing: Flower bonds should be bought when death is clearly imminent. There's little point in holding them for substantial periods before death because they yield very little income. On the other hand, it does no good for the estate to purchase them after death because they won't be applied against the estate tax. In some cases, flower bonds have been bought on behalf of a patient in a coma by a relative or trustee who holds a power of attorney. The IRS has attacked these purchases. But the courts have, so far, sided with the taxpayer.

A power of attorney should be prepared early on. If it's properly drafted, it can cover flower bond purchases and authority for a wide variety of other actions that can preserve the patient's assets and allow for flexible planning.

Income tax planning. A number of income tax moves should be considered. Examples:

Income timing. If the patient is in a low tax bracket, it may pay to accelerate income. The key here is to compare the patient's tax bracket with the bracket his estate is likely to be in. In some cases it will pay to accelerate income to make full use of deductions that would otherwise yield little or no tax benefit. Medical deductions, in particular, may be very high.

Choosing gift property. In making gifts to save estate taxes, it does not pay from an income tax standpoint to give away property that has gone up in value. Reason: The tax basis of gift property is not stepped up. So the recipient will have a potential income tax liability built into the gift. This potential is eliminated if the property is kept in the estate and passes by inheritance. For similar reasons, the patient should not give away business property that has been subject to depreciation.

Copyrights: If a copyright is received as a gift and later sold, the gain is fully taxed as ordinary income. If it's inherited and then later sold, it's treated as long-term capital gain (60% nontaxable).

Other moves. (1) For owners of stock in an S corporation it may pay to accelerate distribution of income particularly if the ill shareholder has previously taxed income that wasn't distributed.

(2) Where death is expected but not "clearly imminent," a private annuity may be a useful way of disposing of property. Reason: IRS regs will key the required annuity payments

to a healthy person's life expectancy.

(3) If the patient owns an unincorporated business or an interest in a partnership, it may pay to incorporate, particularly if the business has substantial accounts receivable or inventory that has gone up in value. Reason: Incorporation can secure capital gains treatment for these assets if the business is later sold.

The Shrewdest Ways To Save Estate Taxes Now

There are a great many saving techniques available for those who want to cut their estate taxes. It's up to you to pick the ones that fit your situation best. Key strategies:

• Reduce the size of your estate by giving money to your heirs during your lifetime. You can give away $10,000 a year to each of any number of beneficiaries completely tax free—$20,000 if your spouse joins you in making the gift. Money you give away now reduces the size of your future estate. And it reduces the tax your heirs will eventually pay.

Example: Your estate is worth $2.4 million. If you wait until you die to distribute the money, your heirs will pay a whopping estate tax. Instead, suppose you and your spouse give $20,000 a year to each of your three children for a period of eight years. At the end of that time, you will have given away $480,000 free of tax. This will save your heirs over $200,000 in estate taxes.

Bonus: When you give money or assets away during your lifetime, you not only remove the assets from your estate, but also any income and future appreciation those assets would earn between the time of the gift and your death.

Timing: The earlier in the year you make tax-free gifts the better. Early gifts remove more income and appreciation from your estate than gifts made late in the year.

• Don't waste one of your $600,000 estate tax exemptions. Married couples often have "I love you wills" in which each leaves everything to the other spouse. No estate tax is payable on the death of the first spouse—the estate is exempt from tax because of the unlimited marital deduction, which allows one spouse to leave any amount of money or other property to the other tax free. But when the surviving spouse dies, estate tax will be due. This tax will be far more than it would have been had the couple made full use of their estate tax exemptions.

Key: Each spouse has the right to leave beneficiaries other than his/her surviving spouse up to $600,000 estate tax free. This is called the "exemption equivalent" or "unified credit amount." The way to save taxes is to make sure each spouse uses his/her exemption equivalent by leaving assets to beneficiaries other than the spouse.

Example: A husband has an estate of $1.2 million. He dies, leaving everything to his wife. There is no tax on his estate because of the unlimited marital deduction. But when his wife dies, leaving an estate of $1.2 million to the children, there will be $235,000 of estate tax due. Only $600,000 of her estate will be sheltered from tax by her exemption equivalent.

Better way: The husband leaves $600,000 to his children (making use of his $600,000 exemption equivalent) and the balance of his estate to his wife. On his death there will be no estate tax payable—$600,000 will be protected by the exemption equivalent and $600,000 by the unlimited marital deduction. On his wife's death—her estate being only $600,000—the full amount will be sheltered by her exemption equivalent.

Estate tax: $0. Estate tax saving: $235,000.

• Family trusts. If your spouse needs the income from the $600,000 you would otherwise leave to your children or other beneficiaries, you can set up what is known as a family trust for your spouse and children. The trustee has the authority either to accumulate the income in the trust or to distribute it to your spouse. On your spouse's death, anything that is left over goes to your children or other beneficiaries.

Trap: You can't put jointly held property into a family trust. That property would not end up in the trust—but in the hands of the survivor of the joint owners.

• Life insurance trusts. If you own a life insurance policy at your death, or own any incidents of ownership in a policy—such as the right to change the beneficiary—the policy's proceeds will be included in your taxable estate. You can avoid this by setting up a trust and transferring the policy to the trust. If the trust is properly set up, it will keep the life insurance proceeds out of your estate and your spouse's estate.

The trust can be devised so your spouse gets money from the trust if he/she needs it. On your spouse's death, or at some other time in the future, the assets remaining in the trust go to your children or other beneficiaries.

Caution: You must live at least three years after the policy has been transferred to the trust for the proceeds to be kept out of your estate. This three-year rule is not a problem if the trust buys new insurance on your life, even if you gave the cash to the trustee to buy the policy. Of course, transfers to the trust are subject to gift tax.

• Make gifts to charity during your lifetime. You get a double tax benefit from such gifts. The value of the gift is deductible for income tax purposes, and the assets you give are removed from your estate—you don't pay estate tax on them. Compare: When you make gifts to charity under your will, you lose the income tax benefit. All you get is an estate tax benefit through the deduction for charitable contributions.

One way to make a lifetime gift to charity is through a charitable remainder trust. The trust pays you an income for life and the charity gets the trust assets on your death. You get a current income tax deduction for the present value of the assets the charity will eventually get.

• Skip a generation and make gifts to your grandchildren. If your children are already well provided for, you can avoid estate tax on their deaths by leaving some of your estate directly to your grandchildren.

Caution: There's a $1 million generation-skipping tax limit per donor on transfers of property that skip a generation. Amounts that exceed $1 million are subject to 55% tax. Note: These transfers are still subject to regular gift and estate taxes.

Reminder: Gifts within the annual exclusion limit ($10,000/$20,000) that are not in trust are not subject to the generation-skipping tax. There are also limited exceptions for certain other trusts.

• Use GRITs, GRATs, and GRUNTs. These trusts involve lifetime gifts that are made for the purpose of getting assets out of your estate at a low tax cost.

• Grantor Retained Income Trusts, or GRITs, are used to take a personal residence out of the estate. The house is transferred to a trust for the ultimate benefit of your heirs. You reserve the right to live in the house for a period of years. At the end of that period, your heirs get the house. If you survive the trust's term, your interest ceases and the value of the house is excluded from your taxable estate.

The transfer of the house into a trust is subject to gift tax. But the value for gift tax purposes is low because you've retained the right to live in the house for a number of years. The taxable gift will be only a fraction of the house's market value.

Key: The estate tax value of the house is frozen at the time of the transfer into the trust. Any appreciation that builds up in the house from the time of the transfer until your death escapes estate tax. Caution: If you die during the trust's term, the full value is pulled back into your estate.

• Grantor Retained Annuity Trusts, GRATs, and Grantor Retained Unitrusts, GRUNTs, are used to take other assets, such as securities, out of the estate. In principle, they work the same way as GRITs but require annual annuity (or unitrust) payments. Property is transferred at low gift tax cost. The estate tax value of the property is frozen at the time of the transfer. Any appreciation is kept out of your estate. If you survive the trust's term, no additional estate tax is payable on the trust's assets on your death.

Note: Tax basis of lifetime gifts is the donor's basis with adjustments, not date of death value. This can affect total savings.

Source: David S. Rhine, partner, BDO Seidman, 15 Columbus Circle, New York 10023.

Clever Estate Planning

Give property to children in exchange for their promise to pay you an annuity for life. Use IRS life expectancy tables to set the size of annuity payments so the annuity's value equals that of the property. Benefit: Estate taxes are eliminated since the property is removed from your estate and the annuity that replaces it stops at death—its value then is zero. Mistake: One person recently tried to set up this type of an arrangement after his doctor told him he had less than a year to live. But the IRS ruled that he couldn't use its life expectancy tables when he knew his life would be shorter. Thus, the transfer to the kids was ruled a taxable gift. Moral: Don't delay estate planning.

Source: Letter Ruling 9133001.

Estate Planning Loopholes...After Death

Much time and effort is put into planning an estate before a person dies...but planning doesn't end with death.

There are many things a person's executor can do to cut taxes.

Executors have many elections, or choices, to make, generally within the first nine months after a person's death. It is these elections that present the biggest tax-saving opportunities. Key elections:

• Loophole: Deciding whether it makes sense for a beneficiary to give up an interest in the estate. In some situations, a great deal of estate tax can be saved when a beneficiary disclaims (gives up) a share of the estate.

Example: A wife leaves $500,000 to her husband, who has an estate of $10 million. No estate tax would be owed on the wife's death because of the unlimited marital deduction. But on the husband's death, the extra $500,000 would be taxed at 55%. The tax would be $275,000. That tax could be saved if, on the wife's death, the husband were to disclaim the $500,000 inheritance and let it pass to the couple's children or other beneficiaries. The gift would not be taxed in the wife's estate because of her exemption equivalent—her right to leave up to $600,000 estate-tax-free to beneficiaries other than her husband.

• Loophole: Whether or not to treat distributions to the surviving spouse as Q-TIP distributions (Qualified Terminable Interest Property distributions). Property in which a spouse is given only a life interest may qualify for the marital deduction as Q-TIP property. If it qualifies, the property will be included in the surviving spouse's estate at death. One of the requirements for qualification as Q-TIP property is that the executor make an unequivocal election on IRS Form 706, Schedule M, to have it qualify.

• Loophole: Choosing a taxable year. Estates can have a fiscal year—any year of the executor's choosing—rather than a calendar year. The estate is entitled to an extra $600 exemption for every fiscal year it has over its life, except for the final fiscal year.

Example: Suppose the decedent dies in February. The executor plans the distribution of assets to take place the following April. He sets up a fiscal year ending on March 31. This would give the estate two $600 exemptions—one for the first fiscal year running from the date of death to March 31 and one for the second fiscal year running from April 1 to the following March 31.

Choose a fiscal year that delays for as long as possible the time the beneficiaries have to report the income earned on estate assets. Suppose, for instance, the executor chooses a March 31 fiscal year. Any income earned from the date of death to March 31 will be taxed to the beneficiaries in that year. The income earned from April 1 to the following March 31 will not be taxed until the beneficiaries file their returns for the following year.

• Loophole: Deciding whether estate administration expenses and losses are deductible on the income tax return of the estate or the estate tax return. (The estate must file both an estate tax return and an income tax return.) If the estate is in a higher tax bracket than the individual decedent, it pays to take the deductions on the estate tax return rather than on the income tax return—the deductions produce a bigger tax benefit because the tax rate is higher.

Example: If the estate is in the 55% bracket and the individual in the 31% bracket, it would pay to take the deductions on the estate tax return rather than on the income tax return.

• Loophole: Deciding whether to redeem stock in closely held corporations. If the decedent owned stock in a C corporation that had high retained earnings, the stock can be redeemed income-tax-free by the estate. The redemption is treated as a capital gain. There would be no income tax payable because the value of the stock is stepped-up to its value on the date of the decedent's death. Normally if you take money out of a corporation's retained earnings without liquidating the corporation, the money is taxed as a dividend.

• Loophole: Whether to pay tax in installments. Where the estate consists largely of stock in a closely held corporation, the executor can elect to defer paying tax for four years and then pay the tax in installments over 10 years afterward. Requirement: The value of the company stock must exceed 35% of the adjusted gross estate.

Bonus: For the first five years, the estate gets a bargain interest rate from the government on the tax on the first $1 million of the taxable estate.

• Loophole: How to allocate items of income. Depending on the terms of the will, the executor may also have the right to allocate which types of income go to whom.

Example: The executor might decide to allocate long-term capital gains to an income beneficiary age 14 or over who has no other income. Any income tax owing from the date of the decedent's death to the distribution date would be taxed at the beneficiary's low tax bracket.

• Loophole: Whether the surviving spouse should file a joint or separate income tax return for the final year. This decision depends on how the spouse's deductions break down. If the surviving spouse has steep medical expenses or other deductions that are subject to

percentage-of-Adjusted-Gross-Income limitations, it may pay to file as a single taxpayer.

• Loophole: Flower bonds. Certain Treasury bonds issued before March 4, 1971, may be applied at par value in payment of federal estate taxes even though they were sold at a discount. These are called "flower" bonds, and the executor should check to see whether the decedent owned them at death.

• Loophole: Income in respect of a decedent. This is income that the decedent earned but was not paid before death. This after-death income may be subject to both income tax in the recipient's hands and to estate tax. There is, however, a deduction on the estate tax return for the income tax paid.

• Loophole: Pension distributions. Pensions are treated the same as income in respect to a decedent and are subject of double taxation.

Trap: Lump-sum pension distributions may be subject to an additional 15% excise tax if they exceed $750,000.

Opportunity I: A surviving spouse can elect to roll over a pension distribution into an IRA and defer the payment of income tax.

Opportunity II: The first $5,000 of death benefits paid by an employer to an employee's surviving spouse are free from income tax.

Opportunity III: Lump-sum pension distributions payable on death may qualify for five- or 10-year averaging, which greatly reduces the income tax on the distribution. More: The part of a distribution that relates to pre-1974 participation in a pension plan may qualify for tax-favored capital gains treatment.

Source: Edward Mendlowitz, partner, Mendlowitz Weitsen, CPAs, Two Pennsylvania Plaza, New York 10121. Mr. Mendlowitz's book is *Aggressive Tax Strategies*, Macmillan Publishing Company, 866 Third Ave., New York 10022.

When Using Gifts To Keep Property Out Of Estates

One of the most effective tools of estate planning is to diminish your taxable estate by giving property to your beneficiaries while you're still alive.

There's a good reason for reducing the size of the estate—the federal estate tax rate now starts at 37% for taxable estates exceeding $600,000 and rises to a steep 55%.

Even people who don't think of themselves as rich may be subject to estate taxes when they consider the value of their homes, retirement-plan accounts and insurance policies.
Traps:

Making a gift that doesn't meet tax law requirements can result in the gifted property being added back into your estate, with high-bracket taxes unexpectedly due.

The biggest mistake people make when giving property away is not giving it away completely—keeping "strings" on the property to retain some benefit from the property's use or the income it produces. Examples:

• Parents give their house to a child, but continue living in it without paying a fair rent.

• A person declares a gift of bearer bonds to a child, but keeps the bonds in his own safety deposit box and continues to collect the income paid on them.

In both these cases, the property would be included in the parent's estate, because the parent kept ownership benefits from the property that was supposedly given away.

Similar problems can arise even if legal title to property is transferred.

Example: Title to a registered bond resides with the registered owner. But if a parent puts registered ownership of a bond in a child's name while retaining possession of the bond and taking the income from it, the genuineness of the gift may be questioned.

It's best to avoid such problems entirely by simply giving property away outright when a full transfer is your intention. Don't retain possession even "for the sake of convenience," for example, by safely storing gifted property for a child. If the child is too young, consider setting up a trust or an UGMA account (see below). Any gift that's not completed may be challenged.
Restricted gifts:

It is possible, of course, to make a less-than-outright gift to a child.

Example: Putting property in trust on the child's behalf. The gift-making parent can serve as trustee of such a trust, and thus retain control over how trust funds are managed. Trap: Retaining too much control.

Example: A parent names himself as trustee of a child's trust, the terms of which enable the trustee to make or withhold payments to the child according to a very vague standard, such as "for the child's comfort." Since the parent effectively retains full control over the trust assets, they may be taxed back to the parent's estate.

Essential: When a gift-making parent serves as trustee for a child, be sure there is some ascertainable standard directing how payments to the child are to be made, so the parent's control over trust assets is limited. Such a standard might name specific expenditures that are to be made for the child (such as tuition payments) or specify an income level for the child (an "accustomed standard of living").

Better: Name a third person to serve as a legally independent trustee. The person may be a relative, close friend or professional advisor (such as a banker) whom you know will follow your intentions. The "retained control" problem will be cleanly eliminated.
Other gift opportunities:

• Uniform Gift to Minors Act (UGMA) accounts. These are just about the simplest way to give a gift to a minor—any bank and most brokers can do it for you. You simply open an account in the child's name and deposit money or property in it. Account income is taxed to the child at the child's own tax rate, which will likely be lower than the parent's rate, if the child is over age 13.

Tax-saving strategy: The "Kiddie Tax" imposed on the income of children under 14 can be avoided by investing in property that pays no current income but appreciates in value—such as Series EE savings bonds—until the child reaches 14. Then the property can be cashed in.

Drawback: Funds in a UGMA account become the child's own property at age 18, with the parent retaining no control over how they are used. So you may wish to limit your UGMA account contribution to an amount that your child will be able to handle responsibly at that age. Also, consider naming a custodian other than yourself—otherwise, if you die before the child reaches age 18, the funds revert to your estate.

• Life insurance. The proceeds of a life insurance policy that you buy will be taxed to your estate if you retain "incidents of ownership" in it, such as the ability to change beneficiaries or borrow against it. You can remove the policy proceeds from your estate by giving away the incidents of ownership, even if you continue to pay the premiums.

Trap: If you die within three years after making such a gift, the policy proceeds will be taxed back to your estate.

Tactic: Set up a trust to hold a life insurance policy, donate money to the trust, and let the trust buy the policy. According to recent court decisions, the policy proceeds won't be taxed back to your estate even if you do die within three years.

• Private annuities. You sell property you own to your children, in exchange for their promise to pay you an annual amount for the rest of your life. The size of the annual annuity payment is determined by the value of the property and your life expectancy under IRS tables.

Advantage: When you die the annuity ends, so nothing is taxed in your estate.

Trap: The annuity is merely an unsecured promise to pay on the part of your children. In future years they may become financially unable—or even unwilling—to pay.

• Annual gifts. The simplest and most flexible way to remove property from your estate is to take advantage of the annual $10,000 gift-tax exclusion—$20,000 when gifts are made jointly by a married couple. You can make any number of gifts of up to this amount to separate recipients each year.

Example: A married couple with six children could give them a total of $120,000 annually free of gift tax—$20,000 for each child.
Appreciating property:

When property is expected to rise in value in coming years, it can pay to give it to members of a younger generation even if you will pay gift tax on the transaction. That's because if the

property rises in value your estate will likely pay more tax when you die. Still, it's possible to minimize the gift-tax bite. Suggestions:

• Real estate. If you own land or a building, it may be possible to give children an annual tax-free gift of a $10,000 (or $20,000) undivided interest in it.

Snag: A property can become difficult to manage when it has several owners with undivided interests, since they all have to agree on any action (such as a sale, refinancing or the construction of improvements) that affects their ownership rights.

Strategy: Set up a partnership or S corporation (which is treated the same as a partnership for tax purposes) to own the property. Then donate shares worth $10,000 (or $20,000) to each child annually. Clear control over the property will reside in those with a majority of shares—which is likely to be the original property owner for at least a number of years.

• Family business. If you own all or most of the stock in a family-run business, don't simply give your shares away to the children. Consider recapitalizing the company with different kinds of stock.
Possibilities:

• By keeping voting shares while giving away non-voting shares, you can retain control of the business even while giving away most of the stock. Also: You can give voting shares to children who are active in the business, and nonvoting shares to those who aren't.

• By keeping preferred shares, which have a set value, and giving away common shares, you may be able to "freeze" your taxable estate by shifting appreciation in the company's value to the next generation. Note: Expert advice is needed to comply with IRS rules.
Bottom line:

Remember, the one type of gift that is certain to avoid estate-tax problems is an outright gift made with no strings attached. If you wish to retain some control over, or benefit from, the donated property, be sure to get advice from an estate-planning expert to avoid making any costly mistakes.

Source: Larry C. Rabun, partner and national director of estate-planning services, Deloitte & Touche, CPAs, 1700 Market St., Philadelphia 19103.

Too Much Reliance On The Marital Deduction

Under current law, you can leave your spouse an unlimited amount of cash or property free of federal estate tax.

However, this may not be the wisest thing to do. It may actually increase the tax that must be paid when that surviving spouse dies.

Reason: Overuse of the unlimited marital deduction wastes another valuable estate tax break—the right of each spouse to leave up to $600,000 to other beneficiaries free of estate tax. This is called the exemption equivalent. Re-evaluate your estate to avoid unnecessary taxes.

Source: David S. Rhine, tax partner, BDO Seidman, CPAs, 15 Columbus Circle, New York 10023.

How To Talk With Your Parents About Their Finances...And Your Inheritance

It's common for adult children with elderly, hospitalized parents to look through the parents' papers and be shocked to find assets they knew nothing about.

Many of my older clients are very secretive about their assets. While everything is going well, they think their finances are their own personal business. But when things aren't going well, especially when illness strikes, their children often find they don't have the information they need to help.

Why parents won't discuss finances:

Most people don't talk about what they own and what they're leaving to their children. Reasons:

• We all feel uncomfortable talking about death. It's simply a taboo subject in our culture.

• Many parents think that as long as they've drafted wills, their children don't need to know exactly what they've got.

• They also think that their estates will change. And as long as that's going to happen, why should they discuss it?

• Some parents are afraid that their children will take advantage of them. Although I've never seen this happen in my practice, it does occur and it is something that parents worry about.

How to talk:

There's nothing wrong with children opening up a discussion with their parents about finances.

How to bring it up: The best thing to say is...

Mom and Dad, I want to discuss your finances. Not because I'm concerned about inheriting the money, but because I want to make sure you have planned properly and are protected. I want to be sure that if there are problems I can deal with them. You don't have to discuss your plans with me, but I do want to make sure that you've done the planning.

If that's too direct for you, approach the subject by saying...

I heard a talk show host recommend...or I just read an article in *Bottom Line/Personal* saying...

Don't push. If you do, your parents' will could be questioned later as having resulted from coercion.

If you think that your parents haven't planned properly and they refuse to discuss their finances, get a neutral third party to discuss the matter with them.

Suggested: The family lawyer or physician, a family friend, another relative of their age or a social worker.

Once your parents agree to talk about their finances, the discussion can be relatively straightforward if you're an only child. Problems often come up, however, when there are siblings. If one child talks to his parents and winds up with a larger inheritance, there's going to be a battle. A private discussion between one sibling and his parents is a recipe for disaster.

Remedy: If you have siblings, discuss your parents' finances as a family.

It's often assumed that the parents are the ones who resist talking about finances and inheritance. But sometimes the children refuse to face the subject.

Example: An only child who's very close to her mother refuses to talk about her mother's finances and her inheritance.

Reason: She doesn't want to think about her mother dying.

In addition, whatever plans the parents have may not work if their children don't know about them.

Example: If a parent keeps stock certificates in a safe-deposit box, his children may never even know they exist.

Parents' responsibilities:

Parents should make comprehensive lists of all their assets.

These lists should include: Life insurance policies, bank accounts, stocks, bonds, CDs, safe-deposit boxes, real estate holdings, etc. Everything should be on one master list so that nothing can be lost or overlooked. And the children must know where the list can be found.

It's also very important to give the power of attorney to one adult child. If you have more than one child, the power of attorney should be given to the one who lives closest to you or the one who would be best equipped to handle your finances.

This device is frequently used by older people as a planning tool for disability.

How it works: Pre-printed power-of-attorney forms are available in many stationery stores. I still recommend that this be discussed with an attorney before signing the document. The power of attorney form must be signed in front of a Notary Public.

Parents should fill out and sign a power of attorney but hold the document themselves. They should tell the designated child where it is but not give it to him until there's an emergency. This arrangement ensures that the child won't use it until it's needed.

Suggested: Keep it with your list of assets.

Source: Daniel G. Fish, partner in the law firm of Freedman and Fish, 233 Broadway, New York 10279, which specializes in the legal rights of older adults.

The Most Common Mistakes In Estate Planning & How To Avoid Them

Most people don't like to think about estate planning. Result: They either do nothing, or they make mistakes—big mistakes—in deciding what's going to happen to their property. Mistakes to avoid:

• Thinking you don't need a will. Some people who have placed all their property in trust or in joint ownership think that they don't need a will at all. Trap: Even if they haven't forgotten to include something— which is highly unlikely—they need a will to cover these possibilities:

• Someone owes them money at the time of their death.

• They inherit property or money that has not been distributed at the time of their death.

• Failing to realize the limitations of a will. Contrary to popular belief, you cannot always use a will to dispose of all your property. Examples:

• Joint property goes automatically to the surviving joint owner.

• Property held in trust goes to the beneficiary.

• Insurance proceeds, pension funds, etc., also go to the beneficiary.

• Money in a joint bank account or deposited in trust for someone automatically goes to the survivor.

Many people are surprised to learn that they can no longer dispose of some of their property through their will. Worse, they may never find out...and the provisions of their will may be based on misapprehension.

• Leaving everything to your spouse to save taxes. It's true that what you leave your spouse is fully exempt from estate tax. But it will be taxed in the spouse's estate when he/ she dies, and you'll lose the benefit of your $600,000 exemption.

Example: A man leaves $1 million to his wife, tax-free. But when she dies, her estate becomes taxable. After the $600,000 general exemption is deducted, $400,000 remains subject to estate tax. Had he taken advantage of his general exemption by leaving $600,000 to his children or others, and the remaining $400,000 to his spouse, his estate would have escaped taxation. And his wife's $400,000 estate would be absorbed by the $600,000 exemption on her estate. Result: No tax on either estate.

If you're worried about leaving your spouse without enough money to live on, use a bypass trust. How it works: You leave $600,000 in trust for your children or others, but stipulate that the income from the property go to your spouse for life, and that the principal may be invaded for the spouse's benefit, if that becomes necessary. Check with your lawyer for details.

• Not keeping your will up-to-date. Estate planning doesn't end at the moment you sign your will. Your financial condition may change. Tax laws may change. Births, marriages and deaths may alter your plan. Your own marriage or the birth of a child may even invalidate your will in whole or in part.

Review your will at least once every three years and whenever there's a substantial change in your finances or your family situation.

• Changing your will by codicil. A codicil is a written amendment to a will. It must be executed with the same formalities as the will itself—witnesses, signatures, notarization, etc.

Having a codicil doubles the chance of mistake or misinterpretation. Better: Have a new will drawn up. This is not very expensive because nowadays most lawyers keep wills on word-processing computers. If the changes aren't extensive, the cost of creating a new will should be minimal. In addition, preparing a new will should take no longer than drawing up a codicil.

• Keeping your will at home. Wills, like anything else, can be lost, stolen or accidentally destroyed.

If you keep your original will at home and it can't be found after your death, the presumption* will be that you destroyed it intentionally, rendering it null and void. Courts will not accept a copy of the will in evidence.

*In New York and many other states.

Leave your original with your lawyer. If, somehow, the lawyer loses the will, the presumption will not apply. Copies or other evidence are acceptable to prove its contents.

• Not planning for incapacity. Mental or physical incapacity is the most neglected problem in family planning. And the results of this lack of planning can be disastrous.

Example: The US Supreme Court decided the case of Nancy Cruzan, a young woman in a coma that doctors deemed irreversible. The Court ruled that her parents had no right to shut off the machines that were keeping her alive, that only Nancy herself could have made the decision, and she had not. The Court strongly intimated it would have upheld a living will, had she made one.

A living will is a signed document, valid in most states, declaring whether or not you want to be kept alive by artificial means if you are no longer able to make the decision yourself. Also helpful: A medical power of attorney authorizes someone to make medical decisions on your behalf. I recommend using both a living will and a medical power of attorney.

You should also plan for someone to manage your property if you are stricken with a disease like Alzheimer's. This will allow you to avoid costly and time-consuming incompetency proceedings. Strategies:

• Open joint bank accounts.

• Establish a durable power of attorney, which authorizes someone to act for you, and provides that the power continue in effect even if you become incompetent.

• Set up a revocable living trust of your property, naming yourself as trustee, with a co-trustee to take over if you become incapacitated.

• Procrastinating. The Cruzan case illustrates how suddenly disaster can strike at any age, and how unprepared for it we generally are.

Most people, for instance, realize that they should have a will, but they just never get around to preparing one. Result: They have no say in who receives their property or administers their estate. Other consequences that are less commonly known:

• Court-appointed administrators must post bond. The estate is responsible for the cost.

• Property that is inherited by children may not be touched until they reach 18 years of age—even if they are in dire financial need—without costly, time-consuming court proceedings.

• Owning your own life-insurance policy. If you own the policy, the proceeds are taxable to your estate.

Instead, the policy should be owned by an irrevocable life-insurance trust (ILIT) that is established for just that purpose and funded with enough money to pay the premiums. Caution: You must divest yourself of all incidents of ownership, such as the right to change the beneficiary.

• Rushing to the safe-deposit box when someone dies. Banks keep records of who opens a box and when. If federal and state tax agents learn that the box was opened within hours of its owner's death they will get very suspicious, and may charge that money or property was removed to evade income and estate taxes.

When someone dies, apply for a court order to open his safe-deposit box. Court orders are easy to obtain in most states, but laws do vary from state to state. Ask your lawyer about the proper way to go about doing this.

*In New York and many other states.

Source: Daniel Fish, a member of the National Academy of Elder-Law Attorneys and partner in the law firm of Freedman & Fish, 260 Madison Ave., New York 10016.

How To Write The Right Living Will

Living wills are often not enforced because of vague language and doctors' fears of lawsuits. For an effective living will:

• Talk with your doctor to be sure your wishes are understood and supported. If not, consider changing doctors.

• Be as detailed as possible. Describe exact treatments that would or would not be ac-

ceptable to you and at what point you would want all treatment to be stopped.

• Designate someone who is familiar with your wishes to make health-care decisions for you. (This should be done in an adjunct to your living will.) Note: A friend is better than a relative...especially if the relative is also an heir.

• Sign the will before two witnesses. Initial and date it a few times a year so that it continues to reflect your wishes. The more recent the date, the more likely it is to be honored.

• Store the original document where your family can easily get to it—not in a safe-deposit box, where you may be the only one with a key. Give copies to your next of kin, clergyman, lawyer and anyone else who might one day be asked to help make decisions for you.

Source: Recommendations from The Society for the Right to Die and Concern for Dying, two non-profit advocacy groups. Free living-will forms, guidelines and information can be obtained by writing to either group at 250 W. 57 St., New York 10107.

Awful Mistakes In Choosing An Executor

The biggest mistake people make in choosing an executor is that they don't give the matter enough thought.

They pick their spouse, or a friend or relative who will do the job for nothing—and simply forget about it. Or, they pick a lawyer whom they've just met for the first time without questioning his qualifications to act as executor.

If people knew what executors did, they would take more time in choosing one. Here are just some of the duties of an executor...

• Select an attorney to handle the probate of the estate.

• Locate and collect all of the assets of the decedent.

• Straighten out the decedent's financial affairs, including gathering any debts and reviewing them to see that they're valid.

• Pay off the decedent's debts.

• Prepare and file estate tax returns and income tax returns.

• Liquidate assets, converting them into cash.

• Close up the decedent's house or apartment.

• Locate personal effects that have been bequeathed to specific beneficiaries.

• Go through safe-deposit boxes.

• Arbitrate disputes among various heirs and potential heirs.

• Make decisions that affect estate tax, such as whether to qualify property for the marital deduction and whether to use special valuation for a closely held business.

Helpful: Most banks have pamphlets that give more details on what an executor and trustee does.

The right way to choose an executor:

Review the work your executor will have to do. Make sure that the person, or bank or trust company you pick has broad areas of expertise to handle the various tasks. Mistakes people make in choosing an executor…

• Mistake: Choosing a contemporary. It's important that an executor, and more importantly a trustee, be alive and able to do the job when the time comes. People in their 60s and 70s, however, often choose a trusted contemporary to act as executor. Then, that person dies before taking on the job or, worse, dies during the administration of the estate. This causes probate to be delayed.

Better: Choose someone younger than yourself, someone who is likely to survive you, to act as executor. If you wish, name the younger person co-executor with a trusted contemporary.

• Mistake: Choosing a lawyer who is not an expert in trusts and estates. Another risky tendency people have is choosing as executor a lawyer who handled another matter for them, such as a real estate closing. This person is not necessarily an expert in trust and estate law, and that's what you want—an expert. It's a very complicated field. State laws can be tricky. If your financial affairs are complex, and you have property in a number of states, you need someone who is familiar with the intricacies of state law.

• Mistake: Choosing a surviving spouse or child as the only executor. These people are likely to be overcome with grief at the time of your death and unable to act competently. You want to have someone who can function at that time with a cool, level head. Also, a spouse or child probably doesn't have the skills to do the job of executor. And, there's the problem of hurt feelings when you name one child as executor. Why did you name that child and not the others?

If you've been married more than once and have children from previous marriages, naming your current spouse as executor can cause serious problems. Children from a previous marriage may view the current spouse as an interloper, and be suspicious of every move the spouse makes in winding up the estate. These problems often end up in court.

Better: Name a competent outsider who has no ties to any part of the family and is, therefore, likely to be impartial.

• Mistake: Choosing a person who will do the job for nothing. The job of executor is a very complex task. Anyone competent enough to do it is not going to be able to afford to do it for nothing. You want to avoid the situation where the executor gives up the job because he's not getting paid.

• Mistake: Failing to name alternate executors—or to designate how alternates are to be chosen. If your executor dies before you, and you haven't named an alternate in your will, the court will select somebody for you. State law may determine who is chosen. If the law does not, a judge will. If more than one person has an equal right to act, they may all be appointed—and fight over what is to be done. This can also result in multiple commissions being paid by your estate. In some states, the person appointed can be a creditor of your estate. These are often people you would not want to have as executor because their interests are opposed to your family's interests.

As a last resort, a public administrator may be chosen to wind up your estate. State public administrators' offices are often very poorly organized. It can take years and years to administer even the simplest of estates. It can also be very costly, since the administrator gets to name the estate's lawyer and that person may charge much more than a lawyer representing a private executor.

• Mistake: Failing to discuss the issue of fees with a lawyer you've chosen to be your executor. When a lawyer acts as executor, there's a great deal of overlap of executor's work and legal work. Most reputable firms will work out an arrangement whereby the lawyer who is named as executor will get the full executor's fee but the law firm will charge only half of the usual legal fee. This matter should be discussed beforehand, at the time you make your will.

• Mistake: Letting the lawyer who prepares your will automatically name himself as executor. This happens a lot and it's something you should guard against. Just because you use a lawyer to draw up a will doesn't mean that person should be your executor. Remember, the person you choose as executor should be an expert in trusts and estate matters and someone you can trust with your life savings.

• Mistake: Thinking a bank or trust company will charge more than private executors. Usually they charge you the same or less than what an individual executor would charge. When a bank or trust company acts as executor, they do all the work for one fee. They hold the estate's stocks and bonds, so you aren't charged a custody fee. They handle the investments, so you don't have to pay for an investment adviser. They do the paperwork, so you don't have to pay for a bookkeeper. And, they do the tax returns, either at no charge or a minimal charge, so you don't have to hire an accountant. It's very difficult to find one individual who is expert in all these fields. Often, specialists must be called in to help the person who is named executor, and they all charge extra fees.

• Mistake: Choosing only one individual or bank to act as executor. In many cases, you're better off naming two executors—a bank or trust company to handle the technical side of administering the estate and an individual to handle the human side. The individual executor can make the important family decisions

that must be faced, such as who receives income if the will presents a choice, and which of the beneficiaries need special help. A family friend or relative is often willing to serve in this limited executorial role without charging a fee.

Source: Peter Van Nuys, Esq., partner, Baker, Nelson & Williams, 800 Third Ave., New York 10022. Mr. Van Nuys, a trusts and estates attorney, is a member of the trusts and estates and tax divisions of the American Bar Association. He is also a member of a committee dealing with legal issues affecting people with disabilities of the Association of the Bar of the City of New York and New York County Lawyers Association.

How To Make Life Better For Your Heirs

Leave your heirs a letter of instructions to ease execution of your will after your death. Include:

• Assets and liabilities list: Brokerage and bank accounts, insurance policies, real estate, art, debts, etc.

• Location of important documents: Birth certificates, will, marriage certificate, tax records, etc.

• Assets that pass outside the estate: Jointly owned bank accounts, real estate, etc.

• Personal requests not in the will: Pet care, funeral preferences, etc.

• Earned benefits: Social Security, work-related, veteran benefits, etc.

Revise the letter annually or after a major change (new job, marriage, etc.). Give copies to your spouse, adult children, close friend, lawyer and executor.

Source: *Julian Block's Year-Round Tax Strategies for the $40,000-Plus Household*, St. Martin's Press, 175 Fifth Ave., New York 10010.

Living Trusts: Pros And Cons

A living trust, which directs the disposition of your assets upon your death, offers advantages…expensive legal fees for probating a will (which may equal a percentage of your estate) are avoided, privacy is maintained (a trust is a private document, while a will is a public one), and a trust is harder to challenge than a will. Drawbacks: You must pay a trustee to administer the trust. Complicated tax and administrative filings are required annually. You will probably need a will anyway (for issues regarding children, etc.). Fallacy: The idea that a living trust saves estate taxes. Whether assets pass through a will or a trust, taxes should be the same.

Source: Donna Barwick, head of trust and estate planning, Ernst & Young, Atlanta, quoted in *Financial World*, 1450 Broadway, New York 10018.

How To Give More To Charity…And Leave More For Heirs

It *is* possible for you to have your cake and eat it, too. By planning carefully, you can increase the amount of money your heirs will receive on your death, benefit your favorite charity and retain a lifetime income for you and your spouse.

Bob and Rhonda:

Bob is 64 years of age and his wife, Rhonda, is 62. They reside in California and have four adult children who are essentially on their own. Bob's investment assets include a portfolio of tax-exempt municipal bonds. Both Bob and Rhonda want to benefit Charity X substantially but they do not want to see their children's inheritance diminished by the gift to Charity X.

Solution:

Step one: In February 1992, Bob's lawyer prepares a charitable remainder annuity trust, the assets of which will flow to Charity X at the death of the survivor of Bob and Rhonda. The trust is set up with $250,000 worth of Bob's tax-exempt municipal bonds.

Bob and Rhonda are named income beneficiaries of the trust, receiving a six percent per annum annuity ($15,000) through the life of the survivor, to be distributed in a single payment annually.

Bob's charitable deduction for his contribution to Charity X is equal to $250,000, minus the present value of the life incomes that Bob and Rhonda will receive, or $107,022. The charitable deduction produces a cash tax benefit of $44,219. (These calculations are based on the applicable federal discount rate for December 1991—9%—since Bob has the right to elect the rate for the month the trust is funded or either of the two immediately preceding months. Further, it is assumed that the approximate maximum income tax rate for California residents is 41.25%.)

The trust retains the $250,000 of tax-exempt bonds with an average annual return of 6.5%, so that the $15,000 annuity, payable to Bob and Rhonda in satisfaction of the trust's 6% payout requirement, is well covered.

Step two: Bob and Rhonda give the sum of $44,219 to the trustee of another newly created trust for the benefit of their four children. (The transfer is handled in a way that avoids both gift tax liability and the use of any lifetime gift or estate tax exemption.) This constitutes the full amount of the tax saving resulting from the transfer of $250,000 to the charitable remainder annuity trust.

The money is used to purchase a universal survivorship ("second-to-die") insurance policy on the lives of Bob and Rhonda.

This policy is issued under a "one pay" plan designed to provide for the children a death benefit substantially greater than the loss to them of the net after-estate-tax value of the $250,000 transferred to the charitable trust.

The approximate amounts of the income tax deduction, the tax savings and the death benefit under the policy to be acquired with the tax saving, for individuals aged 64 and 62 respectively, were determined as follows…

Charitable Deduction	Tax Saving at the 41.25% Tax Rate	Life Insurance Death Benefit
$107,022	$44,147	$358,419

Summary:

As a consequence of these steps, Bob and Rhonda have made a major gift to Charity X but also have retained a flow of annual income for their lifetimes.

Had they done nothing, the $250,000 would have been subject to federal and state estate taxes and, consequently, would have been diminished to only about $112,500 when received by their children.

Now, however, their children will receive, upon the death of the survivor of Bob and Rhonda, life insurance proceeds (from a policy fully paid for by tax refund dollars) in the amount of approximately $358,419.

The children's net inheritance has been increased from $112,500 to more than three times that sum as a result of this transaction. In this case, everyone ends up winning.

Source: Stanley S. Weithorn, Esq., a tax attorney at 40 W. 57 St., New York 10019. Mr. Weithorn specializes in charitable tax planning and sophisticated estate planning.

Is It Worthwhile To Avoid Probate?

It's possible to avoid probate for a good portion of your estate by establishing a living trust...or a revocable trust that directs how your assets will be managed and administered after your death.

But is a trust worth the effort?

Advantages of trusts:

• Cost savings. You may save probate fees, which in some states are a percentage of an estate's total value. You also save court costs and attorney's and accountant's fees, which may be incurred in probate court.

• Privacy. Court records of probate proceedings are public. But the terms of a trust are private.

• Protection. Trusts are generally tougher to challenge than wills. Trusts aren't frozen during a probate period, so the trustee can distribute assets immediately, thus making it more difficult for a disgruntled heir to raise a challenge.

Drawbacks to trusts:

• You still need a will. It's unlikely you'll be able to handle all your assets through a trust. And you'll need a will to handle any unforeseen contingencies that might arise. A will is also necessary to name a guardian for your minor children.

• Cost. In addition to the cost of drawing up the trust, you'll have to pay annual trustee fees.

• Estate taxes. You do not save estate taxes by avoiding probate. Your estate tax bill will be the same whether you use a trust or a will.

• Income tax. While you're alive, having a trust will not save you any income tax. After your death, it's beneficial to have your property pass under your will rather than through a trust. Estates, but not trusts, can pick a beneficial tax year for as long as the estate is in the administration process. Additionally, an estate can continue to deduct, for the first two years, $125,000 of real estate passive-activity losses. A trust can't.

Source: David S. Rhine, partner, BDO Seidman, 15 Columbus Circle, New York 10023. He specializes in estate planning.

Asset List

Make an asset list to be sure your family, not the government, ends up with everything in your estate. The list should supplement your will, not be a part of it. Wills often simply divide estates into bulk portions, leaving heirs to try to track down records, papers and documents to establish the extent of the estate. Better: A separate, clear, regularly updated list of available assets, including such items as pensions, Social Security and veterans' benefits.

Source: *Everything Your Heirs Need to Know* by David S. Magee, Dearborn Financial Publishing, 500 N. Dearborn St., Chicago 60610.

12

Your Home, Your Family

Why You Shouldn't Pay Down Your Mortgage

Many financial planners are advising home-owners that they can save $150,000 or more in interest charges by accelerating payments on their home mortgages. They're only half right.

Although your interest costs will be reduced, you may be losing the use of money that could be better invested elsewhere. If you invested that money in a mutual fund…or in a new business…you could end up with more than you'd save in interest expenses.

Paying down your mortgage also forces you to give up a terrific tax deduction. Now that credit card and personal interest deductions are gone, your home mortgage is one of the last remaining sources of deductible interest. If you're paying 10% on a mortgage in a 40% tax bracket, the mortgage is only costing you 6%. Accelerate your payments and you'll lose that deduction forever.

Trap: If you pay down your home mortgage and then decide later to raise money by refinancing it, you may not be able to deduct all of the new interest expense or the points unless any increase in mortgage is used to improve your home. More problems: Although you'll still be able to take out a tax-deductible home equity loan for up to $100,000, Congress may very well act to restrict use of home equity loans in the near future.

Source: Attorney Martin Shenkman, 1086 Teaneck Rd., Teaneck, New Jersey 07666. He is the author of *How to Buy a House with No (or Little) Money Down*, John Wiley, 605 Third Ave., New York 10158.

Refinancing Traps And Opportunities

Falling interest rates have prompted many homeowners to refinance their mortgages. Those who ignored the tax consequences of refinancing came in for some unpleasant surprises. Keep the following in mind if you're thinking about refinancing…

• Trap: Your interest payments on the new mortgage may not be fully deductible. On a refinancing, home mortgage interest payments are fully deductible as acquisition debt only up to the extent of the old mortgage that was in place at the time of the refinancing.

Suppose you have a $200,000 mortgage. There's enough equity in the house to allow you to refinance for $250,000. The home mortgage interest deduction rules will only permit a deduction for interest on $200,000—the amount of the original mortgage debt.

The remaining $50,000 in this example may or may not be deductible depending on (a) what the money is used for and (b)what other debt there is on the property.

If the money is used for home improvements, then interest on the remaining $50,000 is fully deductible. If it's not used for home improvements, then you have to examine what other debt is on the property.

If you do not have a home-equity line of credit, the interest on the remaining $50,000 would be deductible as home-equity borrowing. (The law allows you to deduct interest on up to $100,000 of home-equity debt.) But if you have already borrowed up to $100,000 of home-equity loans, interest on the remaining $50,000 of the newly refinanced mortgage debt would not be tax deductible as mortgage interest. (It may be deductible as investment interest if you use the borrowed funds to make investments.)

• Opportunity: You can deduct points when refinancing proceeds are used for home improvements. Most people are aware that when they refinance their home mortgage, the points they pay at the time are not deductible up front. The points must be amortized and deducted a bit each year over the life of the loan. What people forget is that if they refinance and use some of the proceeds for home improvements, a pro rata portion of the points that are paid can then be taken as a current deduction on their tax return.

Example: A couple has a current mortgage of $200,000. They refinance for $250,000 and spend $50,000 on home improvements. One-fifth ($50/250$) of the points they pay would be currently deductible. The balance of the points have to be amortized.

• Opportunity: You can deduct the balance of previously amortized points when you refinance your home a second time. Suppose you refinanced your home five years ago. You've been amortizing the points over the life of the loan. Then you refinance again. The balance of the points on the original refinancing are deductible in full in the year that note is paid in full.

Source: Dan J. Hall, tax partner and director of personal financial services, San Francisco and Western Region, Coopers & Lybrand, 333 Market St., San Francisco 94105.

Home-Equity Loan Traps

• Most banks are slow in reviewing applications. You may have to wait up to three months before getting a loan commitment. And there's the possibility of an IRS audit. Tax reform allows you to deduct interest on home loans only up to $100,000 (unless it's used to improve the property). Result: The IRS will be looking closely at equity borrowers to be sure they're not deducting more than they're permitted.

Source: Dr. Michael K. Evans, president, Evans Economics, Inc., 1725 Eye St. NW, Washington, DC 20006.

• Home-equity loans are dangerous propositions—and are often more expensive than other types of credit. Common drawbacks: Excessive up-front point charges and other closing costs, variable interest rates without protective caps, a long payback period (leading to large overall interest charges), and large lump-sum balloon payments at the end of the term. A further trap of a long payback period is that the borrower could be deemed "not creditworthy" and lose his/her line of credit. In this case, the entire balance would be due immediately.

• Home-equity loan traps: (1) Many banks offering equity lines of credit charge an annual fee of $20–$50, whether or not you draw down on the credit line...(2) Several banks have sliding interest scales—the bigger the loan, the lower the interest rate. You may actually save money by taking out a larger loan...(3) Though many banks have stopped charging points, they're now charging "origination fees" that run $100–$450. If you're applying for a relatively small loan (less than $25,000), this fee could add quite a lot to the total cost of obtaining the loan, which also includes appraisal fees, legal fees, and insurance.

Source: Paul Havemann, HSH Associates, Riverdale, NJ quoted in *Money.*

Aged Parents Needing Very Expensive Care

There's nothing underhanded about making an effort to conserve aging parents' assets to pass along to children, while using Medicaid (or, under the new Medicare Catastrophe Act) Medicare to pick up much of the cost of home or nursing-home care. In fact, Congress has made it clear that it doesn't want middle-class families to deplete all their assets for such care.

The key legal device to conserve an elderly parent's assets is the Medicaid Qualifying Trust. The parents divest their assets into the trust and receive annual interest payments. Those interest payments are then used to meet the bills of home and nursing-home care, with Medicaid picking up qualifying expenses over that amount. The principal in the trust would remain intact, to be inherited by designated beneficiaries.

It is essential, however, to get expert legal advice on how this law works in your particular state. Ask your local bar association to recommend lawyers who specialize in legal counseling on the problems of the aged.

Source: Lewis Kamin, partner, Cappa, Kamin and Goldberg, 244-14 Jericho Turnpike, Floral Park, New York 11001, a law firm that works with Corporate Consultations in Aging, Inc.

Don't Pay Too Much

Nearly three out of four mortgage holders pay too much into escrow accounts—set up by lenders with a borrower's money to pay real estate taxes and home-insurance costs. Self-defense: Check monthly payments carefully against copies of all tax and insurance bills. If what's due in taxes is less than the funds in escrow—seek a refund immediately. Bottom line: While you pay monthly, the lender might pay only quarterly—or even annually. Any funds held in escrow until those payments come due are the equivalent of giving the lender a no- or low-interest loan.

Source: Edward F. Mrkvicka, Jr., Reliance Enterprises, Inc., Box 413, Marengo, Illinois 60152.

All About Reverse Mortgages

Reverse mortgages are the opposite of traditional mortgages. They tap the equity in a home to make regular, fixed monthly payments to a homeowner.

These nontaxable loans—they are loans, not income—are becoming a popular financial tool for older Americans and their children who worry about taking care of them.

In the past year, many more lenders have been encouraged to make such loans mainly because HUD's mandate to insure 25,000 of them has led the Federal National Mortgage Association (Fannie Mae) to purchase the loans on the market. That frees up more money so that lenders can make new reverse mortgage loans.

Eligibility:

Owner-occupants aged 62 or older whose houses are mortgage-free, or nearly so, are eligible. The average age of reverse mortgage borrowers is 77. The older you are, the bigger the monthly payment you can get. Reverse mortgages favor older borrowers because the equity is assumed to be paid out over the rest of your lifetime. From the lender's point of view, the shorter that time is, the more cash you can get.

Maximum mortgage varies with a borrower's age, prevailing interest rates and the borrower's equity...and HUD mortgages may have a geographical area limit.

Cost:

There are closing costs and fees associated with taking out a reverse mortgage, just as there are with a regular mortgage. You also pay a sizable insurance premium up front that protects you and the lender in case you outlive the actuarial tables or the house loses value. Unless you or your parents expect to spend a good many years in the house, a reverse mortgage could be a very expensive way of borrowing money. Interest rates can also be higher than with other types of loans, and they are compounded. This means that over time, you're paying interest on your interest.

Guideline: Don't take out a reverse mortgage on a house that won't age well with you or can't be adapted to meet the problems of elderly infirmities. If a house has lots of stairs, for example, it may not be suitable.

Many options:

• FHA-insured reverse mortgages protect you against default by lenders, and the loans are backed by the full faith and credit of the federal government.

They also provide a flexible choice of how your equity is paid to you, including tenure loans—monthly payments to you for as long as you live in the home...term loans—monthly payments for a fixed number of months... or a line-of-credit plan—money whenever you need it—which can be used alone or in combination with a monthly payment.

You can switch from one payment option to another at any time. You don't pay interest on a line of credit until you use it. When a loan term is reached, the monthly payments will stop, but you're not required to repay the loan as long as you continue to live in your home.

Important: All FHA-insured reverse mortgages require "adequate counseling" beforehand by a HUD-approved third party who can explain how the reverse mortgage works and describe other, less expensive community-sponsored options available to elderly homeowners, such as property tax relief or low-interest home-improvement loans.

• Lender-insured reverse mortgages. These are similar to the FHA-insured loans, but lenders form their own risk pools and the cost range is apt to be higher, although payments to the borrower may be larger.

The overall cost of lender-insured reverse mortgages depends on how long you live in your home and how much it appreciates during that time. If you exceed your actuarial life expectancy and your home appreciates at a low to moderate rate, the total cost could be reasonable. But if you live in your home only for a short time or it appreciates at a high rate, these lender-insured loans may be very costly.

• Uninsured reverse mortgage. This term loan is paid out to you in monthly cash advances for a fixed number of years that you select. At the end of the term (or if you die, move or sell the house before the term ends), monthly advances stop and the full amount of the loan, including interest, must be repaid. Ordinarily, this means selling the home. If the loan is not paid off when it becomes due, the lender has the right to foreclose, which could force the owner out.

Such a loan might be appropriate for someone who is very frail and ill, wants to spend his/her remaining time in the home or has made long-range plans to sell or move but needs temporary help—and cash—to do so.

For a free list of current lenders of reverse mortgages, send a postcard to: AARP Home Equity Information Center, 601 E St. NW, Washington, DC 20049. You can also request a free copy of AARP's informative guide *Home-Made Money.*

Source: Bronwyn Belling, housing specialist, American Association of Retired Persons, 601 E St. NW, Washington, DC 20049.

How To Sell Your Home If You Must Sell But Can't

Weak housing markets in most of the country have created a frustrating problem for many people—the house of their dreams is on the market for an unbelievably affordable price, but there are no buyers for their current residence.

Solution: Rent your current home until the market strengthens and buyers return. This allows you to snap up a new house without the burden of two mortgages...two property-tax bills...two insurance premiums...and without maintenance costs on two homes. Advantages:

• Your old house will produce income instead of sitting vacant. Also: Vacant houses deteriorate faster than those that are occupied.

• The sale will be delayed until the market bounces back, so you get a decent price.

• Expenses and any losses resulting from renting are often tax-deductible.

• You get a continued tax write-off for depreciation on the old house.

Drawbacks:

There are drawbacks to consider before you rent your house. Included:

• Good tenants are hard to find and hold. And checking on the tenant's housekeeping habits can be difficult.

• It's harder to sell a tenant-occupied house than it is to sell an empty one.

• The depreciation write-off from the rental may eventually produce a bigger tax when you finally do sell.

More tax angles:

If you rent for too long, you may forfeit one of the best tax breaks available to homeowners—the rollover provision. It allows you to defer any tax on the sale as long as you buy a replacement house that is at least as expensive as the one you sold within two years of the sale.

Catch: To qualify for this break, both the house you sell and the house you buy must be used as your principal residence. The obvious danger is that by renting your old house before you sell it, you may transform its character from that of a principal residence to that of a rental property. And a rental property doesn't qualify for the tax-free rollover.

Solution: Structure the rental so it is clearly a temporary arrangement, designed as a stopgap measure to tide you over until you sell,

rather than a long-term one in which you have clearly transformed your old house into a business property.

There is no hard-and-fast rule about what constitutes temporary. But if you follow specific steps, you can successfully argue that the house you rented out should still qualify for the tax-free rollover if the IRS ever challenges you. Suggested:

• Rent for as short a term as possible. The shorter the lease, the better. Although most renters in a commuter community will want a one-year lease, try to get a six-month lease.

If the prospective tenant balks, offer a six-month lease with a six-month renewal option. (This may not be a problem in a college town, where many students like short-term leases.)

• In the lease, reserve the right to show the house to prospective buyers upon reasonable notice to the tenants. Important: Standard leases don't contain this option, so be sure to insert such a clause.

• Keep the house listed with a broker during the lease term. That demonstrates your intent to sell rather than to continue renting.

• If you're trying to sell the house yourself (without a broker), keep advertising it for sale throughout the rental period. Place an ad in the classified section of the local newspaper at least once a month.

• Include an option to buy in the lease. This also emphasizes the seriousness of your desire to sell the property.

Another opportunity:

If you do find a buyer for your house, and have a good amount of property surrounding it, you can increase your profits on the sale. Strategy: Subdivide the land, sell your house with a smaller yard and sell the rest of the land to a second buyer as a vacant lot.

Will the amount you receive for the vacant lot still be considered proceeds from the sale of your home, and thus be eligible for the tax-free rollover? If the land, including the lot you split off, was always used solely as your principal residence, it may all qualify.

Caution:

In this very tough market, beware of "creative" schemes that some brokers propose to help sell a house.

Example: To attract buyers, the seller is urged to pay the first year's property taxes or the first six months of the mortgage payments. This is a huge mistake, because the seller can't deduct these costs if he/she no longer owns the house.

Solution:

Reduce the purchase price if you must sell the house quickly, and continue deducting every penny of property taxes up until the day of the closing. Obviously, lowering the sale price lowers the broker's commission on the transaction, so your broker probably won't suggest this move, even though it's in your best interest.

Source: Attorney Martin M. Shenkman, who practices in both New York and Teaneck, New Jersey. He is the author of several books on real estate, including *How to Sell Your House in a Buyer's Market*, John Wiley & Sons, 605 Third Ave., New York. $14.95.

Refinancing Barriers

Many home owners are finding that they do not qualify for refinancing because their income has declined…their indebtedness has risen…or the value of their home has fallen. Also, the Federal National Mortgage Association—Fannie Mae—has imposed new restrictions on loans that it buys from banks and other lenders. It now insists that borrowers be able to pay loans at 7% or higher…even if the lender is willing to make a lower-interest loan.

Source: Consensus of bankers and mortgage brokers, reported in *The New York Times*.

How To Negotiate A Lease

This weak real-estate market has made home leasing attractive and very negotiable. In many parts of the country, landlords have empty apartments, offices—even houses—that they're anxious to fill.

The basics of lease negotiation don't change, but this is a good time to review what to do.

Negotiation basics:

•Decide what's important to you. It may be lower rent, free parking or better appliances in the kitchen. Everything is negotiable.

•Always negotiate before you sign the lease. The landlord will be much more likely to agree to changes.

•Establish yourself as a reliable tenant. Tell the landlord: "I'm going to be taking good care of your place. In return, I'd like…."

•Never paint yourself into a corner. Saying, "If you don't give me this, I won't rent the place," could end the negotiations abruptly.

•If the landlord turns down any of your requests, offer to split the cost. Half of what you want is better than nothing.

Source: Jeanne D. Newman, a professional leasing agent. She has helped hundreds of residential and commercial clients negotiate better leases. Newman is the author of *Tenants Timely Tips*, Luna Publishing, c/o Royal Marketing Co., 8721 Santa Monica Blvd. #214, Los Angeles 90069.

Rent Or Buy?

If you expect to move in a few years, renting a home may be more economical than buying one. Reason: To just cover closing costs and sales commissions, it takes three years of appreciation at more than 3% annually. Other considerations: Value of write-offs for mortgage interest and property taxes, expected rent increases, earned income from investing what would be your down payment.

Source: *Smart Money Moves for the 90s* by the editors of *Money*, Oxmoor House, 2100 Lakeshore Dr., Birmingham, Alabama 35209.

Traps In Appliance Service Contracts

Don't assume that all appliance service contracts are worthwhile. A study shows that the average yearly repair bill on washing-machine models ranging from one to ten years old came to only $49. That is $6 under the cost of a typical repair contract.

The study finds that the chance of needing a repair on an appliance in any given year is only one in five. Over the life of the machine, a service-contract holder will in all probability be paying out much more in insurance than the person is ever likely to collect in actual repair services.

The Home Inspector

Always accompany a home inspector when he/she tours a house you plan to buy. This will enable you to ask questions as he inspects. Inspections should cover at a minimum: Structural components (water stains, cracks in walls, floors and roof, etc.)…electrical systems…plumbing…heating and cooling…foundation…basement. For an additional fee, most inspectors will also test for radon, asbestos or formaldehyde…will check the quality of your drinking water…will make sure the septic tank is operating properly. Note: An inspector may estimate repair costs—which you should factor into your offer—but should never solicit work for himself or others. If he does, hire another inspector.

Source: *Money Guide: Your Home* by the editors of *Money,* Andrews & McMeel, 4900 Main St., Kansas City, Missouri 64112.

Home-Repair Scams… How To Avoid Them

Shady handymen can take you for a bundle of money. Some common home-repair rip-offs and how you can avoid them:

•Attic insulation. Although foam insulation that is blown into place is cheaper to install than traditional sheets of insulation, it has many drawbacks. It drifts, leaving some areas uninsulated. And it can obstruct ventilation holes under the eaves, causing moisture to collect in the attic.

•Concrete driveways. Beware of rock-bottom bids. Some contractors keep the price of a new driveway low by eliminating steel reinforcement bars or using inferior-grade cement. This soon results in cracks and potholes.

•Housepainting. Don't leave it to the painter to figure out how many gallons of paint are required. Painters often overestimate…and charge you for the difference. Rules of thumb:

•Outside jobs: One gallon of paint covers 350 to 400 square feet.

•Inside jobs: Figure $1\frac{1}{2}$ gallons per average bedroom—two gallons if you're painting the ceiling. Anything more than two gallons per room is cause to be suspicious.

•Agree beforehand that you will purchase the paint on your own. Benefit: The painter can't add his mark-up to the paint, and you'll be sure to get the paint quality that you've paid for.

•Roofing. When you purchase roofing materials, look for a warranty that offers replacement costs at current market prices, not at the prices that were in effect at the time of installation.

•Vinyl siding. Even some of the most reputable installers claim that vinyl siding never needs to be painted. Truth: All vinyl siding eventually fades with age. Siding fades much more quickly in hot climates. And if it's not properly installed, vinyl siding will expand and contract with changes in temperature and eventually work itself loose or crack.

Better: Wood siding. If properly cared for (yes, that does mean occasional painting), it will last 20 years or more.

•Water heaters. Contractors often recommend replacing a water heater whose only problem is the accumulation of sediment. Better: Drain your water heater once every four months to remove sediment. This will greatly extend the life of most water-heating units.

Source: Johnnie Chouke, owner of Acme Lumber Centers, 1001 Austin St., San Antonio 78208. He is also the author of *The Happy Handyman,* available from the above address.

Before You Renovate An Old House

The positive aspects of renovating an old house are enticing: A sense of accomplishment, an outlet for creativity, and the possibility that it will be a good investment. However, the experience of returning a house to its former glory can be frustrating and overwhelming to anyone who attempts it for the first time without proper understanding.

The worst aspects, according to old-home buffs:

Not knowing what you are getting into.

Living amid the chaos of reconstruction for very long periods.

Some things to consider when buying an old home to renovate:

Choosing the right neighborhood is the most important element on the investment side. If many homes are being renovated in your neighborhood, chances are good that your choice will be expensive. Best: Find a neighborhood where one or two homes have been renovated on your block and several more a few blocks away. There is a strong possibility that the neighborhood will blossom and values will rise.

Speak to owners of similar homes in your area before you purchase. Concentrate on the steps they took.

Get a good engineer's report about the home, and focus on foundation, plumbing, electrical, and mechanical systems. These are the most difficult to restore.

If you want a modern interior and expect to gut most of the house and substitute modern fixtures, find a house that's just a shell. Reason: Old homes with fine architectural details such as marble mantels and restorable wainscoting cost more.

Don't put your last penny into a down payment and take a big mortgage. The fixing-up process can be extraordinarily expensive even if you expect to do much of the work.

Don't get an architect to draw up a master plan for your house immediately. It usually takes a while to know what you want out of a house. Unless you have lived in it at least six months to a year, you will probably make expensive mistakes.

Learn how to deal with contractors. You must hire experienced people. Read the contract. Make sure the contractor is bonded. Possibility: If you are fairly handy, call in a professional to do a small portion. You may be able to finish the job yourself.

Gutting an interior can be done easily by anyone. All you need is a crowbar, sledge hammer, old clothes, and elbow grease. Most homes can be gutted in a weekend. Keys: Hire neighborhood teenagers to help. Find a dumpster for the plaster.

Don't be discouraged by broken beams, crumbling interior plaster, or even a leaking roof. As long as the exterior walls and the foundation are solid, shabby interiors are secondary.

Study local zoning laws before you make major changes.

Most expensive changes: Changing the location of the kitchen or bathrooms. Why: Plumbing. Don't do it if you can possibly live with things where they are.

Way to boost resale value: Organize a walking tour of restored homes in your area. These walking tours are great sales tools.

Source: Benita Korn and Patricia Cole, directors, the Brownstone Revival Committee, Inc., 200 Madison Ave., New York 10016.

Seven Easy Ways To Make Your Old Home Feel Like New

Simple, inexpensive fix-ups can make an old home look almost new. And you don't have to be a home-repair whiz to do them. Some suggestions:

• Paper a room. A real easy job, especially with new, prepasted wallpapers. For walls that are marred, textured papers cover a multitude of sins.

• Kitchen face-lift. A professional renovation can cost as much as $20,000. But simple, do-it-yourself tasks will bring new life to your kitchen. Easy possibilities: Paint the cabinets (use a good-quality enamel)…replace countertops with premade sections sold at building supply stores…replace the sink…install a new floor using attractive vinyl squares.

• Redo the bathroom. Replace the old-style hanging sink with a modern pedestal sink or full vanity. Adding a vanity with drawers for storage allows you to replace an old-fashioned metal medicine cabinet with a full-wall-width mirror, making the room look twice as large.

• Refinish wooden furniture. Refinishing is much easier and more pleasant today than it was 10 years ago. Helpful: Nontoxic, odor-free refinishers have replaced the caustic, smelly products of old. New finishes are also easier to apply and much more forgiving.

• Replace gutters and downspouts. New vinyl gutters look much better than old, aluminum ones and are easier to install. Segments snap together easily for a better water seal and can be cut easily using a regular hand saw. Easy-to-install mounting brackets hold gutters in place.

• Install new storm doors, usually the most visible part of a home. Old-fashioned anodized aluminum doors sag and fall out of alignment, resulting in a shabby look, a poor seal and wasted energy. Newer aluminum storm doors come in colors, have adjustable door frames for easy installation and fit snugly.

• Install a bay or bow window, a project that requires some—but not a lot—of expertise. Modern windows are premade and come in a variety of sizes and styles. Result: A brighter, more "open" room. Trickiest part: Getting the window into place—they're heavy and bulky. Suggestion: Invite a few friends over for a "window-raising" party.

Recommended reading list:

• *Ortho's Home Improvement Encyclopedia* by Bob Beckstrom. Ortho Books, Box 5047, San Ramon, California 94583.

• *Reader's Digest Home Improvement Manual,* Reader's Digest Association, Pleasantville, New York 10570.

• *Renovation: A Complete Guide* by Michael W. Litchfield, Prentice Hall. 200 Old Tappan Rd., Old Tappan, New Jersey 07675.

• *Popular Mechanics Home How-To* by Albert Jackson and David Day, Hearst Books, a division of William Morrow & Co., 1350 Avenue of the Americas, New York 10019.

Source: Arthur Rooze, senior editor, *The Family Handyman*, 7900 International Dr., Suite 950, Minneapolis 55425.

How To Make Home-Improvements Investments That Pay Off

In a troubled real estate market, many homeowners renovate their houses rather than moving into larger or more attractive ones. But remodeling can either be a terrific way to add value to your home…or a very expensive nightmare.

To be sure that your remodeling investment doesn't hurt the salability of your house, you need to analyze your situation carefully…

Are you planning to stay in the house for 10 to 15 years? Or will you need or want to move sooner than that? If you plan to stay for a long time, the remodeling may be worth the cost just for your own family's pleasure. If not, think about potential buyers and their needs. Mistakes people make:

• Forgetting the neighborhood. If you make expensive renovations that elevate your house's value well above others in your area, you'll have trouble getting a buyer. For your asking price, potential buyers can—and probably will—look for a house in a more exclusive or convenient neighborhood.

• Open kitchen-dining room. You may be comfortable with your guests watching you fix dinner, but you are in the minority. Most families prefer to have a dining area that can hide the mess that's in the kitchen.

• Eccentric tastes. You may love the color fuchsia and be comfortable in a brilliantly colored environment, but most people tend to be a bit more conservative. When you put in a costly tile bathroom, for example, keep the color of the tiles and fixtures neutral. You can decorate with towels and shower curtains to

221

suit your own tastes. Keep carpeting, floors and wallpaper in the rest of the house neutral as well.

• Unusual layout. You may have great ideas about turning all three bedrooms in your house into a great master-bedroom suite complete with gym and Jacuzzi, but very few prospective buyers are interested in this bachelor pad layout.

Most families want a house with discrete bedroom areas for children and parents. Adults want privacy for themselves and a separate place where children can play and leave a mess.

Projects to think twice about:

• Fireplaces. Wood-burning fireplaces used to be a big selling point in houses. This is no longer the case. While people love the look of a fireplace, they don't want to have to deal with the bother and the mess (and the inefficiency of old fireplaces). Good compromise: A fireplace with gas logs, which is cheaper to install and requires no maintenance.

• Finished basement. The days of the old wood-paneled family recreation room are over. Buyers want a dry basement for storage and utilities, but most are too dark for people to want to use for living space.

• Swimming pool. Most buyers, particularly those who are living in temperate areas where outdoor pools have a limited season, consider pools to be a liability. They don't want to take on the maintenance…or the worry that neighborhood children might fall in.

• Extensive landscaping. The expense of removing overgrown trees and bushes has become extremely costly. Replacing them can also be very expensive. It is risky, unless this is your hobby and pleasure, to do anything but trim and shape up existing planting. Exception: It does pay to remove an overgrown tree that blocks light from a window.

• Backyard or garage renovations. Buyers are much more concerned with the front of a house and its welcoming appeal for themselves and their guests than with what the backyard or an out-of-the-way garage looks like.

Projects that pay off:

• Ordinary maintenance. You must keep your house painted and caulked, the roof in good repair and the plumbing, heating and cooling systems in good working order. These are priority projects to protect your house for yourself. And you can't sell it unless these things are taken care of.

• Extra bathroom. Good bathrooms are a good investment. A built-in vanity and a shower with sliding glass doors and lots of mirrors appeal to almost everyone.

• Kitchen renovation. If the kitchen is more than 10 years old, you may profit by redoing it. You may be able to simply refinish the cabinets and put on new handles. A tiled floor is a good feature, and new appliances, if the kitchen is out of date, will pay for themselves.

• Skylight. People love light in a house. It makes the rooms seem bigger and the whole space airier and more cheerful. Well-placed skylights can open up dark areas in a very effective way.

• Master bath. Adding extra features to the master bath—a sauna, a Jacuzzi, mirrors, etc.—can help sell a house as long as it's not the only bathroom.

• Front door. A beautiful front door and a beautiful entryway are always good investments. They are the first things you and your guests see when entering the house and they establish its personality.

• Closets. Good storage space, particularly if the shelves are adjustable, will usually pay for itself.

Source: Mary Weir is an international independent restoration and renovation contractor headquartered in Rumson, New Jersey.

Useful Home-Maintenance Checklist

A little timely maintenance can go a long way toward preventing the need for complicated, costly repairs to your home. Easy and inexpensive steps you can take—season by season—to save yourself future headaches…

Spring:

• Check downspouts to make sure they carry rainwater far from the house.

• Check groundslope to make sure that soil is graded away from the basement. Danger: Soil that has been compacted all winter may settle and tend to slope toward foundation walls, bringing water with it.

• Check the condition of the roof. Replace missing or damaged shingles. If more than half the granules have eroded off an asphalt roof, ask a contractor to examine it. You may need a new roof.

• Check inside the attic, especially the ceiling, under the eaves, around chimneys and plumbing vent lines, for signs of leaks. Catching small leaks early can prevent serious damage to interior walls, ceilings and floors.

• Check the basement for moisture. Painting interior basement walls with waterproof paint will considerably reduce minor moisture penetration.

• Clean and lubricate sliding screen and patio doors to prevent yanking, which can destroy alignment and damage the doors.

• Clean the air-conditioning units. For maximum efficiency, vacuum around vents and air intake, replace filters.

Summer:

• Seal the driveway. This is an easy project that will look good, is inexpensive to do (materials to seal asphalt driveways can be purchased at most home centers) and will prevent water penetration that can result in serious deterioration.

• Repair the deck. Check for spots that have begun to soften or rot and replace single deck boards or joists as needed. If you delay, the rot will spread and can lead to major structural problems.

• Check around exterior windows and sills for signs of decay. Fill any cracks or holes with epoxy filler made for outdoor use, then paint. An early "patch and fill" job takes about 10 minutes. Delaying may cost you a full day and a few hundred dollars to replace entire window frames.

• Fill cracks in concrete or masonry steps with a mortar patch. Reason: During the winter, water freezing and thawing in the cracks will gradually cause the masonry to break apart.

• Have the furnace serviced. The furnace should be adjusted and cleaned and the blower lubricated every year or two to prevent winter breakdowns. The quickest and the least expensive time to do this is during the summer, when demand is relatively low.

Fall:

• Caulk any gaps in exterior siding or trim around windows and doors to prevent water leakage and drafts.

• Clean the gutters after the leaves fall to prevent water from backing up and freezing under the shingles and eventually leaking into the attic.

• Repoint brick. Replace mortar where necessary on foundations, walls and chimneys to prevent leaks.

• Secure weatherstripping around exterior doors, especially storm doors.

• Check storm doors for overall fit. The metal frames of most storm doors are easy to adjust. Doors that swing, close and seal properly are more efficient and last longer.

• Lubricate the garage door. Clean and oil the tracks and rollers along the sides. Oil the springs where they make contact with other metal and the device that lifts the door.

• Fertilize the lawn. Reason: Grass roots grow in the fall.

• Repaint exteriors before you notice a serious breakdown of paint. That eliminates the need for tedious scraping.

• Turn off water to outdoor faucets to prevent winter freezing, which can damage pipes.

• Have chimneys cleaned before you start using fireplaces.

Winter:

Stay indoors, keep warm, catch up with reading and indoor projects.

All Seasons:

• Vacuum vents and undersides of refrigerators, washers, dryers. Reason: Built-up dust and dirt impedes air flow and cuts down on the efficiency and life expectancy of these appliances.

• Clean sink drains regularly to prevent clogs.

• Check hardwood floors for signs that the finish is beginning to deteriorate. Repair by doing a light sanding by hand, and applying a top-coat polyurethane or varnish finish.

• Regrout bathroom tile early. You can easily regrout a dozen small gaps in half an hour. If you delay, water leakage can cause the walls to deteriorate. Use caulk, which remains elastic, for the joints around the bathtub and areas where tub and tile join.

Source: Art Rooze, senior editor of *The Family Handyman* magazine, 7900 International Dr., Suite 950, Minneapolis 55425.

Tax Benefit From House Repairs

Repairs after a fire or flood can be tacked on to the original purchase price of the house when the house is sold. That reduces the capital gains tax. Also added to the purchase price: General home improvements, including the cost of materials for do-it-yourself jobs. Caution: Keep invoices to document claims for the IRS.

Source: Phillips et al. v. Comm'r, TC Memo., 1979-239, 6/25/79.

Liability For Injuries To Uninvited Guests

Courts in many states are more likely than ever to hold an owner responsible for injuries to a visitor. That's so even though the person was on the property without an invitation. The old distinction between an invitee (someone asked onto the property) and licensee (someone on the property without an invitation) is breaking down. Traditionally, invitees would be awarded higher settlements for damages.

Now courts in about one-third of the states ignore the distinction between an invitee and licensee and hold the property owner responsible for keeping the property safe for both invitees and the self-invited.

Now: Salespeople, whether they contacted the customer before their visit or not, are generally treated (by courts recognizing the distinction) as invitees.

Buying A Home Pool Without Getting Soaked

Backyard pools are growing in popularity as high gasoline and motel prices keep more people at home. While buyers must still proceed cautiously, there are now plenty of reputable pool dealers around. The industry itself has set standards and flushed out many fly-by-nighters.

Caution: Do not expect to recoup or better your pool investment when selling the house. Real estate brokers consider pools neither a plus nor a minus. Pools frequently reduce the resale value, but can be very attractive to some buyers.

Drawbacks: Pools require considerable maintenance. Neighbors often expect pool privileges. Some neighbors may complain about noise, drainage, and safety. Fencing the pool can be expensive.

Defensive strategy: While the pool is being built, order additional liability insurance coverage.

To find a builder: Ask neighbors with trouble-free pools. Other sources of referrals: Home contractors, swimming pool managers, a national trade group.* Have builders take you to other pools they have built, and ask owners about any problems.

From initial inquiry through completion, the job can take from two weeks to two months. Much depends on what the builder finds when excavating. Underlying rock, for instance, will slow the process. But, on average, construction itself takes three to four weeks. Watch out for contractors who will not sign an agreement for a firm completion date. Reason: pool contractors tend to take on too many summer jobs and push leftovers into the next season.

*National Swimming Pool Institute, 2000 K St. NW, Washington, DC 20006.

Best materials: A Gunite concrete liner, using pneumatically applied concrete, is best. Vinyl liners often tear. They do not fit right. Stainless steel, aluminum, and partly wooden liners are all adequate. Fiberglass is suitable for smaller pools only.

Equipment: A premium-priced filter, plumbing, and pool heating equipment are worth the cost in the long run. Do not buy both an electrical heater and a cover that heats with solar energy.

Body comforts: Plan for a sauna or hot tub in the original design. It probably will add less than $3,500.

Financing: Bank loans run about 19%. They are easily available.

Paying the builder: Do not hand over more than 10% up front. Leave a big payment, at least 25%, until the day of your final inspection and acceptance. Do not forget to ask for the winter pool cover.

The latest fad: Shallow pools. Advantages: A pool 3½ to 5 feet deep saves $1,000 and up in building costs. And children do not have to be watched so carefully, provided that they know the pool is too shallow for safe diving.

If the pool turns out to be more trouble than it is worth, fill it in and plant grass.

It's Easy To Make Your Own Nontoxic Housecleaning Products

Cleaning house should not be harmful to your health. Yet many of the most popular cleaning products are extremely toxic.

All you really need is baking soda, distilled white vinegar, table salt, lemon juice, water and borax. With these inexpensive and easy-to-find products, you can make everything you need to clean the whole house…without harming the housekeeper or the environment. Make your own:

•All-purpose cleaner. Most cleaners contain ammonia, which attacks the skin and irritates the eyes and lungs.

Better: Mix one teaspoon of a vegetable-based liquid soap* or one teaspoon of borax into a quart of warm water. Add a squeeze of lemon or a tablespoon of vinegar to cut through grease and grime.

•Dishwasher detergent. Avoid dishwasher detergents that contain chlorine. It gives off irritating fumes when it comes into contact with water.

Better: Use one part borax and one part baking soda.

•Dishwashing liquid. Use a vegetable-based liquid soap. Or rub a damp sponge on a bar of all-natural soap.**

Add a few slices of lemon to the dishwater to cut grease and impart a lemony scent. If dishes are not greasy, clean them in very hot water with a sponge or dish brush.

•Drain cleaner. Pour a handful of baking soda and a half cup of vinegar down the drain. Cover immediately, and let the fizzing chemical reaction eat through the blocked matter. Rinse with plenty of hot water.

Also effective: Pour a half cup of salt and a half cup of baking soda down the drain, followed by lots of hot water.

•Glass cleaner. Avoid glass cleaners that contain ammonia.

Better: Combine equal parts vinegar and water. Sponge or spray it on windows and glass. Wipe it off with a clean, lint-free cloth. The wax buildup from chemical glass cleaners sometimes causes streaking the first time vinegar is used. Simply rub a little alcohol on the glass first, then use the vinegar and water.

•Oven cleaner. Standard oven cleaners contain lye, which irritates the skin. All contain ammonia, even those that claim to be free of fumes.

Better: Mix together in a one-quart spray bottle two tablespoons of vegetable-based liquid soap, two teaspoons of borax and enough warm water to fill the bottle. Spray the mixture on the oven interior, holding the bottle close to the target so the mixture doesn't get into the air or your eyes. Leave it on for 20 minutes, then scrub with steel wool and a scouring powder that does not contain chlorine. Rub

*Use a biodegradable soap, such as Dr. Bronner's, available at natural-food stores and some supermarkets.
**Choose a soap that contains no added scent, color or deodorizer. Good alternative: A natural glycerin soap or one made from olive oil.

pumice onto stubborn, baked-on spots.

•Scouring powders. Most scouring powders contain talc and chlorine bleach. Talc may be contaminated with asbestos. As you sprinkle the cleaner, a small amount of asbestos may go into the air—and your lungs.

Better: Use a wet sponge sprinkled with salt, baking soda or borax.

Source: Leslie Cerier is a personal fitness consultant, RFD 2, School House Rd., Amherst, Massachusetts 01002.

How To Make Small Yards Seem Larger

Small yard? A lovely garden can still be yours to enjoy. Secret: Create a space that appears to be much larger than it really is. Some techniques:

• Plant the right plants. Included:

• Vertical plants direct the eye up and out of the garden...and don't take up much ground.

• Finely textured foliage and delicate flowers create an illusion of space. Use large-leaved, variegated or unusual plants sparingly as accents to avoid a cluttered look.

• Masses of greenery with a few colorful accents produce a pleasing effect. Too many different plants are confusing to the eye. They tire rather than soothe.

• Adopt the principles of perspective used by artists. Plant taller plants near the house and shorter plants farther away. This will create an illusion of depth.

Also: Plant the most brightly colored flowers close to the house. Shift slowly to pastels—especially blues and grays—the farther away from the house you get. This makes the flowers appear to fade into the distance.

• Create outdoor rooms. Divide the yard into well-defined areas to make it seem larger.

Examples: Build a small brick patio close to the house for entertaining. Or create a shaded sitting area with mid-size deciduous trees. Lovely bonus: Many trees—including apple, shad, crab apple and magnolia—bloom in the spring.

• Divide the yard into two levels. Separate them with a low stone wall or a hedge. Two or three steps between the levels will help define them.

Use the upper level for entertaining. Plant lawn and plants, both flowering and foliage. Use the lower level for a children's play yard—it can be partly hidden by shrubbery.

• Build a deck diagonally across a small, square yard. Place it next to the house. This will divide the yard into two activity areas.

A small pond peeking out from under the deck or partly hidden behind a trellis or shrubbery will create an illusion of space.

• Choose the right fencing. If possible, it should be no taller than eye level.

To create an illusion of distance, place the tallest part of the fence nearest the house and slowly reduce its height as the fence approaches the end of the yard.

In very narrow spaces, use vertical boards for the bottom two-thirds of the fence and trellising for the top third. This creates a light, airy effect.

• Create pathways. Decorative paving focuses interest at ground level rather than into the yard.

Example: Bricks laid in a herringbone pattern help expand visual space.

Paths should have a destination—a bench, a special plant, etc. And soften them with plants spilling over the edges.

• Block offending views. Plant mid-size conifers, a shrub hedge or use a trellis covered with vines.

Source: Bonnie Wodin, Heath, Massachusetts 01346, is a garden and landscape designer who writes and teaches about gardening.

How To Protect Your Home Without Spending A Fortune... Or Living In A Fortress

Effective home security doesn't have to cost many thousands of dollars. By knowing how burglars size up their targets, you can make your home substantially safer for only a few hundred dollars.

For even greater protection, you can install an effective electronic security system for about $2,000.

Contrary to what most people believe, house breakers usually work during the day, not at night. Homeowner's self-defense:

• Make it difficult for a would-be burglar to enter the house without being seen or heard by neighbors.

• Delay an attempted entry for as long as possible. Burglars usually leave if they can't get in within 90 seconds.

First lines of defense:

• Trim shrubbery so it doesn't cover windows.

• Trim the vegetation around entrances so they're also clearly visible to neighbors.

• Put solid wooden doors at all access points from the outside, including the passage from the garage to the house. The test for a door is whether it can be kicked in easily by an adult male. That's the most common means of entry for burglars.

• On doors to the outside, install dead-bolt locks that go at least one and a half inches into the door panel. Buy from a licensed locksmith, not a chain discount or hardware store. Locksmiths have the best-quality locks, and they know how to install them.

• Put iron gratings over basement windows. If a basement room is used for sleeping, install the type of grating that breaks away from the inside—to make escape possible in case of fire.

• If you want a dog to help guard the house, get one that's nervous and loud. Fox terriers are ideal. They'll deter burglars much more effectively than a quiet, 200-pound mastiff. Forget beware-of-dog signs if you don't have a dog. Although, burglars usually aren't too bright, a sign won't fool them. The same is true for phony burglar-alarm signs.

• Install lights to illuminate the property at night. The best are sodium-vapor lights. Their soft glow subtly illuminates an area without making it look like the entrance to Fort Knox. A 35-watt lamp is adequate for most backyards.

Second line of protection:

An electronic security system is necessary if you can't follow through with the simpler safeguards, or if you want the greater peace of mind that an electronic system provides. What to look for:

• A system made by a reputable security firm that's been in business for longer than five years. For recommendations, ask the local police department or your insurance broker.

• Unobtrusive sensors on all windows and doors to the outside. When someone tries to enter, one of these perimeter sensors will trigger an alarm in the house that signals a monitoring service, which subsequently notifies the police.

• Interior detectors that use both infrared and microwave technology to sense an intruder who eludes the perimeter detectors. Dual technology is the most effective because infrared or microwave alone can give false readings. Use only the perimeter sensors when you're home but both systems when you're away.

• Response that takes no more than five minutes from the time of attempted entry to the arrival of the police. If you doubt the manufacturer's claim, ask the police about their experience with the system.

Cost of the system:

About $2,000, plus $10–$30 a month for the monitoring service. Bonus: If you have an electronic security system, most insurance companies reduce rates on your homeowner's policy by 10%–25%.

Source: Joe Mele, associate professor, National Crime Prevention Institute, University of Louisville, Kentucky 40292.

A Safer Safe

A home safe should be rated for fire resistance by the Underwriters Laboratory. Recommended: A class-350 safe, which protects paper documents against high heat for at least half an hour. For floppy disks: Get a class-125 safe, which keeps humidity down to 85%—humidity is an enemy for floppy disks.

Source: *Making the Most of Your Money* by financial writer Jane Bryant Quinn, Simon & Schuster, 1230 Avenue of the Americas, New York 10020.

Checklist For Move To A New House

Arrange for the utilities (gas, electric, water, etc.) to be turned on in the new house or apartment a few days before you move in.

Install the telephone a month before you move (or as early as is feasible).

Enroll your child in the new local school.

Open savings and checking accounts promptly at a bank in the new neighborhood.

Notify companies of change of address (insurance, credit card, magazines, etc.).

If you are moving to a new state, check to see if your auto coverage is applicable.

Notify the IRS of the move both at the time of the move and again when you file your income tax.

Have pharmaceutical prescriptions renewed before moving so that adequate amounts of medication will be on hand.

Ask the previous occupant for a list of reliable local service people (electricians, plumbers, carpenters, etc.) and good nearby stores.

Moving outdoor plants to a new home: For a long move, place them in a plastic bag and cover with wet straw or weeds. If you know in autumn you'll be leaving in the spring, use a spade to cut a deep circle around a shrub or young tree to sever the roots and outline the root ball.

Suggestions For Condominium Hunters

Look for a building about to undergo conversion. If you sublet an apartment in it, you get first crack at buying the apartment.

If you have trouble getting a mortgage, look for a condominium developer who has a mortgage commitment from a lender.

Rent a portion of the condominium apartment to a friend. This helps meet the monthly payments.

How To Protect Your Kids From Violence

With one in five high school students today carrying some type of weapon,* it's important for kids to know how to avoid becoming victims. My advice—which is also useful for adults trying to survive these increasingly violent times...

• Don't stand out from the crowd. Conformity is the rule. Flashy clothes, jewelry and other accessories act as "sight triggers," attracting the attention of predators. Also: Know and avoid wearing the local gang "colors" so as not to attract the wrath of rival gang members.

Examples: In many schools, red and blue scarves or clothing with professional sports team logos—particularly the LA Raiders or LA Clippers—are often associated with different gangs.

• Don't go it alone. Avoid going anywhere—to and from school, walking between classes—alone. Two are safer than one, three safer than two, etc.

• Learn to project an air of self-confidence. Let your demeanor send the message that you're someone not be messed with.

Examples: Don't walk with your shoulders slumped and your eyes downcast. Instead, lift your head up and stick your chest out.

• Know the territory. Know where in school it's safe to be—and avoid places that aren't safe.

• Realize that your watch, wallet, bus pass, etc., are replaceable. Be willing to surrender them if confronted. Remember: Nothing is more important than your own safety. Consider carrying several dollars at all times to appease thieves.

• Alert your parents immediately if you are victimized. Let them report it to school officials and the police.

*According to a study by the Centers for Disease Control.

Source: Edward Muir, director of school safety in New York for the United Federation of Teachers, 260 Park Ave. S., New York 10010.

How Parents Can Walk The Fine Line Between Overprotection...And Neglect

Parents have been sold a bill of goods by the psychology establishment about how much attention their children need.

Result: Exhausted parents—particularly single parents—have succumbed to feelings of guilt and inadequacy when there is no reason for them to chastise themselves. And children, now accustomed to being the center of attention, have become dependent upon and demanding of their parents.

Parents' feelings of guilt don't help children—they destabilize the family. And parents who get too involved with their children's lives don't establish the distance necessary for the youngsters to grow and learn from their own mistakes—experiences that build self-esteem and help children become responsible adults.

Children need to feel secure so that they can go about the business of fulfilling their potential. There are two cornerstones to a child's security...love and discipline.

The essence of discipline is the three Rs—rules, routines and responsibilities. A parent's job is to establish and enforce the three Rs. The love comes naturally.

Child-rearing basics:

There are some simple child-rearing principles that parents should keep in mind throughout the years during which their children are growing up.

• Pay more attention to your marriage—or yourself, if you're a single parent—than you do to the children. Your marriage, if it is strong and satisfying, will give your children more security than any amount of attention. If you are single, your sense of self-respect and fulfillment as a person can act as the same sort of anchor for children.

• Expect your children to obey. Don't apologize for decisions you make in their lives. Children need powerful parents upon whom they can count to be authoritative, decisive and trustworthy. You are in charge of the family. As long as your children live in your house, they don't have a right to make decisions for themselves...you allow them the privilege of making decisions. And you always have the option of revoking that privilege if it is abused.

• Nurture your children's responsibility within this structure. Allow them to make choices, and let them know that they must accept the outcomes. From an early age, expect them to make regular, tangible contributions to the family. That means doing chores they don't get paid for. And it means letting your children take responsibility for their own actions. Don't run after the bus—let your children suffer the consequences of being late or arriving at school without the permission slip they left on the kitchen table.

• Say no, and say it often. I call this a healthy dose of vitamin N. If the response is a tantrum, so be it. Exposure to frustration prepares children for the realities of adulthood and gives them a tolerance for frustration that eventually develops perseverance—a key ingredient in every success story. Your obligation is not to make your children happy, but to give them the skills to pursue happiness on their own. Important: Don't say no arbitrarily—rules must be consistent and the reasons for them explained.

• Where toys are concerned, less is more. Having too many toys destroys a young child's ability to make creative decisions. If a youngster has too many options, he becomes overwhelmed and can't decide what to play with. Then he says he's bored and has nothing to do. A child with too many toys also misses out on the magic of making do, which exercises imagination, initiative, creativity, resourcefulness and self-reliance. The best toys are flexible—they can be whatever the child wants to make of them. An older child can earn the money for the toys he wants by doing extra chores...a teenager who wants a car should prove he can pay for it by getting a part-time job.

• Turn off the tube. Preschool children need to play so they can develop basic competency skills, learned by touching and exploring their environment. Nothing happens when a child sits passively in front of a television screen. Children shouldn't be allowed to watch television until they have learned to read and enjoy books—between the third and fifth grades usually. By that age, watching a few programs that represent the world in a realistic way (nature specials, history-based movies, documentaries, sports and cultural events) can't hurt.

• Don't be intimidated by the experts. Use suggestions and ideas that make sense to you, but remember that all parents make mistakes now and then...and children aren't permanently scarred by them. Raise your children your way—and enjoy it.

Source: John Rosemond, director of the Center for Affirmative Parenting in Gastonia, North Carolina. His nationally syndicated parenting column appears in 100 newspapers in the United States and Canada. His latest book is *Parent Power! A Common-Sense Approach to Parenting in the '90s and Beyond,* Andrews and McMeel, 4900 Main St., Kansas City, Missouri 64112.

Kids And Family Finances

Include children in family financial discussions—in age-appropriate ways. Just don't expect them fully to understand a financial crisis—or, of course, to shoulder the burden. Important: Children must understand that they are not burdens. As cutbacks are necessary, try to make sure that they affect everyone in the family fairly. Helping to decide where the family budget should be trimmed is useful for children.

Source: *Make Your Money Grow* by Theodore J. Miller, editor, *Changing Times,* Kiplinger Books, 1729 H St. NW, Washington, DC 20006.

Raising Happy Children

Parental warmth and affection play the single most important role in determining a child's well-being during adulthood. That parental support can overcome negative influences, such as a parent's early death or alcoholism, divorce or poverty. Parental warmth is more than just cuddling and hugging. It signifies a deep attachment and responsiveness to a child's emotional needs.

Source: A 40-year study of nearly 100 people conducted by Boston University psychology professor Carol Franz, reported in *Parenting,* 25 W. 43 St., New York 10036. 10 issues. $18/yr.

Finally!! How To Get Through To Your Kids

The most common question I hear from parents seeking assistance is, How can I motivate my kids?

The motivational goals vary, from improving the children's grades in school, to having them help more with chores around the house, to more socializing with peers, to improving relations with siblings.

Regardless of what they're aiming for, parents are frustrated because the only effective ways they have found to get youngsters to do the things they want them to do is to nag, threaten or bribe.

But there are positive techniques parents can use with children from about age 10 onward that can bring about desired changes without having to resort to such unpleasant behavior.

However, most parents want a simple quick-fix approach to solving problems with their children. Reality: No single technique works every time. Having a positive, long-term influence on your child's behavior requires multiple methods. Just as you can't build a house with only a hammer, you can't motivate your child with just one behavioral approach.

The most powerful motivational tools you can use to enable your youngster to become self-motivated...

• Establish rapport with your child. This involves seeing things from your child's perspective. You have to see, hear and feel things the way a teenager does rather than the way an adult does, and for most of us that involves going back a long time. Try to remember that teens magnify the smallest slight and may be devastated by actions that adults shrug off.

Example: Your son comes home feeling in the dumps. His clique at school went off to a restaurant for lunch and didn't invite him. He wallows in misery and doubts that he will ever have friends again. Instead of belittling his feelings, translate his experience into something you can empathize with. Imagine you're at your desk at work. At noon you stop by several of your co-workers' desks only to find that they've gone to lunch together—without asking you. Now how do you feel about your son's travails?

• Realize that experience is 10 times more effective than words. Even at ages 10 and 11, most children still are not highly verbal. So to get through to them you need to be as concrete as possible.

Example: Parents worried that their teens were spoiled and didn't respect the house, toys and other family possessions. Instead of lecturing to them, the parents had the kids work in a soup kitchen and day-care center for the needy. Instead of having a fancy turkey dinner at home for Thanksgiving, the kids helped to cook and serve dinner to the homeless. These experiences communicated far more than words could all the privileges this family enjoyed and made the kids finally appreciate how fortunate they were.

• Ask open-ended questions. Instead of asking a pointed question, and then providing the answer yourself, ask a question that enables the child to give the answer. By using such an approach, you help to develop a child's ability to solve his/her own problems.

Example: Take the familiar case of a child who complains that he/she can't do anything right. You might then ask, "You mean you can't think of one time you've done something right?" Your child might reply, "Well, sometimes." You can then say, "Name one." And more likely than not, you'd be on the road to directing your child to look for the positive things in life rather than accepting depression.

• Build your child's self-esteem. One easy way to do this is to catch your teen in the act of doing something right. Most parents are great at this when their kids are young. They can't wait to celebrate their child's first step or first word. But somewhere along the way, they forget how important it is to keep celebrating. If your teen is learning something new and getting parts of the skill right, offer a positive stroke. This is an incentive to repeat the behavior.

Example: Tim had encountered problems with his old English teacher, who handed every paper back with so many marks and slashes it looked as if Zorro had attacked it. His new English teacher was a complete switch. On his first paper, she peppered it with positive comments, such as: "Excellent opening sentence. Sets scene for the rest of the paragraph." She went through the rest of the paper to catch everything Tim had done correctly, not incorrectly. Result: Tim's self-esteem improved, and his grades went from Ds to As and Bs.

• Be specific with your praise. Lack of specificity robs praise of its motivational value. So you need to make an effort to discover what your child does that is praiseworthy. Instead of saying, "You are the most wonderful child a mother could have," you might substitute something along these lines: "That's initiative—three mornings you've gotten up on your own." Or, "When you smile like that, it makes everyone in the room feel your warmth."

• Use specific examples of positive traits. My Dutch grandma, a crusty old lady, instinctively did this when she told me stories about her incarceration as a prisoner of war during World War II. She managed to smuggle a few gold coins into the concentration camp where she was being held. She wrapped the coins in burlap, making buttons for burlap-bag dresses. As the years progressed, she broke the coins into fragments and traded them for the one food she craved, bell peppers. By eating these peppers, which contain more vitamin C than oranges, she managed to avoid the scurvy that was the cause of death for many of her fellow prisoners.

My grandmother's story illustrated the resourcefulness and ingenuity that helped her to survive. And by hearing this account from her, I realized that ingenuity became a living, breathing trait in my grandmother's story. Children build their own personalities from available traits. The more concrete a trait, the more available it is.

• Encourage your children to read biographies. Best: Those of people in careers in which they're interested. Share with your children the stories of interesting people who have led successful lives. By doing so, you bring out examples of positive behavior and give them the additional support of good role models.

Source: Jim Wiltens, leader of parenting workshops and seminars in the San Francisco Bay area, director of Deer Crossing Camp, a summer camp in California devoted to bringing out the best in children and the author of the new book *No More Nagging, Nit-picking and Nudging,* Deer Crossing Press, Box 60517, Sunnyvale, California 94088.

Children's Regressive Behavior

Children's regressive behavior can be an early warning of trouble requiring professional help. Specific warning signs: A child who has learned to talk starts to speak less…one who could walk or ride a bike easily now has trouble doing so…a toilet-trained child starts having frequent "accidents"…children who start to hurt other kids—or themselves. If you are in doubt about the meaning of behavioral changes, talk to a pediatrician or child psychologist.

Source: J. Clifford Kaspar, PhD, supervising neuropsychologist, Charles I. Doyle Mental Health Center at Loyola University, Chicago.

Saving Savvy

Start saving when a child is born in order to have enough for his/her education. The key is regular saving—through stable, income-producing investments such as bond funds and high-dividend stocks. Important: Saving for college alone is no longer enough. More and more parents are now opting to enroll their children in private schools in lower grades. A year of prekindergarten education can now cost as much as $10,000.

Source: John Sestina, a financial planner in Columbus, Ohio, reported in *The Wall Street Journal.*

Home Alone

To leave a child home alone, wait until an appropriate age—usually 11 or 12—make sure there is a neighbor to whom the child can turn in an emergency. Have proper locks on doors and windows—and be sure the child can operate them…practice fire drills…keep emergency phone numbers by the telephone.

Important:

If you have several children, do not overburden the oldest with too much responsibility by being gone too often or for long periods.

Source: *How to Stay Lovers While Raising Your Children* by health and psychology writer Anne Mayer, Price Stern Sloan, Inc., 360 N. La Cienega Blvd, Los Angeles 90048.

Adjusting To A New Sibling

To help a young firstborn adjust to a new baby, enroll the child in a preschool program long before the new baby arrives. It will help the toddler become more independent, giving him/her a meaningful place and significant people that he doesn't have to share with the baby.

Source: Alberto C. Serrano, MD, professor of psychiatry and pediatrics at the University of Pennsylvania School of Medicine and medical director of the Philadelphia Child Guidance Center.

Family Education

Take your children or grandchildren back to the area in which you grew up. If you're bold, ring the doorbell of your former house and ask if you can walk through the yard (you may also be invited inside the house). Visit your school playground, the place where you bought ice cream, the old hardware store, etc. Consider having lunch at the deli. This helps give children a feeling of another era. Perhaps—with proper advance conversation to alleviate sadness—you could also visit the cemetery to see old family gravestones. Good at any time: Construct a family tree so that the kids will know who's who.

Source: *The Ten Commandments for Grandparents* by child-development specialist Caryl Waller Krueger, Abingdon Press, Cokesbury Service Center, Box 801, Nashville, Tennessee 37202.

A What-Matters-Most Memo From Child... To Parents

Don't spoil me. I know quite well that I shouldn't have everything I ask for — I'm only testing you—and...

• Don't be afraid to be firm with me and set curfews and rules. I prefer it. It makes me feel secure.

• Don't protect me from consequences. Sometimes I need to learn the painful way.

• Don't let me form bad habits. I rely on you to detect them in the early stages and give me direction by example.

• Don't make me feel smaller than I am. It only makes me behave stupidly to prove that I am "big."

• Don't correct me in front of people if you can help it. Praise in public. Chastise in private.

• Don't make me feel that my mistakes are sins. It upsets my sense of values.

• Don't put me off when I ask questions. If you do, you will find that I'll stop asking you and begin seeking information elsewhere.

• Don't tell me my fears are silly. They are real to me and you can do much to reassure me if you try to understand.

• Don't suggest to me that you are perfect or infallible. It hurts and disappoints me to learn that you are neither.

• Don't be inconsistent. That confuses me and makes me lose faith in you.

• Don't ever think that it is beneath your dignity to apologize to me. An honest apology makes me feel surprisingly warm toward you.

• Don't forget that I can't thrive without lots of love and understanding. I need your quantity and quality time, and your affection.

• Please keep yourself fit and healthy. I need you and I love you. Please don't die early because you smoke, drink too much or use drugs.

• Because "stuff happens," let's stick together. I believe in you. I need you and hope you believe in me.

Source: From *Weathering the Storm: The Survival Guide for Teenagers* by Dan Clark. Published by British American Publishing, 19 British American Blvd., Latham, New York 12110. Distributed by Simon & Schuster.

Secrets Of Much, Much Better Family Relationships

Even great, great success professionally doesn't compensate for failure in family relationships.

But relationships with spouses and children, as with all other relationships, tend toward disorder and dissolution. Keeping these relationships healthy over the long term is a big task.

It is much easier, though, if you follow what I call a principle-based approach—and live in harmony with such enduring virtues as fairness, equity, justice, integrity, honesty and trust.

To revitalize and enrich your family relationships, give these principle-based practices a try...

• Retain a long-term perspective. Short-term perspectives bog us down. If you only focus on the short-term in your family, a relationship problem becomes just another frustrating obstacle on a fast-track path to self-fulfillment.

To focus on the long-term, envision two lines. The upper one is where your family wants to be, and the lower one is where it actually is. Then, imagine forces that are pushing the family toward the top line—such as jobs inside and outside the house, and common social, psychological and spiritual goals. Then, imagine forces that are pushing the family toward the bottom line—such as selfishness, competitiveness and lack of interdependence.

The point of this exercise is to get the family to identify its driving forces, and to concentrate on building the positive forces that push it toward the upper line. The very process of involvement can transform a family and enable it to integrate its idealistic and spiritual side with the mundane, gritty, everyday side of life.

• Rescript your marriage and family life. Our behavior as adults is based on the "scripts" we received from our parents when we were children. The problem is that these scripts often involve negative ways of solving conflicts. The typical poles in reacting to family difficulties are fight or flight. But as parents, we have the ability to write new scripts for ourselves. In the process you'll come up with more mature ways of solving problems than yelling or withdrawing.

Important: As parents, our day-to-day behavior is far and away our greatest influence on our children.

Helpful: In difficult situations, role-play with other family members—put yourself in their shoes and respect their objections to your approach.

• Consider your roles. Spouses and parents play three roles...producer, manager and leader:

The "producer" does what's necessary to achieve desired results. Father takes out the garbage, mother puts the baby to bed, the children clean their rooms.

Problem: Many producer parents don't know how to delegate, so they end up doing all of the work themselves. They become exhausted, irritable and disappointed that others are not being more helpful.

In the "manager" role, parents may delegate various jobs around the home and yard to the children.

Problem:

Manager parents often become inflexible, methods-oriented and bureaucratic. They tend to focus on doing things right instead of on doing the right things.

In the "leadership" role, parents can bring about constructive change. Here their role is to provide direction through example and vision, to motivate through love and inspiration.

Example: In our family, we have what's known as the 10-minute rule. Each night after dinner, everyone pitches in to help with cleanup duty. I wash off the dishes, one child loads them into the dishwasher, another sweeps the floor and so on. This approach transforms what could have been a lonely, onerous chore into a leadership system that creates team-building. And no one has to spend more than 10 minutes on cleanup detail.

• Don't kill the golden goose. Too many parents focus on the goal—the golden egg—and in their single-mindedness ignore the means of attaining that goal—the golden goose. Take the case of parents who are always after their children to tidy up their rooms. The parents should ask themselves whether they want a clean room (the golden egg) or want the children to clean their rooms cheerfully (the golden goose).

The lesson here is that by using intimidating and manipulative techniques, parents may get the golden egg in the short term, but eventually they will kill the golden goose.

Over the long term, using such a heavy-handed approach will almost certainly backfire. Effective parents should try to preserve emotional assets and resources that enable family members to be productive. Open communications, unconditional love, gentleness, consideration and small courtesies all go a long way toward keeping the golden goose alive.

• Develop a family-mission statement. Too many families are managed on the basis of instant gratification rather than sound principles and a rich bank of shared emotional experiences. When crises occur, members of such families tend to deal with them by repeating old patterns—fighting, withdrawing, becoming critical or silent.

But by pulling together and drafting a family constitution, you will be forced to focus on priorities. This gives a family a fresh perspective and helps everyone to get to the roots of family problems.

To create a mission statement for your family, you need to ask...

What do we value?

What is our family all about?

What is our reason for being?

I can't say that creating a family-mission statement happens overnight. It took my family six months of regular meetings. And as important as the end product—a piece of paper that captures the family mission—is, even more important is the process. If you create an environment in which everyone can express his/her feelings openly, where a real effort is made to understand what is most important to each family member, you will be able to develop a constitution that guides, governs and inspires every member of the family.

Source: Stephen R. Covey, a management consultant who has advised many *Fortune* 500 companies, is chairman of the Covey Leadership Center in Provo, Utah, and the author of six books, including the best-seller *The Seven Habits of Highly Effective People.* His latest book is *Principle-Centered Leadership,* Summit Books, 1230 Avenue of the Americas, New York 10020.

Grandparents' Mistakes Can Be Avoided

Even though they are wiser and more experienced than they were when they were parents, many grandparents miss out on the joys of their new role because they fail to approach their adult children in a way that makes it easy for the generations to meet.

That's a real shame, because grandparents can give their grandchildren a kind of unconditional love, support and perspective that no one else can provide. And now more than ever—with both parents working in the majority of families—children need caring grandparents in their lives.

What grandparents do wrong:

• Mistake: Overreaching. By imposing their ideas about how to raise the grandchildren on their adult children, grandparents make themselves a disruptive force in the family instead of a help.

Better:

It's fine to offer counsel, but only when you are asked. It's great to offer financial help for housing or tuition, but don't dictate what house to buy or which school the child should attend.

• Mistake: Undermining the grandchildren's parents. Even if you disapprove of how your own adult child and his/her spouse are raising your grandchild, you only hurt the child by saying so. His first loyalty will always be to his parents. You can help most by setting limits for the child in your home and helping the youngster make responsible choices in his dealings with you.

• Mistake: Not admitting past mistakes. If you see that perhaps you were too permissive with your own children and they are suffering from a lack of discipline now—or if you now regret being too strict and punitive and hate seeing your children repeat the same pattern with your grandchildren, talk to your children about your new insights. They may be very appreciative...and you'll spare your grandchildren some very difficult times.

• Mistake: Not being flexible about helping. Take your cues from the parents on when and how to contribute to the family. Let them decide whether they need a weekend without the children (you can baby-sit)...or an outing for the whole family that includes you. Be available to listen to the parents or the children without making judgments. Respect their

235

family goals and values even if they are different from yours.

• Mistake: Underestimating resources. Grandparents often have unique talents and experiences to share with grandchildren. If you're a gardener, help your grandchildren plant their own plot. Teach them to play the piano (if they're interested). Take a grandchild to your workplace and show him what your profession is about. Tell about your childhood and your children's adventures while they were growing up.

• Mistake: Not staying in touch with your grandchildren. Grandparents who don't live near their families sometimes don't participate as much as they could in their grandchildren's lives.

Recommended:

Send postcards to grandchildren. Write them letters. Send them small gifts. Call them on the telephone. Even these small gestures can make a child feel very special, and every child needs that feeling.

• Mistake: Being a grandparent only to your own grandchildren. You can play a grandparent's role to children other than your own. Be available to the children in your neighborhood and your community.

Source: Robert A. Aldrich, MD, co-author with Glenn Austin, MD, of *Grandparenting for the 90s: Parenting Is Forever*, Robert Erdman Publishing, 810 W. Los Vallecitos Blvd., Suite 210, San Marcos, California 92069. Dr. Aldrich is a pediatrician and clinical professor of pediatrics at the University of Washington School of Medicine in Seattle and a founder of the Seattle Kid's Place Project.

Wiretapping By Spouses

Wiretapping by spouses is becoming increasingly common in troubled marriages. The equipment is inexpensive, easy to use and may already be in the house. Answering machines, Caller ID and nursery monitor (used anywhere) can become eavesdropping devices. Legality: unclear. Some courts have declared wiretapping illegal, but others have made exceptions for spouses.

Source: Family-law attorney Cary Cheifetz, writing in *New Jersey Law Journal,* Box 20081, Newark, New Jersey 07101.

13

Very, Very Smart Education

How To Get Into Medical School

Undergraduates who want to go to medical school must know what factors are important in getting in. The 126 medical schools in the U.S. and Puerto Rico admit 16,500 first-year students out of as many as 36,000 applicants.

The number of applicants has been declining in recent years, but the competition is still stiff.

Since most students apply to 10 or more schools, a typical medical school is likely to receive 6,000 applications for a class of 180. About 600 applicants are selected for interviews. Here are the bases on which they are chosen.

Grade Point Average (GPA): An admissions committee's first question is whether an applicant can succeed academically. A student's grade point average is the best measure of academic competence. Many schools compute an overall GPA and a science GPA sepa-

rately. Both are important.

Medical College Admissions Test: Since no admissions committee can be familiar with all the colleges that applicants come from, the Medical College Admissions Test (MCAT), required by nearly all medical schools, is the equalizer. If an applicant's GPA is a little low, a high MCAT can make the difference, especially if the undergraduate college's recommendations are strong.

Recommendations:

Letters from former professors are read very carefully. If they are strongly supportive and specific about the student's competence and character, they can make a significant difference. Before asking for a recommendation, a student should ask whether the professor can give a clearly positive report.

The interview and essay:

Medicine is a helping profession that requires commitment and compassion, as well as academic competence. The essay and interview are designed to reveal the kind of human being the applicant is. The admissions committee wants to know whether an applicant has the qualities that will make a good doctor.

Qualities:

Commitment to the profession, ability to communicate, compassion for people, motivation to complete a demanding course of study. The more tangible evidence an applicant can offer from past activities in sports, social activities, jobs, and home life, the better.

Undergraduate schools:

A degree from a top private college may give an applicant a slight edge, but not much. It is most likely to be helpful if an applicant's GPA is a little low. A student's course of study is examined for breadth, as well as for science courses. Doctors don't spend their lives in a laboratory. Thus, a grounding in the humanities and social sciences is important. No matter how high a student's GPA is, if there are too many easy courses on the record, the response will be negative.

Dealing with rejection: If an applicant is not accepted, there is always next year. If your GPA or MCAT scores are too low, spend the next year raising them. If your academic record is fine, but other applicants are given preference, spend the year working in a hospital or other helping profession to prove your commitment to serving people.

More information: *Medical School Admissions Requirements: U.S.A. and Canada,* Assn. of American Medical Colleges, 1 Dupont Circle NW, Washington, DC 20036, and *Getting into Medical School* by S.J. Brown, MD, Barron's Educational Services, Inc., Woodbury, NY 11797.

If The College Of Your Choice Turns You Down

If an applicant has not been accepted at a preferred private college, there is little that can be done.

Reason:

The applicant's admissions folder was carefully reviewed by three or four admissions committee members, who made a decision.

But don't give up.

Options:

Review the application and the instructions for filling it out. Was something that could have significantly affected the committee's decision left out? The applicant's special interests? Achievements? Talents or skills? Also: The application process started in the fall, when the senior year of high school was barely under way. What has the applicant done during the last six months? Built a computer? Raised the grade point average? Started playing French horn with the local symphony? All of these are significant additions to the application. Inform the college of them, and ask for a review.

Call the admissions director and ask: Why didn't I get in? Listen carefully for specifics. Example: Your grades were high, but you didn't take enough tough courses. More likely the director will offer general comments, but will give you a clue to the decision, not wanting to get into an argument about specific issues of judgment.

Go to a college that has offered admission. Strategy: Achieve a top academic record during the freshman year. Then: Reapply to the first-choice college as a sophomore transfer. The admissions folder will still be on file. And the continuing interest in the school will get the applicant a first-consideration rating among transfer applicants.

Take a year off. Chances are that the applicant followed all the admissions procedures correctly but has a record that looks exactly like many other applicants' records. Nothing sets it apart. A year working in a public service job, learning new skills in a private-sector job, or traveling and studying may well make the second application more attractive.

Although an application has not been accepted, the person should not feel rejected. Admissions officers in schools where the competition is murderous say that the thousand applications of those under the acceptance cutoff mark look so much like many of those who were accepted that it is impossible to tell them apart. Chance just worked against them.

College Marketing Opportunities

At first glance, college students seem to comprise a market that's small, difficult to reach, not very affluent and too diverse to fit into familiar demographic segments. But, despite the problems, there are compelling reasons to sell products and services to college students today…

• Many companies shy away from the college market because they don't know how to reach it. There are big opportunities for companies that do go after the college market, because most don't.

• Individual college students don't have as much disposable income as their parents, but cumulatively, their disposable income is an estimated $13 billion.

• Long-term buying patterns often begin in college. When you convince college students to buy a product, you may have customers for life.

Like any other market segment, college students have a unique set of goals and interests that translate into buying habits. What works:

• Products that appeal to status—particularly credit cards. College kids love the freedom to charge purchases just as older people do.

• Products that appeal to image. College-age people also value products that help them gain approval of their peers, that make them look "cool."

Example: One reason IBM had trouble marketing computers to students was that they were perceived as stodgy business machines. Apple's, on the other hand, were seen as flashy and modern. IBM went a long way in changing its image by sponsoring 3-D film festivals and other events that identified it with hip, state-of-the-art technology.

• Instant gratification. Point-of-purchase (POP) promotions can work well to serve this need on campuses because young people like to see immediate benefits.

Examples: Instant rub-off sweepstakes or contests on campus.

Coupons, on the other hand, have a dismal record at colleges, largely because most kids haven't learned much about saving and budgeting and they want immediate gratification. Identification:

Since brand loyalty often develops during college years, companies can profit not only by selling their products, but also by identifying them with something students value.

Examples: Sponsoring concerts, giving prizes that reward achievement, underwriting programs on college radio or television stations (especially since the stations usually don't sell time for commercials).

Zenith Data Systems, for example, recently sponsored alternative music programs, called Disk Drive, on nearly 200 campus radio stations. The company hopes the tie-in with music will give it a youthful image that will translate into the sale of computer products.

To reinforce the radio programs, Zenith also offers student discounts on personal computers, and has set up games at computer stores where lucky students can win free CDs. Research differences:

Since college students are a young and fast-changing group, many conventional types of market research don't work.

Example: There isn't much information available in standard computerized demographic databases that specifically analyzes college students to help marketers. This is because college mailing lists are often out of date a few months after they're compiled.

Also, it's risky to survey consumer patterns on one campus and expect the results to be useful at another.

Reason: The students at any given school, with the possible exception of community colleges, come from all over the country, if not the world. They come from all different economic classes, as well. Better techniques:

• Focus groups.* Interview sessions with groups of students can reveal deep-seated motivations. Marketers can use the information gathered in focus groups to develop promotions and other campaigns that tap these motivations. Focus groups, for example, have helped automakers learn which types of

*Groups of individuals from the market, who are brought together to discuss products, giving marketers insight into consumer attitudes.

239

cars appeal to the status and image goals of students.

• Test marketing. There's virtually no substitute for test marketing. When a product or service is found to work on one campus, try it on another.

Useful: Look for demographic groups and other identifiable consumer groups within student bodies. Examples: Hispanics, auto owners, those who travel frequently.

Caution: The college market is fickle. Once you sell a product on campus, keep in touch with the market. If students begin responding to new ideas, you may be able to alter the product or its positioning to tap the new tastes. Traps:

• Brand loyalty can work both ways. If students buy a product and it doesn't live up to claims in the marketing, they may harbor a grudge for many years to come. Some credit card companies fell into this trap when they gave out cards to students too freely, only to cancel them later. Naturally, some students were angered.

• Overlooking community colleges. They're a huge market that's often more affluent than kids in four-year colleges, largely because community college students frequently have part-time jobs and save money by living at home.

Inside moves:

In developing new promotions (and even doing most types of market research), it's almost always necessary to work with college officials. In most cases, their permission to do business on campus will be needed. At other times, it's just good politics to be liked by the officials.

Essential: When the company approaches the university for cooperation, the promotion must be of value to the school.

Examples: The promotion could offer an education or cultural benefit…or an anti-drug message. Or, in the case of market research, a company can offer to share its findings with the school.

Source: Marilyn Adler, president, Creative Targets, student marketing specialists, Five W. 19 St., New York 10011.

Back To School— To Teach

Many local colleges welcome courses taught by professionals with special skills. No teaching certificate is needed, because the courses are offered through the Community Services or Adult Education division. The college advertises the seminars, mails bills to students and collects fees. Usual split: 60% for the instructor, 40% for the college. To get started: Create an idea for a seminar, send it to the head of the program at the college and follow up.

Source: Adult-education expert Tom Koziol, writing in *The Banker's Secret Bulletin*, Box 78, Elizaville, New York 12523.

College Tomorrow??

If college is only a few years away and you failed to set up an inflation-beating college fund 10 or 20 years ago, there are some crisis methods you can employ. These options should be used only after careful thought and research:

• Home-equity loans
• National direct student loans
• Guaranteed student loans
• Borrowing against life-insurance cash values
• Refinancing a home mortgage
• Loans from an employee retirement fund
• Terminating an employee retirement fund
• Loans against a stock or bond portfolio
• Enrolling in a military program such as ROTC
• Cooperative education (a program that combines classroom as well as on-the-job education)
• Company-sponsored education
• Commuting to a local school

Source: Reprinted from *Get Rich Slow: The Truth—Not the Hype—About What to Do with Your Money and Why* by certified financial planner Tama McAleese, Career Press, 180 Fifth Ave., Hawthorne, New Jersey 07507.

The Purse-String Threat

In our pinched economy, more and more parents are now telling their college-bound children, "We'll sacrifice to keep you in that top school—but only if you get top grades." Danger:

Putting all the emphasis on good grades—and using purse strings as a threat if your child does not live up to your expectations—warps his/her purpose of going to a top-quality school.

Freshman grades are rarely a gauge of what a student can achieve—in school, in a career or in life.

More important: That the young adult learns to work independently, to work hard, to stay healthy on his/her own and to remain in communication with the family during this enormous period of change.

Additional source of pressure on new college students: Because some of the excellent colleges just below the most prestigious names are anxious about falling enrollments, they are beginning to accept some students who find themselves not quite equipped to keep up. (Top-tier schools are still as selective as ever.)

Better: Be realistic if your child is working hard but still feels well over his/her head at the end of freshman year and is very anxious. In this case, transferring to a school where the student can succeed is probably a very sensible choice.

Tuition Tactics-Earn Residency Benefits

Students who attend a state college or university outside their home state pay much higher tuition than do residents of that state. In addition, nonresidents do not have access to statewide scholarship and student aid programs. However, the Supreme Court has ruled that although state colleges and universities can charge nonresidents higher tuition, those students must be allowed to earn residency status during the period of their enrollment.

Public institutions are subsidized by the tax dollars of the citizens of the state. Substantial tuition income is lost when out-of-state students become entitled to lower resident tuition. Therefore, the process is strictly regulated—and requirements are becoming more stringent. A year ago, for instance, the University of California added to its simple requirement of a year's residence in the state the stipulation that a student also must prove financial independence.

Although requirements for residency vary from state to state, most follow similar patterns. All states, for example, require continuous residence for a period of time immediately preceding application—usually one year, but as little as six months in a few states.

Some states require evidence that the student intends to become a permanent resident of the state. However, the emphasis placed on this factor varies greatly. In some states, such as New York, no such requirement exists. In others, the application forms are designed to elicit such information indirectly.

When a nonresident student enrolls, the institution assumes that he is there for educational purposes rather than for a permanent change of residence. Therefore, the burden of proof is on the student to prove desire to become a bona fide resident.

Basic questions a residency applicant is asked:

• Have you filed an income tax return in the state?

• Are you dependent on your parents for support, or are you financially independent?

• Have you registered and voted in the state?

• Do you have a driver's license or car registration in the state?

• Do you have a record of employment in the state? (Students who are seeking financial aid are expected to earn some money through summer and part-time employment.)

Helping Your Child Plan A Career

While many adults feel uncertain about helping their children with careers, there are ways to offer assistance.

Recommendations:

Recognize that both sons and daughters pass through various career attitudes. Most youngsters spend their childhood believing that they can become anything, from fire fighter to the president of the U.S.

During every phase, you must treat your child as a growing person. Don't snuff out the child's interests with your prejudices. Allow exploration and curiosity about all sorts of work.

Promote a sense of worthiness in your offspring. Give them the chance to make choices, even if they seem to be bad ones.

After the age of 17, your child considers a career realistically. Help your child to be practical. But don't stifle experimentation. After all, we spend most of our lives at work. We should find a job we enjoy.

Source: How to Help Your Child Plan a Career by Dean L. Hummel and Carl McDaniels, Acropolis Books, Washington, DC.

How Top Private Colleges Select Their Students

The most selective colleges do not apply the same admissions standards to all applicants. They seek variety and sort their applicants, usually into five categories. This means that applicants don't compete for admission with all the others who have applied, but only with those in their category. Different colleges give varied weight to each category.

Intellectuals. Top academic records are likely to get applicants admitted anywhere. Those who have taken tough courses in high school, graduated at or near the top of the class, and score well on the standardized tests are almost certain to be accepted no matter what other qualities they do or do not have.

Specially talented. Varsity-level athletes predominate in this group. If the athletic department is looking for a fullback, a long-distance runner, or a hurdler, the admissions office is likely to cooperate. Occasionally an exceptionally talented artist, musician, sculptor, or poet will be given preference.

All in the family. Private colleges depend on alumni for financial support and for time and effort spent on behalf of the institution. Family traditions within a school are highly valued. A parent, grandparent, or close relative who has been a loyal and generous supporter of the college gives the applicant an edge. It's still necessary to meet the college's academic standards. But most colleges are generous in judging the applicants from kinfolk of alumni.

Affirmative action. In recent years, most top colleges have placed a strong emphasis on the recruitment of academically competent blacks and other minority-group members. They have considered it an obligation. Students from disadvantaged backgrounds are often judged more on their potential than on their previous academic accomplishments.

All-American boys and girls. This is by far the largest group. It includes all the bright, mannerly, good-hearted kids who are competent in many things, but aren't outstanding in any single area. Because of the large number of applicants in this category, the competition is tough. Note: This group makes up the largest percentage of all those admitted to the top private colleges.

Applicants who are bright, but who don't get into a top school, shouldn't despair. There are many excellent colleges that will accept them and provide a top-notch education. Also: That kind of education will be just as good as, perhaps better than, the one offered by a school thought to be superior.

Source: *Playing the Private College Admissions Game* by Richard Moll, Penguin Books, New York.

How To Get More Out Of College

Some students get more out of college than others. They are more assured, speak up in class often, are involved in many campus activities. Quieter, more diffident students often do well in their studies and enjoy college life generally. But they may be hesitant to join in class discussions and never get to know their professors except on a classroom basis.

Specific ways to enrich your college years:

Recognize that most college professors choose their profession because they like teaching and working with young people. They are eager to share their knowledge.

Don't be afraid to ask questions. Ignorance is no sin. You are in college to learn more.

Use your teachers' conference hours. You will be welcomed.

Some professors are better teachers than others. Good teachers are still learning—they are adult students.

How To Qualify For College Financial Aid

The biggest mistake families with bountiful assets or high current incomes make about college financial aid is to assume that they couldn't possibly qualify for outside assistance.

Important: Don't be turned off by the advice of friends, co-workers, etc., in similar circumstances who say that they tried—and failed—to get aid. The application process is complex. And the precise formulas used to decide whether or not a family will receive aid are not made public. You won't know if you qualify unless you try.

Opportunities:

The formulas used to determine how much a family can contribute to college expenses take into account about 30 variables. Included: Family size, age of the older parent, number of children in school, unusual medical expenses and the form in which assets are held.

It's not impossible for a family earning $120,000 a year to qualify legitimately for aid if it has more than one child in college, graduate school or high-tuition private secondary school at the same time. And families rich in assets sometimes do exceptionally well under some state-aid programs that use different criteria from the so-called Congressional methodology formulas used in other financial aid applications.

Example: In New York State, the aid formula is based on taxable income. College students whose parents own millions of dollars in tax-free municipal bonds or breeding farms, apartment houses or other real estate that shelters income may be eligible for the full amount of state financial aid.

Don't disqualify yourself:

Parents often make mistakes in filing financial-aid forms that reduce the aid they get or disqualify them from receiving any aid at all.

Example: They list assets they don't have access to—funds in Keoghs, IRAs or pension accounts. Or they forget about certain expenses, such as medical insurance premiums that are automatically deducted from their paychecks.

Information provided on the financial-aid forms is audited and verified to detect income or assets that are not reported. But these audits do not uncover errors that overstate income or assets.

Don't forget to plan:

Another major mistake wealthier families often make is failing to plan far enough in advance.

Example: A family's income and assets for the current calendar year—1992—is the base that will be used to determine eligibility for students entering college in the fall of 1993. Since these students are now juniors in high school, few of their parents are giving much thought now to what they can do to qualify for aid.

There are several things parents should not do during the base year (or during the next three years while the child is in college, because financial-aid packages are reconsidered each year). Included:

• Don't sell securities on which there are capital gains to pay for college expenses.

Better: Sell those securities and take capital gains before the child enters his/her junior year of high school. Capital gains are considered income and considerably reduce eligibility for assistance.

•Don't take money out of pension programs—401(k) plans, IRAs, profit-sharing, etc.—in anticipation of meeting college expenses. You will have to pay taxes (and perhaps penalties) on the money. And it will increase the income that the financial-aid formulas take into account in determining your eligibility for aid.

Better: Borrow the money while the child is in school and then pay back the loan by taking assets out of pension accounts after the child graduates.

As your child approaches junior year in high school, your investment, savings and tax strategies should all take into consideration the impact on your family's eligibility for financial aid.

Some actions necessary to increase the family's chances of obtaining financial aid make no sense from any other standpoint.

Sad but true: Encouraging your child to earn and save by holding a part-time job during high school may be wonderful for the child's character, but the money earned will reduce his/her eligibility for aid.

Income earned by the child in the prior year is assessed heavily—up to 70% of that income is considered available to meet college expenses. So if a child earned $3,000 the year before college, the family may qualify for $2,100 less in financial aid than it would if the child had not worked.

Warning: Many accountants advise their clients to put assets in a child's name once he/she reaches 14 so that income will be taxed at the child's tax rate. But this tactic can cause you to lose financial aid.

Don't procrastinate:

Get the financial-aid applications filed by the deadlines determined by the colleges. Don't wait until a child is accepted at a school.

Financial aid is granted on a first-come, first-served basis, and the amount of money available at any particular school is limited. You may be as qualified as the family whose ap-

plication was reviewed just ahead of yours…but they may have gotten the last buck.

The process begins by completing a financial-need analysis document—in most cases the Financial Aid Form (FAF) or the Family Financial Statement (FFS). Copies of these forms are available from high-school guidance counselors. The catalogs of schools your child is interested in will say which form is required.

Send your form in as soon as possible after January 1 of the year in which your child will enter college. That means if you aren't able to get your taxes completed by the deadlines, you should use estimated information.

Schools have different deadlines. Be sure you know what they are. And send the forms by certified mail, return-receipt requested—even if the form says it's not necessary to do so. It's important to have proof of the date on which you mailed the form.

If you get a financial-aid package from one school that is much better than the one offered by the school your child really wants to attend, don't hesitate to negotiate for a better package. The strategy is often successful.

And don't be discouraged because you read that financial aid is getting tighter and tighter. Reality: The budget compromise struck between Congress and the administration late last year actually increased the amount of college financial aid available from the federal government.

Source: Kalman Chany, president, Campus Consultants, 338 E. 67 St., New York 10021. The company guides families and students through the financial aid process.

How To Send Kids To College...Free

If you have children in college, you know that loans, scholarships and grants rarely cover the entire cost. But there is a way to offset virtually every expense students will have during their years at college. In some cases, you may actually make money from the plan.

Key steps: Take out a commercial education loan and/or a PLUS loan (Parent Loan for

Undergraduate Students), a type of financing colleges rarely tell you about. Then buy a house or apartment in the town in which your child will be attending school. Use a 5%-down new mortgage or assume an existing mortgage. Have your child live there (instead of paying rent to the school or a stranger) and rent space to other students. Use the appreciation to pay off the loan four or five years later when your child graduates.

At first, buying out-of-town real estate might sound like a complicated and risky way to pay for a child's education. But when it's done right, there's surprisingly little time or effort involved.

The loans

Because most financial-aid officers are trained only to help with government student loans, they don't generally volunteer information about parent loans. (Actually, PLUS loans are also available to grandparents and even financially independent graduate students.)

Advantage:

Parents don't have to prove financial need, as they do with most other types of college loans.

PLUS loans provide up to $3,000 a year, or a maximum of $15,000, and money can be borrowed as needed. Repayment starts within 60 days.

Since you're likely to need more money, also take out a commercial education loan from one of the three institutions that now offer them.*

These education loans can pay up to 100% of tuition, but they may be restricted to certain states and to families that earn at least $30,000 a year. Repayment usually begins after the student graduates. A few local banks also offer tuition loans.

The property:

Buy a house or an apartment within easy transportation distance from the school. It must have four bedrooms so it can house your child plus three other rent-paying students...and be easily sold when your child leaves college.

*Mellon Bank Edu-Check Program in Philadelphia, Knight Tuition Payment Plans in Boston and Education Financing Group's Tuition Plan in Concord, New Hampshire.

Since property in college towns is among the most sought-after in the country, there is a very good chance that it will appreciate in value during your child's college years. Your profit on the ultimate sale of the property can be used to pay off the college loans.

If you've invested well, you could emerge with a significant gain. You may even choose to keep the property and continue renting it out as a source of income.

Safety: Insist that the parents of the tenants co-sign the leases, and specify that the leases run for a full year. Furnish the house as inexpensively as you can—preferably with cost-free discards from your own home and the homes of friends.

The mortgage

Don't fear that banks will shy away from mortgaging a house to an out-of-town buyer. In fact, most loan officers will love lending to a family with a child in college who also has paying tenants.

Since financing will probably be easy, realtors in the town will also be eager for your business. Let them have the job of introducing you to loan officers.

Tax breaks:

Residential real estate is one of the last legitimate tax shelters still left after Tax Reform, and purchasing an apartment for your child to live in may provide major tax benefits...

• If you make personal use of the house or apartment yourself during the year (perhaps during the students' vacation break), it may qualify as a second residence and entitle you to claim a full mortgage-interest deduction on the loan used to finance it—providing you with tax-favored financing for an investment that should appreciate in value.

• Under Tax Reform, someone with an Adjusted Gross Income (AGI) of less than $100,000 can deduct up to $25,000 of losses from a rental activity against regular income (smaller deductions are allowed for individuals with an AGI of between $100,000 and $150,000).

Key: Depreciation on real estate is a major no-cash-cost deduction that can produce tax-shelter–type losses that protect your regular income from tax, even if the property is producing a positive cash flow.

In any case, expenses incurred while owning the property (insurance, maintenance, etc.) can be deducted against income derived from it. Consult your tax adviser about how an investment could affect your specific situation.

Act now

Now is the time to start this kind of house-hunting, since it takes time to find one, close the deal and sign up tenants for September rental. Moreover, right now residential prices are depressed in many areas, including Boston, New York, Washington and the Southwest.

The only possible risk in the plan is that your child may suddenly want to transfer to another school or drop out before graduation. But even that risk can be largely eliminated by first sending your child to a local community college if there's any doubt about his/her university plans.

Once the child settles on an academic path and shows the determination to graduate, allow him/her to transfer to a four-year college. Then you can go ahead and implement the loan-and-property plan.

In the past, a student couldn't always transfer all community-college credits to other institutions. Today many community colleges have completely transferrable credits. And they still charge only nominal tuition.

Source: Charles J. Givens, a financial planner who specializes in accumulating wealth while minimizing risk, heads the Charles J. Givens Organization, 921 Douglas Ave., Altamonte Springs, Florida 32714. He is author of *Wealth Without Risk*, Simon & Schuster, 1230 Ave. of the Americas, New York 10020.

How To Get Much Better Test Scores

Multiple-choice tests—the most common format for major tests—are extremely unfair. Because answers are intentionally misleading, test-takers are often tricked into making the wrong choice, even when they actually know the correct answer.

Self-defense: Understand how these tests work. This knowledge will protect test-takers against deceptive questions and enable them to improve their scores with enlightened guessing techniques.

Caution: These guidelines should be used to augment—not override—your own knowledge. If you're certain that an answer is right—and the right answer doesn't meet the following guidelines—go with what you know.

Ground rules:

• The first time through, answer only questions that you are absolutely certain of. After you've gone through the entire test, go back to the troublesome questions and try them again. By then, your brain will have warmed up, your memory will be stimulated...and you'll probably be able to recall some of the answers you missed the first time.

• Answer every question. There are no points for unanswered questions. If you can narrow your answers, it's to your advantage to guess.

• Develop a healthy level of contempt for the test. This will prevent you from being intimidated by it.

General strategies:

• Balance every answer. After reading a question, read and judge the reasonableness of answer A. Then read answer B and "balance" it against A to decide which is more correct. Balance the better choice against C and the better choice of that comparison against D. The winner of this final match is the right answer. Important: Study every option before you choose your final answer. This can be time-consuming, but it's worth it.

• Avoid creativity. Give the test-makers the answers they are looking for. Don't use the test to editorialize or express your personal philosophy.

• Avoid picking the same letter choice on three consecutive questions. It's rare for the same one to be correct three times in a row.

• Don't review questions that you've already answered. Unless there's a good reason to suspect your choice (new information revealed later in the test or the same answer repeating three times), you'll start to doubt your judgment…outguess yourself…and may change a right answer to a wrong one.

Specific strategies:

• Eliminate negatives. The correct answer is usually stated in a positive or neutral tone.

Example: How is the character of Don Quixote best described?

(A) Clever   (C) Blundering
(B) Chivalrous   (D) Idealistic

Eliminate C. The correct answer, of course, is D.

• Look for repeating elements. The right answer often has similarities to other answers.

Example: In the human body, most digestion takes place in the…

(A) Mouth   (C) Small intestine
(B) Stomach   (D) Large intestine

Best odds: B and C. The correct answer is B.

• Avoid answers stated in absolutes. These include always, never, exactly, etc. The exclusive and unforgiving situations that these statements describe are highly unlikely.

• Eliminate synonyms. If two of the choices are synonymous, they are both going to be wrong.

• Look for multiples. In a math question, if two of the choices are multiples, one of them is likely to be the correct answer. Two is the most common multiple factor.

Example: $3(3+2)=$

(A) 6   (C) 15
(B) 8   (D) 30

Best odds: C and D. The correct answer is C.

• Look for numbers that are close in value. Generally, the correct choice will be one of those answers.

Example: $49+13=$

(A) 52   (C) 63
(B) 62   (D) 44

Best odds: B and C. Best guess: B (which is the correct answer).

• Select B or C over A or D once you've narrowed the options to a choice of two. For some reason, test-makers tend to designate more B and C responses than A or D responses.

Source: John Garland Peyser, teacher of test-taking skills to students and adults. He is the author of *Muscling the Multiple Choice: The Slightly Subversive Guide to Super-Guessing*, available from TW Concepts, 1836 River Rd., Middletown, Pennsylvania 17057.

Too Much Of A Head Start Hurts Children's Learning

Contemporary fast-track mothers and fathers want to be super-parents at home as well as super-achievers at work. They have the resources to give their children every advantage—sports and art lessons, private nursery-school classes and sophisticated "educational" toys.

Their aims are understandable. They believe that they are helping their children get an early start on the road to success. They see themselves as giving their youngsters a leg-up on a rich and rewarding life in a competitive world.

But there's a dangerous trap in this…we hear from the very knowledgeable David Elkind.

This kind of head start misfires. Instead of helping toddlers master their world, early academic or motor training actually jeopardizes youngsters' successful passage through important developmental stages.

Personality crises:

Child development experts recognize a series of important "crises" in the development of a healthy personality that occur during the early years of life.

During the first year of life, for example, an infant either learns to trust that the world is a safe place to be in—or he becomes apprehensive and unable to function well in it. This sense of trust comes from an attachment to warm and responsive parents who are able to anticipate and meet the infant's basic physical and emotional needs.

Parents who are constantly flashing word cards at an infant in a misguided effort to teach the baby to read years before his peers are not responding to the child's emotional needs.

In their second and third years, children begin to develop an important sense of autonomy and control over their own bodies. Mastering these basic motor skills give children the confidence to have a healthy sense of independence later on. If a child is pushed too soon toward the mastery of motor skills that he cannot handle at this time, he will come to doubt his innate abilities and feel shame for his failure.

Using language:

Children need to be praised and appreciated for the inherent motor skills they master at their own initiative during these years. That is why the handling of toilet training, which usually takes place during this phase, is considered so important by child psychologists.

In their fourth and fifth years, children are beginning to develop their own initiative for understanding the larger world that is around them. They experiment with language and ask questions.

Sensitive parents are able to follow their youngster's lead. They answer questions at the child's level. Helpful: Answer a question with a question to be sure you understand what it is that the child really wants to know. A six-year-old who asks you what sex is may not want to know the facts of life. He may only be asking about gender differences.

Trying to teach children academic subjects at this time kills their natural initiative for exploring the world. It creates an inappropriate framework for learning by demanding right and wrong answers instead of encouraging more questions.

Socialization:

Four-year-olds, for the first time, can begin to interact with peers. Children at this age are ready for socialization and their experiences with their peers may well determine how they get along with others the rest of their lives.

To succeed in socialization, young children need a strong sense of belonging at home. If they are to benefit from the group experience at nursery school, they must feel comfortably part of the family.

Security at home allows children to then become happy members of a group elsewhere. Without a strong sense of belonging—first at home, then at school—children may become permanently alienated from society.

Pushing children into activities and lessons that frustrate them destroys their sense of acceptance and belonging. It makes them feel inadequate and alienated at home and at school.

Learning styles:

Young children learn through direct encounters with their immediate world. They explore everything around them with all their senses and each experience is a fresh first-time encounter. This is fundamental and manipulative learning.

Only as we get older can we learn through symbols such as words and project what we learn onto the future or compare it to the past. This is symbolic and derived learning, the basis for academic studies.

Given a three-dimensional tabletop maze, a young child will trace a path through it with his hands, feeling each dead end with his fingers before finding the way out by trial and error. An older child, on the other hand, will look at the maze from above, study the paths and then, having already worked out the route, run a finger through the correct path.

Human development demands both types of learning in sequence. Only after a certain degree of manipulative learning can a child master symbolic learning. It is miseducation to try to teach children symbolic and derived curricula before they are ready.

The risks of miseducation:

Pushing children into learning situations that they cannot handle will frustrate them, undermine their confidence and make them feel helpless at school. Ironically, children who are not ready to learn to read until first grade quickly catch up with peers who started reading in kindergarten—or before. Those who learn to read later, in fact, often surpass their peers later on.

In a comparison study of kindergarten curricula in Louisville, Kentucky, boys who were given only age-appropriate manipulative materials in kindergarten were tested in eighth grade against boys who had been taught to read in kindergarten. The boys who had not been taught to read in kindergarten showed a 12-month advantage in reading and a 10-month advantage in math.

In Denmark, formal reading instruction is not introduced until the second grade. Children in kindergarten and first grade receive a rich manipulative language experience. They are read to, talked to—and encouraged to dictate stories.

Result: Denmark has almost 100% literacy. Our rate: 75%–80%.

French children are taught to read in kindergarten through a state-mandated program. Close to 30% of French children have reading problems.

Bottom line:

Parents in the 1970s tended to hurry their children into growing up too fast.

That is different from miseducation. Miseducation is deliberately trying to manipulate a child into being a super-kid.

Miseducation not only doesn't work—but the price that is actually paid in later life is very high. Infants and young children accept and participate in miseducation mostly because it pleases those to whom they are attached—their parents—and not because they find it interesting or enjoyable.

This sets up internal conflicts that usually leave a child with lifelong emotional disabilities.

Source: Dr. David Elkind is professor of child study and senior resident scholar at Tufts University. President of the National Association for the Education of Young Children, Dr. Elkind is also the author of 12 books, including the recent *Miseducation: Preschoolers at Risk.*

Better Parent-Teacher Conferences

Plan in advance. Ask your child what he/ she would like you to mention to his teacher… arrive a little early to get extra time if the previous conference is already over…avoid irrelevant talk—start discussing your child immediately…take notes…watch the clock— bring up complex problems early in the conference…think of at least one positive thing to say to the teacher at the end of the meeting.

Source: *Erasing the Guilt: Play an Active Role in Your Child's Education No Matter How Busy You Are* by marriage, family and child counselor Nancy Wright, The Career Press, 180 Fifth Ave., Hawthorne, New Jersey 07507.

Home Schooling: What You Need To Know And Do

Children from an estimated 180,000 families are now being educated at home rather than in public or private schools. Most parents who choose to educate their children at home do so for one or more of the following reasons…

Religious. They are dissatisfied with the lack of moral values taught in traditional schools.

Disciplinary. They are alarmed by the lack of discipline in schools, particularly the use of drugs and alcohol among schoolchildren.

Academic. They are disappointed at the schools' failure to teach adequately.

All 50 states permit home schooling in one form or another. But just because a state "allows" home schooling doesn't mean it's easy to be an at-home teacher in that state.

Example: While most states do not require home schoolteachers to be certified, many require "equivalency" of curriculum and local approval. Some local authorities have interpreted equivalency to mean the teacher must be certified.*

Educating your child at home doesn't have to be daunting. Some guidelines…

• Contact a local home-school support group. Operating nationwide, these groups act as information clearinghouses. They'll be able to answer questions on local and state laws, direct you to sympathetic attorneys and answer many other questions. Most of these groups are small, are not listed in the phone book and do not advertise. For a list of established home-school support groups, see the *Home Education Resource Guide,* by Don Hubbs.** Also helpful: Word of mouth. Talk to people at church, community groups, even at your child's public school.

*For legal informaiton concerning state regulation of home schools, contact the Home School Legal Defense Association, Box 159, Paeonian Springs, Virginia 22129. 703-882-3838. Or, contact the National Association for the Legal Support of Alternative Schools, Box 2823, Santa Fe, New Mexico 87504.
**Blue Bird Publishing, 1713 E. Broadway, #306, Tempe, Arizona 85282.

• Develop your own lesson plan. This can be done in several ways…

• Individualize teaching for your family. Draw upon your own knowledge and let your child's natural curiosity guide you. Tutors are available for teaching subjects that extend beyond your area of expertise.

• Purchase packaged curricula from a home-school publisher or correspondence school. These include complete lesson plans (textbooks, teaching guides and other materials) either prepackaged or tailored to your child's needs. A comprehensive list of curriculum publishers and correspondence schools appears in the *Home Education Resource Guide.*

• Work in partnership with your local school district. According to one study, 62% of at-home schooling was conducted with the approval of school authorities. Half had obtained formal approval, half informal approval. Some of the more progressive school districts have inaugurated cooperative programs between traditional schools and home-education programs.

Example: The San Juan Ridge Union School District in Nevada City, California, operates a program called Independent Study. Sanctioned by the state, the program develops individualized study for home-schooled elementary school students. Once each week, they visit the school to review their work with the program director. Similar cooperative programs are in operation in Massachusetts and Louisiana.

Source: Cheryl Gorder, the author of *Home Schools: An Alternative,* Blue Bird Publishing.

What You Can Do To Enhance Your Child's Education

Most Americans are all too familiar with the failings of our educational system—how test scores continue to drop, how our children are being outclassed by children of other nations, how the US is becoming ever less competitive in the global economy. Yet despite the good intentions of our elected officials, much-publicized education reform efforts and the expenditure of billions of dollars, the typical American public-school education remains haphazard and poorly focused.

Parents can make a big difference in their children's education—and not just by becoming politically involved to promote education reform. There are plenty of small but highly practical steps parents can take to change what their kids are learning and how they are being taught.

Encourage learning outside the classroom:

Ninety percent of a child's first 18 years is spent outside school, so it doesn't make sense to leave a child's education entirely to teachers. Recommended:

• Encourage your child to read books beyond those assigned in school.

• Take the family to visit museums, concerts, libraries and other cultural events and institutions.

• Discuss current events.

• Choose books for the family to read aloud. Follow readings with discussion.

• Be sure to provide for your children's ethical and moral education as well.

• Be a role model.

• Encourage participation in athletics, religious institutions, scouting groups, etc.

Monitor your child's progress:

Most parents have only a vague sense of what their children are being taught in any given week, so they have only a vague sense of what their kids are supposed to know.

Better:

Determine exactly what your child must know in order to be promoted to the next grade, and also to perform well on a monthly, weekly, even daily basis. Then make sure your child is keeping up. If the class is studying fractions, for instance, informally test your child to make sure he/she's making progress in that area.

Helpful: If the teacher is hard to reach, suggest that he/she set up an answering machine with daily announcements about what's being taught. Parents can phone the machine each evening for an update. Those who have questions or comments can leave a message.

Help with homework:

Check your children's homework for completeness, correctness and neatness. Even if the subject material is unfamiliar to you or over your head, odds are you know whether the assignment "looks right." But remember, your role is to help check over homework, not to do it yourself.

Press for accurate information:

In a recent survey of results of standardized tests, 48 states claimed that their schoolchildren were performing at or above the national average. Clearly, something is amiss, since one would expect half the states to have scores above average and about half to have below-average scores.

Explanation:

State education officials and the companies that design these tests are eager to dispense good news. Everything is calculated to make the system look good.

Sad result: In many communities parents never learn the truth about how their children are doing.

• Learn to interpret report cards. Teachers' comments on report cards are almost always positive—or neutral. That's unfortunate, because the first step toward improving a child's academic performance in school is realizing that there is a problem.

Self-protection:

Scrutinize report cards. Read between the lines. If your child's grade seems out of line with the teacher's overall assessment, or if there is some other puzzling aspect to the report, schedule a meeting with the teacher.

Become a school volunteer:

Many school districts welcome volunteers, yet few parents make the effort. If you can spare the time, ask school officials or individual teachers if there's anything you can do. If you have a particular area of expertise, work in a field that may be of interest to students or have taken an interesting trip, offer to give students an informal talk. Parents who are too busy to volunteer can ask the grandparents to do so.

Planning ahead:

It pays to select the best teachers and schools. Most parents are content to let the local school board determine not only what their children will learn but also which school their children will attend and which teachers they will have.

Better:

• Poll other parents to find out the best schools and teachers.

• Check the results of standardized tests (usually published in the local paper on an annual basis).

• If necessary, petition school officials to reassign your children.

• While school administrators are understandably reluctant to honor special requests, in many cases the best schools and teachers are no more than a phone call or letter away. Note: In some cases, several different "schools" operate within the same building.

Source: Chester E. Finn, Jr., PhD, professor of education and public policy, Vanderbilt University, and director of the Educational Excellence Network, a nonprofit organization dedicated to improving education in the US. A close adviser to federal education secretary Lamar Alexander, Dr. Finn is the author of *We Must Take Charge: Our Schools and Our Future*, Free Press, 866 Third Ave., New York 10022.

Better Studying

Take frequent 5- to 10-minute rest breaks. Reason: We remember best the first and last items in a study sequence and breaks introduce more "first" and "last" items. Also: We remember more 5 to 10 minutes after studying than immediately after—and a rest period allows this consolidation to occur.

Source: *The New Brainbooster* by Robert W. Finkel, PhD, chairman, physics department, St. John's University, Walker and Company, 720 Fifth Ave., New York 10019.

Sex Education Trap

Early classroom discussion aimed at preventing child sexual abuse is often the only information on sex that children get in a formal setting.

Result: All they hear about sex is that some adults force children into it—and that it can lead to AIDS. Needed: Discussion of the risks in a broader context that also deals with family life and everyday sexuality.

Source: Pamela Wilson, past president, Sex Education Coalition of Metropolitan Washington, writing in *Education Week*, 4301 Connecticut Ave. NW, Washington, DC 20008.

Children And School

Before placing your preschooler into a fast-track education program, realize that, for most kids, socialization is more important than academics.

Important:

Unless he/she is internally motivated, forcing a preschooler into advanced academics may cause him to lose interest in school altogether.

Source: *Getting Through to Your Kids* by parenting experts Susan K. Golant, MA, and Mitch Golant, PhD, Lowell House, 2029 Century Park E., Suite 3290, Los Angeles 90067.

Student Myth

Top students often don't excel in the "real world". The best high-school graduates—valedictorians and salutatorians—often go on to further academic honors in college. But most are not headed for eminence in creative or ground-breaking careers.

Source: Ten-year study of top high-school graduates from Illinois, led by Karen Arnold, assistant professor of education, Boston College.

14

Car Smarts

The Most Common Auto Insurance Problems... And How To Solve Them

Consumers spend billions of dollars a year on automobile insurance, but, fortunately, few of us get a chance to test whether the coverage we've been paying for is really worth it. It's only after we're involved in an accident that we discover the cards are stacked in favor of the insurance company.

Unscrupulous companies capitalize on consumers' unfamiliarity with the complexities of the system. The companies deal with these tricky insurance matters day in, day out. And they count on the fact that most drivers file a claim only once or twice in their lifetimes.

The most common auto insurance complaints we hear about—and suggestions on how to deal with them...

• Wrongful denial of a claim. Always ask to see the exact contract language a company is invoking if it denies a claim. Of course, some-times a company may be right.

Example: If your policy has a $500 deductible and your claim comes to only $486, the company is perfectly right to refuse payment because you haven't yet satisfied your deductible.

But the situation may be less clear-cut if the policy language is ambiguous, with regard to coverage while driving a rental car, for example. I've seen companies refuse to pay claims when policyholders were involved in accidents while driving rental cars, even though the language in the contract does not bar such coverage.

Solution: In such ambiguous cases, point out to your company that an insurance policy is a contract of adhesion. This means that the party that wrote the contract (the insurance company) had total control over the terms of the contract, while the party that signed it (you, the policyholder) is stuck with it. Then remind the company that the courts, over and over again, have interpreted the language of such one-sided contracts in favor of the party that did not write it. So, if there's any ambiguity in the contract language about what is and is not covered, chances are that you'll win in court—and the insurance company knows it. It simply needs to be told that you're aware of your rights in order for it to act responsibly.

• Slow payment of claims. Unscrupulous companies will take as long as they can before they pay a claim. Reason: The longer they have your money, the longer they can keep it invested. Don't accept this foot-dragging.

When to expect payment: If there's no question who caused the accident, you should receive payment from either your own or the other driver's insurance company within 30 days. If there is a question of who was at fault, you may have to wait until the matter is settled between the two companies or between you and the other driver, perhaps through arbitration.

If your insurance company is taking too long to pay, complain in writing to your insurance agent and to the manager of the claims department. If this doesn't work, contact your state insurance department. Many states have laws that mandate a timetable for claims handling. These laws require insurers to respond to claims, begin investigating them and reach settlement within a certain number of days.

• Shaving the claim. Some companies refuse to "make you whole" after an accident. Typically, the problem arises with a car in good condition that is totaled. The company will usually offer the Blue Book* value of that car. But this value is based upon the average vehicle of that age and manufacture. Perhaps yours was a real gem, garaged and driven only to church once a week. If you can document that your car was worth more—perhaps through photographs, mechanics' records, etc.—the company should reimburse you accordingly.

I am not suggesting that you inflate the claim. This hurts everyone since it drives up the costs of insurance to both good and bad drivers.

• Not being able to afford adequate insurance if your driving record is less than perfect. If you've been involved in several accidents

*Available in most libraries.

or accumulated a lot of tickets, don't automatically buy insurance from your state's "assigned risk plan" or "joint underwriting facility." This insurance coverage, in which all insurers licensed in the state must participate, is designed for high-risk drivers who might otherwise not be able to purchase protection.

This insurance often costs more than comparable coverage for "non-standard" drivers that you might be able to buy directly from a particular company. Because it lumps together the worst drivers in a state, assigned risk coverage tends to be a scavenger's market and a high-profit business for the companies that offer it. But, be careful—some "non-standard" policies are ultra high cost. Don't pay more than the assigned risk cost. You may do better to buy coverage on the open market, especially if your violations and/or accidents were not major ones.

• Signing away rights before the full extent of injuries are known. Say someone driving another car hits your car and it's clearly his/her fault.

That driver's insurance company may present you with a release form offering you a certain sum of money—perhaps $500. The release will state that the $500 is full payment to you and that you relinquish the right to make any further claim.

Beware:

Sign such a release only if you are absolutely sure the sum covers all damages. If you were injured even slightly, don't sign such a release. But don't ever fake an injury in an attempt to increase your settlement—you could wind up losing your coverage.

• Getting duped by "soundalikes." Some companies that have very high rates have names that sound a lot like the names of companies offering low rates.
Self-defense:

Comparison shop carefully to make sure you are working with a company that charges reasonable rates.

• Not getting the correct insurance rating. Most people haven't a clue about how a company's underwriting department has evaluated them. Generally, all consumers see is a code that consists of a bunch of apparently meaningless letters and numbers. But these letters and numbers represent important data about your age…driving record…address…and other factors that determine the level of your premiums. If the code is wrong and misrepresents your true situation, you may pay much more for your coverage than you should.

Solution: Make sure you are rated correctly by asking the complete meaning of the code you have been assigned.

Not all rating mistakes are intentional, by the way. The person processing your application may simply have checked the wrong box.

• Assuming the company offering the widest variety of discounts is the cheapest. Some companies, generally those whose policies are sold by agents, can offer up to 20 different discounts—for things from car-pooling to nonsmoking. But their prices are often higher than companies that offer just a few discounts.

Reason: The discounts are a selling tool for the agents, who use them to proclaim that they've managed to cut the (inflated) premium price to a fraction of what it would have been. Self-defense: Compare the net cost of one policy to the net cost of another.

• Assuming that companies will automatically give you all the discounts to which you're rightfully entitled. Recently, several states have taken insurance companies to court for failing to give customers contractual discounts for features such as air bags, automatic seat belts or car alarms. As a result, the companies are being forced to repay millions of dollars in excess charges.

If you think you have not received discounts to which you were entitled, notify the company in writing. They should repay you for any overcharge and immediately apply the discount to all future premiums. If the company doesn't satisfy you about this, write a letter to your state's insurance department. States tend to be strict in this area.

Source: Robert Hunter, president of the National Insurance Consumers Organization, a nonprofit educational group, 121 N. Payne St., Alexandria, Virginia 22314.

Car-Buying Strategy

The best time to buy a car is during the last week of the month. Reason: Automobile salespersons and sales managers are judged according to their monthly sales performance. The end of the month is the time when they feel the most pressure to make a lot of sales in order to meet their quotas and earn bonuses.

Source: *The Import Car Buyer's Survival Guide* by James Underwood, E. P. Dutton, 375 Hudson Ave., New York 10014.

New-Car Options: What To Buy And What Not To Buy

The right optional equipment can transform an automobile that's okay…into one that's truly outstanding—not only in terms of safety, comfort, and convenience but also in terms of resale value. Which new-car options are good choices, and which are a waste of money?

• Air conditioning. Except if they're to be used exclusively in frigid climates, all cars should be equipped with air conditioning. Besides raising your comfort level during warm weather, air conditioning boosts a car's resale value.

• Automatic transmission. This feature simplifies driving, especially in urban areas. Like air conditioning, it usually boosts a car's resale value. Drawbacks: Increased cost, reduced fuel economy, more sluggish performance. Before deciding which transmission to order, test drive cars equipped with each.

• High-performance engine. A decade ago, many standard-equipment engines were so underpowered that they made driving unpleasant and, at times, unsafe. Today's base engines are usually more than adequate…and any increase in performance afforded by a power plant with turbocharging or extra cylinders must be weighed against the higher cost, and the reduction in fuel economy and the potential for higher insurance premiums.

Bottom line: Unless you need extra power for specialized application, order the base engine.

Note: If you tow a trailer, inquire about special trailer-towing packages that combine a larger engine with automatic leveling, beefier shocks and springs, heavier-gauge wiring and special engine-cooling equipment.

• Anti-lock brakes. These make driving safer, and in many cases they qualify owners for lower insurance premiums. Well worth the money.

• Rustproofing. Most new cars have adequate protection against the elements, thanks to standard factory-installed rustproofing. Dealer-applied rustproofing is not only unnecessary, but also potentially harmful to a car's corrosion resistance.

Similarly, special dealer-applied paint protectants and upholstery treatments generally are not worth the cost.

• Rear defroster. This low-cost option—now mandatory in Michigan and some other states—dramatically improves rearward visibility in inclement weather. Worth the money.

• Heated windshield. This sounds great to everyone tired of scraping snow and ice. However, heated windshields are coated with a thin metallic heating film that subtly cuts visibility—especially at night. And, they cost more to replace than standard windshields. They also reduce the range of radar detectors.

Bottom line: Unless you frequently leave your car outside in icy or snowy weather, save your money.

• Sunroof. If you want one, make sure it is factory-installed. Dealer-installed sunroofs are more vulnerable to breakdowns. Warning to taller drivers: Sunroofs limit interior headroom.

• Power controls. Power locks make it easier to lock a car's doors, so they're sensible from a safety standpoint. Power windows are more of a trade-off. While more convenient, they are more expensive to repair if they break down. Power seats, though expensive, may help you to get more comfortable in a car, especially if you are smaller or larger than the average person. Power rearview mirrors make sense only for cars driven by several people. Power steering is now standard on all but the tiniest economy cars.

• Adjustable steering wheel. A wheel that tilts upward for easier ingress and egress is well worth the small additional cost.

• Handling packages. Stiff springs, beefier shocks, stabilizer bars and larger tires dramatically improve a car's ride and handling—if you prefer a stiff, responsive ride. If you prefer a softer ride, opt for the standard suspension. If you're not sure, arrange for extended test drives in cars equipped with one type of suspension.

• All-wheel drive. Many cars and mini-vans are now offered with a "full-time" all-wheel drive option, in which power is applied to the road through four wheels instead of the usual two. It improves traction on ice, snow or sand, giving an uncanny sense of surefootedness, and may be worth the additional expense.

• Active suspension. Infiniti offers this option, which uses computer-actuated springs to "iron out" road bumps. Sounds great—but not worth the current exorbitant cost.

• High-performance tires. Many drivers pay extra for super-high-performance tires—not realizing the tiny additional improvement in dry-weather handling is often outweighed by the big decline in wet-weather handling. Unless you live where it almost never rains or snows, go for the standard all-weather rubber.

• Special seats. Performance-minded motorists spend hundreds of dollars on seats made to hug the body. Surprise: Most motorists find standard-equipment seats more comfortable, especially for extended stints behind the wheel.

Source: An industry expert who has been evaluating cars and options for 10 years.

Gas Rip-off

Service stations are selling regular gas under the higher-priced premium label. Where to watch out for this: States where agencies do not inspect service stations— Indiana, Michigan, Missouri, Montana, Oregon, Tennessee and Washington.

Source: US General Accounting Office.

Safety Statistics You Should Know

Vehicles with the highest occupant death rates: Chevrolet Corvette Coupe...Chevrolet Sprint two- and four-doors...Chevrolet Camaro...Ford Mustang...Nissan 300ZX... Yugo two-door...Chevrolet Spectrum two-door...Pontiac Fiero. Models with the lowest rates: Volvo 240 station wagon...Saab 900 four-door...VW Vanagon...Olds Cutlass Cruiser station wagons...Pontiac Safari/Parisienne station wagon...Volvo 740/760 four-door...Volvo 240 four-door...Acura Legend four-door...Audi 5000 four-door...Lincoln Town Car...Mercedes SDL/SEL...Toyota Cressida.

Source: Insurance Institute for Highway Safety, 1005 N. Glebe Rd., Arlington, VA 22201.

How To Protect Yourself From Common Car-Repair Scams

You don't have to be a mechanic yourself to be a smart consumer when you take your car in for maintenance and repair jobs.

Read your owner's manual carefully before you take the car to the shop. Ask questions if something doesn't sound right to you, and don't be taken in by these very common ripoffs...

• Brakes. You have been charged for rebuilding your car's brake system when all it really requires is new pads or shoes.

Self-defense: Ask why the car needed more than new pads, and ask to see the parts and why they need to be replaced.

• Alignment. You have been charged for a complete alignment check, but only one aspect of this three-part job was done.

Self-defense: Ask to see the alignment readings before and after the alignment is done.

• Cooling-system flush. You are charged for a complete flush when only one gallon was changed.

Self-defense: Also have the thermostat replaced to ensure a complete change.

• Oil change. You are charged for but do not get:

• Top-quality oil. Cars made since 1988 need SG grade oil, and some car warranties are invalidated if you don't use the correct oil. Self-defense: Insist on seeing the specifications on the oil can.

• New filter. Self-defense: Mark the old one so you can tell if it's still there.

• Full oil replacement. Instead, the engine is underfilled or overfilled. Self-defense: Check the oil level yourself before you pay.

• Lubrication. You have been charged for a lube job on key parts of the car, but the joints are sealed and don't need this service.

Self-defense: Check the owner's manual to see what should be lubricated.

• Disc brakes. You are charged for new brake pads, but they were installed without the antisqueak clips that come with better brands and you are stuck with the noise.

Self-defense: Purchase complete pads and hardware kits from the car dealer and take them to the mechanic for installation.

• Tune-up. You have been charged for a whole laundry list of things you may or may not need. There is no standard definition of what a tune-up is, so the sky is the limit.

Self-defense: Using your owner's manual as a guide, make a list of the things you want done in a tune-up. Keep a record of when you have different filters changed, for instance, so you don't have it done more often than necessary.

• Computer-alert problem. You are charged for a long list of faults based on codes in the car's computer.

Self-defense: Find a mechanic who has dealt with car computers before. When one fault happens, it often triggers the computer to register other "phantom" faults. Auto-computer–literate mechanics know this and can correctly repair the one part that is at fault.

• Diagnostic analysis. You have been charged for diagnostic time when the car is in for repairs that don't need to have diagnostics performed.

Self-defense: In advance, specify that you do not want a diagnosis done. If the car has less than five years/50,000 miles, it is against EPA rules to charge for diagnostic testing that involves emission repairs.

• Overlapping repairs. You have been charged for separate repairs when the labor time for one of the repairs involves repeating work done on the other repair.

Example: You have to take off the brake shoes to either repair the wheel cylinders or replace the brake shoes. You shouldn't have to pay twice for taking off the brake shoes if you have both jobs done.

Self-defense: Ask for estimates of both jobs ahead. Then ask for a price that takes overlapping into account. Shop around.

Source: Dré Brungardt is publisher and editor of *Nutz & Boltz*, a consumer newsletter for car owners, Box 123, Butler, Maryland 21023.

The Most Deceptive Auto Advertising

Beware of these claims that often appear in auto-dealer advertising…and that are often deceptive:

• Only a few dollars over dealer cost. Various incentives provided by the manufacturer to the dealer make the dealer's true cost much less than the cited cost.

• Discounted from suggested retail price. The manufacturer's suggested retail price is often grossly inflated.

• Free products or services provided. The cost of the "free" incentive is usually included in the vehicle's base price.

• First-year payments reduced or deferred. Deferred payments are added to the end of the payment period so that, with interest, the buyer winds up paying more.

• A price discount and a rebate. There's no mention that the price discount is based on the rebate.

Source: Mark Schienberg, executive vice president of the Greater New York Auto Dealers Association, quoted in *Everybody's Money*, published by the Credit Union National Association, Box 431, Madison, Wisconsin 53701.

Best Ways To Protect Your Car From Thieves

A quality security device installed on your car will more than pay for itself on insurance-premium savings alone…

• Many insurance companies provide premium discounts for cars that are equipped with antitheft systems.

• One of the best ways to reduce premiums is by increasing the deductible on your insurance policy. A good antitheft device will help cut premium costs by increasing your deductible—while reducing the risk that you will ever have to pay it.

Antitheft basics: You want the car thief to know that you do have a security device on your car. Therefore, make sure you let your system show—the little red light under the dashboard is an excellent deterrent—also, you should put a sticker advertising the alarm system in a window.

But you also want to make it difficult for the thief to figure out what he has to do to beat your system, and give him very little time to do it.

Trap: Thieves are very familiar with the most popular security systems, such as those installed on new cars at the factory, and can defeat them quickly.

Self-defense: Start by hardening your car's "soft spots." Thieves know the vulnerable spots on your car better than you do. Here are some examples:

• Many GM cars are stolen by "peeling" the steering column casing, a technique used to expose a little rod that can then be moved almost as easily as a key to start the engine. If your GM car has a plastic steering-column casing or one made of lightweight metal, buy a reinforced collar—either one that you have to remove every time you start the car or one that is installed permanently. (One source that specializes in fitting columns to GM cars is Steadfast. Call 800-342-5911 for information on your nearest dealer.)

• On many Japanese-made cars, key mechanisms are vulnerable—namely, the steering column and the trunk. The Japanese don't have a serious car-theft problem, so they don't put much effort into improving the quality of their locks. A lock shield may deter a thief skilled in taking advantage of this weakness.

It's a mistake to rely entirely on a sturdy bar that locks the steering wheel in place so the car can't be driven, as many people do. Under US auto-safety standards, the steering wheel must collapse easily in a crash.

Result: Thieves find it easy to cut into the steering wheel and remove the bar.

Easy and effective

Some simple security steps that work:

• When you park against a curb, turn the front wheels sharply to the right—or left—and make sure the front of the car is not pointed outward, which would make it too easy to tow away. The thief would then have to tow the car from the rear—and won't because the angle of the front wheels makes the car almost impossible to control.

• Buy a car alarm that sounds when a car is tilted, again to defeat towing.

• Have all the windows and major parts (doors, fenders bumpers, tops and fancy wheels) etched with the car's Vehicle Identification Number (VIN). Body shops that know they are subject to search by the police won't accept parts that are marked this way—and thieves know that. Most effective: Put a sign in the window noting that the parts have all been marked.

• Install a simple toggle switch (Cost: Less than $5) on the wire that runs from the ignition to the starter and hide it amid the wires under the dash or run it under a car seat. Turn the switch off when you leave the car. Catch: Read the warranty on a new car first. Some manufacturers make it difficult to buy anything but a dealer-installed system by voiding the warranty on the car's electrical system if a wire is cut to install a security device.

To learn about a range of more sophisticated devices that won't be familiar to most thieves, call the Vehicle Security Association* for its brochure on selecting an alarm system and a list of its member manufacturers—the upper echelon of the industry. Also read the ads and articles about security systems in reliable trade magazines—*Car Audio* and *Electronics*, etc.

High-tech tracking:

Recovery strategies for already stolen cars: There are sophisticated security systems that will track your car after it has been stolen.

• Lo-Jack system, now operating in Massachusetts, New Jersey and southern Florida, hides a tracking unit about the size of a chalkboard eraser somewhere in your car. If your car is stolen, you call the local police and give them your Lo-Jack code number. They then use the Lo-Jack tracking system to locate your car.

• Teletrac, soon to be available in the Los Angeles area, does not depend on a call to the police. A thief who hot-wires the car or tows it initiates the tracking system automatically.

• Code-Alarm's Intercept system, which will use the Coast Guard's Loran C Navigation System to track cars, will be available in several coastal areas.

One California company has recently announced a system that will use satellites to hunt down stolen vehicles.

Meanwhile, don't forget the simplest and most effective auto-theft prevention system of all: Always take the car keys with you when you leave the vehicle. One out of five auto thefts occurs because the keys were left in the ignition.

*202-828-2270. 2101 L. St. NW, Washington DC 20037.

Source: Ken MacKenzie is an investigator with the Richardson, Texas, police department and an officer of the International Association of Auto Theft Investigators, 255 S. Vernon, Dearborn, Michigan 48124. Barnet Fagel is first vice president with the Vehicle Security Association, 2101 L St. NW, Washington, DC 20037, and public safety liaison manager, International Teletrac Systems, 9800 La Cienega Blvd., Inglewood, California 90301.

Motorist Do's And Don'ts

• Don't use dealer financing plans to buy a car. Borrowing from a bank, a credit union, or against an insurance policy costs much less.

• Don't buy a factory-installed AM/FM radio. They're priced too high and aren't very good. Instead, order the least expensive AM radio plus stereo speakers. This provides the necessary wiring. Then buy a quality radio and quality speakers and have them installed.

• The best time to buy a car is after the first severe winter weather of the year, especially snowstorms. Sales are slow then, and automobile dealers are very eager to move their stock.

• Testing a new car for leaks: Put some clean white paper (shelfpaper is good) under the entire car at night. Don't worry about clear spots, which are probably moisture that has condensed around the air conditioner. Oily pink leaks are likely to be transmission fluid. Dark leaks are engine oil. Dry pink leaks are gasoline. Engine-coolant leaks depend on what color the coolant is, either yellow-green or pink.

• Fanbelt adjust test: Press your thumb down on the belt at the midpoint between the pulleys. You should be able to press the belt in about a half-inch by pressing down moderately. (If more or less pressure is called for, an adjustment is necessary.) Also, always carry an extra belt in the trunk.

• In the long run, synthetic lubricants are a better buy than natural products. Advantages: Better reduction of friction and absorption of engine contaminants. Users report as much as 50,000 miles of driving between oil changes. And there is little evidence of wear on engines that have logged 250,000 miles.

• Radial tires signal impending trouble before they blow out. Early warning signs: Difficult or erratic steering, rough ride under normal conditions, or a bulge on the tire.

• Sell your old car yourself rather than trade it in. The dealer will only allow wholesale value on the car—or even less.

• Lengthen the life of old windshield-wiper blades by rubbing the edges with a knife or the striking part of a matchbook cover. This exposes the softer material underneath and improves wiping ability.

• Preserve the car's finish by washing it with cold or lukewarm water. But never wash the finish with hot water, which may damage it in some way.

• Run the air conditioner at least 10 minutes every week. This procedure will maintain coolant pressure and avoid costly air conditioner breakdowns.

• When you stop for service, get out of the car and watch gas station attendants carefully, particularly if you have an out-of-state license. When the oil is checked, make sure the dip stick is inserted all the way. Reason: Some attendants may show you a dipstick indicating that oil is low, then use an empty can and pretend to add a quart of oil.

• Never fill up while the gasoline station is getting delivery of fuel. Reason: Gas pumped in stirs up sediment that has settled at the bottom of the dealer's tanks. Recommended: When traveling, get gas where the truckers do. They usually know which stations are the good ones.

• Bargain tires marked "blems" are perfectly serviceable except for minor cosmetic blemishes on the sidewalls.

• Clean corrosion off battery terminals. Use a wire brush or steel wool to scrape battery posts and cable clamps. Clean the top surface with a mild solution of baking soda and water. (Don't let it seep under cell caps.)

• Prevent wind resistance, which reduces performance by as much as five miles per gallon, by keeping the car windows closed while you are driving.

• Extended auto-service plans aren't a good deal. The typical luxury-car contract covers very little. The owner pays the full cost of tune-ups and other maintenance, plus a deductible for each repair under warranty (engine, drivetrain, etc.). Also, the owner is locked into using the dealer's repair shop.

• Substitute for dry gas on cold winter mornings when you can't get the car started: Denatured alcohol, a pint per tankful, into gasoline tank. It's cheaper, too.

• Sports cars and two-door cars are much more likely to be stolen. Least likely: Four-doors in all sizes, from subcompacts to full size.

• A dealer's emblem doesn't have to be affixed to your car. When ordering, specify that you want no emblem, and make sure the instruction shows up clearly on the order. When you speak with the dealer on subsequent calls about one detail or another relating to delivery, remind him about the emblem so he doesn't go through with that procedure, which is almost automatic.

• Diesel fuel and gasoline shouldn't be mixed. Despite the advice of some diesel-car manufacturers, recent evidence shows that this practice is dangerous. Temptation trap: Wintertime addition of gasoline to increase diesel fuel combustibility for easier starts.

• Caring for radials: Rotate radial tires differently from bias tires to ensure that they wear evenly. Bias-plys are changed front left to rear right and front right to rear left, in an X. Radials are changed front left to rear left, and front right to rear right, in two parallel lines. The bottom line: Don't mix radials and bias-ply tires. If you must, use radials as rear tires. Never mix radials and bias-plys on the same axle; the combination is dangerous.

• Start the car in neutral, not in park. Reason: There is less drag on the engine.

• Don't turn your wheels while waiting for traffic to clear before making a turn. Recommended: Keep the wheels pointing forward until you actually begin to move into the turn. Reason: If your car is hit from behind, it will go straight ahead rather than into the path of oncoming vehicles.

• Overheated car. When caught in traffic, if needle on indicator moves up or red light comes on, car can probably make it to the next service station if these steps are followed: (1) Turn off air conditioner. (2) Turn on heater to draw heat away from engine. (3) Put transmission into neutral (when stopped) and race engine slightly. Note: Check water level as soon as possible. If it's adequate, thermostat may be malfunctioning.

• Tire-changing aids. All-purpose penetrating oil helps loosen lug nuts encrusted with rust. Keep a can in the trunk. Also helpful: Lifting and positioning the spare is easier with leverage. Place an X-shaped lug wrench flat on the ground. Roll the tire onto it. Then, using the wrench as a two-footed crowbar, raise its other legs until the tire and lugs match up with each other.

• Shock absorbers. The sure sign they should be replaced is when they begin to look damp and oily. Reason: Absorbers are filled with fluid. After 40,000 to 45,000 miles, the seal holding the fluid usually gives out.

• Keep a golf tee in your car tool kit. Two suggested uses: (1) When removing contact points on the distributor, slip the tee into the hole in the advance plate. This keeps the just-removed screws, which could slip out of your hand, from dropping through the hole—a mishap that requires removing the entire distributor. (2) When working on the distributor, plug the tee into the end of the vacuum line while setting the engine timing.

• Scam. A class of costly car-care products, called "sealer/lusterizers," is said to help preserve your car's exterior finish. But this claim has not yet been substantiated, at least not to the satisfaction of automakers and chemical producers.

• Rustproofing is advisable for any new car that you plan to keep in a corrosive climate for three or more years (generally the Northeast, the Snowbelt, and coastal areas of the Southeast). Note: The rustproofer should apply the spray at a pressure of 960 pounds (or higher). Otherwise the material may not adhere properly.

• Automated car washes may do more harm than good. Reasons: (1) Rotating brushes, if adjusted for down-sized cars, may apply too much pressure to a full-sized model and scratch the finish. (2) Many car washes use recycled water. The salt picked up from previous washings can hasten rusting. (3) Hotwax processes can damage vinyl tops. Bottom line: Old-fashioned washing, done in the shade, is safest. Never wax vinyl tops.

• Removing a bumper sticker. Apply heat to the sticker. Use a cloth dipped in hot water or a hair blower. Caution: Don't hold the blower too close if the sticker is on the trunk;

it could melt the paint. After the sticker has been removed: Wipe away the adhesive residue with mineral spirits. Note: Usually mineral spirits will not remove car paint. But before applying it to a prominent painted surface, test it on a hidden part of the car.

• Exploding batteries. Car batteries can release explosive hydrogen fumes. (There are over 8,000 battery explosions each year.) Accidents are most common in winter, when drivers try to start dead batteries with jumper cables. Safety rules: Don't smoke while attaching cables. Take off battery caps to vent gases. Remove ice before attaching cables.

• Gasoline poisoning increases. It's another effect of inflation—striking inept siphoners. Hospitals report a twelvefold increase in poisonings. Caution: There's no right way to transfer gas by sucking on a tube.

• The safest color for cars and trucks is yellow. It is most visible under almost all traffic conditions, particularly in fog or hard rain and at twilight. Second best: Light green. Both yellow and light-green vehicles are two to four times more visible than dark-colored cars and trucks under poor driving conditions.

Source: Minnesota Department of Safety.

• Carbon-monoxide poisoning is suspected as the cause of many of the annual 14,000 fatal single-car accidents for which there is no other apparent reason. Protective steps: Have the car's exhaust system inspected on an overhead rack twice a year, or whenever the muffler or tailpipe is damaged. Drive with a front vent or window open to let in fresh air. (This helps ward off highway hypnosis, too.) Danger signs: Shortness of breath or a slight headache while driving may indicate that there is carbon monoxide inside the car.

Source: *The Road Ahead.*

Beat Radar Guns

Radar guns can be foiled occasionally. What to do:

Position your car close to other cars when-

ever possible. Police officers generally cannot match you with the speed indicated on their guns unless they have an unobstructed view of your car. In most states, motorists can also make use of radar detectors, devices designed to alert drivers to radar early enough to allow them to slow down before police officers can get a good reading. If you do a lot of driving, a detector is a sensible investment if it is legal in your area.

Gas Pump Rip-Off

Don't be cheated at the gas pump. Use the lowest grade of gasoline practical. That may be what you're getting anyway. Trap: Some stations are pumping lower grades of gas than what is posted on their pumps. Solution: Although you can't verify octane without a lab test, there is one defense. Check your owner's manual and see what grade of gas your car requires. If it doesn't state high-octane, you may not need it. Most gas-station switches occur at pumps labeled high-octane. More than 90% of cars operate just fine on mid-level or regular octanes. Premium gas is not only more expensive, but it burns dirtier, causing more pollution. And many don't need the engine cleaners that gas marketers claim are so good for them.

Source: Robert Krebs, director of public and government affairs, American Automobile Association, Potomac, Maryland.

Parking-Lot Protection

Don't park next to vans—they are the vehicle of choice for kidnappers. If your car doesn't start and someone offers help, refuse—this person may be the one who disabled the car. If you are putting packages in your car and then going back for more shopping, move your car to another part of the lot.

Source: Dré Brungardt, editor, *Nutz & Boltz*, Box 123, Butler, Maryland 21023.

Beware Of Car Waxes On New Car

Nearly all car waxes contain abrasives, which are needed to remove the effects of oxidation in older cars but can destroy new car finishes. Tip-off: A wax labeled as a cleaner and polisher will scratch. To protect your car during the first year: Use silicone, available at paint-supply stores, instead of wax. Regularly wash the car using car soap and nonabrasive towels, such as diapers. Don't go to a car wash that uses brushes—they scratch the paint. After a year, choose mildly abrasive waxes to remove built-up debris.

Source: Dré Brungardt, editor of *Nutz & Boltz*, Box 123, Butler, Maryland 21023.

How To Buy A Used Car Safely

Despite their ghastly reputation, used cars are often a good investment—if you know how to avoid the traps. To learn how to pick a peach from among the lemons, we asked the expert—Jack Gillis, author of The Used Car Book*—the right questions...

Just how popular are used cars?

Very. Each year, Americans buy 18 million of them, for a total of $126 billion. We buy 10 million new cars a year—$150 billion.

Does it make sense financially to buy a used car?

Yes. The average used car costs less initially than a new car ($7,000 versus $15,000) and is cheaper to operate. Example: If you drive 10,000 miles a year, buying a new car and driving it until it has to be junked costs about 38¢ a mile. Buying a four-year-old used car and keeping it until it goes south costs about 26¢ a mile.

Where should I buy one?

From a trusted friend. Next best...from a private seller. Reason: No overhead—the seller may accept less than the car's retail value. Private sellers also are more likely to give ac-

*The Used Car Book, Harper & Row.

curate information about how well the car was cared for. New car dealers usually get top-dollar, have a wide selection of high-quality vehicles—and they often offer warranties. Used-car dealers have lower prices than new car dealers. However, cars sold by used-car dealers are usually sold "as is." Buying from a car-rental company has several advantages, including full access to the car's maintenance history. However, these cars usually have high mileage.

What about auctions?

Cars sold at auctions are often those that would be difficult to sell elsewhere—because of accident damage or some other problem. And auctions are often intimidating to the average buyer.

How can I avoid "odometer fraud?"

It's been illegal to disconnect or roll back odometers since 1972. Yet each year, an estimated three million cars have their odometers rolled back. Average: 32,000 miles! To avoid the problem:

• Look for maintenance stickers on doorposts or on the air filter. These often give the mileage when last serviced.

• Check pedal wear. If the pedals are badly worn and the odometer reads less than 20,000 miles, assume it's been rolled back.

• Check the ignition lock and dashboard. Scratches or missing screws suggest tampering.

• See if all numbers on the odometer line up. Rolled-back odometers often have misalignments.

• Study the title carefully. Be suspicious of those that have stamps, staples or folds through the odometer reading.

What do I look for when evaluating a used car?

• Study the upholstery. Stains and lumpy seats suggest heavy use.

• Look under the floor mats. See how much wear the surface underneath sustained before the mats were installed.

• Check the pedals. They should operate freely, without excessive play or binding.

• Examine the doors. Discoloration on the upper part, where the driver's arm rests, suggests heavy use.

- If the car smells musty or heavily perfumed, it probably leaks.
- Make sure everything on the dashboard works—radio, windshield wipers, heater, air conditioner, clock, horn, etc.
- Turn on the ignition without starting the car. See that the alternator and oil-pressure lights go on.
- Make sure all the windows work.
- Check the glove compartment for original owner's manual and warranty papers.
- If the car originally belonged to someone else, contact that person.
- Be especially careful when evaluating convertible tops. Park in bright sunlight to see if there are any holes or cracks. And hose down the car to check for leaks.

What about the exterior?

Check the glass and test the lights. Look for rust—especially in the wheel wells and along window moldings. (If the car has a vinyl roof, push it with a finger. A crunching noise means there's rust underneath.)

- Examine the paint. A newly repainted car may have been damaged in an accident.
- Make sure the doors, hood and trunk open and close easily. Look inside the trunk. Make sure all the tire-changing tools are there. A spare with uneven wear may have been exchanged with a front tire to hide a front-end problem.
- Check for leaks. Anything besides a water leak from the air conditioner means trouble.
- Stick your finger inside the tailpipe (make sure it's cool first!). It should come out with a white or gray powder. A residue that's sooty or gummy means engine trouble.
- Check the tires. Wear alone is not necessarily bad. Uneven wear is. It suggests alignment problems.
- Test the shocks by pushing up and down on a corner of the car. When you stop, it should bounce no more than once.
- Make sure the frame is aligned. Squat down about 20 feet behind the car and make sure the wheels line up perfectly. Shake the wheels. Excessive play suggests a bearing problem.

Anything else?

Yes. You've got to check under the hood. Check inside the radiator (make sure it's cool first!) for an oily film. This indicates oil is leaking into the cooling system—a costly problem.

- Check the oil and air filter. Dark, gritty oil or a dirty air filter means the car may not have been properly maintained.
- Check the engine compartment for cleanliness.
- Look for maintenance stickers. These give you an idea of how frequently the car was serviced.
- Check fan belts and wiring.
- Check levels of all fluids—brake, steering, windshield washer, etc.
- Check the battery. A new battery in an old car suggests electrical problems.
- If the car has automatic transmission, check the automatic-transmission fluid. Start the car, put the transmission in park and activate the parking brake. Locate the transmission-fluid dipstick and have a look. If the fluid is not reddish, there could be trouble. Note: This is an important check. If you can't do it yourself, ask a mechanic for help.

What tools will I need to do all this?

You'll need a flashlight and screwdriver for poking around in the wheel wells and under the hood, rags to clean your hands, a magnet for spotting plastic body filler and a sparkplug wrench for removing a plug to gauge engine condition.

It's a good idea to bring a friend for moral support, plus a notebook in which to record details of each car you examine.

Taking a test-drive is clumsy.

Yes, but it's important. Test the car on a variety of road surfaces and a range of speeds. Check brakes, steering and wheel alignment. Listen for unusual sounds. Good idea: Contact the AAA for a complete evaluation of the car. This is worth the average cost of $50.

How can I get the best price?

Consult the National Automobile Dealers Association (NADA) Official Used Car Guide beforehand to determine the car's value (it's available in most libraries.)

Before you talk price, road-test the car and decide the maximum price you're willing to pay. Use a notebook. This not only helps you keep track of things, but also suggests to the seller that you have other options. Point out dents and other problems. Stay emotionally detached—and don't be intimidated by silence. Make an offer about 20% below your maximum price.

If the negotiations bog down, take a second look at the car. This puts the seller on the defensive. Bottom line: Always remember that you can walk away from the deal at any time. That's the ultimate trump card in any negotiation.

What are the best choices among used cars?

There are several good choices in each category...

Subcompact:
- Acura Integra (1986-89)
- Chevrolet Nova (1986-88)
- Geo Prizm (1989)
- Dodge/Plymouth Colt, Mitsubishi Mirage (1985-88)
- Honda Civic (1981-89)
- Mazda 323 (1986-89)
- Nissan Sentra (1982-86)
- Toyota Tercel (1983-89)

Compact:
- Dodge Aries/Plymouth Reliant (1986-89)
- Honda Accord (1982-89)
- Toyota Camry (1985-89)

Intermediate:
- Buick Century, Chevrolet Celebrity, Oldsmobile Cutlass Ciera, Pontiac 6000 (1987-89)
- Ford Taurus/Mercury Sable (1988-89)

Large:
- Buick LeSabre, Oldsmobile 88 Royale, Pontiac Bonneville (1988-89)
- Chevrolet Caprice (1984-89)
- Dodge Caravan/Plymouth Voyager (1987-89)
- Ford LTD/Mercury Marquis (1981-82)
- Ford Crown Victoria/Mercury Grand Marquis (1983-89)

Luxury:
- Lincoln Continental (1980-81)
- Lincoln Town Car (1982-89)
- Volvo 740 (1987-89)

Sporty:
- Honda Prelude (1984-89)
- Mazda RX-7 (1988-89)
- Toyota MR-2 (1985-89)

Source: Jack Gillis is director of public affairs for the Consumer Federation of America, the nation's largest consumer-advocacy organization, 1424 16 St. NW, Washington, DC 20036.

How To Buy A Car Without Getting Taken For A Ride

Just any dealership won't do:

There's more to buying a car than price. Where you buy it counts, too. Take the time to evaluate different dealerships. Go to a few and walk around. When a salesperson comes up to you—and one will—say, "I'm just looking around. I'll come to you when I'm ready." Don't let any of them intimidate you.

Walk through the service area and sit down. Stay for about a half hour. Observe:

Is it orderly and run efficiently?

Is the manager there and working?

Are the customers treated with respect?

Proceed into the service lot and look at the license-plate frames. In a good dealership you'll see frames from competing dealerships, too.

Don't choose a dealership that's out of the way. The salespeople know that they have just one chance to make a sale, and they lean on you hard. Also avoid multifranchise dealerships. Too many people run different parts of the operation, causing confusion in service.

Choose your salespeople—don't let them choose you. Speak with several. Ask:

- How long have you been at this dealership? (The longer, the better.)
- Where else have you worked? For how long?
- May I get the name and number of a recent customer? (Follow up with a phone call.)

If there's a lot of turnover, leave—the dealership is unstable. Trap: Looking for a salesperson who's a member of your ethnic group because you think you'll get special treatment. You won't, and you'll be letting your guard down.

Knowledge is power:

Educate yourself. Get as much information as possible about a car before you sit down with the salesperson. Collect brochures (dealers don't usually keep them on display, because they want you to approach the salespeople) and read consumer magazines that rate autos.

Don't let salespeople woo you into trusting them with their "impressive" knowledge of a car. That's how they try to establish authority and take control of the sale.

Know the competition, too. If you say that you're considering a competing brand, the salesperson will knock it and be very convincing if you're uninformed.

Know what you want:

If you're not firm about what you want, you could easily end up with what the salesperson wants to sell you—the most expensive model, with the most extravagant options, at the highest price.

Once you show serious intentions of buying, the salesperson will offer you a test drive, during which he will talk glowingly about the car to get you to take mental ownership of it. He is seducing you. Resist.

Trap: Negotiating to buy when you're tired of shopping. Salespeople are attracted to this kind of customer like bees to honey. They know that if they promise you what you've been looking for—whether they have it or not—you'll probably buy on the spot. Buy only when you're in an energetic mood.

Few salespeople ask idle questions. Seemingly irrelevant questions are actually attempts to find out about your lifestyle, income, driving habits, etc. Avoid answering these questions.

Unscrupulous tricks:

Options are where dealers make their money. Common tactic: The dealer says, "Sorry, but all the cars arrive with power windows. If you don't want them, I'll have to place a special order. It could take several months." Result: You end up paying for an option that you don't want. But if you stand firm, he'll work something out—he wants the sale.

Another trick: Cars for the lot are ordered without carpeting, and customers are told that carpeting is extra when it's really standard. Read the dealer's brochure carefully. It lists every standard option and every extra.

Also make sure every option has the car's name on it: That means the dealership is responsible for it if it breaks. For example, Honda uses Alpine brand radios, but Honda's name is on the faceplate—which means Honda is responsible.

To get the best price, get a range of prices from several dealerships and write them down. When you're at the first one, don't let the salesperson know it. When he asks what other dealers have quoted, say, "Why don't you give me your best deal and we'll take it from there."

Read the sticker carefully: D.A.P. stands for Dealer Added Profit. Locator Cost means the dealer located the car. Procurement Cost means that the dealer procured the car. All these charges are negotiable.

Take particular note of a common price-padding tactic: A prep fee of $100 or more (whatever the dealership thinks it can get away with). The cost of preparing your car for delivery is already included in the manufacturer's sticker price.

Salespeople's trick: Constantly consulting with the manager and pretending that they're really on your side. They aren't—they work on commission.

Don't shop for price by phone because salespeople will quote anything just to get you into the dealership. Shop for financing in advance so you'll know a good deal when you hear one. Don't believe salespeople who claim that they can get you good insurance rates—they can't.

Trap: Accepting a trade-in price for your old car that you know is too high. The dealership will make up the difference on the price of the new car or on the options.

Being "turned over":

Don't let yourself get "turned over." If a salesperson feels that he's not in control of the sale, he'll say that he's going on coffee break and will "turn you over" to another salesperson. In a high-pressure operation, this could happen three or four times, until they wear you down. How to resist: Go out for a walk, have a cup of coffee at a nearby diner, say that you need to think about it. Get away from the salespeople so you can think clearly. Now you own it:

When the deed is done, inspect your new car thoroughly before you leave the dealership. Make sure everything is working correctly. Final dirty trick:

The car was dented in transport, so the dealer parks it close to a wall to hide the damage—which greets you when you arrive home.

Source: Two veteran car salesmen who wished to remain anonymous.

Make Your Car Hard To Steal

• Lock your car.
• Take your keys.
• Park in well-lighted areas.
• Park in attended lots. Leave ignition key only (not trunk key) with attendant.
• Install a burglar alarm.
• Activate burglar alarm or antitheft device when parking.
• Don't put the alarm decal on your car.
• Install a secondary ignition switch.
• Park with wheels turned toward the curb.
• Remove rotor from distributor.
• Install a fuel-shut-off device.
• Remove coil wire from distributor cap. (Especially useful for long-term parking at airports.)
• Close car windows when parking.
• Replace T-shaped window locks with straight ones.
• Install a steering-wheel lock, and use it.
• Install an armored collar around the steering column to cover the ignition.
• Don't hide a second set of keys in the car.
• Never leave your car running when no one is in it.
• Don't let a potential buyer "test drive" alone.

• For front-wheel-drive cars, put on emergency brake and put in park.
• Back your car into your driveway. A potential thief will then be forced to tinker with ignition system in full view of neighbors.
• Lock your garage door.
• Lock your car in your garage.
• Be sure inspection sticker and license tag are current and were issued by the same state.

Source: Aetna Life and Casualty.

All About Speeding Tickets

The best way to avoid speeding tickets is, of course, to avoid speeding. But all of us drive over the limit occasionally.

Here are some suggestions to help you avoid tickets:

• Know the limits. It's no illusion that police officers generally ignore cars driving just slightly over the posted speed. In fact, many departments set threshold speeds (six miles an hour above the limit in one state, for example) at which officers are to take no action. You might be able to slip by at 65 mph in a 55 mph zone, but you're unlikely to do the same at 70 mph.

• Be selective. Most speeding tickets are written during the morning and evening rush hours, when there are more motorists and more police officers on the road. Late night and very early morning are not watched as carefully.

• Drive unobtrusively. Flashy cars attract attention, something to keep in mind if you drive a red Maserati. The same applies to flashy driving styles. Don't tailgate slower cars to force them aside. Don't weave in and out of traffic.

• Be vigilant. The likeliest spot to get nabbed on the highway is just beyond a blind curve or the crest of a hill, the best hiding places for patrol cars. Learn to recognize likely traps, and reduce your speed whenever appropriate.

• Remember that police officers can nab speeders from virtually any position—the rear, the front, the side or even from aircraft. Be on the lookout at all times. An unmarked car on the side of the road with its trunk open is especially suspect. (A radar device may be inside.)

• Fight back. Radar guns can be foiled occasionally. What to do: Position your car close to other cars whenever possible. Police officers generally cannot match you with the speed indicated on their guns unless they have an unobstructed view of your car. In most states, motorists also can make use of radar detectors, devices designed to alert drivers to radar early enough to allow them to slow down before police officers can get a good reading. If you do a lot of driving, a detector is a sensible investment if it is legal in your area.

• Use psychology. All is not lost even if you are pulled over. Police officers feel vulnerable when stopping speeders—you could be speeding away from a murder for all they know, and consequently they are usually nervous. Put them at ease. Sit still, keep your hands in plain view (on the steering wheel is a good place). Be courteous and respectful. Above all, be honest. If you have a good excuse for going over the limit, state it. Otherwise, admit guilt and apologize. Police officers can be surprisingly lenient if you're cordial.

Safer Winter Driving

Remove all snow and ice from the hood, roof, trunk, lights and windows before you begin to drive…avoid damage to wiper blades or motor by making sure the wipers are "off" before starting the engine…prevent the windshield from fogging by running the heater for several minutes before turning on the defroster…wear clothing that provides warmth and comfort—and freedom of movement—both inside and outside of the car. Best: A jacket that zips up…thin leather gloves.

Source: *Consumers' Research Magazine*, 800 Maryland Ave. NE, Washington, DC 20002.

How To Trade In A Used Car

Selling a used car on your own inevitably brings more money than unloading the same car as a trade-in. However, if you're too busy to sell your car independently, steps can be taken to maximize your car's trade-in value…

• Know the approximate value of your trade-in car. To get an idea of your car's value, check the prices listed for similar cars in your local paper's classified ads. Also: Consult *The Blue Book*, available at local libraries and banks. It lists the high and low price for every car. Unless your car is in particularly bad condition, aim for the higher price.

• Discuss a trade-in only after you've agreed on a purchase price for the new car. Be sure to get it in writing—verbal contracts are meaningless. Otherwise the salesperson is likely to "pad" the price of the new car by the estimated value of your trade-in. If the salesperson asks if you plan to trade in your present car, say you haven't yet decided and that you'll discuss that possibility later.

• Wash, wax, and vacuum your trade-in car. Clean cars sell better than dirty cars. However, performing extensive repairs wastes time and money. Never clean under the hood. That suggests there's an engine problem you're trying to hide. If your car's exterior finish is hazy or cracked, consider having it repainted.

• Have your trade-in car appraised at night. Scratches, dents and other flaws are harder to spot in dim light. Important: Do not drive your trade-in car onto the dealer's lot until you've settled upon a price. Have a friend drive you, or park a couple of blocks away and walk. Otherwise the dealer may surreptitiously appraise the value of your car as you and the salesperson negotiate.

• Bring your service records when having your trade-in car appraised. Cars with detailed service records are more valuable than cars without such records.

• Beware of cash rebates. Because they are taxable as personal income, they are less desirable than a higher trade-in offer. If the salesperson offers you $500 for your trade-in car and a cash rebate of $1,000, ask instead to forgo the rebate and get a trade-in of $1,500. Bonus: Getting the money "up front" reduces the purchase price of the new car, thus minimizing the sales tax you must pay.

Source: Dré Brungardt, editor of *Nutz & Boltz*, Box 123, Butler, Maryland 21023.

Secrets Of Safer Driving

Safe, efficient driving means more than obeying traffic regulations and wearing your seat belt.

Safety subtleties:

• Position rearview mirrors carefully. Properly aligned mirrors provide an unobstructed and complete rearward view. Problem: Motorists often position the exterior and interior rearview mirrors so that the view in one partially duplicates that in the other. Result: Blind spots that often lead to accidents. Remedy: Position mirrors so that one mirror "picks up" where the other leaves off. (For most motorists this means aiming the driver's-side exterior mirror a little farther to the left and the right mirror more to the left.) Always scan your mirrors whenever backing up or changing lanes. Important: Also glance briefly over your shoulder to make sure you've got room to maneuver.

• Know your brakes. In cars equipped with conventional brakes, the driver must manually "pump" the brake pedal in order to steer in panic situations. This is accomplished by stomping on the brake pedal until the wheels lock and begin to skid, then reducing pedal pressure slightly to free the wheels, then rapidly repeating again and again.

In cars equipped with antilock brakes, however, the brakes are pumped automatically whenever the brake pedal is depressed firmly...so there's no need for the driver to pump them.

Bottom line: Manually pumping antilock brakes reduces rather than improves stopping efficiency.

If you don't know what kind of brakes your car has, check your manual or phone your dealer.

• Know which wheels drive the car. A car's handling characteristics depend in part upon which wheels transmit power to the road. Front-wheel-drive cars typically "understeer," meaning that they require greater rotation of the steering wheel to negotiate a particular corner than does a comparable car with rear-wheel drive. In addition, front-wheel-drive cars typically are more apt to skid if a corner is taken with excessive speed.

Note: This is not to suggest that rear-wheel drive is inherently safer than front-wheel drive. Safe drivers know which kind of car they're driving and adjust their technique accordingly.

• Hold the steering wheel properly. Wrong: Casually draping your hands over the top of the steering wheel. This not only reduces your ability to control the car in a panic situation but also exposes you to the danger of having your hands dislodged from the wheel in case an air bag inflates. Right: Position your hands at nine and three o'clock.

• Look as far ahead as possible. Aim your eyes parallel to the road and scan far down the road to give yourself maximum time to respond to approaching hazards.

Important: If you're following another car closely, also look through its rear window and windshield—to see the road ahead.

• Avoid needless downshifting. Before the 1950s, brakes were notoriously unreliable, and wary motorists often selected a lower gear to reduce speed. Today brakes are extremely reliable, so there's no longer a need for this precaution. In fact, downshifting affords no greater safety and serves only to speed transmission and clutch wear.

• Avoid needless accidents. Ninety percent of all automobile accidents could be avoided if motorists knew how to react one second sooner in an emergency situation.

If you suspect that you're being followed, fight the urge to speed. Stay below 40 miles per hour and head directly for the nearest police or fire station, shopping mall, public school or other "safe zone." Going faster will only increase your risk of having an accident that disables your car and gives your pursuers a chance to corner you.

Source: Bill Buff, a former race-car driver and founder and the president of Driving Dynamics, an advanced driving school headquartered at 25 Bridge Ave., Red Bank, New Jersey 07701. A one-day course at the school costs $360, a two-day course $650. For more information, write…or phone 908-219-0404.

Beware Of Antilock Braking Systems

Antilock braking systems aren't always best. Problem: When the entire road surface is wet or slick with oil, people tend to pump their brakes. With ABS, this can trigger loss of control.

Self-defense:

When approaching hazardous road conditions, slow down. Take your foot off the gas, and drive slowly so you won't have to brake hard enough to activate the ABS. Don't downshift or accelerate. If you must apply brakes, apply steady pressure and allow the ABS computer to do the work for you.

Source: Dré Brungardt, editor, *Nutz & Boltz*®, Box 123, Butler, Maryland 21203.

Car Sense

Only one automaker in the world—General Motors—has devised a good deterrent against auto theft. Its high-end models—Buick, Oldsmobile and Cadillac—now have electronic resistors on the ignition key. If a car's computer doesn't "read" the resistor when the ignition is turned on, the fuel system shuts down—instantly. Result: Many expensive GM cars (for example, Corvettes), once high on lists of cars most often stolen, are now off the lists completely. Contrast: Most Japanese cars can be broken into—and driven off—using just a screwdriver and a hammer. Other US and European cars—even top luxury models—aren't much better. GM's system does not protect against cars towed away by thieves.

Source: Dré Brungardt, editor, *Nutz & Boltz*®, Box 123, Butler, Maryland 21023.

15

Consumer Savvy

The Smart Consumer

Too many consumers are willing to tolerate defective or shoddy merchandise rather than risk trying to return the goods. They allow themselves to feel guilty about their flawed decisions. Unfortunately, stores are aware of this and some actively discourage returns.

Many people mistakenly believe that once you wear a piece of clothing, you cannot return it. But this is simply not so. While I certainly don't suggest returning a cocktail dress that you've bought just to wear to an important party, there's nothing wrong with returning a girdle that doesn't hold you in, or a pair of energized panty hose that sag in the first hour you wear them, or athletic socks with elastic that stretches out after one wearing.

It's quite easy to take almost anything back—off-tasting food, poorly made clothes, difficult appliances, cosmetics or unused concert tickets, etc.

First step: Recognize that you can't return something if you don't try.

Secrets of successful returns:

• Don't feel guilty. Returning merchandise is neither illegal nor immoral. In fact, consumers are far more often the victims of sales and marketing hypes than are the manufacturers and stores who hawk the merchandise. A store can resell merchandise that is returned in good condition, or return damaged merchandise to its suppliers for credit.

Furthermore, losses incurred by stores for merchandise that cannot be sent back represent a legitimate cost of doing business and are already figured into the price of the merchandise. You're actually paying for the right to return. So exercise it.

• Have a valid reason for the return. This can range from a poorly fitting garment, to damaged or defective merchandise, to a gift that is just not your taste.

L.L. Bean, one of the nation's largest mail order companies, has an exemplary return policy that allows customers to return anything purchased from the company at any time, even years after an item was purchased,

271

and they will replace the item, offer store credit or give a refund.

• Be honest. You may be returning an item because you discovered after you bought it that you could get the same thing for less someplace else. If you level with the store, it may be willing to match a competitor's price rather than lose a sale.

• Be polite. It's much more helpful if you are pleasant when making a return, rather than storming in and making a big scene. But that doesn't mean you should immediately cave in if the retailer resists your return.

Just recently, a store manager balked when I was returning something, so I just raised my voice a bit, and was a little more firm. I said— in a voice that all the customers around me could hear—that I couldn't believe the store's inflexible return policy. After he glanced around, and saw the other customers intently listening to us, the manager decided to honor my return request.

• Deal with the person in charge. If a sales clerk is having a bad day, he may refuse a return request that ordinarily would be honored. If you ask to speak with the manager, who usually has a much broader view of the importance of maintaining customers, chances are that you'll get a more sympathetic hearing.

• Vote with your wallet. If a reasonable return request is denied, let the merchant know that you won't shop at the store again. And let the store know that you'll suggest to your friends that they avoid the place as well. Sometimes, the threat of a small-scale boycott will make a store reconsider. Or—the management will reconsider their policy, helping others in the future.

• Beware of discount stores and small boutiques. Such establishments often have very stringent return policies, and may be totally unwilling to negotiate. In general, I find that major department stores have the most lenient return policies.

One standout:

Nordstrom's, which has the return policy of giving the customer what the customer wants. In essence, it means never saying "no" to cus-tomers, because satisfied customers will keep coming back.

• Use a charge card. Credit cards give you more leverage in making returns. If a store refuses to honor a reasonable return request, for example, you can threaten to withhold payment. If that doesn't work, go ahead and withhold the payment…but first contact your credit card issuer in writing and explain your reason for doing so.

• Save receipts. This way you'll have evidence of the date and place of purchase. Should you lose the receipt, don't give up hope. If you've paid by credit card, the card issuer should be able to produce a copy of the original transaction.

• Be sure of a store's return policy before you make your purchase. If you're buying a present for someone months in advance, first find out if there is a time limit for returns. If a store has a 7-day limit, for example, you may do better by taking your business to an establishment with a more lenient policy, particularly if the recipient of the gift is finicky.

• Don't take no for an answer. I once bought an expensive piece of cookware that melted when my husband overheated it on the stove. A pot made for cooking should not melt, even when used by a clumsy husband. The local Bloomingdale's branch refused to exchange the pot for a new one, claiming that the cookware had been abused, so my husband took the melted-down pot to another Bloomingdale's, where they gladly exchanged it for a new one.

• Know your legal rights. Generally, stores are required to post their return policies in a public spot. If they don't, they usually must give you your money back, rather than refuse to accept the return or require you to accept a store credit. If a store won't take back defective merchandise, you can always try to return it to the manufacturer. And if all else fails, you can take the merchant to your local small claims court.

Source: Arlene Singer, a media buyer for an advertising firm in the Washington, DC area and co-author, with Karen Parmet, of the book, *Take It Back! The Art of Returning Almost Anything*, National Press Books, 7200 Wisconsin Ave., Suite 212, Bethesda, Maryland 20814.

Phone Scam

Beware: 800-number scam. You get a post-card saying you have won a prize and should call a toll-free 800 number to claim it. During the call, a computerized voice starts giving instructions and says—not always clearly—that you will be billed. You stay on the line, thinking all 800-number calls are free…learn you have won a minor prize…later get a bill that looks like an official phone bill and is for more than the value of the prize. Several states are probing the scam.

Source: Consensus of state, telephone company and consumer-rights officials, reported in *The New York Times*.

Questions To Ask Before Retaining A Lawyer

Before you hire a lawyer to handle even a simple matter like an uncontested divorce or a fender-bender case, follow these steps to be sure that the lawyer will accomplish exactly what you want and that you won't be surprised by the final bill…

Finding a lawyer:

Start your search by getting recommendations from respected friends and associates.

Other helpful resources: State and local bar associations—a lawyer who has experience and expertise in a particular field is especially needed.

Then, conduct telephone interviews with several candidates who "feel" best. Ask:

• Are you taking cases?

• What is your experience in the field?

• What are your fees and what are the fee options?

Fees

Lawyers' fees are generally negotiable, based on one of the following four fee structures:

• Flat fee. You know exactly what the cost will be, regardless of how long the matter drags on.

• Hourly rate. If a lawyer is unsure how much work will be incurred on a case, he/she will often quote an hourly fee. Caution: Unless some limits or controls are placed on this practice, a case can become extremely expensive.

• Contingency fee. When you are suing for a sum of money, the lawyer may ask for a percentage of the award. The percentage may be steep (often 30% to 40%), but the lawyer gets paid only if he wins. This way, you avoid large payments up front, and the lawyer bears the risk of loss in the case of a small (or zero) recovery.

• Percentage fee. Such an arrangement is usual for a probate case, where the lawyer takes a share of the estate being settled. Again, the amount of the percentage the lawyer receives is negotiable.

The lawyer may be willing to combine some of types of fee options. This could reduce his/her economic risk and your fee.

Examples: An up-front fee combined with a limited hourly rate, or an up-front fee combined with a smaller percentage fee.

Making a choice

Arrange in-person interviews with two or three lawyers who sound best suited to your needs. Most will not charge for the initial consultation, while some will charge a modest fee.

Questions to ask:

• How long will the case last?

• What is an educated guess of the outcome?

• Does the lawyer recommend any options other than litigation?

• Who will pay expenses (court fees, expert witnesses, etc.)?

• Is the lawyer willing to sign a client-attorney agreement in which all this information is spelled out?

• What happens if the two of you fall into a dispute?

When disputes arise:

Most disputes with lawyers center on fees. Expect the lawyer to agree to offer the dispute for arbitration. Even though most arbitration panels are composed of bar association lawyers (some also have nonlawyers on the panel), their decisions are usually fair because they make a special effort not to show bias.

Important: Be wary if a lawyer is not willing to explain the strategy he/she will adopt for the case, or if he is not forthcoming about fee structures or seeking ways to save you money.

Source: George Milko is the director of the education department at HALT, a Washington, DC, group that advocates legal reforms. For more information about dealing with lawyers, consult the book compiled by the HALT staff, *Using a Lawyer*, Random House, 201 E. 50 St., New York 10022.

Credit-Card Calling

When you have more than one phone call to make from a hotel or pay phone, don't hang up after each call. Push the # button between calls. This will allow you to stay connected with your chosen long-distance carrier. Added benefit: Most hotel computers will register several calls made this way as a single local call, saving you surcharges.

Source: *Travel & Leisure,* 1120 Ave., of the Americas, New York 10036.

Recycling Danger

Using plastic bread packaging for wrapping sandwiches or freezing foods. Problem: Lead found on the outside of the wrapper of 18 of the 20 national brands tested can flake off into food when the bag is turned inside out.

Source: Bernard Goldstein, MD, director, Environmental and Occupational Health Sciences Institute, University of Medicine and Dentistry of New Jersey, Piscataway.

Paper Cups Vs Plastic Cups

Paper cups are more harmful to the environment than plastic foam cups (Styrofoam),

contrary to popular belief. Study: The chemicals and energy used in making paper cups and the emissions from burning or burying them afterward have a more harmful impact on the environment than does making and disposing of plastic foam cups. Making paper cups uses 12 times more steam and 36 times more electricity than making foam cups.

Source: Martin B. Hocking, chemistry professor at the University of Victoria, British Columbia, quoted in the *Wall Street Journal.*

Easy Way To Unstick Your Stamps

Save stuck-together stamps by putting them in the freezer for an hour or two. They should then unstick and be usable.

Source: *Practical Problem Solver, Substitutes, Shortcuts, and Ingenious Solutions for Making Life Easier,* published by The Reader's Digest Association, Pleasantville, New York 10570.

Unlisted Number Trick

If you want an unlisted number but don't want to pay the phone company the extra charge for this privilege, have the number listed under a fictitious name and give it only to your close friends and associates.

Source: *Wouldn't You Rather Be Rich?* by Clyde Albert Paisley, Cherokee Publishing Co., Box 1730, Marietta, Georgia 30061.

All About Listening Devices

Eavesdropping devices are more sophisticated—and at the low end, less expensive—than ever before. It's easy for anyone to bug a telephone, an office or a private home—and to get all the tools you need from a catalogue or the nearest Radio Shack. Milo Speriglio, director-in-chief of Nick Harris Detectives, the second-oldest detective agency in the country, tells us what's out there...

Much of this electronic eavesdropping is illegal, even though the law is rarely enforced. In four states (California, Florida, Michigan and Pennsylvania), both parties to a phone conversation must consent before the call can be recorded.

In other states, it is still legal to tape your own calls without informing the person you are speaking to.

But it's definitely illegal for a third party to record conversations between two other people, even if one of those parties is a spouse in the third party's home.

Other devices can be legally used to pick up conversations on the streets and in other public areas, but not within private buildings. With these limits in mind, here is a range of snooping gadgets now available to the public:

• Voice-activated telephone recording system plugs into the wall jack and turns on automatically whenever a call is made. Even cheaper: A one-party induction coil consists of a rubber suction cup, which attaches to the phone's earpiece, plus a jack which connects to a tape recorder.

• Amplifying devices can pick up a whispered conversation up to 100 feet away. They function as ultra-hearing aids, and are disguised as portable Walkman-type radios with earphones. Three models:

• Whisper 200
U.S. Buyers Network, 1 American Way, Roanoke, Virginia 24106.

• Sonic Air 9000
Sonic Air, Box 769, Vinton, Virginia 24179

• Power Hear
EMP Sales, Box 1735, Hicksville, New York 11802.

All of these should work, but the technology is crude.
Danger:
If you're out in the street and someone blows a car horn nearby, it may shatter your eardrum.

• Portable voice stress analyzers: Primitive lie detectors. They are packaged to look like hardcover books. More sophisticated models feature voice-activated tape recorders and have elaborate print-out capabilities. Other versions offer a coded digital read-out which purports to tell you whether the subject is telling the truth.

Drawback: These devices don't measure heart, pulse or breathing rates, which limits their reliability. A more expensive model ($3,000 and up) may be 75%–80% accurate. A bottom-of-the-line analyzer is right only 60% of the time—little better than a coin flip. (A full-scale polygraph, by comparison, has an accuracy rate of 90%-plus.)

• Infinity Transmitter (Criminal Research Products, $595) is an effective room bug. When screwed into a telephone's mouthpiece, it transmits any conversations in the room through the phone lines. The eavesdropper simply has to dial the phone number from outside. (The device prevents the phone from ringing.)

• Cellular phone scanners can pick up conversations within a 30-to-40-mile radius on any frequency that you dial. Available from Radio Shack and other audio-equipment stores.

• Voice-activated tape recorders are smaller and more versatile than earlier models. Easily concealed in a room, the latest generation can record up to 14 hours on one tape—usually enough for at least four days of conversation.

Source: Milo Speriglio was one of two experts called to testify before the National Wiretap Commission, which led to changes in federal law governing eavesdropping devices. His office is located at 16917 Enadia Way, Van Nuys, California 91406.

Electronic-Checkout-Scanning Ripoffs

Out of 33 supermarkets inspected by the New York Department of Agriculture, only one did not overcharge customers. Alarming trend shows human error in programming the scanners...prices advertised for goods are lower than what the scanner reads.

How To Buy A Lordship

Many Americans live like lords. Now some can even be lords. Since 1981, between 1,000 and 1,500 British lordships have been sold through auction or private treaty. Americans have bought about 150 of them. (Our source must keep names confidential.)

What's being sold: Feudal lordships—also called "manorial lordships" or "lordships of the manor"—grant certain rights. Among them are the ability to use the title—for instance, John Smith, Lord of the Manor of Winchester...and the right to a coat of arms. Other valuable rights are mineral rights, which may cover from 400 to over 6,000 acres, hunting, shooting and fishing rights, and rights to sell goods on your land.

Most of the manorial lordships date back to William the Conqueror and his Domesday Book (1086), which inventoried the real estate of the country he and his Norman barons had conquered. Through a curious quirk of English law, manorial lordships are still treated as real estate and can be bought and sold freely.

Note: Most lordships don't include land— only certain rights to the land. And the title involves no real responsibility other than spelling it correctly on your stationery, and holding on to some very old papers.

Some lordships are accompanied by rare and valuable historical documents. Example: The lordship of Garforth, York, included a grant with seals of Charles I dating from 1639.

Other lordships are valuable for their historic connotations. In spirited bidding last year, the lordship of Stratford-on-Avon sold for £87,000 ($134,850), a record for manorial lordships.

The "lordship market":

The Manorial Society of Great Britain (104 Kennington Rd., London SE11 6RE, 011-44-1-735-6633) holds four auctions a year. At an auction on October 6, 1988, about 40 manorial lordships were knocked down to the highest bidder.

Two highlights from the sale are indicative of the social value of manorial lordships:

The feudal lordship of a royal manor in Cheshire brought in excess of £100,000 ($155,000). After the Church of England, the Queen is the largest holder of manorial titles. The title—like those of other royal manors—is so valuable because its owner can say that it was granted by the Crown, leaving his listeners to wonder what marvelous service he performed for the royal family.

An Irish feudal barony was sold by the Earl of Shannon for £20,000–£35,000 ($31,000 to $54,250) because its owners will be called Baron and Baroness, titles that far outrank Lord and Lady.

Most manorial titles sell for much less, with many of them selling for less than £10,000 ($15,000). However, the market has been rising. In 1981, the average price for a feudal title was £2,500 ($4,000) and it will probably rise even higher after the Manorial Society's October and December auctions.

Practical perks:

There are practical advantages to being a lord or a lady. When it appears at the top of your stationery, the title will impress your bank manager, a co-op board, the admissions committee of a very selective school you want for your kids or a club you wish to join. One lord, a Scarsdale real-estate developer, says that his title gets him free use of first-class lounges at airports and a good chance of being bumped up to first class, even though he always flies economy.

Good Health, Good Lives, And $25,000,000,000+ A Year

The problem: A massive, widespread, well-organized and lucrative web of consumer fraud (taking money under false pretenses) known as "quackery"...the promotion and selling of questionable therapies, remedies, and diagnostic tests—advertising them to be safe and effective. At the heart of the problem: Staggering profits—and clever deceits.

The cost: In the US alone, $25 billion a year, as well as untold damages to human health and premature loss of life. The elderly are spending $10 billion of this. Phony cancer cures account for $4 billion to $5 billion.
Deceit by omission:

A method of disease prevention or treatment is accepted by the medical and scientific community when it has been objectively, reliably and reproducibly shown in the professional journals (not the tabloid press) to be...

1. More effective a preventive or treatment than either using a placebo or doing nothing.

2. As safe as doing nothing.

3. Or...if less safe than doing nothing, having a potential for benefit exceeding its potential for harm.

The deceit involved in health fraud is most often the omission of the facts that effectiveness and safety have not been responsibly demonstrated, and/or omission of the contraindications that have been so demonstrated.

Example: A misleading ad that claims eating more wheat bran can "reduce our risk of some kinds of cancer." Facts: There is no evidence that Americans who eat wheat-bran cereal have less cancer than those who don't. Research done on rats indicates that too much wheat bran actually promotes colon cancer. A recent study of colon cancer in women showed it to be most frequent in those women who ate the most cereal. Too much bran can promote iron, zinc and calcium deficiencies and can cause intestinal obstruction. It is important to eat adequate fiber (not less than 15 gm or more than 35 gm daily) from a variety of fruits, grains and vegetables. Bottom line: Too much of anything, including bran, can be harmful to one's health.
Tip-offs to quackery:

• Quacks quack—they crave publicity.

• Quack cures may sound miraculous. General rules: If it sounds too good to be true, it's probably not true. If it's reliable, it probably won't sound miraculous.

• Reliance on testimonials as evidence of effectiveness. The placebo effect and natural pathology are rarely credited. When investigated, cancer testimonials usually fall into one of five categories:

1. The patient never had cancer to begin with.

2. The cancer was cured or remitted due to responsible therapy.

3. The cancer is silently progressing.

4. The patient is dead.

5. The patient had a spontaneous remission, while a hundred others died using the same "cure."

• Frequent use of the language of fear. You may be told that "establishment" doctors are really unenlightened butchers, that hospitals are death traps, that surgery is actually "cutting" and radiation is "burning," that our food supply is "poisoned" with additives.

The New York State Department of Agriculture found the same pesticide residues in food sold in health-food stores as in similar foods sold in supermarkets, but the "health food" was twice the price.

• Misrepresentation of credentials or display of meaningless degrees.

• Use of specious tests—hair analysis, cytotoxicity testing, iridology, nutrient-deficiency questionnaires.

• An "informed consent" form that does not inform you of adverse effects or that you are the subject of an experiment.

• Encouragement to exercise "freedom of choice" by selecting an "alternative" treatment or cure. In fact, it is impossible to make an informed free choice if you lack reliable information. "Alternative" means "alternative to what is known to work." To a promoter of health fraud, freedom of choice equals freedom to deceive.
Worst offenders:

• Laetrile. Trade name for amygdalin, much-promoted as a cancer cure, a compound that is 6% cyanide by weight and accounts for $1 billion a year just for the product. Patients on Laetrile suffer slow, progressive cyanide poisoning.

• IAT (immunoaugmentative therapy). Pooled samples of blood product from patients are processed, then sold to other patients for injection. No cancer-treatment benefits from IAT, a $20 million a year business, have been reliably documented.

• Chelation therapy. Injections of EDTA (Edetate), into the veins of patients with atherosclerosis on the claim that it clears the coronary arteries of calcium deposits.

• Nutrient supplements. Just about every nutrient in megadoses is toxic. Myth: Excesses of water-soluble vitamins are harmlessly urinated out. Fact: They can do major harm before being excreted. Example: Kidney toxicity is reported from megadoses of vitamin C. (Half of all Americans take supplements of vitamin C, which studies indicate do them no good.)

While purveyors of health foods decry the use of preservatives in food, many are happy to sell you a concentrated BHA or BHT preservative on the theory that it will help to preserve you. One gram daily of either is fatal to rabbits, but the effect on humans is unknown. Cost: About $15 for one $^2/_3$oz. bottle.

• Other quackery. Bee pollen (highly allergenic), RNA pills, coffee enemas (can result in cardiac arrest), Gerovital (mostly procaine), DMSO and green-lipped mussel extract for arthritis (among other "cures"), evening primrose oil.

• Probably most widespread: Weight-loss scams.

Most vulnerable:

Fraudulent cures always have an audience among the desperate—those with chronic, painful or fatal diseases. But quackery can also appeal to those susceptible to miraculous claims (Effortless weight loss while you sleep!) and those who are naturally hostile to established practices. But perhaps the largest number of victims of health fraud are the unsuspecting.

Organized promoters of health fraud:

There are several organizations that are devoted to the vigorous protection of the right to misinform and thereby defraud the public.

• The National Health Federation (NHF) wants anyone who claims to have an effective treatment or product to be able to market it without scientific proof that it works, and without interference from the government. The chairman of the board of NHF, Kurt Donsbach, has been convicted of practicing medicine without a license, among other counts

of illegal activity. Despite the enormous income he apparently derived from the sale of food-supplement formulas, books, tapes, and treatments, he filed for bankruptcy in 1987 owing $3 million to over 100 creditors.

• American Quack Association members oppose "any penalty whatsoever against anyone employing any form of treatment for cancer or any other disease."

• The Council for Responsible Nutrition (CRN) is a trade organization made up of 70 vitamin and mineral pill manufacturers whose "deception by omission" is apparent in their very name. Advertising by CRN member firms tends to be similarly misleading.

How to protect yourself:

• When in doubt, get a second opinion.

• Unless you are a lawyer, do not accuse. Report suspected cases of quackery to the FDA, the FTC or the Postal Service (surprisingly, the most effective).

• For responsible information regarding health frauds, contact the American Cancer Society, the Arthritis Foundation, the National Council Against Health Fraud or the National Better Business Bureau.

Source: Dr. Victor Herbert, professor of medicine and chairman, Committee to Strengthen Nutrition, Mount Sinai Medical Center, New York, and chief, Hematology and Nutrition Laboratory, Veterans Administration Medical Center, Bronx, NY. Dr. Herbert is widely published in the field of quackery. In December of 1987, he filed a landmark lawsuit against alleged promoters of health fraud, the American Quack Association and 25 other defendants. Contributions may be sent to the Herbert Anti-Quackery Litigation Fund, c/o Michael K. Botts, Esq., Box 33008, Kansas City, MO 64114.

Low-Tech Burglary Defense Good Doors And Locks

Most burglars just walk in the front or back door because—crazy as it may seem—many people either don't bother to lock their doors or simply forget.

Of course, if your door lock is more than 10 years old, especially if it's loose or wriggly, it offers only marginal protection.

Most new locks are effective. Important: The throw, the shaft that slides out when the key is turned, should extend at least one inch into the door jamb.

Avoid: So-called pick-proof locks. They are three times more costly than regular locks and aren't worth the extra investment. No crook is going to stand at your front door for 10 minutes trying to pick a lock.

Also avoid combination locks. They, too, aren't worth the extra cost—unless you rent the house or use it as a vacation home and don't want to carry a key. If you do get a combination lock, be sure you can change its code easily.

More effective: Double-cylinder locks. They should be avoided, however, if the door has a glass window within 40 inches of the lock. Important: If you use double-cylinder locks, when home leave the inside key in place. Avoid single-cylinder locks. It's much too easy for a burglar to break the window and reach in to turn the lock.

Doors: Many doors are hollow—and attached to weak jambs. Burglars know this and often just kick in a door for fast entry. To thwart this: Get a solid door with a sturdy jamb. And, obvious as it may seem, be sure the hinge pins are not on the outside, where a crook can easily slip them out and remove the door.

How To Find Almost Anybody

The most direct ways of getting an unlisted phone number—from credit applications, personnel records and other nonpublic documents (including, of course, the telephone company records themselves)—are all illegal.

This is why information bureaus and most private detectives don't handle this kind of work. Those who do charge at least $300 to find a single number.

Warning: If you do hire a detective, specify in writing that payment is to be made only for obtaining the number…not trying and failing.

Key to doing it yourself: Find a public document on which the individual has supplied his/her unlisted telephone number. Beyond motor vehicle department records, commercial loan filings, court documents, and voter registration forms, you can also try checking local tax collectors' records for payment of a municipal tax, school tax, or water tax. These records may contain an individual's telephone number.

These methods aren't guaranteed to give you the access you seek, but with persistence you ought to be able to "reach out and touch" many people whose telephone numbers are unlisted.

Source: Ralph Charell, former CEO of his own Wall Street securities firm and a former network television executive.

A Shopper's Guide To Bargaining

The biggest problem most shoppers have with bargaining is a feeling that nice people don't do it. Before you can negotiate, you have to get over this attitude. Some ammunition:

Bargaining will not turn you into a social outcast. All shopkeepers see when you walk in is dollar signs. If you are willing to spend, they will probably be willing to make a deal. They know that everybody is trying to save money.

Bargaining is a business transaction. You are not trying to cheat the merchant or get something for nothing. You are trying to agree on a fair price. You expect to negotiate for a house or a car—why not for a refrigerator or a winter coat?

You have a right to bargain, particularly in small stores that don't offer discounts. Reasoning: Department stores, which won't bargain as a rule, mark up prices 100%–150% to cover high overhead costs. Small stores should charge lower prices because their costs are less.

The savvy approach:

Set a price limit for a particular item before you approach the storekeepers. Be prepared to walk out if they don't meet your limit. (You can always change your mind later.) Make them believe you really won't buy unless they come down.

Be discreet in your negotiations. If other customers can overhear you dickering, the shop owner must stay firm.

Be respectful of the merchandise and the storekeeper. Don't manhandle the goods that you inspect. Address salespeople in a polite, friendly manner. Assume that they will want to do their best for you.

Shop during off hours. You will have better luck if business is slow.

Look for unmarked merchandise. If there is no price tag, you are invited to bargain.
Tactics that work:

Negotiate with cash. In a store that takes credit cards, request a discount for paying in cash. (Charging entails overhead costs that the store must absorb.)

Buy in quantity. A customer who is committed to a number of purchases has more bargaining power.

When everything is picked out, approach the owner and suggest a total price of about 20% less than the actual total. Or, if you are buying more than one of an item, offer to pay full price on the first one if the owner will give you a break on the others.
Storekeeper's alternative:

You spent $500 on clothing and asked for a better price. The owner couldn't charge you less, but threw in a belt priced at $35 as a bonus.

Look for flawed merchandise. This is the only acceptable bargaining point in department stores, but it also can save you money in small shops. If there's a spot, a split seam, or a missing button, estimate what it would cost to have the garment fixed commercially, and ask for a discount based on that figure.

Variation: You find a chipped hair dryer. When you ask for a discount, the manager says he will return it to the manufacturer and find you an undamaged one. Your reply: "Sell it to me for a little less and save yourself the trouble."

Adapt your haggling techniques to the realities of the situation. A true discount house has a low profit margin and depends on volume to make its money. Don't ask for more than 5% off in such a store. A boutique that charges what the traffic will bear has more leeway. Start by asking for 25% off, and dicker from there.

Buy at the end of the season, when new stock is being put out. Offer to buy older goods at a discount.

Neighborhood stores: Push the local television or appliance dealer to give you a break so you can keep your service business in the community.

Source: Sharon Dunn Greene, co-author of *The Lower East Side Shopping Guide*, Brooklyn, NY.

How To Complain Effectively

Basic rule when dealing with defective merchandise:

Save receipts, warranties and all other papers. Then:

• Have your facts straight before you act. Be clear about dates, prices, payments and the exact nature of the problem.

• Meet with the salesperson or store manager. Describe the problem. Give him/her copies of the relevant documents. Then ask for a replacement or other compensation. Be polite but firm.

• Be specific about what you want done— repair, replacement or refund.

• In response to whatever excuse the merchant uses, repeat your demand like a broken record.

• Give reasonable deadlines for action you expect to be taken. (A week for store personnel to look into a problem, for example.) Deadlines move the action along.

• Write to the manager, going over the points made in the conversation. Include in the letter copies of the sales slips as well as a statement of intention to refer the matter to the Better Business Bureau, a consumer agency or the manager's superior.

• Send copies of receipts. Keep the originals for your records. File copies of all correspondence and notes (with dates) on any telephone dealings. Those records may be the pivotal factor if negotiations are prolonged or you must take your complaint elsewhere.

• Be businesslike in your attitude, and make it clear that you expect a businesslike response.

• Find out where you can go if the seller fails to make good, and indicate your intention to follow through. Government agencies, such as a state attorney general's office, may need the very kind of evidence that your case provides to move against chronic offenders. Licensing boards or regulatory bodies are good bets for complaints against banks, insurance companies or professionals.

• If that fails, write directly to the president of the company, not the customer-relations department. Manufacturers of products are listed in the *Thomas Registry*. Names of executives and addresses of companies are in *Standard & Poor's Register of Corporations*. You can find both of these books at the public library.

• Recount the facts and the demand for compensation. Include copies of paperwork. Make sure you send a carbon to the store's local manager.

• As a last resort, call a consumer agency. State consumer offices are generally in the attorney general's office. There are 140 Better Business Bureaus in the country and more than 100 consumer hot lines. Complete listings of hot lines are available from Call for Action, Inc., 575 Lexington Avenue, NY 10022.

Additional recourse:

• Consumer-action centers sponsored by local newspapers and radio and television stations often get swift results.

• Small claims court. If you can put a monetary value on your loss, you may get a judgment by suing in small claims court. Collect- ing can be a problem (you must take the initiative yourself), but the law is on your side and the psychological benefits are enormous.

• Trade associations can be effective with their member organizations but not with outside companies.

Source: Nancy Kramer, co-author with Stephen A. Newman of *Getting What You Deserve: A Handbook for the Assertive Consumer*, Doubleday, New York.

Buy PC Clones

Personal computer "clones" costing only a few hundred dollars offer far greater versatility and value than comparably priced typewriters or personal word processors. Word processors are designed only for writing, but PC clones use software that permits countless uses—writing, information storage, financial planning, education, games and more. Best bet: Any reputable manufacturer's IBM PC AT clone, available through local computer stores or via mail order. Cost: About $600, plus $180 for a printer.

Source: Tina Rathbone, the author of *Thousands of Fascinating and Unique Uses for Your Home Computer*, Computer Publishing Enterprises, Box 23478, San Diego 92193.

Computer Self-Defense

Never buy the newest-and-latest anything. Everything new has flaws—and problems. Give the company time to correct them—without using you as a guinea pig. If you really want new hardware or software, rent before buying.

Source: *Computer Wimp No More* by John Bear, Ten Speed Press, Box 7123, Berkeley, California 94707.

How To Pick The Right Camcorder

When you are shopping for a camcorder for home use, the two main issues are comfort and price:

• Comfort. It has to feel good in your hand and have controls that are easy for you to use.

Although camcorders come in three formats—8 mm, mini-VHS and standard VHS—only the first two make sense for home use. Standard VHS cameras are simply too big and heavy.

• Price. The price for smaller camcorders ranges from $400 to $1,000 retail. Prices vary widely among stores.

When you go shopping:

• Visit several stores and in each one find a helpful salesperson. Get a clear explanation of the different cameras' various features.

• Try different camcorders. In the store, shoot some tape and then play it back. Consider: The quality and sharpness of the different camcorders' video output...how wide and how narrow the lens can zoom...differences in how they sound.

• Decide which "bells and whistles" you want. These are anything beyond the basic video and audio output.

Examples: Editing capabilities that allow you to move portions of the film around...a flying erase head that produces smooth transitions when you stop and restart the camcorder (without one, a little hash of black and white lines appears in your film)...or a memory that allows you to create titles to superimpose over images you shoot later.

Source: Al Thaler, a former CBS news producer who went shopping for a camcorder for his own use.

16

Very, Very Personal

The Pill: What We Know…And Still Don't Know

The birth control pill celebrated its thirtieth birthday in 1990. While the continuing flow of information shows the Pill to be effective, safe and ultimately beneficial to women's health, misconceptions and fears about oral contraceptives persist…

• Sixty million women worldwide currently use the Pill. Eleven million of them are in the US. Among American women, 82% of those who have used contraceptives have used the Pill at some time in their lives.

• The Pill is the most popular form of birth control in the US, the choice of 28% of American women at risk of unintended pregnancy. Tubal sterilization is next most common at 25%, followed by the condom at 13%. Average duration of Pill use is four to five years.

• Using any form of contraception, including the Pill, is safer and healthier than using no birth control. Contraception prevents about 1,500 hospitalizations per 100,000 women annually, and saves 120 to 150 lives per 100,000.

• The Pill protects against ovarian cancer. The risk is lowered by 30% for women who have used the Pill for four years or less, compared with women who have never used it. Among women who have used the Pill for five to 11 years, the risk is decreased by 60%…and by 80% after 12 years of use. The protection is detectable within a few months of starting the Pill, and lasts for at least 15 years after use is stopped.

• The risk of being diagnosed with breast cancer by age 55 is the same for women who have ever used the Pill and never-users, when all age groups are taken together.

Women who first used the Pill at age 25 or later have the same incidence of breast cancer as never-users, regardless of duration of Pill use. But risks and benefits differ for women in different age groups.

Young women: Current or former Pill use is

associated with a slightly higher risk of breast cancer for women under 35, when the disease is relatively rare.

Older women: The Pill is associated with a lower risk of breast cancer among women aged 45 to 54, when the disease is much more common.

The statistics: According to a study by the Centers for Disease Control, women aged 25 to 29, who have used the Pill for at least 10 years, will have nine diagnoses of breast cancer per 100,000 per year, compared with six cases for never-users of the same age. Long-term or current users in their thirties and early forties will have seven to 11 more cases of breast cancer per 100,000 than never-users. But women aged 45 to 54 will have 19 to 21 fewer breast cancers per 100,000.

Cancer perspective: Overall, the net impact of Pill use on cancer is small. By age 55, there will be 500 fewer annual diagnoses per 100,000 of all cancers of the reproductive system for women who have ever used the Pill, compared with never-users.

• Pill use compounds the risk of heart attack, two kinds of stroke and venous blood clots for heavy smokers (those who smoke 25 or more cigarettes a day). The added risk to women under 30 is extremely small, but increases with age. Important: At all ages, the key risk is smoking, not Pill use.

However, the Pill is not recommended for women who have risk factors for cardiovascular problems (diabetes, obesity, high blood pressure, family history and sedentary lifestyle) which are more frequent among older women.

• Pill users have 93 more hospital admissions per 100,000 for gallbladder disease compared with other women at risk of unintended pregnancy. The risk virtually disappears after the first year of use.

• The Pill protects against benign breast disease—the longer the use, the lower the incidence—can prevent hospitalizations for ovarian cysts and reduce by half the incidence of pelvic inflammatory disease (PID), or infection of the upper genital tract.

What we still don't know:

• The exact relationship of the Pill to breast cancer. Hypotheses: Pill users may be screened for breast cancer more often than non-users, resulting in earlier detection. The hormones in the Pill may accelerate the growth of certain kinds of breast cancer, but do not initiate or cause the cancer, an effect that would be consistent with the temporarily increased risk of breast cancer during pregnancy. Women who use the Pill for long periods may have other health or behavioral characteristics that increase the risk of breast cancer.

Example: Deferred childbearing.

• Why the failure rate for the Pill, though relatively low, is still higher than clinicians believe it should be. Problem: Many women fail to use the Pill correctly. (The pregnancy rate in the first year of use is thought to be about 0.1% for women who use the Pill correctly, but it is 6.0% among current users.) Research is examining ways to improve ease and compliance of use.

Source: Jacqueline Darroch Forrest, PhD, vice president for research at the Alan Guttmacher Institute in New York City and co-author of *Preventing Pregnancy, Protecting Health: A New Look at Birth Control Choices in the United States,* The Alan Guttmacher Institute, 111 Fifth Ave., New York 10003.

Sexual Side Effects Of Widely Used Medicines

Many illnesses can themselves cause lack of libido and impotence, but in other cases it is the medication that brings on changes in sexual desire and capability. Research in this area is scant, and the sexual side effects of many drugs are not universal. Discuss your own situation with your doctor. However, the drugs listed below are known to have affected the sex lives of many who take them regularly.

High Blood pressure medicines:

•Esimil and Ismelin (guanethidine) may cause impaired ejaculation and lack of potency in men.

•Aldomet, Aldoclor and Aldoril (methyldopa) can decrease sexual desire and make holding an erection difficult for me. In rare cases, they cause a man's breasts to develop.

•Diupres, Exna-R, Rau-Sed, Regroton, Salutensin, Ser-Ap-Es and Serpasil (reserpine) can cause reduced libido and potency, delayed ejaculation and enlarged breasts.

•Catapres (clonidine) may produce impotence in men and failure to achieve orgasm in women.

•Eutonyl and Eutron (pargyline) may bring on impotence, delayed ejaculation or delayed orgasm.

•Inderal and Inderide (propranolol) rarely cause side effects, although difficulty with erections have been reported.

Digestive-tract drugs: Many of the older, commonly prescribed ulcer drugs such as Banthine, Bentyl, Donnagel, Donnatel, Pamine, Pathibamate and Pro-Banthine have been associated with sexual problems. The more recent medication Tagamet (cimetidine) has been reported to reduce male potency and enlarge breasts when given in very high doses.

Tranquilizers: Librium and Valium have quite opposite effects on different individuals. For some, these drugs reduce inhibitions and increase sexual desire. In other cases, they decrease libido.

Birth-control pills: Regardless of brand, the sexual effects vary among women. Many report increased libido, which may simply be a release from the fear of pregnancy. Some women claim to experience decreased sexual desire while taking the Pill, which may be caused by the drug's effect on hormonal regulation.

Antidepressant drugs: Depression itself often causes a lack of interest in sex. Antidepressant drugs sometimes increase libido and sometimes decrease it. Other sexual side effects vary widely and are not well recorded. Possible problems include impotence, testicular swelling, breast enlargement and milk secretion, impaired ejaculation in men and delayed orgasm in women.

Antipsychotic drugs: Many medications used to treat mental illness have adverse sexual side effects that have not been fully documented. Among the symptoms are impotence, difficulty in ejaculation, irregular menstruation, abnormal lactation, increased and decreased sexual desire and even false positive pregnancy tests.

Source: Joe Graedon, a pharmacologist and the author of *The People's Pharmacy* and *The People's Pharmacy-2*, Avon Books, New York, and *The New People's Pharmacy*, Bantam Books, New York.

When Condoms Prevent Disease And When They Don't

Condoms offer protection against some venereal diseases (gonorrhea, nongonococcal urethritis and yeast infections). They are less effective against herpes, venereal warts and chlamydiae which are small enough to pass through the pores of the condom. If either partner has an active urethral infection or genital lesion, the only safe course is sexual abstinence.

Source: Dr. Michael Carrera, professor of health sciences, Hunter College School of Health Sciences, City University of New York.

Best Time For Older Men To Have Sex

Older men who have trouble attaining erections at night may do better with morning sex. Testosterone levels are higher earlier in the day.

Source: *Medical Aspects of Human Sexuality.*

Better Sex

How to exercise your love muscle and have better sex. The Kegel exercise, which strengthens the pubococcygeal muscle—the muscle responsible for controlling urination—can enhance your love life. Reason: It can prevent premature ejaculation in men and allow them to make love longer...and can help women experience better orgasms. How to perform the exercise: For 10 minutes each morning and evening, contract this muscle as if you were holding back the flow of urine. Do 36 contractions at a time and rest for a couple of minutes before beginning again. For best results, practice this exercise for several weeks.

Source: Dr. Domeena Renshaw, Loyola University Medical School, Chicago.

Safer Sex For Heart Patients

Location: A familiar, quiet setting. A strange environment can add to stress. Time: When rested and relaxed—perhaps in the morning or during the day, after a nap. Eat one to three hours before so digestion is complete. Take medications—nitroglycerin, etc.—beforehand to prevent chest pain. Positions: Whatever is most comfortable and familiar—it's not usually necessary to change these habits to decrease possible strain on the heart. Helpful: Foreplay. It gradually prepares the heart for the increased activity of intercourse.

Source: *Medical Aspects of Human Sexuality*, 500 Plaza Dr., Secaucus, NJ 07094.

The Prostate Gland Can Be A Blessing Or A Burden

When it's working properly, the prostate gland contributes to a man's sexual pleasure. But when dysfunction occurs, it not only hinders a man's sex life but can cause other kinds of distress as well.

What are the usual things that go wrong with the prostate?

Among younger men—ages 20 to 40—we see a lot of prostatitis, an inflammation of the gland. The condition produces a wide range of symptoms—sexual dysfunction (including premature ejaculation and impotence), discomfort in the lower abdomen or genital area and difficulty in urination (such as a frequent and urgent need to urinate). In most cases, the disease is caused by a virus or bacteria and requires treatment by a physician.

Variation: Prostatosis, a congestion of the gland that is not as serious as prostatitis. It's usually not caused by an infection. But doctors aren't sure what causes it.

Are there home remedies for alleviating the distress?

Fortunately, prostatosis sometimes responds to home treatments...warm baths of 10 to 15 minutes twice a day, drinking plenty of fluids, staying away from spicy foods and alcohol. But there's not much you can do at home to treat prostatitis. As we learn more about prostate diseases, we're finding that some of the treatments we thought were effective really do nothing.

What about prostate massage? Many men claim it brings relief.

We used to think it was important, but now we realize that increased sexual activity is just as good...and more pleasurable.

Is there any connection between frequency of ejaculation and problems with the prostate?

We think not. The illness is too vague to make any connection obvious.

What about sexual activity?

It depends on the patient. If problems develop during a period of frequent sexual activity, we advise him to cut back. But if an attack occurs during a lull in activity, we suggest increased frequency. It often helps. We also know that sometimes the episode has an emotional component. But, frankly, we're not sure whether the attack causes the emotional reaction or the emotions cause the attack.

What about enlarged prostates?

This disease is fairly common among older men, 60 and up. What happens: Since urine flows through the hole in the doughnut-shaped prostate, when the gland becomes enlarged and the hole is made smaller, the patient has trouble urinating. The only medical treatment is surgery—removal of the part of the gland that's enlarged, not all of it.

How does removal of part of the gland

affect sexuality?

There's no negative effect on overall health. Usually a man can still get an erection and ejaculate—but instead of ejaculating through the penis, the semen sometimes falls back into the bladder—retrograde ejaculation.

Can the patient still father a child?

If he's intent on it, yes. It's possible to collect the semen from the urine and impregnate his wife by artificial insemination.

And cancer of the prostate?

Again, there's no way to prevent it. Once it occurs, treatment is either surgery to remove the entire gland or radiation if it hasn't spread.

Source: E. Douglas Whitehead, MD, urologist and director of the Association for Male Sexual Dysfunction of New York.

Prostate Trouble Confidential

The prostate is a chestnut-size gland below the bladder that produces fertility-promoting substances. It is susceptible to enlargement and cancer—especially in middle-age men. Scary statistic: Prostate cancer kills more men than any other form of cancer except cancer of the lung. This year it will strike approximately 85,000 Americans, causing 26,000 deaths. The incidence of prostate cancer is on the rise.

Many men have prostate cancer without being aware of it. Autopsies performed on 50-year-old men show that between 30% and 50% had microscopic evidence of prostate cancer (even though it may not have been related to the cause of death).

By age 80, that figure increases to between 50% and 80%. Clearly, the risk of prostate cancer increases with age.

Scientists aren't sure exactly what causes prostate cancer. Recent studies in Japan suggest, however, that sexual activity plays a role. At highest risk: Men who become sexually active when very young, have many sexual partners, marry late or stop their sexual activity early. Levels of the male hormone testosterone, which stimulates the prostate and affects sexual drive, could be a factor. Testosterone seems to stimulate tumor growth.

Prostate cancer doesn't always cause obvious symptoms. In about 25% of men with advanced cases, however, there is pain in the pelvis and spine, the ribs and the long bones. Most cases of prostate cancer are detected during routine rectal exams.

The American Cancer Society currently recommends that men have annual rectal exams after age 40. During the exam (known as a digital exam), the physician places his gloved finger into the rectum and examines the prostate for lumps. Cost: $60 when performed by a urologist, $20 when done by a family doctor.

A new technology, transrectal ultrasonography, uses high-frequency sound waves to detect tumors that are too small to be detected with a digital exam. Comparison: A digital exam can locate tumors half a centimeter in diameter or larger. Ultrasonography can spot tumors less than half that size. Biopsies are then performed to confirm the presence of cancer.

At one time, treating prostate cancer by radical surgery was likely to cause impotence. But today, many treatments are effective without serious side effects. Options: surgery, external radiation, internal radiation and hormone therapy. Treatment is tailored to each individual, based on age, health and tumor size.

If the cancer has not spread, surgical removal of the prostate (prostatectomy) or radiation therapy offers the best chance of cure. If it has spread, removal of the testicles (orchiectomy) or treatment with estrogen is most appropriate.

A new technique known as the Walsh nerve-saving method reduces the incidence of postsurgery impotence from 90% to 20%–50%. And the 5%–10% of surgical patients who become incontinent can be treated in several ways, including the use of an artificial urinary sphincter.

Other treatments have side effects as well.

Some 30% of the patients undergoing radiation therapy also become impotent. Orchiectomy can inhibit libido. Estrogen therapy has been found to cause heart attacks and blood clots in 6%–8% of cases.

Prostatectomy costs about $15,000 and requires seven to nine days of hospitalization. Implanting radioactive pellets in the prostate (to treat small tumors) costs about $10,000, with five to seven days in the hospital. External radiation therapy for advanced cancer costs about $7,000 for 35 treatments spread over six to seven weeks. Orchiectomy can be done on an outpatient basis for about $1,500.

Chemical castration for patients with advanced disease can be achieved with the drug leuprolide, which blocks the release of testosterone. This $250-a-month drug, which can cause hot flashes, has to be injected daily.

The second leading prostate problem is enlargement, also known as benign prostatic hyperplasia (BPH). This occurs when the gland swells and begins to press upon the urethra. Half the men past the age of 40 have at least microscopic evidence of BPH.

BPH symptoms: Difficulty in initiating urination, the need to urinate frequently at night, slow urination, dribbling.

Surgery for enlarged prostate, known as transurethral resection of the prostate (TURP), involves the insertion of a telescopic instrument down the urethra into the prostate. TURP requires three to four days of hospitalization.

Bleeding and incontinence may develop following TURP. There may also be fertility problems, since the surgery occasionally causes ejaculation into the bladder. Very rarely, some men complain that they enjoy sex less following surgery.

Alternatives to surgery: A drug called dibenzyline reduces difficulties with urination in about 30% of patients. There are also antiandrogen medications that interfere with the action of testosterone, which in turn helps shrink the prostate.

Source: Dr. Gerald Chodak, professor of urology, University of Chicago Medical Center.

The Easy Cures For Male Infertility

- Male fertility problems result from the inferior production, quality and movement of sperm. Some factors to take into account...
- Age. Sperm production drops sharply after age 30.
- Alcohol. Too much lowers the production of the male hormone testosterone.
- Caffeine. Coffee and medications with caffeine appear to make sperm sluggish.
- Cimetidine. Prescribed to treat ulcers, it decreases testosterone levels.
- Clothing. Tight trousers or underwear can overheat sperm-producing cells in testicles, which lowers sperm count.
- Diethylstilbestrol. A drug used during the 1950s to prevent miscarriage, it has been found to cause fertility problems in men whose mothers used it.
- Hot tubs. Frequent use can lower sperm count by overheating sperm-producing cells.
- Infection. All sexually transmitted diseases can have an adverse effect on fertility.
- Partner's vaginal douches, lubricants and sprays can immobilize sperm.
- Recreational drugs. Marijuana and other drugs may decrease testosterone levels.
- Smoking. Lowers sperm count and slows sperm mobility.

Source: *A Doctor's Guide to Men's Private Parts* by James H. Gilbaugh, Jr., MD. Copyright 1989 by James H. Gilbaugh, Jr., MD. Reprinted by permission of Crown Publishers, 201 E. 50 St., New York 10022.

Sex And Headaches

Study: 33% of women experienced substantial relief following intercourse. In another study, 23% reported long-lasting relief and another 23% reported at least temporary relief from headache pain. Theory: Sexual arousal prompts the release of a pain-reducing substance.

Source: Studies led by neurologist James R. Couch, Southern Illinois University, reported in *Medical Aspects of Human Sexuality*, 249 W. 17 St., New York 10011.

How To Reject Sex...

How to reject sex without rejecting your partner. Give a reason why you're not interested in intercourse at that particular moment and suggest another time...and take responsibility for initiating sex the next time.

Source: *Not Tonight, Dear: How to Reawaken Your Sexual Desire* by Anthony Pietropinto, MD, Doubleday, 666 Fifth Ave., New York 10103.

Good News About Menopause

Menopause improved sex for 29% of women surveyed—mostly by making it more spontaneous once there was no risk of pregnancy. In cases where estrogen loss causes vaginal dryness and painful intercourse, hormone treatment is highly effective: Ninety percent of women who reported a lack of desire before the treatment had increased desire and sexual activity within three to six months.

Source: Study by Yale University School of Medicine, reported in *McCall's*, 110 Fifth Ave., New York 10011.

Sexual Pressure

Men are pressured into sexual activity almost as often as women are. Researchers from the University of Kansas polled almost 1,000 college-aged men and women... and found that 98% of women and 94% of men reported having engaged in unwanted kissing, petting or intercourse. Men's reasons: Desire to appear "macho" or "experienced" or be popular...and because of verbal or physical coercion. Men are more likely than women to engage in unwanted intercourse. Women are more likely to engage in unwanted kissing. Women often feel that they should allow themselves to be kissed, whereas men often feel they are expected to have sex, especially in a committed relationship.

Unwanted-sex avoidance advice: Be assertive...communicate openly with your partner...don't act on vague assumptions.

Source: Researchers Stephen Cook, University of Missouri, and Charlene L. Muehlenhard, University of Kansas.

Sex Without Desire

Sex without desire is common. Both men and women report engaging in sexual behavior without desire—usually to please a partner. As a group, men report feeling desire more often than do women.

Source: Study of almost 150 college students, aged 18 to 54, led by J. Gayle Beck, PhD, department of psychology, University of Houston, reported in *The Journal of Sex Research*, Box 208, Mt. Vernon, Iowa 52314.

Women And Impotence

Women take the initiative to cure their partners' impotence. More than half of the calls to the national Impotence Information Center are from women with impotent partners. And women are far more willing than men to discuss the problems in detail.

Source: Impotence Information Center, 11001 Bren Rd. E., Minnetonka, Minnesota 55343.

Arthritis And Sex

Decreased libido is a result of pain or depression that comes with the disease. Often, too, sufferers are concerned about changes in their physical appearance. Good news: Arthritis seldom has an effect on the sexual organs, so the problem can be solved if a couple will discuss it with a doctor or therapist.

Source: Psychiatrist Joyce Brothers, quoted in *Taking Control of Arthritis* by Harvard Medical School professor and arthritis specialist Fred G. Kantrowitz, MD, HarperCollins, 10 E. 53 St., New York 10022.

Psychological Intimacy

Important relationships are held together by psychological intimacy. Key: The willingness to tell about one's private experiences and to listen respectfully to the other person tell about his/hers. Trap: Psychological intimacy is inherently short-lived and must be re-established frequently.

Source: Stephen Levine, MD, medical director, Center for Human Sexuality, University Hospitals of Cleveland, the author of *Sex Is Not Simple*, Ohio Psychology Publications, 2599 E. Main St., Suite 140, Columbus, Ohio 43209.

Divorce Does Not Have To Be As Tough On Kids As It Usually Is

One of the major factors influencing a child's reactions and adjustment to divorce is the child's age. Parents should be aware of the problems specific to each developmental stage.

Infants and toddlers:

Infants and toddlers feel confused and disoriented by divorce. It seriously disrupts the continuity of their lives. Most upsetting: New caregivers and new settings.

Infants and toddlers are extremely sensitive to the emotional states of their parents. They may be frightened and overwhelmed by what their parents are experiencing, especially if there is a lot of arguing and fighting.

Signs of distress: Reverting to earlier patterns of sleeping, eating, talking and toilet training...becoming clingy when a parent leaves the room...becoming overly upset out of proportion to what is going on around them...getting angry often and showing it by yelling, biting and kicking...acting fearful when around unfamiliar adults...acting listless and withdrawn. How to help:

• Consult a pediatrician or family doctor. Make sure the distress doesn't have a physical cause.

• Maintain a regular daily schedule. Children need to know where they will be and who will care for them.

• Don't fight in front of the children. Make peace, even if you feel hurt or angry.

• Respect and respond to the developmental needs of children.

Example: Joint custody—which means shuttling children back and forth for long periods—ignores their need for environmental consistency.

Preschoolers:

During ages three to five, children have a lot of trouble distinguishing fantasy from reality. For children of divorce, this leads to fantasies of being abandoned by their parents or punished for an angry feeling.

Preschoolers are also struggling to achieve independence. When parents divorce, their feelings of security are threatened. This makes it more frightening for them to venture forth into the wider world.

Signs of distress: Delaying bedtime...insisting on sleeping with a parent...eating only a few types of food...refusing to ride a bicycle ...refusing to draw or color...reverting to using *me* instead of *I* in making personal references...refusing to participate in previously enjoyed group activities. How to help:

• Listen closely to preschoolers and observe their behavior. Look for: Frightening fantasies and self-blame. Explain: That the divorce wasn't their fault...what the divorce will mean for them in terms of living arrangements and visitation.

• Be willing to adopt different parenting strategies.

Example: Steve felt rejected by his mother when he had to visit his father. His parents rearranged visitation so he saw his father more often but for shorter periods of time. Result: His distress diminished.

• Use displacement communication. Talk to children about problems they are experiencing in an indirect, nonthreatening way.

Example: Steve's mother told him, I "know that a boy might get angry about having to visit his dad because he feels his mom doesn't care about him anymore. But when a boy's mom sends him to visit his dad, she's doing it because she wants him to stay close to his

dad and have a good time with him."
Early elementary school children:

Young elementary-school children often get depressed in the early stages of divorce. They experience their parents' fighting as the loss of their niche in the world.

A major source of stress is an overly anxious, lonely or depressed custodial parent. Needy parents endanger children's sense of having a supportive, trusting home base, undermining their ability to turn their attention outward to school and friendships.

Signs of distress: Crying...looking sad... denying that the divorce is occurring ...thinking that parents will reconcile... getting angry over not getting enough attention...whining ...complaining...developing nervous habits, such as nail biting. How to help:

• Empathize with the child's loss. Let children know that you understand the sadness they are likely to feel soon after the separation.

Example: Jane's mother told her, "Lots of kids feel sad when their parents split up. But it does get better."

• Structure special time with your children. Children of this age are especially sensitive to feelings of loss. Children see any change in a parent's behavior toward them as a sign that they're no longer lovable.

• Arrange for frequent and predictable visits to noncustodial parents.

• Get help for yourself if the divorce is causing long-term feelings of loss and depression. How you feel will affect how you relate to your children.

Late elementary-school children:

Youngsters between 9 and 12 can realistically understand divorce events. Whereas younger children suffer from frightening fantasies and self-blaming beliefs, older children suffer from competing wishes and concerns.

They may have the impulse to side with one parent against the other, which gives rise to uncomfortable, divided loyalties.

Children this age also may develop elaborate psychological defenses to protect them from the painful emotions that divorce engenders. They often convert their feelings of helplessness and sadness into anger. This prevents them from feeling unhappy and emotionally vulnerable.

Signs of distress: Fighting with peers or siblings...directing bitter, verbal aggression at one or both parents...developing psychosomatic complaints—such as headaches and stomachaches...becoming socially withdrawn. How to help:

• Don't mount frontal assaults against children's defenses. Again, use displacement communication.

Example: Frank's mother told him, "Sometimes boys have pretty angry feelings when their parents divorce. They take those feelings to school and get into fights. Can you think of any better ways for a guy to work out his feelings?"

• Don't place children in an adult role. They should not be asked to be a co-parent or confidant.

• Don't ask children to be messengers between you and your former spouse. And don't pump them for information on your ex's drinking, dating habits, etc.

Adolescents:

When parents divorce, adolescents face the formidable task of adjusting to two sets of significant changes in their lives—their own rapid changes and the loss of the stability, support and protection of the family unit.

During the teenage years, most youngsters come to see their parents as complex human beings with limitations as well as admirable qualities. Divorce often derails this process as adolescents start to see their parents as being merely selfish, stupid, weak or even cruel.

Teenagers have an especially difficult time with divorced parents dating or remarrying. Already overwhelmed by and confused about their own sexual impulses, they are forced to confront their parents' sexuality as well.

Signs of distress: Abusing drugs or alcohol... slipping academically...getting into trouble... engaging in precocious/promiscuous sexual behavior...fighting...being self-destructive... being accident-prone...running away from home. How to help:

• Discuss any plans to start dating. And talk about the difference between adult and teenage relationships, particularly in terms of sex.

• Be flexible. Try to maintain the difficult

and delicate balance between direct and indirect communication. And show respect for the adolescent's emerging autonomy.

Source: Psychologist Neil Kalter, PhD, director of the Center for the Child and Family at the University of Michigan at Ann Arbor. He is the author of *Growing Up with Divorce: Helping Your Child Avoid Immediate and Later Emotional Problems*, The Free Press, 866 Third Ave., New York 10022.

Troubled Marriages Can Be Saved

Couples whose marriages are in trouble are increasingly trying to create a better relationship instead of heading for the divorce court. This is a great contrast with how problem marriages have been handled during the past 10 or 15 years.

The most important thing about this trend is that it can work: It's not just possible to save your marriage, it's very likely you can if you're determined to turn around the things you can.

The disadvantages of divorce:

We've begun to realize that divorce itself has clear disadvantages…

• It rarely solves the problem it is intended to solve. Too many people get out of the marriage only to find similar problems in future marriages or single life.

• Divorce often creates new problems, such as needing to make moves—geographical moves—and dealing with diminished financial resources. Not the least of these problems is the incredible pain a divorce causes, even when both people want the divorce—and it is amicable. Couples who really wanted to divorce find themselves 10 years later still feeling an emptiness inside.

• Divorce is a tremendous adjustment for children. Most children will tell you that if they could choose, they'd want their parents together.

Practical divorce busting:

I have been very successful in helping people to save their marriages—85% of the couples I counsel stay together.

Key to that success: New technologies. I use solution-oriented brief therapy. This is a method that helps people come up with solutions quickly. It doesn't require long introspective journeys into the past, which is often just back-pedaling. Instead, I help people identify where the trouble really lies.

Then we expand the actions that work and do away with the actions that don't work. The couple moves toward the future instead of looking back.

This method is based on the work of Milton Erikson, an extraordinary psychiatrist who died in 1980. Although traditionally trained, he had some very untraditional ideas about how people solved problems.

Erikson was not at all interested in how problems developed. He was interested in how solutions developed. He would look for the glimmer of hope and expand on that.

Over the past years, many brief therapy models with an Eriksonian feel have been popping up all over the world. Their objective is to focus on people's strengths and resources instead of on their weaknesses and limitations.

Erikson's solution-oriented brief therapy can be extremely successful. I have fine-tuned these techniques for use with couples.

When a couple comes to see me, I immediately ask what their goal is. In traditional therapy, that might not happen for some time.

Of course, they don't always tell me about their goal. They may be more interested in their problem. I shift their attention and ask about positive aspects.

Example: If a couple says, "We're just not communicating at all," I simply ask, "What's different about the times when you did communicate better?"

That question shocks people. But the vast majority are able to identify very specifically what they do differently when their communication works.

Example: We communicate better when we spend more time together. Or—we communicate more when the relationship is more physical.

Next I ask them what makes their communication work.

Example: We get a baby-sitter…we do

more fun things together and we communicate more then.

As a result, it becomes very evident that they don't have to wait for this magical loving feeling to return. They can leave my office and do something different immediately that will hopefully trigger this positive feeling. Common problems for couples:

Ultimately what dissolves the marriage are not differences but hopelessness. When even one person reaches the point of thinking that the future is just a miserable extension of the past, that's when a marriage is really in trouble. But if at least one person thinks that there may still be an unturned stone, there's hope.

There are certain complaints that I always hear: My husband can't communicate…my wife nags.

Women, particularly, complain about the lack of communication in relationships. In the 1960s, we thought that perhaps we could eliminate some of the gender differences. Now we're finding that men and women have distinctly different styles of communication.

Men tend to be more action-oriented. But this doesn't mean that a man is any less committed to the relationship or any less in love if he doesn't talk about his feelings.

A woman communicates in a different kind of language. She talks about different kinds of things with her women friends than she does with her husband. Women may want to think that a day will come when men will be more like women. As far as I can see, that isn't going to happen.

Men complain that their wives nag them all the time. What really happens is that women often take the responsibility for being the relationship regulators. When things seem to go off track, women will notice it and say something. Often this takes the form of nagging. A wife may not be asking for the thing that is apparently on the surface. Sometimes she just wants a response.

Caution: A man should worry when his wife stops nagging—because that's usually when she's no longer interested in making things better. She is the woman who will come into my office and say, "I am absolutely out of this marriage…I can't take it anymore."

Men seem to have a radar for anything that smacks of control. If a woman says: "Honey, I want to spend more time with you," he may interpret it as nagging because he feels controlled—even though she's just trying to reach out and be closer.

A few of the couples I've worked with do eventually decide to split up. The couple decides, either unilaterally or together, that they want to get out of the marriage.

If one person wants "in" and the other wants "out," sometimes I will work with the person who wants "in" to help figure out what has to be done differently to turn the marriage around.

If this doesn't work, the person usually ends up feeling better and more ready to handle the inevitable divorce. Two-career vs. traditional marriages:

In my experience, there's no difference in the number of problems you see in traditional marriages versus two-career marriages. There can be problems in either kind—they're just different problems.

One thing I see in two-career families is that people don't make the relationship a priority. They will go weeks without going out to dinner with each other—after work they take care of the kids because they feel that they haven't spent enough time with them.

If you want to do something for your kids, make your marriage a priority.

In traditional families, often the woman is eager for her husband to come home so she will have an adult to talk to. But that adult is often so exhausted that he can't even put energy into a conversation.

Wives in that situation often say that they had to get out of the marriage because their own needs weren't being met.

Whether a marriage is in good or bad shape has very little to do with who works outside the home. New directions for therapy:

Therapists have tremendous interest in these new techniques. Last year I gave the keynote address at the American Association for Marriage and Family Therapy* on divorce-

*To find a therapist in your area who does solution-oriented brief therapy, call the American Association of Marriage and Family Therapy at 800-374-2638.

busting, and the response I got was tremendous. More and more therapists seem to believe this is the way to go.

But believing this and knowing how to do solution-oriented brief therapy are two different things. Gradually more therapists are getting training, and many more are eager to learn.

Bottom line: The most important point is that even if just one person wants to save the marriage, the couple shouldn't give up hope. If they can get themselves to a divorce-busting therapist or read my book, there's a very good possibility they can turn the marriage around. Unlike that old adage that it takes two to tango, it does not always take two to save a marriage. It can take one to tango, as long as that person is willing to take the initiative and change first.

Source: Michele Weiner-Davis, the author of *Divorce Busting: A Revolutionary and Rapid Program for Staying Together,* Summit Books, 1230 Avenue of the Americas, New York 10020.

AIDS Risk

Neurological exams in which the same pin for pain-receptor tests is used on more than one patient.

Source: *Nurses' Drug Alert.*

Beyond The Obvious Differences Between Men And Women

As a reaction to outmoded Victorian concepts about women being the weaker sex, we've just gone through a long period of downplaying the differences between men and women.

But common sense alone dictates that men and women must have innate differences. We were probably built to complement each other, to function together in order to maintain our evolutionary advantage.

It has been known for a long time that there's more variation within one sex than there is between the sexes. But we are beginning to find distinctive differences between the behaviors of the sexes when they are averaged out.

Math versus verbal ability:

One of the big differences that various tests are beginning to show is that, on the average, women really are more verbal and men are more spatial. Women speak sooner and more fluently as children, they learn foreign languages faster and far fewer suffer from dyslexia. Men excel at math, at abstract problem-solving, at maps and mazes.

From an evolutionary perspective, there are some sound reasons for these differences. We were hunters and gatherers for 4 million years.

Women, the gatherers, talked while they worked in order to scare away the animals. Also, in every society the women raise the children, and a tremendous amount of culture and training are passed on through language.

Men, the hunters, used spatial skills to scout, track, roam large distances and find their way home. The one thing you really cannot do while hunting, however, is talk.

Aggression:

Anthropologists have found that men around the world are more aggressive and women are more nurturing. Even in the least aggressive societies, where the most aggressive men are nowhere near as aggressive as our least aggressive men, men are still more aggressive than women. There seems to be a link between the male hormone testosterone and the level of aggression.

Both aggressive and nurturing traits gave us an evolutionary advantage. Someone had to protect the group. Someone had to nurture the young. We're still seeing that division. Men, on the whole, are still the ones who fight wars, even though a woman can shoot a gun as well as a man can. And most children are still raised by women, even though men can nurture effectively.

Brain differences:

There are very few differences we can define between male and female brains, but it is generally accepted that the bridge between the two sides of the brain, called the corpus callosum, is larger in women than in men. This has led some scientists to believe that the two sides of the brain are better connected in women than in men.

How this affects thinking: Scientists have experimented with temporarily putting half a person's brain to sleep. They asked a woman a logic question when the logical side of her brain was asleep, and she struggled until electrodes attached to the brain showed that she was trying to solve the problem with the other part of her brain. She eventually came up with some kind of answer. Men, on the other hand, cannot use another part to compensate as efficiently as women can.

This difference shows up in what we call women's intuition. Women are better at picking up nonverbal cues.

Example: A woman will say, "I think he feels uncomfortable," because she observes the swaying of someone's body, the clenched hands, the tone of voice.

Women do better in tests of nonverbal communication. Reason: Their brains are more generalized and can absorb more information simultaneously than men's brains.

This tendency toward specialization means that both geniuses and idiots are more likely to be men. When men are good at something, they tend to be very good. But when they're defective, they can't use another part of the brain to compensate.

This difference may also explain why it's so much easier for women to express emotions than it is for men to do so. We can't communicate our feelings very well without good connections between the emotional center and the language center. Since these connections may be better developed in women, women are probably more fluent at expressing their emotions.

Battle of the sexes:

One of the main reasons men and women have problems with intimacy is that women seek it by looking face-to-face and talking and men seek it by sitting side by side and doing. Women's most common complaints about

their mates are, "He doesn't talk to me...he doesn't discuss our problems...he doesn't listen." Men who watch the football game together experience closeness by doing something together. Women don't understand that. Their mode of intimacy is verbal.

The situation isn't hopeless, however. Women can learn spatial and visual skills. Men can learn verbal skills. Like anything else, you get better with practice.

I met a man who actually went to a class to learn to be more verbal. Even though attending the class was his wife's idea, it made him feel better because he could communicate better and be a much better person.

Women, on the other hand, must learn to watch football games with their mates—and not call them silly. They need to acquire a taste for male-oriented activities in order to foster intimacy in the less-verbal areas where men feel most comfortable.

Source: Anthropologist Helen E. Fisher, PhD, department of anthropology, American Museum of Natural History, New York. Dr. Fisher is the author of *The Sex Contract: The Evolution of Human Behavior.* William Morrow, 105 Madison Ave., New York 10016.

How Very Safe Sex Can Be Fun

Although most people think safe sex is boring because it limits sexual expression, it also can have unique and very positive aspects. Safe sex prolongs the courting phase of a relationship. It forces couples to get to know each other before they have sex. And delaying intercourse can bring back the excitement of being a teenager again.

Why people hate safe sex:

Stopping to put on a condom can suddenly pull you back to the reality of how dangerous sex can be today. You start asking yourself, "How well do I know this person?...Am I being 'bad?'" Conscious and unconscious guilt get mixed together and block pleasure. Problem: None of this is compatible with being swept away, an experience that many people enjoy.

In addition, most couples today are choosing what seems to be the easy way out. Instead of taking a creative approach to safe sex, they equate the term with using condoms (which are not considered 100% safe). Problem: They have sex a few times, decide that they like and trust each other and stop using condoms. Trap: Just because someone's nice doesn't mean he/she doesn't have AIDS.

What does safe sex really mean?

Ideally, safe sex means having sex only with someone who is not involved with drugs and who you're absolutely, positively, 100% sure has not had sex with anyone else in years.

In reality, although it can be very difficult to develop and maintain such a relationship, safe sex means not having sex until you trust a person and have thoroughly discussed his/her background.

Even better: Don't have sex until you and your partner have been tested for AIDS. And don't have the AIDS test until you've been dating for a long time (recent research shows it can take years for the AIDS antibodies to show up).

In the meantime, be as creative as you can... Frustration can be fun:

If it's treated as an opportunity to experiment and have fun rather than as a hindrance to sexual expression, delaying intercourse can be very exciting.

Remember how thrilling petting and necking were when you were a teen? Remember what a turn-on it was being pursued (or pursuing someone)...and constantly saying (or being told) no?

Most of us have exciting memories of adolescence, which was a very sensual period—a time when you couldn't and you shouldn't but you wanted to. Analogy: Being on a diet and not being able to eat candy. You get obsessed with it. Safe sex can give the same charge to sex.

A lot of sex is just game-playing anyway—a regressive activity in which adults get to play like kids again. Rationale: Sex, which is physical, takes people back to infancy, when the only way they could relate to the world was through being held, cuddled and stroked.

Instead of having businesslike, goal-oriented sex—which is supposedly mature, adult sex but isn't half as much fun—we can have playful sex. For most of us, that's very healthy. We can enjoy suddenly being forced to do something that we really wanted to do anyway. More safe-sex strategies:

• Revive the art of courting. Send a bouquet of flowers, enjoy a quiet candlelit dinner. This very important part of every relationship became almost obsolete during the sexual revolution.

• Make out. Do it in the back of the car, on the front porch or wherever you found it exciting as a teenager. Or do it in the park, on the beach, in an airplane or in any other setting where you can't actually have intercourse.

• Oral sex. More women have orgasms with oral sex than with intercourse. Caution: Semen carries the AIDS virus. The ejaculate taken internally can be dangerous—though there are no clearly defined cases of transfer of AIDS heterosexually through oral sex.

• Treat condoms as sexual toys. The woman should put them on the man...slowly and seductively. Recommended: Some condoms come with an applicator, which many people leave on because it enhances the size and duration of the erection.

Source: Dagmar O'Connor, director of the sex-therapy program at St. Luke's–Roosevelt Hospital Center in New York City and the author of *How to Put the Love Back into Making Love*, Doubleday, 666 Fifth Ave., New York 10103.

If This Is Love, Why Do I Feel So Insecure?

The world is full of confident and accomplished people who become fearful and anxious—even obsessive—in their quest for love.

Exactly what is anxious love?

It's the sensation of being kept constantly on the edge by a lover who may or may not be fickle. Anxious love is as volatile as the stock market—up one day, down the next. And an anxious lover's passion rages all the more intensely when he/she is least sure that it is being reciprocated.

Doesn't everyone feel this way at least some of the time?

Although most people have felt anxious love at one time or another, some people feel insecure about most of their romantic relationships. It appears that these people actually bring the insecurity—insecurity that lies within them—to the relationship.

Anxious love can also be caused by the partner. The more ambiguous and inconsistent he/she is in expressions of love and affection, the more anxious and upset the insecure partner becomes.

How do you know whether it's you or your partner who's generating the anxiety?

It depends on whether your insecurity is a pattern or an isolated incident. If you've felt secure in past relationships and your current partner makes you feel insecure, chances are something he's doing is causing the insecurity.

But if you have always felt insecure about each of your lovers, it's probably coming from your past. Or you may be choosing partners who make you feel insecure. Helpful: If you think your partner is behaving in a provocative or inconsistent way, ask a close friend if he sees the behavior as you do.

Does anxious love breed obsession?

Although they often go together, they are two different things...

•Anxious love is worrying about losing the relationship, worrying about whether or not your love is reciprocated.

•Obsession is a tendency to be fully absorbed and preoccupied with the partner. It's a love-at-first-sight longing to see the loved one every day, to go live on a deserted island together. To the obsessed lover, rejection would feel like the end of the world.

What causes people to be anxious lovers?

Childhood experience, essentially. Romantically anxious women usually come from families in which there was open conflict between the mother and the father...often active warfare.

Her father's relationship with her was hostile, controlling and dominant. Her mother was more relaxed. Result: The daughter empathized with her mother and took her side in arguments with the father.

Because the daughter wound up with a weak emotional attachment to her father, she developed an inability to discern how the opposite sex feels about her. And she learned to expect that things don't go well in romantic relationships.

Later in life, if the cues from her partner are ambiguous, she becomes anxious and upset.

What, then, would compel a woman to become obsessed with a man?

Most women who develop obsessive love had an even weaker relationship with their father when they were young. He was distant, neglectful and rejecting. Women who are prone to obsession are filling a void in their lives.

What kind of background creates an anxious male lover?

Sons are not as affected as daughters by parental conflict. Most insecure men come from families in which both parents emphasized achievement yet were also cold, unaffectionate and nonnurturing.

Although the son later tries to find the emotional security he lacked at home, he doubts that he can, since his past efforts met with disapproval and rejection from his parents.

How should an anxious lover deal with a partner?

State your needs without inflicting guilt or meting out punishment. Concentrate on your own feelings, not your partner's lack of consideration. Describe exactly what you want from your partner and ask for a commitment.

What if a person's partner refuses to comply?

No matter how a talk like this turns out, just asserting your needs is an antidote to insecurity. If it upsets you that your partner is indifferent to your needs, you need to evaluate what this relationship means to you and whether it's worth continuing.

That's the advantage of raising issues early, before you become fully committed to a relationship. You'll have time to get out of it without being devastated emotionally.

Source: J. Conrad Schwarz, PhD, professor of psychology at the University of Connecticut and co-author of *If This Is Love, Why Do I Feel So Insecure? The First Major Comprehensive Study of What Causes Anxiety, Obsession, Jealousy and Depression in Romantic Relationships*, Atlantic Monthly Press, 19 Union Sq. West, New York 10003.

Low Sex Drive?

If one partner's sex drive seems unusually low, he/she should see a doctor and a psychologist to rule out a possible medical or psychological problem. If no problem is found: Be open and honest during erotic situations—suppressing your feelings leads to anger and resentment. And compromise. Helpful compromises: Plan to have sex at a later time... agree to sex play, with the less desirous partner trying his best...masturbation, preferably with the partner nearby or participating...oral sex...massage or prolonged touching (this may arouse the low-libido partner)...look for creative ways to stimulate the less amorous partner.

Source: E. Douglas Whitehead, MD, and Shirley Zussman, EdD, editors, *Sex Over Forty*, Box 1600, Chapel Hill, North Carolina 27515.

Answers To Questions About Sexuality From Middle-Aged Couples

In almost two decades as a practicing sex therapist, I have encountered nearly every sexual problem imaginable. Yet for all their differences, most couples—especially middle-aged couples—share a remarkably similar set of concerns, including passion, fidelity and compatibility. Here are the questions I get most often, along with my answers.

My husband fears he is losing his virility. What should we do?

This is an especially common question. In my view, the problem stems not so much from the realities of aging as from the cultural fallacy that a man must be physically powerful to be a good lover. Compared with younger men, men in their 60s and older do take longer to get an erection and achieve orgasm, and their orgasms are often less intense. But these changes need not hamper a man's ability to enjoy sex and be an exciting lover. In the vast majority of cases, a middle-aged man's growing self-knowledge and life experience can more than compensate for the slight decline in his physical capacity.

Crucial: A willingness to take sex more slowly and deliberately, with less emphasis on performance and more emphasis on the pleasures of stroking and caressing. For men of any age suffering from impotence or other forms of sexual dysfunction, effective treatment is available. Some cases of impotence have specific, reversible physiological causes. These should be investigated by a urologist.

Will menopause ruin our sex life?

Many middle-aged women worry that menopause will destroy their libido and ruin sex for them—and their partners. Menopause can bring about certain physiological changes—vaginal dryness or a loss of sensation, for example. Fortunately, these problems are usually treatable via the use of lubricants, estrogen-replacement therapy or homeopathic herbal remedies. Moreover, many women find that menopause actually improves their sex life. Following menopause, for instance, sex is often more spontaneous, as there is no longer any need for contraception.

Bottom line: As long as both partners are emotionally prepared for menopause, there is no physical reason that it should interfere with sexuality.

We have fallen out of sync sexually. Why?

Middle age affects men and women quite differently. Many women find middle age a time of sexual liberation. After years of relative inhibition—brought on in part by the time constraints and emotional demands of child rearing—middle-aged women begin to seek greater satisfaction from lovemaking. They have become more comfortable with their bodies, so they are more willing to experiment sexually, and they begin to want more from their lovers. Unfortunately, this increasing sexuality among middle-aged women often clashes with the changing sexuality of their husbands.

Reason: Unlike their wives, middle-aged men often find themselves becoming less, rather than more, interested in sex.

Happily, this rift can usually be repaired. Crucial: Honesty, communication, playfulness, tenderness, an openness to sexual experimentation and self-exploration, including masturbation. However, where there are specific sexual problems or dysfunction, sex therapy is essential. In such cases, the couple may be asked to refrain from sexual intercourse while learning once again to derive pleasure simply by touching and through foreplay.

Forgoing intercourse in this manner seems strange to most couples who have been having intercourse for decades. But the payoffs in enhanced pleasure and greater intimacy are well worth the effort. For couples who are willing to work together with love and sensitivity, middle age can be the time during which they first learn how to make love rather than merely copulate.

What's happened to my sex drive?

In some cases, a loss of libido can be traced to a crisis outside the marital bedroom: Serious illness, a death in the family, the loss of a job, failure in business, increased work load, unresolved feelings of anger or resentment, etc. All can cause one or both partners to lose interest in sex. Happily, desire usually returns upon resolution of the crisis. All that's required is a little patience.

Other cases of waning desire are more complex. For example, some people find that their libido diminishes the more intimate they become with their partner. A middle-aged man may lose interest in his wife because they know each other so intimately...and in the same way a middle-aged woman can lose interest in her husband. In such cases, the trouble usually stems from some early emotional trauma resulting in a fear of intimacy. For couples who feel that this phenomenon is playing a role in their relationship, the best solution is psychotherapy.

Why doesn't my spouse turn me on anymore?

Your premise is wrong. Your spouse doesn't turn you on, nor does he/she turn you off. Each of us is responsible for turning ourselves on and off. If you are no longer aroused by your spouse's loving touch, the question to ask is, Why am I turning myself off? In many cases, the answer can be traced to unexpressed or unresolved feelings of anger or resentment. If you have difficulty becoming aroused, scan your mind for such feelings, then discuss them with your spouse. In other cases, a spouse unwittingly sabotages the arousal process by reviewing a mental list of his/her partner's flaws.

Better: Run a list of his/her good points. Instead of letting your thoughts wander, try focusing directly on yourself, on just how pleasurable it is to be held and caressed. Remember, the brain is your most sensitive erogenous zone.

Why do my spouse and I argue so much these days?

For most couples, middle age is the time when the kids leave home and strike out on their own. This emptying of the nest seems innocuous enough. In many cases, however, it profoundly alters the emotional dynamic that exists between a husband and a wife. Reason: After years of concealing their sexuality and focusing on child rearing, the couple suddenly find themselves alone, with nothing and no one to keep them apart. Typical: Points of conflict that once were glossed over "to spare the children" flare up into big fights.

Good news:

While often scary, fighting is not without its practical side. It helps couples negotiate important emotional boundaries, providing emotional "space" when necessary. A more congenial way to accomplish the same thing, however, is to learn to state your needs directly to each other, and not wait until resentment turns into a fight. If you feel grouchy, for instance, ask your mate for a couple of hours alone. That way you can create some distance without causing a fight. But remember, a little fighting is healthy.

We just don't have time for sex anymore:

Many couples who complain of not having enough time for sex are really filling their time with other activities—often so that they can avoid intimacy.

Very, Very Personal

And no wonder. Though they can't admit it, even to themselves, most people are terrified by true intimacy. All too many of us grow up in dysfunctional households, seeing our parents argue, suffering harsh discipline and perhaps even abuse or incest—all from the first people with whom we are close, our parents. As we grow older, we fear intimacy out of a sense of self-protection. If you really want to have sex and be intimate with your partner, you can find ways to make the time.

Source: Dagmar O'Connor, PhD, lecturer in psychiatry at Columbia University, New York City. A practicing sex therapist for two decades, Dr. O'Connor was the first Masters & Johnson–trained female sex therapist in New York City. She is the author of *How to Make Love to the Same Person for the Rest of Your Life—and Still Love It* and *How to Put the Love Back into Making Love,* Bantam Doubleday Dell, 666 Fifth Ave., New York 10103.

17

Nutrition, Fitness, And Exercise

Diet Plan Dangers

Avoid weight-loss plans that…emphasize one particular food above all others…guarantee that you will lose a certain number of pounds…use fanciful theories to explain how combinations of certain foods can lead to weight loss…omit one food group or major nutrient…recommend a total daily intake of fewer than 1,200 calories…suggest megadoses of vitamins and mineral supplements to make up for losses in foods.

Source: *The Wellness Encyclopedia* by the editors of the *University of California, Berkeley Wellness Letter,* Houghton Mifflin Co., One Beacon St., Boston 02108.

Dieters' Pitfalls

Judging portion sizes incorrectly…adding extra calories (usually from fat) while preparing food…choosing a diet plan that doesn't fit your lifestyle or food preferences…following a diet that is not nutritionally balanced…consuming too few calories a day…failing to exercise in addition to cutting back on calories…not planning ahead for special events to prevent overeating…weighing yourself more than once a day…not forgiving an occasional overindulgence…not rewarding yourself for successful dieting.

Source: *Dr. Jean Mayer's Diet & Nutrition Guide,* Pharos Books, 200 Park Ave., New York 10166.

How To Lose 10 Pounds In 8 Weeks

Holidays are hard on the waistline, and revelers who face the new year with their belts unnotched are often ready for a new eating regimen.

The Harvard Square diet may be the best-humored, most sensible and least restrictive weight-loss idea for starting off 1993 or any other year.

What distinguishes this diet from hundreds of others is its acknowledgement of your habits and tastes. You are not asked to give up anything you like to eat or drink, only to cut down your portions. You stick to your diet only five days a week, which lets you go to a restaurant or to a party without jeopardizing your program. Key premises:

• You can eat and drink exactly what you are accustomed to having. The change is to eat and drink less of your choices and do it more slowly in three regular meals. Breakfast—as long as you are not used to having four jelly doughnuts—remains the same. At lunch and dinner, you simply halve your portions of everything.

• If you must snack between meals, confine the habit to twice a day—and halve your usual amount of goodies. (Dole yourself out a small portion in a small container and savor every crumb.)

• Start your main meal with a low-calorie salad (greens—not beans or pasta). It will make your smaller servings of meat and potatoes that come afterwards seem more filling.

• Take advantage of low-calorie foods and drinks that taste good to you. Many are excellent and make calorie-saving substitutes for their normal counterparts. If you really don't like just lemon juice and herbs on your salad, use a reduced-calorie dressing. If you feel deprived without a sweet after dinner, try an artificially sweetened dessert.

• Burn up an extra 300 calories a day with exercise five days a week. Walk briskly for an hour, play tennis for 45 minutes or dance to a rock band for 30 minutes. The choice is yours as long as you make a point to do it.

Key promises of the plan:

• You will lose a minimum of 10 pounds in eight weeks.

• It will stay off because you lost it slowly and your eating habits will have been modified for the better.

• You will not have compromised your health in any way.

Calories do count:

There is no gimmick behind this diet. It deals with basic scientific reality—if you take in more calories than you burn off, you will gain weight. And, if you burn off more calories than you take in, you will lose weight.

A pound of body weight is made up of 3,500 calories. If your normal pattern of eating and drinking averages 2,000–2,500 calories a day, by halving everything you normally eat after breakfast (and making judicious substitutes for some items), you could save at least 600 calories a day. If you work off an extra 300 calories in additional exercise, you will be using up 900 calories a day. Multiply that by five days that you diet each week and you have 4,500 calories or 1.28 pounds worked off each week. In eight weeks, it is 10 pounds.

It is slow, but it is sure—and more importantly, you will not have starved or shocked your system with an abrupt change in diet. In fact, you should be well prepared to maintain your new weight with a minimum of effort. Or you will be ready to lose even more if you need to.

Importance of exercise:

There comes a point where just eating less to lose weight becomes self-defeating. If we starve ourselves, we risk our health and we can't build good habits that will sustain us for a lifetime.

Exercise has more benefits than simply allowing us to enjoy food and stay slim. It burns off extra calories after a heavy meal—you can literally work off an indulgence. And it decreases appetite, firms muscles, helps circulation and eases tension.

Little things mean a lot:

If losing weight were truly effortless, there would be no pudgy people. It takes commitment and willpower, even when you follow the Harvard Square diet. Ideas that seem to work:

• Take small bites and chew them slowly. You must satisfy your jaw muscles as well as your stomach to feel full.

• Enjoy and appreciate your meals so that they are satisfying experiences.

• Keep regular mealtime hours. You will be less likely to get ravenously hungry and to want to overeat.

• Study calorie charts so you can avoid needlessly high-calorie foods and methods of cooking.

• Fend off urges to snack by putting off the decision for 10 minutes, or jump into some other engrossing activity or think ugly thoughts about the snack (picture it on your hips, for example).

• Keep low-calorie snacks like raw vegetables prepared and keep high-calorie treats inconveniently out of reach.

• Indulge yourself in a tiny sweet—three maraschino cherries or a tablespoonful of raisins—a half hour before a meal to stave off hunger.

• When going to parties or restaurants, think ahead about how you want to handle drinks, canapés and other temptations. Be ready with your substitute order—mineral water with lime, for example—so you won't get trapped.

• Eat less and exercise more the day before and the day after you know you will eat—or have eaten—more.

Maintaining your weight loss:

It is easy to keep the extra pounds off if you stay vigilant. Weigh yourself once a week. If you have put on a couple of pounds, cut back in your eating and step up your exercising until they are gone.

Plan ahead for holiday periods by eating a little more carefully and exercising a little more before and after.

Enjoy special occasions and treats, but in moderation.

Give away the clothes you needed when you were heavier—or have them altered to your new size—so you will feel the pinch immediately when you start gaining back unwanted pounds.

Source: Dr. Fredrick J. Stare, professor emeritus and founder of Harvard University's department of nutrition. He is co-author, with Dr. Elizabeth M. Whelan, of *The Harvard Square Diet*, Prometheus Books, 700 Amherst St., Buffalo, NY 14215.

How To Lose Weight And Keep It Off

At the age of twenty-five, after failing miserably at countless diets, Larry "Fats" Goldberg lost 175 of his 325 pounds. He lost "a whole Goldberg." Larry has kept the weight off for 32 years...even the years he was running New York City's prize-winning Goldberg's Pizzerias.

We wanted to know how he succeeded where so many others have failed, so we asked...

What's your secret?

"Controlled Cheating." I allow one day a week to eat anything I want, all day long. The Cheating Day is combined with a low-fat diet for the rest of the week, regular exercise and plenty of water. Once an ideal "goal" weight is reached, two Cheating Days are allowed.

That's all there is to it. It's simple—and it works.

How does your system work?

The major reason people can't stay on diets is they can't face the thought of a future without their favorite foods. Sooner or later they cheat, and afterward torment themselves with guilt and feelings of failure. Then they decide they lack willpower and give up their diets in despair.

But anyone can keep to a diet that only lasts six days, when they know they can eat how they choose on the seventh day. Reasons:

• With Controlled Cheating, you don't have to give up any foods—just delay eating them for a few days.

• Controlled Cheating takes the guilt out of cheating, because you know what you are going to do every day—when you will diet and when you will cheat.

• Controlled Cheating is a structured way of eating that imitates how normal people eat. Overweight people benefit from learning to eat this way. Once you've started, it's easy to stay with the plan for the rest of your life—and never gain weight again.

Why does it work?

Controlled Cheating works because people simply can't eat too much in a day. Fact: A person has to eat 3,500 calories to gain a pound, and burn 3,500 calories to lose a pound. So if you eat about 1,500 calories a day for six days, and as much as 5,000 on the Cheating Day (a lot for anyone) you're averaging 2,000 calories a day. Subtract the 500 calories a day you burn exercising, and you are averaging 1,500 calories a day…and you're losing weight.

What are the "rules" for Controlled Cheating?

• Set your goal weight. Goal weight is something most people know about themselves. This is the weight at which you feel most comfortable, healthy and attractive. Discuss with your doctor your ideal weight and how many calories you should be eating to lose weight safely. Once you've set your Goal Weight, think of the weight you must lose in five-pound "bites."

• Choose your Cheating Day. You can pick any day of the week, but once you decide, do not change your Cheating Day.

• Follow your eating plan. Monday is usually the best day to start. But don't eat like crazy the week before you start your diet.

• Stay on the plan for two full weeks. Then you may cheat for one day.

After your Cheating Day, you must go back on your diet. You may cheat one day a week until you reach your goal weight. Weigh yourself every day.

• Reach your Goal Weight. This is a slow process. But when you reach your Goal Weight, you may cheat two days, three to four days apart, and only weigh yourself on the morning of your Cheating Days.

What is the eating plan?

I use a low-fat, low-calorie, high-fiber and complex carbohydrate, balanced diet based on the US Department of Agriculture booklet, Nutrition and Your Health—Dietary Guidelines for Americans: Eat a Variety of Foods, available free from the Consumer Information Center, Dept. 527Y, Pueblo, Colorado 81009. The basics:

• Eat real food. Do not use diet pills, appetite depressants or over-the-counter weight-loss aids.

• Eat a variety of foods. Be flexible.

• Eat plenty of starches, fiber, vegetables, fruits and grains.

• Eliminate fat—as much fat as possible. And…cut out the sweets, salt and alcohol. Use lean meats, low-fat milk products, unsaturated oils.

Save the grease, sugar and salty snacks for your Cheating Day.

What's the rest of the plan?

• Exercise. You must exercise, or the plan will not work. Walk more. Take the stairs. Consult with your doctor if you do not have a regular exercise program.

• Drink water. Drink at least eight to 10 glasses every day, including your Cheating Day.

Any helpful hints from your years of dieting success?

• Eat slowly. This one is hard, but it works. Put the fork or spoon down after every bite…chew…swallow. Then pick it up again.

• Eat lots of little meals. Don't skip breakfast or starve yourself.

• Eat a big breakfast, medium lunch, small dinner. Stop eating by 6:00 PM—or certainly by 7:00 PM.

• Eat crunchy foods that keep your jaws busy (carrots, apples, low-cal breadsticks, etc.)

• Use low-fat and low-calorie products—such as salad dressings and soft drinks.

• Plan your Cheating Day. Look forward to your Cheating Day, and use it for the foods you truly love. Avoid cramming calories just because you can.

• Expect your weight to fluctuate. You will reach plateaus when it will seem as though you'll never lose another pound. Stick with the plan. Your body will adjust and gradually begin to lose again.

• Learn to eat only when you're hungry. To handle cravings: Take a walk. Drink flavored water. Fantasize about your Cheating Day. If you're really hungry, gnaw on vegetables or a bagel.

• Enjoy your food, your exercise…and your new svelte self. Controlled Cheating is a healthy way to eat that produces other healthy changes. As I followed the plan over the years, I naturally became more relaxed, energetic and positive about myself. I don't use food to counteract depression or nervousness…I no longer enjoy the feeling of being stuffed…and I crave fewer "junk" foods—though I love my grease, dough and sugar with a passion!

Best of all, I know I will never be fat again.

Source: Larry "Fats" Goldberg, author of *The New Controlled Cheating Weight Loss and Fitness Program*, Andrews and McMeel, 4900 Main St., Kansas City, Missouri 64112. Mr. Goldberg, the former proprietor of Goldberg's Pizzerias in New York City, now conducts food and other theme tours of his hometown, Kansas City. He weighs 160 pounds.

Losing Weight Without Following A Structured Diet Plan

If you create your own diet plan, you are more likely to keep weight off than if you follow a structured diet program devised by someone else. Also important: Supportive family members and friends...good problem-solving skills...and good, old exercise.

Source: Judith S. Stern, ScD, professor of nutrition and internal medicine, and Susan Kayman, PhD, University of California, Davis.

Simple Secret Of Weight Control

Last year Americans spent $32 billion on diet books, products and programs—and every cent of that vast expenditure was wasted. Dieting simply doesn't work. Dramatic, lasting weight loss—like that touted by the many weight-loss programs*—is essentially mythical.

Reality: 98% of these "successful" dieters regain all the lost weight within five years...and 33%–73% wind up with metabolic changes that cause them to grow even fatter.

Typical scenario: A woman's weight is stable at 150 pounds on a diet of 2,500 calories a day. She goes on a 1,500-calorie-a-day diet until she loses 10 pounds. When she returns

*Fourteen commercial weight-loss programs are currently under investigation by the Federal Trade Commission for possible fraud.

to 2,500 calories a day, her body continues to burn calories at the reduced—1,500-calories-a-day—rate. Result: She regains all the lost weight—and probably more.

This woman feels like a failure, but in truth it's the diet that has failed. Even if she holds her post-diet weight gain to the original 10 pounds, she is worse off than she was before dieting.

Reason: Although her weight has not changed, the percentage of her body composed of fat is now significantly higher, because the slight amount of muscle tissue inevitably lost while dieting is usually replaced in part by new fat cells. Each time a weight loss/weight gain cycle recurs, this increase in fat cells makes getting back to the desired weight harder.

Recent evidence has found that this "yo-yo" dieting is more harmful to a person's health than being consistently overweight.

Weight-control secret:

The key to weight control—known by 4.5 billion instinctive eaters—is to eat only when you're hungry, and not to eat when you're not hungry. That sounds simplistic, but it is the only surefire technique for controlling weight.

Dieting doesn't work because it forces people to reverse the process by which instinctive eaters avoid weight gain—that is, eat little or nothing even when they're famished and then stuff themselves when they really aren't hungry. Dieters spend so much time thinking about eating that they fail to heed the hunger/satiety signals that are the crux of weight control.

Obesity myths:

Before you can become an instinctive eater, you must shed common misconceptions about obesity. Many believe that fat people are fat because some psychological defect causes them to overeat, or because they lack willpower, or simply because they're gluttonous.

Fat people themselves get so much criticism that they too begin to believe these misconceptions.

Reality: Obesity is often hereditary. If one or both of your parents are fat, odds are that

305

you too will be heavy—and there isn't a great deal you can do about it.

Self-defense: Naturally heavy people must realize that while they might want a model's body, they do not need such a body. They can be happy and successful with the body they have. And, contrary to what most people believe, there are no health reasons to lose weight—so long as their weight remains stable.

Exception: People who are extremely overweight—those more than 50% above their ideal body weight—should see a doctor about how they can control weight gain.

Most overweight people whose weight is constant have no more health problems than thin people. It's when they start starving themselves that they get into trouble. Yo-yo dieters are at increased risk for diabetes, heart disease and other serious ailments. Someone whose weight stays a constant 190 pounds faces fewer health risks than a person whose weight fluctuates between 120 and 160.

Most people have a sense of how much they should weigh, but this perception is often far off the mark. Problem: They confuse ideal and optimal weight.

• Ideal weight is that which each of us, for reasons of vanity, would like to reach. Unfortunately, many of us would have to literally starve ourselves to reach this weight…and once we reached it, we would probably be unhealthy and miserable.

• Optimal weight is that at which our bodies feel and function best. For a few fortunate people, ideal weight coincides with optimal weight. For many, optimal weight is several pounds above ideal weight.

Principles of instinctive eating:

Learning to eat instinctively does not guarantee that you will reach your ideal weight. But it does ensure that you will reach your optimal weight, and that is more than good enough.

Illustration: One woman who attended one of my seminars had ballooned from 110 pounds to more than 200 pounds. She learned the principles of instinctive eating but for the following six months remained as heavy as ever. Then, almost imperceptibly at first, her body began to shrink. Now, several years later, she is down to a size 14. She may never again reach her ideal of size four, but she has stabilized her weight at an acceptable level. More important, her self-disgust at being overweight has ended.

To eat instinctively…

• Learn to recognize hunger. Different people feel hunger differently—some people feel a gnawing sensation in the stomach…some get a feeling of tension in their chest…others get a headache or feel weak.

Unfortunately, many signals taken to be signs of hunger are really symptomatic of illness, fatigue, sadness, nervousness, or some other condition. To eat instinctively, you must learn to tell the difference.

Self-test: If you think you feel hungry but are unsure, have a bite to eat. Wait several minutes. If the sensation is somewhat alleviated, you truly were hungry. If the sensation persists, however, you were not. Do not continue eating if not hungry. Instead, go for a walk, call a friend, take a nap, or do something else not involving food.

At first, it may be difficult to tell hunger from other sensations. Eventually, the process will become automatic.

• Determine what you're hungry for. The body is a machine, and, like any machine, it requires different kinds of maintenance (food) at different times. Hunger is the body's way of requesting fuel. To make sure you feed your body the right fuel, run through a mental checklist.

Protocol: Instead of grabbing the first thing that looks appetizing, break foods down into their specific attributes.

• Temperature—do you want something hot, cold, or room temperature?

• Taste—do you want something sweet, sour, bitter, or salty?

• Texture—do you want something smooth, crunchy, chewy, or fibrous?

In many cases, you will be just as satisfied by a low-calorie, nutritious food as by a calorie-dense, nutrient-poor food. This checklist cannot reduce how much you eat or how often, but it can reduce your caloric intake and make your diet more wholesome.

Example: A hungry overeater heads to the freezer for ice cream. But after running through the food attribute checklist, she finds that she really craves not cream, but sweetness. So instead of a bowl of Rocky Road, she enjoys a ripe pear—thus providing her body with nutritious food and saving herself several hundred calories.

• Eat sitting down. Eating while standing or on the run not only encourages you to eat more often, but also makes it more difficult to tell how much you are eating. Pick one spot in your home and always eat your meals there. Don't eat in bed, while watching television, while talking on the phone or while involved in any other activity.

• Eat slowly. After the first bite of food, it may take 20 minutes or so for the body to "realize" that it is no longer hungry. Unfortunately, the average American meal is consumed in under seven minutes. By the time we feel full, we've already consumed hundreds of calories more than we needed or even wanted.

Helpful:

Never rush your meal. To indulge your sense of anticipation, look at your food before eating. Chew thoroughly. If you have trouble pacing yourself, make it a point to chew with empty hands—place your knife and fork on the table while you chew and swallow. Eating slowly sounds easy, but for many people it is the single most challenging aspect of instinctive eating.

• Learn to recognize satiety. Just as instinctive eaters know how to tell when they're hungry, they're also able to recognize when they are full. Again, the process depends upon paying close attention to the signals your body gives you.

Procedure: After each mouthful of food, pause briefly to ask yourself if you are still hungry. If so, continue eating. But if you no longer feel hungry, stop eating at once. Do not let yourself eat out of habit. Do not let yourself be pressured into eating for social reasons.

• Don't be tyrannized by numbers. Many overweight people pay such close attention to their weight, calorie counts, and other numerical measures of diet that they lose sight of the natural hunger/satiety mechanism.

Helpful: Get rid of your scales, listen to your body and forget about calorie counts.

• Don't accept criticism of your body. Few of us tolerate attacks on our religion, ethnic heritage, profession, etc. Why put up with comments like, You could stand to lose a few pounds? Accepting such criticism not only makes obese people feel bad, it engenders a sense of hopelessness that reinforces and encourages overeating.

Better way: Love yourself at your current weight, even if that weight is well above your optimal weight. If someone puts you down for your weight, just ignore him.

Source: Steven C. Strauss, MD, a board-certified internist practicing in New York City and author of *The Body-Signal Secret*, Rodale Press, 33 E. Minor St., Emmaus, Pennsylvania 18098. Dr. Strauss's *Lighten Up* seminars, given in New York City and Washington, DC, teach participants to control their weight permanently without dieting.

Is Snacking Before Meals Bad For You?

For most people, a low-carbohydrate, high-protein snack is good, since it promotes weight loss. For example, a cup of chicken soup (only 50 calories), about 20 minutes before a meal, stimulates the release of the hormone cholecystokinin (CCK) in the small intestine, creating a sense of fullness.

Source: Steven Peikin, MD, associate professor of medicine, Thomas Jefferson University, and author of *The Feel Full Diet*.

The Fiber/Calcium Connection

Dietary fiber can prevent the body from absorbing calcium. Recommended: Eat high-fiber and high-calcium foods at different times.

Source: *American Health*, New York.

To Boost Fiber Intake

Add garbanzo beans to salads…try such ethnic foods as bean enchiladas and hummus …eat at least four servings of cooked or raw vegetables a day—and have at least three servings of fruit…use cooked barley or bulgur instead of rice in stuffings and soups…substitute whole-wheat or spinach pasta for regular…bake with whole-wheat flour instead of white flour.

Source: *Safe Food: Eating Wisely in a Risky World* by Michael F. Jacobson, PhD, executive director, Center for Science in the Public Interest, Living Planet Press, 558 Rose Ave., Venice, California 90291.

Healthier Baking

Substitute apple sauce for butter or margarine to reduce fat, calories and cholesterol. Apple sauce provides moisture and stability when used as a fat alternative, performing best in recipes that contain other moist ingredients such as skim milk or fresh fruit.

Source: Cornell University Cooperative Extension, reported in *Working Woman,* 342 Madison Ave., New York 10173.

Changing Eating Habits

Eating habits change slowly, even among most people who know they ought to eat more healthful foods. Reason: People place health concerns fourth on their list of reasons to change what they eat—behind taste, price and convenience.

Source: Harry Balzer, vice president, NPD Group, a Chicago-based market research firm that surveyed 2,000 households' eating habits, reported in *The New York Times.*

Beware Of Soy Sauce

The worst sodium offender among condiments: Soy sauce. Regular soy sauce contains more than 1,000 milligrams of sodium per tablespoon. Disturbing: Although "light" versions have 30% to 40% less sodium, they still contain approximately 600 milligrams per tablespoon. Note: The recommended maximum daily intake of sodium is between 1,800 mg and 2,400 mg.

Source: *The Wellness Encyclopedia,* Houghton Mifflin, One Beacon St., Boston 02108.

The Benefits Of Fish Oil

Fish oil cuts triglycerides—fats in human blood cells that are linked to coronary artery disease. Fish oil seems to make human blood less likely to form clots that can block blood vessels and bring on heart attacks.

Recommended:

Eat fish once or twice every week—especially salmon, mackerel, tuna, anchovies and sardines, which have the highest levels of beneficial fatty acids.

Source: Research led by Alan Geisler, DO, director, Lipid Disorders Clinic, School of Osteopathic Medicine, University of Medicine and Dentistry of New Jersey, Stratford, New Jersey.

Large Doses Of Niacin

An inexpensive B-vitamin—are an effective way to lower blood cholesterol and triglycerides…but not for everybody. Problem: Side effects…including nausea and the niacin flush—when the skin acquires a redness and burning sensation. On rare occasions, megadoses of niacin have caused liver damage. Solution: If your doctor approves, large doses of niacin can be taken slowly in a time-release pill or capsule. Helpful: Start with 250 mg of the time-release niacin three times a day…and have blood tests after three and six months to determine the effectiveness at that dosage and to check liver function.

Source: Robban Sica-Cohen MD, Center for the Healing Arts, 325 Post Rd., Orange, Connecticut 06477.

Vitamins Fight Cholesterol Plaque

The primary cause of hardening of the arteries. In lab studies, vitamin C was shown to be 95% effective in preventing LDL (low-density lipoprotein—"bad" cholesterol) oxidation, which leads to plaque formation. Also: Beta-carotene, a form of vitamin A, was found to be 90% effective and vitamin E was found to be 45% effective.

Source: Study by Ishwarlal Jialal, winner of the American Heart Association's "Young Investigator Award," reported in *Cardiac Alert*, 7811 Montrose Rd., Potomac, Maryland 20854.

Good News For Pasta Lovers

Pasta is an excellent, low-fat source of carbohydrates. The National Academy of Sciences recommends we eat five or six servings of carbohydrates daily. (Whole grains, potatoes, cereals, and breads are other good carbohydrate sources.) Choose wisely what you put on those carbohydrates. Avoid cream, butter, cheese, and fatty meats. Calories from pasta provide the body with energy. But they don't come with many micronutrients (minerals and vitamins), so also eat foods rich in these substances—fruits, vegetables, low-fat dairy products. Also important: Lean meat, chicken or fish. Note: Different varieties of pasta—spinach, tomato, etc.—all have about the same nutritional value.

Source: Henry N. Ginsberg, MD, head of the division of preventive medicine and nutrition at Columbia University's College of Physicians and Surgeons in New York City.

Garlic's Healthful Properties Are Overrated

Studies were flawed, with too few subjects and too short a test period. Problem: The amounts of garlic used in these studies (7 to 28 cloves a day) are impractical for people to consume every day, and garlic supplements haven't been proven effective. Trap: Large doses of fresh garlic can cause dermatitis, stomach problems, and sometimes even allergic reactions.

Source: *Mayo Clinic Health Letter*, 200 First St. SW, Rochester, Minnesota 55905.

What To Eat To Prevent Cancer...And What Not To Eat

Although scientists continue to debate the role specific foods play in the development of cancer, there's now a consensus that Americans could dramatically lower their cancer risk by altering their eating habits—specifically, by eating less fat and more fiber.

The fat connection:

Most Americans consume 38% to 40% of their total calories in the form of fat—well above the 25% to 30% fat consumption considered desirable.

This makes us highly susceptible to cancer of the colon, breast, pancreas and prostate.

No one knows exactly why eating too much fat promotes the development of cancer, but the evidence—drawn from studies on both animals and humans—is compelling.

Different foods contain different types and quantities of fat...

• Saturated fats are found in beef and other meats, fried foods, and poultry skin.

• Monounsaturated fats are found in peanuts, olives, and a few other foods.

• Polyunsaturated fats are found in corn, safflower, and other cooking oils.

• Very unsaturated long-chain fatty acids are found in cold-water fish, such as herring and salmon.

It's important to keep track of what kinds of fats you eat because nutritionists now recommend that these fats be eaten in a 1:1:1 ratio. In other words, each day we should eat equal portions of polyunsaturated, monounsaturated and saturated fats. For most of us, this means cutting down on saturated fats while increasing intake of monounsaturated and polyunsaturated fats.

To reduce your consumption of saturated fats, eat less fried foods, trim the fat off beef and other meats and trim skin off poultry. These small sacrifices have big health payoffs.

About fish: Although fish contains oils that are highly unsaturated, it's still unclear what, if any, role this oil plays in preventing cancer. There is some early evidence, however, that eating large amounts of fish reduces cancer risk and lowers serum triglycerides—lipids that may be associated with heart disease.
The fiber connection:

While we're eating too much fat, we're also eating too little fiber. On the average, Americans consume only 10 to 12 grams of fiber a day. Instead, we should be eating 25 to 30 grams of fiber every day. (One gram is equivalent in weight to three pennies.)

Big problem: Our diet consists of highly refined, easy-to-chew foods instead of high-fiber fruits, vegetables, and grains.

There are two basic kinds of fiber:

• Insoluble fiber, found primarily in wheat bran, is fiber that is not broken down by bacteria in the intestine. By helping waste pass quickly through the colon, it helps prevent colon cancer, diverticulitis and appendicitis.

• Soluble fiber, found in oat bran and in most fruits and vegetables, is fiber that is broken down by bacteria. It helps to prevent heart disease (by lowering cholesterol) and diabetes (by lowering the blood sugar).

Nutritionists now recommend that Americans should double their intake of dietary fiber...fruits and vegetables as well as grains. Pears, for instance, at 4.6 grams of fiber each, contain more fiber than any other fruit. Other good fiber sources: Red kidney beans (7 grams), lentils (4 grams), apples (3.3 grams), bananas (2.7 grams) and grapefruit (1.5 grams per half).

Caution: Don't consume more than 40 grams of fiber a day. Too much can be almost as bad as too little. In animals, excessive consumption has been found to cause bulky stools that can result in a form of constipation.

There also is some early evidence that alfalfa and certain other grains may actually increase the risk of developing colon cancer. Self-defense: Until the final verdict is in, don't rely just on grains for your fiber...eat a wide variety of fiber-rich foods.
Beyond fat and fiber:

Other than increasing fiber and reducing fats, evidence linking dietary choices to cancer is less reliable.

Still, there are things to do that probably will help prevent cancer...and which won't hurt in any case.

• Eat a wide variety of foods. This limits your exposure to any carcinogens that might be found in a particular food...and eliminates the need for vitamin and mineral supplements.

• Increase your consumption of vitamin A. A powerful antioxidant, it keeps our cells from being attacked by oxygen, and thus prevents cancer. Vitamin A seems particularly effective in helping prevent lung cancer in smokers. To a lesser extent, it also seems to help stave off colon cancer, breast cancer, and lung cancer. Best vitamin A sources: Carrots, squash, and other orange and leafy vegetables.

• Increase your intake of selenium. Selenium is a trace element found in most vegetables. To get more into your diet, eat more vegetables. Alternative: Selenium supplements.

• Limit your consumption of smoked and pickled foods. They have been tied to stomach cancer. An occasional dill pickle won't hurt you, and neither will an occasional barbecued meal. But a daily regimen of pickled vegetables and smoked meats is imprudent.

• Avoid obesity. Obesity is clearly linked to cancer of both the endometrium (the lining of the uterus) and the breast. Also, obese women with breast cancer are far more likely to succumb to the disease than are normal-weight women diagnosed with similar breast cancer.

Keeping track of your diet is one step toward controlling your weight. Also extremely helpful: Exercise.

Watching TV, working in an office, and other aspects of a sedentary life-style all are associated with cancer.

Although it's not yet clear exactly how exercise helps prevent cancer, the incidence of colon cancer is much higher in men with sedentary occupations than men who are active. Women athletes have lower rates of reproductive-tract cancer than sedentary, out-of-shape women. And animal studies have demonstrated that moderate exercise cuts the risk of breast, pancreas, liver, and colon cancer.

Caution: Too much exercise may actually be almost as bad as too little. Several studies have indicated that extreme exertion (like that necessary to complete a marathon) temporarily weakens the immune system, opening the way for infectious bacteria and viruses—and possibly the development of cancer.

Evidence: At the turn of the century, stomach cancer was common in the US. Now that refrigeration is almost universal—and we rely less on pickling and smoking to preserve our foods—it is a rarity. In Japan, however, where pickled and smoked foods remain common, stomach cancer rates are among the highest in the world.

• Limit your consumption of simple carbohydrates (sugars). Evolving man ate very little sugar. As a result of this, our bodies are not set up to properly digest it.

Problem: Simple carbohydrates cause the pancreas to produce a large amount of insulin very rapidly, and there is now some evidence suggesting that this can have a harmful effect on the pancreas. Better: Complex carbohydrates—found in pastas and breads.

• Limit your caffeine consumption. Caffeine has been tied to a variety of cancers, including those of the pancreas and bladder. More recent data suggest caffeine does not cause cancer. Nonetheless, caffeine is very clearly a potent drug, and it makes sense to consume it in moderation.

• Limit your alcohol consumption. Drinking to excess (more than a couple of drinks a day) has been linked to cancer of the mouth and throat. People who drink and smoke are at high risk. Most patients with head or neck cancer are alcoholics or near-alcoholics with poor nutritional habits who smoke regularly.

Source: Leonard A. Cohen, PhD, head of the section of nutritional endocrinology, the American Health Foundation, One Dana Rd., Valhalla, New York 10595. Dr. Cohen's specialty is in the area of nutritional carcinogenesis.

From All The Fats In Your Food

Many misconceptions about foods and fats have found their way into our culture in recent years. The most common…

• Myth: 2% milk is low-fat because only 2% of it is fat.

Truth: Although this figure is correct, it represents a percentage of the product's weight, and doesn't reflect the calories per serving.

In other words, 2% milk has only 2% fat by weight, but more than 38% of its fat calories* come from cholesterol-raising saturated fat.

Recommended: Switch to 1% milk (which gets 17% of its calories from fat) or skim milk (which contains virtually no fat). Each contains as many vitamins and possibly more calcium than fattier versions.

• Myth: Lean hamburger is low in fat and is a healthy choice for red-meat lovers.

Truth: So-called lean ground beef isn't truly lean. Federal regulations say that lean meat may contain no more than 10% fat by weight, and extra-lean no more than 5% fat by weight. However, ground beef is exempt from these rules. So lean ground beef may contain 21% fat by weight and get 64% of its calories from fat after cooking—hardly a low-fat product! Bottom line: Ground beef is the most commonly eaten meat in the US, and no other single food contributes more cholesterol-raising saturated fat to the average American's diet.

Recommended: If you want truly lean ground beef, buy a round steak, have it trimmed of all fat by a butcher and then ground. Or try ground turkey.

• Myth: Processed turkey products are much healthier than processed beef and pork products.

Truth: Just because a label says chicken or turkey doesn't mean the food is lean. The label on Butterball Turkey Bologna says it's 80% fat-free, and is 20% fat by weight, but a slice of it gets 77% of its calories from fat. And Thorn Apple Valley's Chicken Bologna gets

*A healthy guideline is to stick to foods that get no more than 30% of their calories from fat and preferably less than that.

90% of its calories from fat—that's even more than regular bologna. Bottom line: The word chicken or turkey doesn't guarantee a low-fat product.

Recommended: To avoid excess fat, opt for oven-roasted chicken or turkey breast instead.

•Myth: Frozen diet dinners and entrées are convenient and low in fat.

Truth: Many of these dinners merely sound lean. Budget Gourmet's Slim Selects entrées get about 32% of their calories from fat. And the Weight Watchers line is one of the worst, with its products averaging about 38% of their calories from fat. Although the calories are relatively low (about 300 per meal), watching calories isn't enough. You need to get the fat out of your diet.

Recommended: ConAgra's Healthy Choice meals average a mere 14% of calories from fat per meal, and Stouffer's Right Course meals average 20% to 25% calories from fat per meal.

• Myth: Part-skim cheeses are a low-fat alternative to whole-milk cheeses.

Truth: Most part-skim mozzarella, ricotta, and "light" cheeses have one-third less fat than their whole-milk counterparts, but they're still not low in fat. For instance, Weight Watcher's Natural Cheddar and Kraft Light Cheddar Cheese both get more than 50% of their calories from fat.

Recommended: Lite Line's pasteurized processed cheese products contain about three grams of fat per two slices.

• Myth: Trimming the fat from red meats will make them low-fat.

Truth: Even very well trimmed pork or beef provides a large portion of saturated fat when compared with chicken or fish.

Recommended: Limit these to an occasional three-ounce serving and choose a center-cut pork chop (very well trimmed), pork tenderloin, eye-of-round or bottom-round cut of beef or a well-trimmed sirloin steak. Veal is not much leaner than beef. Worst: Porterhouse and T-bone steaks.

• Myth: Eating salads is the best way to cut down on fat.

Truth: The word "salad" is not guarantee you're eating light. A salad can be very fatty if you make the wrong choices. Taco Bell's Taco Salad is the fattiest food on its entire menu, containing about 14 teaspoons of fat and almost 1,000 calories. At a salad bar, whole-milk cottage cheese, croutons, cheese, bacon bits, and a regular dressing can make the fat content soar.

Recommended: McDonald's Chicken Salad Oriental and Burger King's Chicken Salad deserve special credit for being low in fat. Each contains about one teaspoon of fat and a total of about 140 calories. At a salad bar, choose fresh fruits and vegetables and reduced-calorie or water-based dressings, or, even better, a squirt of lemon juice.

• Myth: Non-dairy frozen desserts, because they are not made from animal products, are low in fat.

Truth: These products contain oils and can be as fat-packed as premium ice creams. For instance, Ice Bean has as much fat as Breyer's regular ice cream and Tofutti is almost as fatty as Häagen-Dazs.

Recommended: Stick to nonfat frozen yogurt. If you can't tolerate dairy products, try Tofutti Light.

• Myth: Pizza is an absolute no-no if you're cutting fat from your diet.

Truth: Pizza doesn't have to be fatty if you make wise choices. Try ordering pizza without any cheese, asking instead for mushrooms and green peppers. If you just can't give up cheese, keep in mind that two slices of Domino's plain cheese pizza contain about 2½ teaspoons of fat. But if you order fatty toppings—sausage, double cheese, etc.—that can more than double the fat content.

• Myth: Granola is often touted as a health product, so it must be low-fat.

Truth: Most granola cereals get about 25% of their calories from fat. With so many lower-fat cereals on the market, granola—which also contains very little fiber—makes a poor choice. And granola bars—many of which contain chocolate chips, peanut butter, and other fatty additions—are really just "health-food" candy bars.

Source: Jayne Hurley, a nutritionist at The Center for Science in the Public Interest, 1501 16 St. NW, Washington, DC 20036.

The Best Junk Foods Now...And The Worst

With the pace of life getting faster and more meals being eaten on the run, snack foods have become a fact of life.

Good news: Not all snack foods are terrible for your health. Some are even good for you.

Trap: Some foods that seem healthful are among the worst for you.

Biggest offender: Fat. Many junk foods are loaded with it. Fat is linked with more ills—particularly certain cancers and heart disease—than any other dietary component.
Obviously bad:

- Candy bars. Even a tiny piece is packed with saturated fat and calories.
- Chips. Potato chips get 60% of their calories from fat—even if they're labeled "no cholesterol." There are 150 calories and 9.8 grams of fat in one ounce of potato chips (10 or 12 chips), and most people don't stop with that many. Corn chips aren't much better.

Alternative: Guiltless Gourmet tortilla chips are baked, not fried. An ounce of these contains 110 calories and only 1.4 grams of fat.

- Soda. Drinking one can of soda is like eating 10 packets of sugar and washing it down with water. And soda actually makes you thirstier—your body demands more fluids to dilute all that sugar.

Alternative: Fill a glass half with flavored seltzer and half with fruit juice. A 16-ounce glass of this refreshing drink has only about 55 calories. And the sugars in the fruit juice quickly take the edge of your appetite.
Junk foods in disguise:

Many of the foods that have a reputation for being healthy aren't. Included:

- Granola. It's high in fat, often saturated fat such as coconut oil. Granola bars are even worse—they require a lot of fat to retain their bar shape.
- Muffins. The old-fashioned kind Grandma made were healthful—the small, crumbly muffins that fell apart when you tore the paper off. Most of the muffins for sale now are 4½ to 6 ounces, at about 100 calories per ounce, and contain as much fat as three pats of butter.

- Peanuts. People substitute a jar of peanuts for a skipped meal and think the protein in peanuts makes this a healthful choice. Peanuts do contain protein—but 74% of the calories in peanuts comes from fat. A small bag of dry-roasted peanuts from the vending machine contains 170 calories and 14 grams of fat, the equivalent of almost three pats of butter.

Peanuts are also slow to be digested—your brain doesn't get the feel-full signal until you've consumed great quantities.

- Cheese. Cheese contains some protein and a significant amount of calcium. But it also has one of the highest saturated-fat contents of any food. Cheese can be a good diet supplement, but it should not be a diet staple.
Best snack foods:

- Cereal...(except granola!) With skim milk and fruit, dry cereal is soothing, nutritious and simple to fix, whatever the time of day.
- Bagels. Only 160–180 calories, and almost no fat.
- Fudgesicles. If you crave chocolate, these are a great way to get the chocolate flavor without the fat. They're only about 100 calories each (35 calories for the diet version), compared with 250 to 300 calories in the average candy bar.
- Hershey's chocolate syrup. Unlike fudge sauce, which is made with cocoa butter, Hershey's syrup is made with dry cocoa powder and has very little fat. Mix it in a blender with skim milk and ice cubes for a low-calorie chocolate shake...pour it over low-fat ice milk for a sundae.
- Soft pretzels...sold in frozen-food sections of supermarkets. They contain almost no fat and are quite similar to bagels in calorie content.
- Pizza...if you ask for very little cheese and lots of mushrooms, peppers, onions. Pizza can be a satisfying snack or light meal that's high in calcium and in vitamins A, B-complex and C.

Source: Connie Roberts, MS, a registered dietitian at Brigham and Women's Hospital in Boston, where she manages the Nutrition Consultation Service. She is nutrition editor for the *Harvard Heart Letter,* Harvard Medical School Publications Group, 164 Longwood Ave., Boston 02115.

Prescriptions
For Walking

If you are overweight or have diabetes: Distance is more important than speed. Try to walk for 45 minutes to one hour at a self-selected pace. Heart or lung disorders: Exercise indoors in a climate-controlled, pollution-free environment, especially if the temperature is above 88° and humidity is greater than 85%. Sports injuries or arthritis in the back or lower extremities: Avoid steep hills. They stress weight-bearing joints. To reduce stress or improve aerobic fitness: Increase intensity of exercise, aiming for a 15-minute mile or better. To increase heart rate, use handheld weights, walk up stairs or hills, and pump your arms.

Source: *Walking Medicine: Lifetime Guide to Preventative & Therapeutic Exercisewalking Programs* by Gary Yanker and Kathy Burton, McGraw-Hill, 1221 Ave. of the Americas, New York 10020.

Whole Truth About
Walking Shoes

A few years ago, as fitness walking began to boom, the major athletic-shoe companies announced that walkers had different needs than runners and developed a new category—the walking shoe.

The truth: Many walkers don't need walking shoes...and some walkers would even be better off with another kind of shoe.

Whether you are a casual fitness walker or a dedicated power walker (with a focus on technique, pace and heart rate), you can probably be well-served by tennis shoes, cross-trainers or running shoes—as long as they are of high quality. Running shoes can be very well-suited to walkers. Reasons:

• As you age, there is some atrophy of the fat in your foot pads—the heel pads, in particular. If you walk on hard surfaces, you will benefit from the extra cushioning in running shoes.

• People who over-pronate (roll in excessively) need the support of a straighter last (the form the shape of the shoe is built around) and stronger support features—which running shoes have.

The most important criterion in choosing a shoe is a good fit—for both length and width. Since most athletic shoes are not sized for width, the more options you have, the better.

Bottom line: When buying a shoe for walking, seek out the model that best suits your needs. Don't restrict yourself to a specific category.

Source: Tom Brunick, director of The Athlete's Foot Wear Test Center at North Central College, Napierville, Illinois.

Women's Exercise Shoes
Vs Men's Exercise Shoes

Women in men's exercise shoes are probably more comfortable than they would be in women's shoes. Reason: The average exercise shoe made for women is narrower than the average woman's foot. Men's and boy's shoes are cut more generously and will fit many women better. Self defense: Both sexes should shop in the men's or boy's shoe department.

Source: Francesca M. Thompson, MD, assistant clinical professor of orthopaedic surgery, College of Physicians and Surgeons, Columbia University.

How To Build
A Home Gym

When I tell people I'm a home fitness consultant, the first question they ask is, If I buy just one piece of exercise equipment, what should it be? There's no easy answer. It all depends on the individual.

Most important: Before buying anything, make a serious commitment to exercise. Without a commitment, you'll probably waste hundreds—or thousands—of dollars on equipment that goes unused. How to shop:

• Consider your needs and wants. If you love outdoor biking but live in northern Minnesota, buy a stationary bike. If you sit behind a desk all day, choose a machine you can use while standing.

Other considerations: How much space you have…how much motivational feedback you need (don't buy high-tech options you'll never use)…who else will be using the equipment. Buy a unit with a timer and other performance readouts. Reason: Feedback gives goals and helps with motivation.

- Try the equipment out before you decide to buy. Don some comfortable clothes and athletic shoes and head to the store for test runs on different types and models of equipment. And really work out for at least 5 to 10 minutes.
- Buy from a specialty store. They usually have the best selection and service, as well as the most knowledgeable sales staff. Despite the money-back guarantees, I do not recommend buying through the mail.
- Buy quality. Don't buy cheap equipment thinking that you'll upgrade it later with something better. A poor-quality machine that is uncomfortable to use will turn you off exercise completely.

Aerobic equipment:
- Treadmills.
- Benefits:
- Habit-forming—they have the highest adherence of all home exercise equipment.
- Healthful—doctors say weight-bearing exercise helps prevent osteoporosis and also burns lots of calories.
- Safe—walking (not running or jogging) is easy on the joints.
- Drawbacks:
- Expensive.
- Stressful—running and jogging are hard on joints. If you want to run: Buy a shock-absorbing model. And don't run if you have an orthopedic problem.
- Large—they take up a lot of space.
- Stationary bikes.
- Benefits:
- Easy to use. You can even read or watch TV while exercising.
- Small—they don't require much space. Exception: Recumbent models.
- Drawbacks:

- Painful. They can be a pain in the rear—literally—to use.
- Limited—they exercise only the lower body, unless you buy a dual-action model.
- Cross-country ski machines.
- Benefits:
- Versatile—they tone hips, thighs, buttocks and calves.
- Rigorous—a great aerobic workout.
- Drawback:
- Hard to use—the motion can be difficult to coordinate, especially with some of the flywheel models.
- Stair climbers.
- Benefits:
- Versatile—they tone hips, thighs and calves—main trouble spots for most women.
- Small—they don't require much space… about the same as a bike.
- Drawbacks:
- Limited—they don't work the upper body (unless you get a dual-action unit).
- Cheatable—users tend to lean on the handlebars, which lessens the work load.

Muscle-building and strength training:
- Free weights.
- Benefits:
- Versatile—the best, time-tested way to tone and strengthen all major muscle groups. And they require greater range of motion than machines do.
- Complete—they work to support muscle groups as well as allow the key muscle in each exercise to be developed.
- Inexpensive—much cheaper than multigyms (see below) and single-station weight machines.
- Drawbacks:
- Hard to use safely—you should have someone assist you, specifically with heavier weights and bench-pressing. Highly recommended: a full-length mirror (for proper form).
- Multigym (strength-training) machines.
- Benefits:
- Safe—you can train without supervision.
- Easier to use than free weights.
- Drawbacks:
- Large—they take up a lot of space.
- Expensive.

Getting started/keeping going:

Developing a good personal fitness program depends more on your fitness level than on your age. However, anyone over 35 should see a doctor—especially if you've had heart problems or if there's a history of heart problems in your family—before beginning a new fitness regime for a complete checkup. Exercise minimum:

Maintain your target heart rate* for at least 20 minutes three times a week. Other advice:

• Set specific fitness goals. Having a goal that is important to you (not your spouse or anyone else) provides needed motivation. Common trap: Picking a goal that is not attainable—if you have a large frame you'll never have the slender body of a runner...if your frame is slight, you'll never look like Arnold Schwarzenegger. Your doctor or personal trainer can help you set realistic goals. Examples:

Within a year, I want to reduce my body fat from 23% to 18%...run an eight-minute mile ...lose two pounds a week.

• Distract yourself. Indoor exercise can be very boring. Make sure your exercise room has some sort of diversion—a stereo or a TV—or read.

• Diversify. Once you know you're committed, you may want to purchase additional pieces of equipment to add variety to your workouts and develop different muscle groups.

• Stretch. Muscles that are too tight are more easily strained—whether from playing sports or just getting out of bed in the morning. Typically, people feel old when their muscles lose flexibility. Recommended: Enroll in a yoga or stretch class, or follow a video or book on the subject.

Rules of safe stretching:

Warm up with a couple of minutes of light aerobic exercise before you stretch...stretch in a slow, smooth motion—never bounce... stretch for a minimum of 2 to 3 minutes before your workout and 3 to 10 minutes after.

*To determine your target heart-rate range: Subtract your age from 220. Multiply this number by 0.7 and 0.83. Your target heart rate, in beats per minute, is within this range.

Source: An industry insider who continually tests the latest home exercise equipment.

Sports Drinks

Special sweetened mixtures of carbohydrate (sugar) and sodium—do not enhance athletic performance. Most sports do not cause the body to burn so much carbohydrate or expend so much sodium that supplements would be required during the activity. Exceptions: Marathon running and cycle road racing. For most other athletes, however, the real value of sports drinks is after exertion, when consuming carbohydrates and sodium may help to speed the body's return to its resting equilibrium.

Source: *The Lancet*, 34 Beacon St., Boston 02108.

Exercise Helps Sleep

People with sleep problems who engaged in one hour of aerobic exercise per day, five days a week for six months, reported significant improvement in their sleeping patterns. According to a recent study, participants who exercised reported falling asleep more quickly, awakening during the night less often, and feeling more refreshed in the morning.

Source: Study results reported by Michael Vitiello, psychologist, University of Washington, quoted in *American Health,* 80 Fifth Ave., New York 10011.

Workout Warning

Regular, moderate exercise is more healthful than more intensive but sporadic workouts, a comprehensive analysis confirms. Data from 66 studies show that a person lowers "bad" cholesterol and raises "good" cholesterol in proportion to the time spent in physical activity. But high-intensity exercise by itself has no effect. Bottom line: A brisk walk or slow jog for 30 minutes a day is better than a heavy weekend workout.

Source: research at the University of Colorado, cited in *The Harvard Medical School Health Letter*.

Can Exercise Really Help A Back Injury?

Doctors generally believe a poor response to back surgery means other treatments will fail as well.

Reality: Patients whose operations fail often get more benefit from exercise than ones whose surgery succeeds.

Possible reason: Some back injuries respond less to surgery than to carefully supervised programs to strengthen muscles.

Source: Hubert Rosomoff, MD, director, University of Miami Comprehensive Pain and Rehabilitation Center, Miami Beach.

Exercise: The Real Aphrodisiac?

Researchers and common sense have long held that exercise enhances health and makes people feel better about themselves and their bodies. This, in turn, makes them more sexually attractive and responsive.

Now studies are suggesting that exercise is a potent stimulus to hormone production in both men and women. It may, in fact, chemically increase basic libido by stepping up the levels of such hormones as testosterone.

Source: *Whole Body Healing* by Carl Lowe, Rodale Press, Emmaus, PA.

Sex Before Exercise Myth

If you exercise, you've probably heard the myth that sex before an athletic event leads to poor performance.

Fact: At worst, sex before strenuous physical activity has no effect on performance. At best, it may improve performance due to the sense of well-being it produces.

Allergies To Exercise

Allergies to exercise can cause itching, hives, swelling and fainting spells. Exercise-induced anaphylaxis (EIA) is most frequently brought on by jogging and aerobic exercising. Some people can induce EIA simply by walking briskly.

Helpful: Don't eat before you exercise—some foods increase the risk of an attack—and avoid taking aspirin and ibuprofen. If you are prone to EIA, don't work out alone...stop exercising at the first sign of itching or faintness...and bring along an adrenaline kit.

Source: Research by Matthew Liang, MD, and Albert L. Sheffer, MD, Harvard Medical School, reported in *Omni*, 1965 Broadway, New York 10023.

Exercising In The Car

To unlock rush-hour tension while in your car, breathe deeply a few times...sit up straight and grip the wheel with both hands...go with the flow of traffic (honking or screaming at the car ahead won't change the pace)...listen to pleasant music on the radio or to books or educational tapes on your tape deck.

Source: *Be Well, Work Well: Your Guide to On-the-Job Fitness* by "Dr. Jock," fitness columnist Marilynn Preston, Dartnell Corp., 4660 Ravenswood Ave., Chicago 60640.

Morning Warning

Don't roll out of bed and go straight into your workout. Always wait at least an hour after waking before exercising.

Reason: During a night's sleep, the disks in your spine expand with fluid, making them tighter, tenser and more vulnerable to irritation when you first get up.

Source: Augustus A. White III, MD, Harvard Medical School, quoted in *Self*, 350 Madison Ave., New York 10017.

Vigorous Exercise Pays Off

Helps fend off diabetes. For every hour of vigorous exercise that a man does in a week, he can lower his risk of developing non-insulin dependent diabetes mellitus (NIDDM) by 6%.

Non-insulin dependent diabetes usually begins in those older than forty, often among overweight people. A study was done of nearly 6,000 men whose exercise habits and health patterns were observed for 14 years.

Source: Susan P. Helmrich, PhD, an epidemiologist at the University of California, Berkeley.

Hot-Weather Workouts

Hot-weather workouts should be done with less intensity—it takes 4 to 10 days for your body to adjust to exercising in the heat. As you feel yourself adjusting, gradually build up to your normal workout.

Recommended:

Swimming—good exercise that helps control body temperature in hot weather.

Source: *Get in Shape, Stay in Shape* by the editors of Consumer Reports Books, 101 Truman Ave., Yonkers, New York 10703.

Heat, Cold And Injuries

Apply ice when tissue is first injured—cold reduces swelling and acts as a local anesthetic. Use heat once bleeding and swelling have stopped—usually after 72 hours. This increases blood flow to the injury and removal of waste products from the area—speeding healing.

Beware: Using heat too soon greatly increases swelling and bleeding into tissues…making the injury worse.

Source: Kim Edward LeBlanc, MD, staff physician, Gary Memorial Hospital, Breaux Bridge, Louisiana, writing in *Running & FitNews,* 9310 Old Georgetown Rd., Bethesda, Maryland 20814.

Safer Night Cycling

Don't look directly into oncoming car headlights (they can blind you temporarily)…don't travel on high-speed roads…don't wear headphones.

Do invest in halogen head- and taillights…do wear reflective fluorescent-colored clothing and patches across the full width of the back and on arms, chest and helmet…do use a rearview mirror…do ride with traffic.

Source: *The Wellness Encyclopedia,* Houghton Mifflin Co., 2 Park St., Boston 02108.

A Healthier You

Aerobic exercise isn't enough to keep you in shape as you age. Also important: Strength training and flexibility exercises. Muscle strength, endurance and flexibility enable people to continue to perform routine daily tasks—bathing, dressing, etc.—as they age.

Source: *The Strength Connection,* Institute for Aerobics Research, 12330 Preston Rd., Dallas 75230.

A Proper Fit

Bicycle helmets reduce the odds of head injury by 85%—if they are worn properly. Look for a helmet that fits your head snugly…touches your head at the top and on all sides without squeezing…comes with "sizing pads"—additional pieces of foam for better fit…has adequate ventilation.

Source: *Consumer's Research Magazine,* 800 Maryland Ave. NE, Washington, DC 20002.

Hikers, Beware

Limber up before you go hiking to prevent muscle problems from developing later. Stretch your hamstrings, calves, feet, shoulders and back muscles using slow—not bouncy—stretching movements.

Source: *Backpacker*, 33 E. Minor St., Emmaus, Pennsylvania 18098.

Exercise Overcomes Depression

People who describe themselves as depressed say they feel significantly better after exercising. Exercise also leads to an improved self-image.

Source: Study of more than 80 college students, led by Paula Stein, PhD, psychology department, Hofstra University, Hempstead, New York 11550.

18

More Funtime

How To Win At Blackjack...Without Counting Cards

Of all the casino games, only blackjack allows a player to gain a long-term advantage over the casino.

The big edge comes from mastering intricate card-counting techniques. This entails hours of practice, intense mental concentration and the risk of detection. (In Nevada, casinos can evict card-counters from the premises.)

But there is an easier way for beginning players to win at blackjack...a set of principles based more on common sense than higher mathematics. If you follow these principles, you can reduce the casino's advantage to a bare minimum—less than .01%. At those odds, you have a fighting chance to win at any given session.

Follow a good basic strategy. This tells you when to...

• Stand (refuse any more cards).

• Hit (take another card).

• Double down (double your bet and receive one and only one more card).

• Split (double your bet by playing each of two equal-valued cards—two aces, for example, or two 8's—as a separate hand).

You can find a basic strategy chart in almost any book on blackjack.*

• The fewer decks in play, the better your chances of winning. In Nevada, make a point to seek out single- or double-deck games. In Atlantic City, virtually all games are six or eight decks.

• Seek out a casino with the most favorable rules. Some rules—such as a 3-2 payoff for a player's blackjack—are universal. But others vary from house to house.

Examples: When a casino allows you to double down after you split a hand, it cuts the house edge by .14%. Also advantageous: The "surrender" option, which enables a player to sacrifice half the original bet (and retrieve the other half) before drawing any additional cards.

*Most reliable sources: Lawrence Revere (*Playing Blackjack as a Business*) and Jerry Patterson (*Break the Dealer*).

• Gauge the mood of the table before you play. If players are smiling and betting more than the minimum, the cards are probably flowing their way and against the dealer.

• Manage your money with betting progressions. For best results, beginning players should vary their bets according to general card-counting principles but without keeping a cumulative count of every card that has been played.

Example: If you sit down at a $5-minimum table, begin play with a $10 bet. Watch all cards exposed by both players and dealers. If you see more small cards (2's through 7's) than large cards (9's, 10's and aces), and you win the hand, increase your wager to $15…and start a fresh count of small and large cards.

As long as the small cards predominate on each hand, and as long as you keep winning, continue to increase your bet as follows: $20, $30, $45. Stay at $45 until you lose or until the dealer shuffles, then revert to a $10 bet and begin again.

If you lose a hand and the large cards predominate, reduce your wager to $5. Keep it there win or lose until you reach a hand where the smaller cards come out ahead, then return to $10.

Limitations:

This system works best with single- or double-deck Nevada games. In Atlantic City and Nevada, where there are six- and eight-deck games, the large number of decks makes counting less valuable—begin at $10 or double the table minimum. If you win, increase your wager as follows: $15, $20, $30, $45, $60. Remain at $60 until you lose or the dealer shuffles, then go back to $10.

Source: "Mr. Blackjack," a professional gambler who has made his living at the tables for more than 10 years. For professional consultations or further information, he can be contacted through any gambling-book store in Nevada.

How To Profit When You Play State Lotteries

The trick to making state lotteries a better gambling proposition is to carefully choose unpopular numbers—numbers that are selected less often than the norm by the lottery-playing public.

When you hit a jackpot with unpopular numbers, you have a chance of being the only winner. And if you do have to share your jackpot, you'll probably share it with fewer people. This makes a significant difference.

Example:

If a $1-million jackpot is split four ways, each winner takes only $250,000. Assuming a 20-year payout (typical for state lotteries), a single winner would receive $50,000 a year (minus taxes).

In a four-way split, the winner would receive only $12,500 a year.

How to pick unpopular numbers:

• Play numbers higher than 31. Many lottery players choose numbers based on birthdays and anniversaries and other special dates—making the numbers 1 through 31 more popular than the rest.

Note:

Don't make all six of your choices higher than 31. Reason: Many savvy players are already doing this. If you hit a jackpot with six numbers of 32 or higher, you'll probably have to share it with several of them. Better: Play a blend of three lower numbers (below 32) and three higher numbers.

• Avoid numbers in the visual hot zone. For psychological reasons, players who mark their lottery cards purely on visual impulse often use numbers from the third horizontal row down to the middle.

They avoid numbers located in the outside vertical columns.

• Restrict your plays to large hold-over jackpots that are not heavily promoted.

After the big jackpot goes uncollected for several games in a row, it can grow to five or six times the normal size. But when jackpots are at their largest, media-induced lottery fever generates much heavier betting by a larger player pool—which dilutes your advantage.

Watch for oversized jackpots in states that do relatively little lottery promotion. Other opportunities:

Giant jackpots that are overshadowed and pushed out of the newspapers by major news events.

Source: Gambling authority Mike Caro (a.k.a. "America's Mad Genius"). He heads a national brain trust of experts who quote odds on current events and broadcast them over Las Vegas radio superstation KBEG. Caro has written six books including *Caro on Gambling,* Gambler's Book Club, Box 4115, Las Vegas 89127.

Are Pro Basketball Games Fixed?

Background:

During one season, the Washington Bullets had a home record of 28 wins and nine losses. On the road, their record was only nine wins and 26 losses. The same home/away contrast holds true for every team in the NBA.

The fix:

Team owners, who want to attract crowds to their home arenas with the lure of victory, require visiting teams to take the earliest scheduled flight on game day, which often demands a 6 a.m. wake-up call...the home team usually has the night off before the game, while the visitors may have played several consecutive nights in different cities in different time zones.

Source: Reprinted with permission from *The Washington Monthly.* Copyright by The Washington Monthly Co., 1611 Connecticut Ave. NW, Washington, DC 20009.

Atlantic City Vs Nevada

Gamblers who like to play the slots should gamble in Atlantic City instead of Nevada for the best odds. New Jersey law requires that slot machines pay out at least 83% of the draw. Newly regulated Nevada machines are required to pay only 75%, and older machines are exempt from the rule.

Source: The New Jersey Gaming Commission and the Nevada Gaming Commission.

Winning Sweepstakes Strategies

Winning a major sweepstakes prize is often no more difficult than addressing an envelope. Yet many people never enter, assuming that the odds against winning are astronomical or that they'll have to buy some unwanted item to have a chance.

In reality, sweepstakes are a major marketing tool used by many of our largest corporations and rigorously monitored by the Federal Trade Commission. By law, no purchase can be required. A sponsor may package a sweepstakes with Yes and No envelopes, for example, to imply that entrants have a better shot if they buy the product. In fact, the odds remain the same.

But you can improve your odds by using simple strategies. Not all sweepstakes are created equal...some are more winnable than others.

Random-draw sweepstakes: In these traditional sweepstakes, the number of entries (on either official forms or facsimiles) is unlimited. Winners are picked from a drum or by computer. The more times you enter, the better your odds of winning. Your chances also improve when there are more prizes and fewer total entrants.

The most profitable draw sweepstakes are held between April and September. (When potential entrants are on vacation, fewer are likely to compete.) Other positive factors:

• A television qualifier, in which players must watch a program to obtain words they need to make an entry eligible.

• An overlong qualifier. If entrants have to print more than six words ("Duncan Hines Mix/Frosting/Brownies/Chocolate Chip Cookies Chocolate Lovers' Sweepstakes"), they are less likely to submit multiple entries. If you have more patience, your chances soar.

• A healthy number of solid middle and lower prizes rather than a single gigantic grand prize. There will be both fewer entrants and more chances to win something substantial.

After targeting a given sweepstakes, you can use more specialized strategies:

• If winners are to be chosen from a drum or barrel, fold your entries on the diagonal or into an accordion shape. This increases their surface area, giving the judge more to grip.

• Use oversize envelopes for mail-in sweepstakes. Again, the rationale is that you are giving the judge's hand something larger to latch on to.

• If you are planning to enter a dozen or more times, mail just a few entries each day. Some judging organizations select a few winning envelopes from each mailbag they receive.

Game sweepstakes: In this category, you find out on your own (by matching, scratching or decoding) whether you are a winner. Since the number of game pieces is predetermined by the sponsor, the chance of winning with any one game piece from any specific sweepstakes is fixed. But you can improve your chances by obtaining more pieces.

Second-chance sweepstakes: Prices unclaimed in a game sweepstakes are dispensed through a new, random-draw "second-chance" competition with new entries and a new deadline. Often 80% or more of the prizes are awarded through the second chance. In a few cases, every second-chance entry we submitted won a prize. Many entrants are unaware of these sweepstakes, since their rules are buried in the fine print of the original game. Savvy players will find their more lucrative opportunities in this category.

Second-chance strategies: Write for a winners' list soon after the original game sweepstakes has concluded. This will tell you how many prizes remain. Ask for instructions and the entry deadline for the second-chance drawing.

The more difficult the game, the more prizes will be left unclaimed. Your best second-chance bets are match and decode games, where entrants may be required to visit a store to find out if they've won in the original sweepstakes. Less favorable: Instant-win "scratch" games, where it is relatively easy to determine a winner.

Source: Jeffrey and Robin Sklar, authors of *Winning Sweepstakes*, Perigee Books.

Secrets Of Doing Crossword Puzzles Much Faster

Successful people play to win. They know the rules, devise plans of attack and follow their plans with discipline whether it's on the job, in the stock market—or just doing a crossword puzzle. To get all the answers...

• Start with the fill-in-the-blank clues. These are usually the easiest and the least ambiguous.

• Next, try to fill in an across answer on the top row or a down answer on the left side. You can then proceed to answers that start with a known letter...and they're always easier to solve than answers where the known letter is in the middle.

• In a thematic puzzle, the longest blanks on the grid always relate to the theme.

• When the clue is expressed in the plural, the answer is probably plural. Most clues that are expressed in the past tense have answers ending in *-ed*. Most clues that are expressed in the superlative have answers ending in *-est*.

• Remember that *e* and *s* are the most popular word-ending letters. Also, puzzles use a disproportionate number of common letters and very few rare letters, such as *q, z, x, j*, etc.

• When you are missing one or two letters in a word, scan the alphabet. Plug in all possible letters or combinations...one is bound to work.

Source: David Feldman, author of *How to Win at Just About Everything*, Morrow Quill, William Morrow, 105 Madison Ave., New York 10016.

How To Become A Game Show Contestant

Getting an audition as a contestant on a game show is easy. But the contestants who make it onto a show—and go on to win—have special qualities. The edge: These players know how to put their best face forward, and they know their game. To get an audition:

• Target the game show. Your favorite game as viewer may not be the game you play best. Important: Choose a vehicle for your best skills and personality traits, matching them to one of the four game show categories: Trivia/quiz, word/puzzle, personality and kids/teens.

• Prepare diligently. Expertise at a game will compensate for almost any shortcoming. The game show producers want you to win. Game shows are popular in proportion to the excitement they generate. Winners are exciting.

Key: Watch the game regularly—daily is best. Tape it if necessary. Know all the rules, and be familiar with game "lingo."

Essential: Practice, practice, practice. The best ways: (1) Play along as you watch the game. (2) Play mock games. (3) Play board games, read books and periodicals, and play video/computer games.

• Get an audition. Some shows, such as "Let's Make a Deal" or "The Price Is Right," pick directly from the studio audience, with little or no preliminary interviewing. More common: Watch for a trailer at the end of the show that supplies addresses and/or telephone numbers to contact for audition information. Best: Call rather than write. Calling is faster, and you can get immediate answers to your questions.

Smart questions to ask when calling a show: I am planning a trip to Hollywood during the period of _____. When will you be interviewing during that time? Will I have time to get through all my audition interviews during that time? If I qualify, will I be able to tape my shows during that time? Will you be conducting a contestant search in or around my area in the coming months? What is your audition process?

Important: Be polite and to the point in all your conversations.

• At the audition:

Jitters are expected, but it's important to pay attention and be yourself. Guidelines:

• Play up your best qualities. Rule of thumb: Be yourself—your best self. What game-show contestant coordinators look for: Someone with good eye contact, an outgoing personality, enthusiasm, a voice that projects. Turn-offs: Someone who is abrasive, who boasts of never having seen the show, who is extreme in some negative way (is constantly self-deprecating, etc.).

• Listen to who's talking to you. This includes the contestant coordinator, the show host or your partner. Pay attention only to what relates to you.

• Don't focus on the competition. Forget the crowds.

• Don't think about prizes. It adds pressure and takes away from having fun. Better: Just relax and enjoy playing the game.

• Wear something you feel comfortable and attractive in. An all-new outfit or "new look" will distract you.

Bottom line: A game show shouldn't be a teeth-clenching endurance test. Contestant selection is tailored to pinpoint people who will enjoy themselves and give the show a good feeling.

Source: Greg Muntean, former game-show contestant coordinator for "Jeopardy!" and "Wheel of Fortune."

Radio Contests: More Than Luck

Almost every popular radio station uses giveaways. Rewards include cash, cars, vacations and other prizes, ranging from record albums to TV sets. Playing the contests won't make you rich, but there's nothing like the thrill of hearing your name announced over the radio—as a winner.

Although chance plays the major role, you can greatly increase your odds of winning by understanding how call-in contests are run.

To begin: Pick a few stations that have entertaining contests and good prizes. Listen to each closely for a few hours, and phone in several times to get a feel for how the game is played.

The more contests you enter, the greater your chance of winning. The trick is to do this without spending your life on the phone. The key: Each program's disc jockey has a format that he/she follows closely.

Example: My prime listening time is from 11 p.m. to 1 a.m. By monitoring four stations, I have found that one holds regular contests at 42 minutes after the hour, another at either 15 or 45 minutes after the hour, another at either 5 or 35 minutes after the hour and another at 5 of the hour. I tune in these stations only at those times.

After the contest has been announced, several factors determine how quickly you should place your call:

• The winning number: The number of the winning call often corresponds to the station's location on the dial. For example, one station, at 95.5 FM, always rewards the 95th caller. If you dial right way, you'll be about number 20 (stations generally tell you your number when your call is answered). So wait 35 seconds before dialing. By the time the call goes through and the phone rings a few times (at least five seconds per ring), you'll be pretty close to call number 95. It usually takes the station 70–75 seconds to reach that call.

• The number of lines at the station: This helps determine how quickly they get to the winning number. A station with only two phone lines moves more slowly than one with 22. If you ask, most stations will tell you how many lines they use for contests.

• The number of people answering the phones: Stations that have two or more people handling the calls move more quickly than those where it's left up to the DJ. After you've played the contests a few times, you'll get to know the voices—and the number of phone answerers at each station.

• Individual speeds: Some DJs get the contest rolling quickly, others slowly. Get to know their habits.

There's always an element of chance. The difference between being caller number 94 and caller number 95 is a split second, and there's no way you can control that. But you can greatly increase the odds of winning.

Don't give up. If you get a call through and you're five or more numbers away from winning, hang up and try again. And don't let a busy signal discourage you. Hint: Many stations have a recording telling you "Please try again later" if all the lines are busy. Stay on the line. Your call will be answered…sometimes in the middle of the recording, sometimes soon after it is completed.

Some DJs award the prize at random rather than counting through the calls to, say number 95. Others announce that caller number two will win, so they don't have to answer 95 calls (and with such a low number, it's really no contest at all). Your only recourse in such a situation is to complain to the station's management. If lazy DJs know they've been caught, they'll improve.

Source: Bob Gross, who has won more than $10,500 in cash and prizes in radio contests over the past five years.

The Wonderful New Art Of Dining At Home

Gone with the extravagant 1980s is the nonchalant going out for $100 dinners-for-two several nights a week.

Today's two-wage-earner families are tired at the end of the day. Their idea of fun is to entertain at home—but in small numbers and serving simple food.

In contrast, at-home chefs from the previous generation took great pride in being able to turn out culinary triumphs like Beef Wellington with Sauce Perigueux that were the rage in the 1960s and 1970s when everyone aspired to be like Dione Lucas or Julia Child. Today's twenty- and thirtysomethings often can't cook at all and may never really need to. Despite the seemingly endless number of cookbooks published each year, very few are best sellers and many have a very short life.

Fresh and healthy:

What is undeniably true today, however, is a tremendous emphasis on health. We are all watching our weight and cholesterol, and many of us don't want to eat beef, much less the rich duxelles and foie gras stuffing that goes between the filet and the pastry wrapping in a classic Beef Wellington.

Among the favored entrees today: Fish and chicken…and even totally vegetarian creations.

Also popular: Chili, pasta dishes and such homey American favorites as chicken pot pie —and good ones can often be purchased ready-made.

Instead of serving three or four courses, most of today's hosts and hostesses settle for a light starter—perhaps a cold or hot soup— or maybe just a few simple hors d'oeuvres, an entree accompanied by a vegetable or salad and a small but elegant dessert, followed by decaf espresso.

A little help…helps a lot:

What's made entertaining at home a lot more doable for working people these days is the wide variety of foods and specialties that can be purchased from outside sources.

From freshly made pastas (with sauces and trimmings) to crispy cooked chicken…to an endless array of tempting precut salad ingredients…a whole meal can be put together with very little chopping or time-consuming preparation by the hosts.

If you're throwing something on the grill, for example, it's very easy to foil wrap a few sliced vegetables like eggplant, onions and zucchini with colorful peppers and roast them, too. Pick up one of the interesting premade pasta or potato salads to serve on the side.

While almost everyone loves a rich little dessert treat, almost no one has to make one anymore. Virtually every town or suburban hamlet has a patisserie or a special bakery that turns out tiny little fruit tarts or sinfully rich chocolate truffles. Or serve mixed fruit with some elegant cookies. Even some supermarket frozen desserts are becoming quite acceptable. Examples: Chocolate-covered ice cream bonbons, frozen cheesecake that can be dressed up with fresh berries and a raspberry sauce.

Concentrate on the ambiance:

Although there are many fine small caterers around these days who are more than willing to prepare at-home dinners, my sense is that few people are using them. Even those who could afford to use a caterer perceive that they cannot…or feel that this would seem pretentious in the hard-pressed 1990s.

As we go forward in this decade, there will be less and less need for people to learn to cook, unless they just love cooking as a creative outlet.

Where most of us will use our creativity, however, is in concocting an interesting menu, putting various food items together and setting a pretty table. Important: Offering a warm and inviting environment in which guests can relax and unwind from the cares of the day.

Helpful: Choose a nice wine and serve it in appropriate stem glasses…have a few flowering plants or fresh flowers around.

Put some thought into the presentation of foods that have been purchased elsewhere. If you're serving deli potato salad, for example, be sure to garnish the platter with leafy green lettuce or radicchio. Snip a little fresh parsley, dill, basil or tarragon over salads.

For those who feel somewhat more adventurous this summer, try putting together a hearty salad meal such as tuna nicoise—with fresh broiled tuna, green beans, tomatoes, anchovies and black Kalamata olives with sliced new potatoes vinaigrette. Take a cue from the many fine restaurants that are now serving salad meals using various combinations of fresh vegetables and baby lettuces with warm sliced broiled chicken or fish.

Bottom line:

When entertaining at home today, almost anything goes so long as it's fresh, looks pretty, has color and texture and, of course, tastes good. After all, the point is to get together with friends, not to prove you can outdo Julia Child.

Source: Irena Chalmers, a food writer and author of many cooking/food books. Her latest is *The Great American Food Almanac*, HarperCollins, 10 E. 53 St., New York 10022. She is currently at work on a massive new project, the *Whole Earth Book of Food*.

Winning Craps Strategy

While craps is the most exciting and emotional casino game, it has always had one major drawback—it appears to be unbeatable. It differs from blackjack, where card-counters could gain an edge against the house in certain situations.

New way: Using systems I've learned from a professional gambler known as the Captain, who has won consistently at craps for the last 10 years, I've found that the casinos can indeed be beaten.

The key to winning at craps is to capitalize on a "hot" roll. You need to be betting when a shooter establishes a "point" (4, 5, 6, 8, 9 or 10)...and then throws the dice a dozen or more times before rolling a 7 ("sevening out").

Problem: Craps players are routinely devastated by a series of "cold" shooters, who seven out within a few rolls of establishing a point. By the time a hot shooter comes along, they have lost so much money that they don't have enough left to invest and recoup.

The Captain observed that craps games tended to run in streaks...long, cold periods would be interspersed with briefer hot ones. If players could conserve their money by not betting during the cold streaks, he reasoned, they could come out ahead over the long haul.

This principle led him to the 5-Count. It's a very simple strategy that would prove more effective than any previous craps system.

The 5-Count automatically eliminates the horrendous rolls that can swallow a player's stake. It allows you to stay afloat while you wait for the "wave" of a hot roll to bring you a profit.

Even if that wave fails to arrive at a given session, the "5-Count" will keep you from drowning.

How the 5-count works:

When a shooter takes the dice for his/her first "come-out" roll, you do not place any bets. Instead, you wait for the shooter to complete five successful rolls of the dice, as follows:

• On the first roll, the shooter must hit a point number—4, 5, 6, 8, 9, or 10—for the 5-Count to start. If the shooter rolls 2, 3, 7, 11, or 12 on the come-out, the count has not begun.

• On the second, third, and fourth rolls, any number except 7 is included toward the 5-Count. (As soon as the shooter sevens out, the count is terminated and begins again at zero.)

• On the fifth roll, the shooter must again roll a point number for the 5-Count to be completed. Your betting begins only after the successful completion of this sequence.

The easiest way to win:

In his own play, the Captain uses his "Supersystem." While this method requires no special mathematical skills, it is too intricate to describe within the confines of this article.*

There is, however, a simpler variant that has also proven successful—the Limited Bankroll System. More conservative than the Supersystem, it can still produce a steady profit.

Assuming you play at a $5-minimum table (the cheapest available in Atlantic City or Las Vegas), that System calls for you to "place"** $6 on the 6 and $6 on the 8 after the "5-Count" is completed.

The play:

• Unless the shooter rolls 7—in which case you'd lose, and would start a new 5-Count—you keep both of your place bets working for five rolls.

• If neither the 6 nor the 8 hits within five rolls, tell the dealer that your bets are off, and keep them off for two rolls. Then put both bets on again for three rolls. If you still fail to win, take your bets off for the next two rolls, and maintain this pattern.

• As soon as either the 6 or the 8 hits, give yourself five more rolls for either one to hit again.

• After your numbers have hit a total of six times on the same roll, you must "press" (double) your bet on the number that represents your seventh win. Example: After you've won four times on the 6 and twice on the 8, the shooter rolls another 8. At that point you increase your bet on the 8 from $6 to $12.

• After the eighth hit, you must press your bet to $12 on the opposite number—in this case, the 6.

• From that point on, you press your bets on the 6 and 8 after the fifth and sixth hits—to $24 on each, and then (on the rare occasion that you hit another six times before the shooter sevens out) to $48.

*A full description is in my latest book, *Beat the Craps Out of the Casinos*.
**In a "place" bet, you're wagering that the number you've bet on will be rolled before the shooter sevens out. A winning place bet on the 6 or 8 pays $7 for every $6 wagered.

One advantage of The Limited Bankroll System is that you can play comfortably with a stake as small as $150. Another plus is that you're highly unlikely to get wiped out in a hurry—a common hazard for more conventional craps players.

Worst-case scenario: There are times when the shooter will repeatedly seven out on the sixth, seventh or eighth rolls—a deadly sequence for anyone playing the 5-Count.

How to handle it: If you lose one-third of your stake ($50, if you start with $150) within 20 to 30 minutes, change tables. If you quickly lose another one-third at the next table, call it quits for that session. As with any system, there are days when it just doesn't pay to play. Bottom line:

Both the Supersystem and the Limited Bankroll System are designed to "grind" out modest but profitable results. They are not get-rich-quick schemes. They reward patience and discipline—and players who stay within their strict guidelines.

Source: Frank Scoblete, a regular contributor to Win magazine, and author of *Beat the Craps Out of the Casinos*, Paone Press, Box 610, Lynbrook, New York 11563.

How To Turn Slot Machine Odds In Your Favor

As an engineer and designer with 20 years' experience in the slot machine industry, I know the game from the inside out.

I also know that you can't make a consistent living from these machines...the odds almost invariably favor the casino. But—with the proper strategies—you increase your chances of striking it rich with one lucky pull.

Key factor: The machine's payback percentage...the proportion of the money wagered that is returned to the players over the long run. If the payback is 95%, the machine returns $95 for every $100 wagered—with $5 held as casino profit.

If the payback is 85%, the machine would return only $85, with $15 going to the casino.

A higher payback percentage will help conserve your stake, and make it less likely that you'll "bust" before your casino visit or vacation is over. At the same time, it will allow you more opportunities to hit a big jackpot.

- Best place to play: Las Vegas, where the payback runs 92%–97%.
- Next best: Reno, at 92%–95%.
- Least favorable: Atlantic City, at 85%–92%.

In Las Vegas, the best machines of all can be found at large casinos off the Strip (Las Vegas Boulevard), such as Sam's Town, the Gold Coast, the Santa Fe and the Showboat. These casinos cater less to tourists and more to discerning local players, who will go wherever the odds are most favorable.

100+% payback: In their never-ending game of one-upmanship, several off-the-strip casinos are now offering slot machines that pay back more than 100%. The longer you play at this type of machine, the more you could expect to win.

The catch: There is no way of telling where these machines are located.

On the other hand, if you find a near-deserted bank of machines in an otherwise busy casino, it's likely for a good reason...the players have migrated to where the paybacks are better.

Advice: If you have a choice, play where it's busy.

Wherever they gamble, too many slot players are led astray by the popular myths.

- Myth #1: Play the machine nearest the door or on the aisle. Years ago, casinos might have tried to attract passing tourists by placing their higher payback-percentage machines in high traffic areas. But now the machines have become so popular that casinos have no need for such tactics.

Fact: The only reason to play a machine on an aisle is for your comfort, as you won't be crowded by other players on either side of you.

- Myth #2: If the machine pays back with hot coins, it's a "hot" machine.

Fact: Coins come out of some machines hotter than others because of their proximity to lights or other electrical components in the machine. Their temperature has nothing to do with the machine's payback percentage.

• Myth #3: "I've put so much money in it, it has to be ready to hit." Today's slot machines are controlled by microprocessors. These miniature computers generate random outcomes of winning or losing symbols, according to the millisecond that you insert your coin or pull your handle. There is no such thing as a "pay cycle" or "cold cycle" on these machines. Each play is independent of the next. Since jackpots are produced by timing, rather than any given number of pulls, there is no way to predict when a machine is more likely to "hit."

Let's say you play a machine for an hour and lose $50 before you end your session. As you collect what's left of your stake, another player pulls the handle of "your" machine and hits a four-figure jackpot on his very first try. Before you start cursing your luck, remember —had you stayed to play, the odds are overwhelming that you wouldn't have won that jackpot. The hit was triggered not by the pull of the handle, but by the precise timing of the play.

• Myth #4: If a machine isn't paying, stop playing the maximum number of coins. Drop down to one coin and increase your bet to the maximum when the machine "warms up" again.

Fact: You should always play the maximum number of coins (generally between two and five), for the simple reason that the top jackpots award a significant bonus for maximum plays. If you play less than the maximum, you'll be donating an extra 2%–5% advantage to the house.

Strategy: If you can't afford to play the maximum, drop down to a lower-denomination machine.

Example: It's more advantageous to play four quarters (assuming that's the maximum) than one dollar on a machine with a two-dollar maximum.

Smart money strategies:

The most successful slots players are those who are disciplined in their money management:

• Set a strict gambling "budget" for your trip—a sum you can afford to lose without guilt or hardship.

• Divide your stake by the number of days you plan to play. If you've budgeted $300 for a three-day weekend, you can risk no more than $100 per day.

• Set a time limit for each session (an hour or two is reasonable) and buy a limited number of coins—say, $25 in quarters.

• Don't play back any coins that drop in the tray. Use only your original "buy." When those coins run out, take stock of what's in your tray. If you're ahead, cash in at the change booth and place your profit in the "winning section" of your purse or wallet. This money is untouchable. If you're behind, add whatever you have left to your original stake.

• If you're behind, take a break. If you're ahead, buy more change with another portion of your original stake and play that out. Proceed as above.

• If you've played half your stake and have lost most or all of it, change your game plan. Change to a lesser-denomination machine (quarters instead of dollars, nickels instead of quarters, three-coin instead of five-coin).

• If you're ahead and your machine keeps you ahead with each cash-in, keep playing. But once your last cash-in amount is considerably less than the amount of stake spent, it's time to move on to a new machine—if only for psychological reasons.

• If you've played your allotted time and still have some of your original session stake, consider yourself lucky. Move what's left to your "winnings" pocket. This money is also untouchable—never bet your winnings!

Bottom line:

If you play on indefinitely for a big jackpot without conserving your smaller wins, the casino's advantage is almost sure to wipe you out.

Even if you eventually hit your jackpot, it's unlikely to outweigh your accumulated losses. You must accept every win, no matter how large, for what it is—a victory against the odds.

Source: Dwight Crevelt, a senior engineer on the technical staff at IGT, a Las Vegas slot machine manufacturer. He is co-author (with his mother, Louise Crevelt) of *Slot Machine Mania*, and has recently come out with a second book, *Video Poker Mania*. Both are published by Gollehon Press and are available at most major bookstores.

Getting In On The Ballroom Dance Revival

Ballroom dance is making a comeback. Couples are dancing in one another's arms again, and dance studios are back in business. A whole generation that never learned partner-dancing is just starting, while their elders are returning to the studios to brush up on their techniques.

Where to go to learn:

Choose a studio that offers an inexpensive introductory special. Look for a combination that includes group classes, short private lessons and evening practice sessions.

Important: Complete all three before committing to any further lessons. Then start by paying for one month at a time. Reason: You need to take some time to find the program that works best for you. Wait till then to take advantage of price savings on longer-term packages.

Making the most of lessons:

Go over the steps you learn on the same day as the lesson. Walking a new pattern, without music, takes less than five minutes and pays big dividends.

Helpful: Think through the steps at odd times—while waiting on lines, riding in elevators, etc.

Since even the simplest dance steps can be quickly forgotten...practice to music frequently between lessons. Even five minutes at a time helps.

Purchase audio tapes from your studio. These are well worth the $8 to $10 usually charged. Reason: The studio will have picked out the kind of slow, easily heard tempos needed for practice. Tapes are also advertised in Dancing USA magazine. Note: It's best not to wear rubber-soled shoes for ballroom dancing.

Basics for beginners:

• Take small steps. Instructors have to exaggerate dance movements so that students can see them clearly. Follow the pattern they demonstrate—but make it small.

Rule: Never take a step longer than the distance between your shoulders.

• Advance slowly. Learn how to do a few basic steps well. This may mean repeating introductory classes several times.

Common mistakes: Rushing ahead to the next level too quickly. Studios, unfortunately, rarely discourage students from moving ahead for fear they will lose their business. Good motto: Festina lente—make haste slowly.

• Mix the private and group lessons. Use the group lessons to learn steps. Perfect the steps with your private instructor. Don't be embarrassed to ask your instructor to repeat an explanation or demonstration—or to lead you repeatedly in a step you are having trouble with. It's no disgrace to need a dozen or even two dozen tries before a step begins coming out right.

Couples can decide to take private lessons together. Trap: Arguing over the steps afterward. Just resolve to put aside differences until the next lesson. Instead of arguing, concentrate on the steps you agree about. Alternative strategy: Take private lessons separately. Many couples enjoy dancing together more if they take their lessons apart.

The best learning strategy:

Study three or four dances at a time. This way you are learning as much as possible in a short period of time—without being confused by too much information at once.

Suggested sequence: Start with American Swing, Foxtrot, and Merengue. These dances are the easiest to learn. They make it possible to dance whether a band plays ballroom style (Foxtrot and Swing), or Latin style (Merengue). Most of the more difficult dances build on the styles learned in these three.

Suggested consecutive sequences: Stick with your favorite among the three dances and add two others. Example:

First sequence: Swing, Foxtrot, Merengue.

Second sequence: Swing, Waltz, Rumba.

Third sequence: Swing, Tango, Salsa (Mambo).

Allow one to three months before going on to a new sequence.

Having fun right away:

As soon as you know more than one dance, begin attending studio parties. These are really practice sessions with low lights and refreshments. Wait, though, at least two months before going out to a club or attending a dance. Heavy traffic is hard for less-experienced dancers to handle.

• Switch partners even if you arrive as a couple. At studio parties, fellow students of either sex feel free to ask for a dance. Dancing with an unfamiliar partner is the real test of skill. And it's a large part of what old-fashioned social dancing is all about: Getting to meet members of the opposite sex under pleasant, controlled circumstances.

Source: Peter Shaw and his wife have been studying for three years at Paul Pellicoro's Dancesport International Ballroom and Latin Dance Studio, 1845 Broadway, New York 10023.

Pool Water And Teeth

Water that is too acidic can erode tooth enamel. Risk factors: A pool-water pH below six, plus considerable time in the water daily for three to four weeks—for instance, daily swimming of laps. Not a significant risk: Leisure time in a home swimming pool. Self-defense: Test pool pH routinely.

Source: Tom Reeves, Centers for Disease Control, Atlanta, quoted in *Cooking Light*, 820 Shades Creek Pkwy., Birmingham, Alabama 35209.

Enjoy An Amusement Park Visit

Go on Monday or Tuesday when it's least crowded...check the opening hours (some actually open a half hour before the posted time)...aim first for the ride or activity that's most important to you and then work your way around in a circular pattern...check ahead for special admission packages and discounts (entering after 4 PM, groups of 10 or more, affinity group discounts)...call before you go to be sure that the park is open (they can be booked for company parties).

Source: *AAA World*, 12600 Fair Lakes Circle, Fairfax, Virginia 22033.

Better Putting

Take hands "out of the putting stroke"— and swing from shoulders with arms hanging freely. After picking the line of the putt, focus on speed. On short putts, the putter should go farther on followthrough than backswing. Make sure the putter sits squarely on the ground—if the heel or toe is up, the ball will go off line. Recommended: Practice short putts with eyes closed, to get the proper feel.

Source: Women's golf star Beth Daniel, quoted in *USA Today*.

Photo Project

While a Polaroid print is still developing, you can get unexpected colors and patterns from the emulsion by manipulating it with a knitting needle or other pointed object. Start as soon as the print comes out of the camera and be careful not to puncture its surface (the chemicals inside are caustic). Protect the tabletop you are working on with newspaper.

Source: *Parenting*, 25 W. 43 St., New York 10036.

Super Bathtubs For Fun...For Health

Whirlpools—tubs with jets—are more popular now than ever—and come in more varieties than ever.

Inexpensive whirlpools resemble standard tubs (as small as 5' by 32") equipped with four jets. More expensive: Tubs with up to eight jets...usually larger ovals or rectangles— and those that come in designer colors. They may take deep, free-form shapes and are as large as 8' by 8'. Some seat four. Details:

Cost: For basic whirlpools—$1,000–$3,000. For high-end whirlpools—up to $8,000.

Material: Lighter weight acrylic tubs are easier to install than those of enamelled cast iron, but acrylics scratch more easily if cleaned with abrasives.

Brands: Jacuzzi, Kohler and American Standard are three widely respected brands. Kallista offers only high-end tubs, has unique shapes and will produce any color the buyer desires.

Possible problems:

- Need for more hot water: Most homes have 40-gallon hot water heaters. A big tub demands that much, leaving none for other uses. Solution: Put in a larger (60- to 75-gallon) hot water heater. Cost: $600 + labor (labor rates differ: $40/ hr.–$100/hr.).

- Vibration: Without proper installation, the tub can cause noise in the room below it. Discuss this with your contractor very thoroughly.

- Access to the motor is essential if repairs are needed. Usually—but not always—this can be managed without great trouble. Often, the motor is installed near a closet or in a cabinet.

- Structural problems caused by the weight. A structural engineer should check an old house (pre-1930s) before a tub is installed.

- Electrical: In most states, a whirlpool must be run on a special circuit that blocks any surge of current into the tub—to protect against electrocutions.

Source: Sheldon Malc, general manager of Davis & Warshow, the largest distributor of whirlpools in the New York area, 150 E. 58 St., New York 10155.

Common Garden Mistakes

We each garden for our own reasons—love of beauty, relaxation, satisfaction, food, increasing the value of our home—but we share a common goal: Lovely, successful gardens.

Still, we all make mistakes. The most common—and how to avoid them...

•Mistake: Trying to be a super gardener. Start small and expand next year. Rule of thumb: One new project per year allows enough time to maintain the rest of the yard. A little self-knowledge goes a long way: Ask yourself how much time you really will be able to put into your garden...and plan accordingly.

•Mistake: Planting without proper soil preparation. Cultivating, or tilling, and adding "organic matter"—compost, composted manures, decayed mulches, leaf mold, etc.—is the most important garden chore.

Add a two inch layer of compost to annual garden beds yearly, then turn it under. For shrubs and perennial gardens: "Side dress" by scratching around the roots of each plant in early spring with a hand cultivator and adding a layer of compost. Water deeply and well.

Exception: Do not disturb the roots of azaleas.

For depleted soils, consider a rotation of cover crops. These are cut while young and tilled under to decay and enrich the soil. Best: Alfalfa or buckwheat. They break up compacted soils...clover or vetch increase nitrogen in soil...rye or winter wheat condition soil during the winter.

•Mistake: Bad timing. Yes—there is a time to reap and a time to sow. Gardens exist on their own schedule. A successful garden depends on paying attention to that schedule. Whether it's pruning, planting, thinning, weeding, watering or harvesting that's needed, the garden will continue growing with or without you. It will not wait until you make time.

•Mistake: Not knowing the plants. Seek help from knowledgeable friends and neighbors, the local garden center or garden club. Consult plant encyclopedias and catalogs. Find out about:

•Horticultural needs: Sun/shade, wet/damp/dry conditions, hardiness zone, etc.

•Growing habits: Annual/biennial/perennial, mature size and how long it takes to be reached, spreading, self-seeding, bushy/narrow, tall/squat, evergreen/deciduous, color of flowers and/or foliage, blooming period, what happens after flowering or fruiting, required ongoing care.

•Mistake: Hole in the flower bed. After blooming, many perennial flowers die back. To avoid the hole, place the early bloomer behind a late blooming perennial or among annual flowers that will fill in the space.

•Mistake: Not practicing restraint. Never buy a plant without a spot to plant it in mind. For visual impact, avoid the speckled effect. Get several of each new plant (three, four or seven depending upon the size of the garden). Plant them in a mass.

•Mistake: Not trusting the experts. A packet of tomato seeds will grow 100-plus plants. Use it over several years, storing the extras in an airtight jar in a cool, dark spot. Space plants and rows as far apart as recommended.

•Mistake: Not watering properly. Overwatering and underwatering spell doom to any garden. Proper watering: Wait until the top layer of soil is dry but the plants are not wilted. Water deeply...one half hour or longer. Deep watering promotes deeply rooted, healthy plants that are better able to withstand dry conditions. Best: Water-saving soaker hoses—with holes all along—that lie on top of the soil or are buried an inch or two deep deliver water to the root zone where it is needed.

•Mistake: Being afraid to make mistakes. This year's mistakes can be changed next year. A long-season melon can be traded for a short-season variety, spinach can be protected from direct sunlight by planting it in the shade of the peas, etc. If a flower color combination displeases you, cut off the offending flowers. Take note, and move the plants around in the fall for more pleasing combinations. With proper care, shrubs and even young trees can be moved.

Source: Bonnie Wodin, of Golden Yarrow Landscaping Designs, Heath, Massachusetts 01346, also lectures and leads workshops on landscaping and related topics.

Index